FRANKLIN *and* NEWTON

Memoirs of the

AMERICAN PHILOSOPHICAL SOCIETY
held at Philadelphia
for Promoting Useful Knowledge

Volume 43

FRANKLIN

and

NEWTON

An Inquiry into Speculative Newtonian
Experimental Science

and

Franklin's Work in Electricity as an
Example Thereof

I. BERNARD COHEN

Associate Professor of the History of Science
and General Education, Harvard University

THE AMERICAN PHILOSOPHICAL SOCIETY

INDEPENDENCE SQUARE

PHILADELPHIA

1956

TO

ALEXANDRE
KOYRÉ

PERRY
MILLER

Preface

The major aim of this study is to illuminate the nature of scientific thought by considering the interaction between the creative scientist and his scientific environment. I have chosen the physics of the eighteenth century as a field of inquiry primarily because it provides an example of the profound influence exerted by the work of a single man, Isaac Newton, to a degree that is unique in the development of modern science. In studying the dissemination and transformation of the Newtonian point of view, I have focussed attention on the growth of concepts of electricity during the mid-eighteenth century. The reason is that the subject of electricity became an exact experimental science only after the death of Newton and thus affords a splendid opportunity of seeing the formation of Newtonian concepts in a post-Newtonian framework.

Though much has been written about Newton and Newtonianism, most of the literature in the recent past has tended toward a static, rather than a dynamic, point of view. General works on intellectual history, and even books on the growth of science or of physics in particular, have concentrated on Newton's positive achievements, rather than on the guideposts he set for the advancement of experimental science. In such books we learn of the invention of the calculus, the analysis of white light and of color, and the principles of dynamics. For the most part, however, we do not find much about Newton's speculations and hypotheses concerning subtle elastic fluids, the nature and structure of matter, or the interaction between matter and radiation—all of which were the source of inspiration for the heroic creations of the speculative experimenters of the eighteenth century.

In the following pages, therefore, I have attempted to present Newton as the men of the eighteenth century knew him. The point of view which I have expressed has grown out of fifteen years of study and reflection, based on an examination of books, pamphlets, manuscripts and journal articles of the late seventeenth and the entire eighteenth century. This has been supplemented by the study of scientific books and articles of the nineteenth century since they contain the keys to discovering which of the concepts and theories of the eighteenth century were genuinely fruitful in the advancement of physical science.

The choice of Franklin as an eighteenth-century Newtonian scientist presents a special challenge in that Franklin was without mathematical training and thus appears to be wholly outside the Newtonian tradition as usually conceived today. The very fact that Franklin was referred to as a " Newton " indicates that the concept of " Newtonian " science in the eighteenth century had a connotation quite different from that which is generally found in our present-day histories. Thus the burden of this monograph may be said to be a search for the connotations of " Newtonianism," to be found in the writings of the practising scientists of the eighteenth century, and the denotations of " Newtonianism," to be found in the Newtonian textbooks and the scientific dictionaries of that age. Although I have stressed the speculative experimental aspect of the Newtonian philosophy, I have not totally neglected the mathematical, exact science of Newton.

Part One is an attempt to see how the personalities of Franklin and of Newton were related to certain characteristic qualities of their scientific thought and to their scientific reputations. Part Two displays those aspects of Newton's scientific work which were particularly important in the growth of the experimental sciences. Part Three documents the general point of view by a somewhat extensive consideration of the most important Newtonian works studied by experimental scientists in the eighteenth century. In addition, it presents the formation of Franklin's concepts in electrical science in relation to the general background of eighteenth-century Newtonian science, as well as to the earlier work in electricity. The conclusion, Part Four, contains information as to the reception, application, and eventual influence of those concepts.

The writer hopes that his work may appeal to a varied class of readers: scientists, philosophers, historians, and students of the history of science. The materials have been arranged, therefore, in such a fashion that each reader may select for study those parts most relevant to his special concerns. With this end in view, each chapter has been divided into sections, fully listed in the table of contents. Thus such particular interests as these may be served: Newton's scientific personality, the character of Newton's scientific concepts, the spread and influence of Newton's ideas, the transformation of Newtonian concepts in the eighteenth century, Franklin in relation to the Newtonian tradition, science in the " Enlightenment," the role of phenomenon and hypothesis in Newton's thought, the relation of concept formation in science to techniques of experimentation, the contrast between methodological precepts and scientific practice, and the like.

Two of the major themes of this work concern the role of the
personality of the creative scientist in producing the kind of concepts
he uses in formulating his theories and explanations, and the intensely personal manner in which the creative scientist interprets and
transforms the general scientific point of view of his age. The quite
different reactions of two great men, separated by two and a half
centuries, may illustrate the highly individual effects of the same
book on different personalities in different ages. According to
Conduitt's memoirs, young Newton looked upon Euclid's *Elements*
" as a book containing only plain and obvious things," and put it
aside in favor of the analytic geometry of Descartes. Let us compare
this statement with that of Einstein in " Autographical Notes," in
which he describes the " wonder " he felt at the age of twelve when
he encountered " a little book dealing with Euclidean plane geometry." Here, said Einstein, " were assertions, as for example, the
intersection of the three altitudes of a triangle in one point, which
—though by no means evident—could nevertheless be proved with
such certainty that any doubt appeared to be out of the question.
This lucidity and certainty made an indescribable impression upon
me."

The variation in the esteem accorded Newton's own book on
optics, according to the age, is a similar commentary. In the eighteenth century the *Opticks* was the inspiration of experimental
scientists in many fields; in the nineteenth, the concept that the
phenomena of light are due to interactions between waves and corpuscles was rejected, and Newton was damned for his espousal of
the particulate theory of light. In our own time Newton's work has
again attracted attention and he has been hailed as a precursor of the
duality of light. But even in the eighteenth century men had differing reactions to Newton's speculations; some tried to explain
electrical and thermal phenomena by slavishly applying Newton's
concept of variations in æther density, while others invented new
concepts that were in some ways similar to Newton's, in order to
account for the phenomena of heat and electricity.

Since this study deals with the first scientific stage of electricity in
relation to the background of Newtonian scientific ideas, the two
central characters of necessity are Newton and Franklin. I trust no
reader will be led to assume that this juxtaposition implies a belief
that Franklin's scientific genius may be equated with that of Newton. Franklin was, as I hope to have shown, a major figure in the
history of science and in the development of electricity in the eighteenth century. He was a scientist steeped in the Newtonian tradition,
and his work showed the power inherent in the Newtonian approach

to the study of natural phenomena. It is not the task of an historian of science to award first, second, or third class medals to scientists of the past. In my judgment, however, Newton stands with Archimedes and Einstein as one of a triumvirate of physical scientists without peer. If compelled to an even more precise discrimination, I should place Newton first.

One of the happier results of this kind of study is the clarification that ensues when one topic is juxtaposed to another, as: Newtonian science and the rise of electricity; Newton and Franklin as creative scientists; theoretical science and experimental science; the science of the seventeenth century and that of the eighteenth. Similarly, the dimensions of Newton's extraordinary genius become manifest when we observe both the magnificent solutions he made in problems in mathematical physics (as in the *Principia*), and the courses he charted by his experiments and speculations (notably in the *Opticks*), the latter of crucial importance in the rise of the new experimental sciences in the eighteenth century. When we examine the spread of Newton's ideas, and Franklin's study of these ideas during the decade or so before he began to explore electrical phenomena, we can the more easily understand how Franklin was prepared for his fundamental contributions to physics. Furthermore, as we study the scientific writings of the eighteenth century, we are again and again reminded that there were at least two kinds of " Newtonian philosophy," and that the one most often then considered of major importance has been largely ignored by writers in the twentieth century. Similarly, it will be seen that in the eighteenth century there was general agreement among Newtonian scientists that there is a duality between the exactness of mathematics and the exactness of experiment. Newton, in the *Opticks*, had given for each theorem a " proof by experiment," whereas in the *Principia* he had given only mathematical proofs; but the eighteenth-century Newtonians presented the dynamical principles based on experiment rather than geometry, in a large number of treatises.

Throughout the present work two scientific attitudes are contrasted, that of the experimental scientist and that of the theoretical scientist. I trust no reader will consider any statement here made with respect to this problem as a generalization outside our specific context. As may be seen in all the examples cited, the goal of the theoretical physicist is to comprehend the findings of experiment and observation in a theoretical structure, the highest form of which is written in the language of mathematics. The worth of his creation is gauged by his ability to predict the findings of experiment and observation, both those already known and those to be discovered.

The goal of the experimental scientist is not only to produce new experiential data, but also to relate all such experiential data to existing conceptual frameworks, or to use them to modify such frameworks, or even to create new conceptual systems as experiment proceeds. The major experimental scientists are those—like Newton, Franklin, Lavoisier, Faraday, J. J. Thomson, and Rutherford—whose discoveries in the laboratory led them to develop new concepts and new theories which in turn led them to still further experiments of importance. Thus the experimental scientists of the highest rank are not usually simple " empirics," whose aim is to produce a " history " of nature in some Baconian sense—though many first-class contributions have been precise measurements or new techniques of investigation which have transformed the whole character of a particular branch of science. The most fruitful experimentation has usually been guided by theory, and has resulted in new theories. The difference between the experimental and the theoretical scientist lies not so much in their respective aims, but in their points of view, their methods.

Franklin formulated his theory of electrical action by meditating on the operations he was performing in the laboratory. In the same manner, Newton created out of laboratory data his theory of light and color and the properties of matter. In the *Principia*, Newton devised a mathematical system without his having had to draw on laboratory experiment (save for a minor point here and there), although he did depend on exact astronomical observations to check his results and to provide the numerical values of his parameters. As a typical mathematical physicist, Newton explored in the *Principia* not only the consequences of a law of force that varies inversely with the square of the distance (as in the law of gravitation), but also other laws of force depending on other powers of the distance. For a mathematician the theoretical interest of the latter is equal to that of the " true " law, even though such laws may not seem to apply to the phenomena of experience.

In the phrase, " electrical action," found repeatedly in this study, the usage of a past age is invoked. Thus in his *Lessons in Electricity*, delivered at the Royal Institution in 1875-1876, John Tyndall referred to " the fundamental law of electric action, which is this:— *Bodies charged with the same electricity repel each other, while bodies charged with opposite electricities attract each other. Positive repels positive, and attracts negative. Negative repels negative and attracts positive.*" This statement implies that there exists a general class of phenomena, in which one body may influence or be influenced by, or may affect or be affected by, one or more bodies with respect to electrification. The phrase "electrical action" thus is intended to encompass the way or ways in which such influences or effects are produced. It is thus similar to the phrase, "chemical action," referring to the way in which one or more substances may alter or be altered by some other substance or substances in a chemical sense. In general, I have tried to follow present-day usage of those vexing words, "electric," and "electrical," but in discussing eighteenth-century concepts this distinction cannot always be made.

At the present time, two great scholarly endeavors regarding Newton and Franklin are under way. An edition of all Franklin's correspondence and his other writings is being prepared. This project is financed by a grant to Yale University from *Life* Magazine on behalf of Time, Incorporated, and a grant from the American Philosophical Society. The project is administered by a joint committee of representatives of Yale and the Society, under the editorship of Professor Leonard W. Labaree at Yale, and Professor Whitfield J. Bell, Jr., in the Library of the Society. The American Philosophical Society possesses the largest collection of Franklin's original papers, and for many years has published studies based on those holdings and has, through grants for research, forwarded investigations on the different aspects of Franklin's career and the science of his time. An edition of Newton's correspondence, under the editorship of Professor H. W. Turnbull, F. R. S., is being sponsored by the Royal Society of London, one of the richest repositories of material concerning Newton and the science of the seventeenth and eighteenth centuries. It may be pointed out that there have been a number of editions of Franklin's works, each making some pretense to completeness; but the edition of Newton's correspondence is a pioneering effort of vast complexity and technical nicety. Readers will rejoice that these two editions are in such able hands, and that they will appear under such appropriate and distinguished sponsorships.

This book is respectfully dedicated to two scholars whose brilliant investigations have clarified so many aspects of the age of Newton and that of Franklin. It may be fitting to say here that one, Professor Alexandre Koyré, has undertaken to collaborate with the author in the preparation of a critical and variorum edition of Newton's masterpiece, the *Principia*.

Acknowledgments

The pleasantest part of writing a preface is the acknowledgment of indebtedness to friends, colleagues, and institutions. I have had the honor of being able to discuss with Professor Alexandre Koyré (Ecole Pratique des Hautes Etudes, Sorbonne) many aspects of my explorations of the thought of Newton. He has kindly read Chapters Three, Five, and Six in typescript. Anyone who has explored the background, nature, and influence of the scientific ideas of the seventeenth century is aware of the penetrating insight that Professor Koyré brings to these topics. Professor Marshall Clagett (University of Wisconsin) read the whole typescript in a preliminary state and allowed me to profit from his great store of learning and his acute critical sense. Two former students and friends, Professor Duane H. D. Roller (University of Oklahoma) and Professor Robert E. Schofield (University of Kansas), have helped me, over a period of years, to clarify certain major ideas. I have particularly profited by discussions with Professor Roller concerning the interpretation of electrical experiments and the nature of the concept of "electric fluids." Professor Schofield read the whole work in typescript to its considerable improvement. Professor Marie Boas (Brandeis University) has given me a critical view of Chapters Four and Seven, and Professor Sanborn Brown (Massachusetts Institute of Technology) has read Chapter Eight. I have a special debt to Dr. Erwin N. Hiebert (Harvard University), who critically read the galleys and helped to check all quotations and references.

I am especially grateful to H. W. Robinson, Esq., formerly Librarian of the Royal Society of London, for his assistance in locating certain manuscript sources which I have used and to the Council of the Royal Society for permission to print some documents from their archives. For similar kindness, I am grateful to the British Museum and the Académie des Sciences (Paris). I record my thanks to the Burndy Library (Norwalk, Conn.) and its director and founder, Col. Bern Dibner, for making available to me many works that I would have otherwise found difficult to consult, and for providing materials used in the illustrations. The American Academy of Arts and Sciences has granted permission to reproduce illustrations from the "Bowdoin MS." Franklin's purse is reproduced through the courtesy of the British Museum. The Historical Library (Yale University School of Medicine) generously sent on loan certain rare books, and I am especially grateful to Dr. John F. Fulton and Miss Madeline Stanton for their personal assistance with certain vexing problems. Mr. Edwin Wolf II answered many queries about the presence of books in the Library Company of Philadelphia in the 1740's. I thank Mr. David P. Wheatland, Curator of the Collection of Historical Scientific Instruments (Harvard University), for the loan of many eighteenth-century books.

Most of my research was undertaken in two great libraries, the Harvard College Library and the American Philosophical Society Library. The resources at Harvard—in the Widener and Houghton Libraries and the George Sarton Collection in the History of Science —have made my task far easier than I might have dared to hope. The American Philosophical Society is the major center for Franklin manuscript material. All visitors to the Society's Library are equally impressed by its magnificent treasures and the courtesy, learning, and helpfulness of every member of the staff. In particular I should like to acknowledge the kindness of Dr. William E. Lingelbach, Librarian, and of Mrs. Gertrude D. Hess, Assistant Librarian. I gladly record my further indebtedness to the American Philosophical Society for making to me a research grant from its Penrose Fund and for doing me the honor of including this monograph in its *Memoirs*. Mrs. Jane Gardner helped to prepare the typescript, Mrs. Blanche B. Cohen checked the Bibliography, and Mrs. Katharine Strelsky helped to revise the proofs. I have reserved for the last the recording of my lasting obligation to Mrs. Marion Van Aman, who attended to all secretarial details, checked the page proofs and prepared the index.

Note on Bibliography, Sources and References

In the section of Sources and References following each chapter, books and articles are cited briefly, by author and date only: e. g., Franklin (1769). These may be readily identified in the Bibliography at the end of the volume, where all works are listed by author and—under each author's name—in the order of the date of publication. The general principles of citation are explained further in the Sources at the end of Chapter One (page 25).

Owing to certain unavoidable delays which supervened between the completion of the typescript and the time of publication, the dates of the literature cited do not, save in a few notable cases, extend beyond 1954.

Although all quotations in this monograph are taken word for word from the original printed or manuscript document, I have in general presented a " modern " text, but not a " modernized " one. Thus I have dropped to lower case the many capital letters used by seventeenth- and eighteenth-century printers, I have largely changed the extensively used italic forms (as in proper names) to roman, and

I have spelled out common abbreviations: *that* for y^t, *the* for y^e, *referred* for referr'd, *etc.* for &c., *Sir* for S^r, and so on. Here and there I have corrected an obvious misprint: *emitted* for omitted, *an* for and, and the like. At times, when the sense is hard to grasp, I have also altered the punctuation though not the order of the words. But in the case of certain letters published here for the first time from the manuscript, I have printed them *verbatim et literatim*, maintaining all vagaries of capitalization and punctuation.

June 1956   I. B. C.

Contents

xvii

Illustrations

FIG. 1. Portrait of Sir Isaac Newton. The print bears the following legend:

> Drawn and scraped MDCCLX by James MacArdel from an original portrait painted by Enoch Seeman now in the possession of Thomas Hollis F. R. and A. SS.

> Les Italiens . . . . Ces peuples ingénieux ont craint de penser; les Français n'ont osé penser qu'à demi; et les Anglais qui ont volé jusqu'au ciel, *parce qu'on ne leur a point coupé les ailes*, sont devenus les précepteurs des nations. Nous leur devons tout depuis les lois primitives de la gravitation, depuis le calcul de l'infini, et la con-naissance précise de la lumière si vainement combattus, jusqu'à la nouvelle charrue et à l'insertion de la petite vérole, combattues encore. Ode sur la mort de Madame de Bereith avec une lettre par Mons. de Voltaire.

> (In transcribing the above note of Voltaire, certain minor errors of the engraver have been corrected.)

FIG. 2. Portrait of Benjamin Franklin showing the lightning rod he erected in his house in September 1752. This portrait was painted by Mason Chamberlin in 1762 when Franklin was fifty-six years of age and is repro-duced from an engraving made after the portrait by Freeman, and, according to the legend, was " Sold by M. Chamberlin in Stewart Street, Old Artillery Ground, Spittalfields." The price was five shillings. Shown are the two bells with which the portions of the lightning rod terminated, the little ball [or clap-per] suspended by a thread between the bells, and the two balls suspended by strings from the bell on the right, forming an electroscope, and indicating the presence of an electrified cloud above.

FIG. 3. Two pages (402-403) from the first edition of New-ton's *Philosophiæ Naturalis Principia Mathematica* (London 1687), showing the " Hypotheses " that ap-

PART ONE

Introduction:
Franklin and Newton

CHAPTER ONE

THE STUDY OF EIGHTEENTH–CENTURY NEWTONIAN SCIENCE

Nature and Nature's laws lay hid in Night;
God said, *Let Newton be,* and all was Light.
—ALEXANDER POPE (eighteenth century)

It did not last: the Devil howling, " Ho,
Let Einstein be," restored the status quo.
—SIR JOHN SQUIRE (twentieth century)

THE WRITINGS of all great men stand as a perpetual challenge to each succeeding generation which attempts to make an interpretation suitable to its own age. This phenomenon is familiar enough to students of literature and philosophy, but it is one that also appears in science. For 250 years the writings of Isaac Newton have been carefully studied, and have produced a series of interpretations that vary from the temper of one age to the next and that display within any single age the several schools of thought in science and philosophy then current. Newton evidently left enough obscurity in his analysis of natural phenomena to provide ground for a wide range of interpreters; we may legitimately suspect that the alterations he made in the " status quo " were not as all-embracing as Pope would have had us believe, and that the twentieth-century revolution in physics was not simply a destruction of a marvelous clarity. For in a sense, that twentieth-century revolution was in a direct line of descent from the seventeenth-century problems in physical science which Newton could neither reduce to mathematics nor adequately illuminate, and which were explored in a fruitful way during the eighteenth century.

These remarks apply more to Newton's physical speculations than to his principles of mathematical physics. Mathematical demonstrations as such may be considered to partake of a quality of absolute truth that can never be found in physical theories. For, as Hermann Weyl has said, we must " distinguish the ' mathematical space,' whose laws are logical consequences of arbitrarily assumed axioms, from the ' physical space,' the ordering scheme of the real things, which enters as an integral component into the theoretical construction of the world ": a sentiment like Einstein's, " As far as the propositions of mathematics refer to reality they are not certain, and in so far as they are certain they do not refer to reality." [1] Newton himself, in the third " book " of the *Principia*, indicated the distinction between " principles of philosophy," including science, which are " not philosophical but mathematical," and the demonstration from those principles of " the frame of the system of the world." But we must keep in mind the fundamental difference between laws of mathematics and mathematical laws of nature, even if they may be formally similar. The permanent truth value of any mathematical law holds only so long as the mathematical symbols are not required to have a unique one-to-one correspondence with objects in the physical world, or even with concepts based upon the observed behavior of such objects. Newton's binomial theorem * creates no problem of interpretation because it is an abstract expression rather than a description of some aspect of a supposed concrete reality or an interpretation of the events in the world around us. Compare it with Newton's crucial theorem of gravitation theory: if a homogeneous sphere may be considered as composed of uniform small elements of matter (each of which attracts and is attracted by a particle external to the sphere with a force that is proportional to the product of their respective masses and inversely proportional to the square of the distance between them), then the total mutual attraction of the sphere and the external particle will be the same as if all of the mass of the sphere were concentrated at a point at its center. This is one of the basic theorems of Newton's *Principia*, and its implications for the interpretation of Nature are more profound than the words themselves can possibly indicate.† If Newton's proof is mathematically sound, this theorem is true. Yet it does not by itself tell us anything about the physical world because it provides no information as to whether such small elements do in fact attract

---

* In 1676 Newton stated the binomial theorem—in effect—as follows: [2]

$$(P + PQ)^{m/n} = P^{m/n} + \frac{m}{n} AQ + \frac{m-n}{2n} BQ + \frac{m-2n}{3n} CQ + \cdots$$

where A is the first term of the expansion (i. e., $P^{m/n}$), B the second term, C the third term, . . .

† This particular theorem has notable implications for the growth of physics and will be discussed in those terms in Chapter Five. At this point, however, we may observe that this theorem was a stumbling block of considerable magnitude in the way of Newton's initial development of celestial dynamics. The suggestion was made by John Couch Adams and J. W. L. Glaisher that the twenty-year delay in Newton's announcement of the law of universal gravitation arose from Newton's failure to solve the problem of the gravitational attraction between a sphere and an external particle which was relatively near the sphere. More recently, Florian Cajori advanced this argument in a convincing way by supplying a mass of additional evidence to support it. [3] We may also observe that the theorem holds for a sphere made up of homogeneous concentric shells and also may be applied to two spheres, each of which acts gravitationally as if its total mass were concentrated at its center.

all others in the supposed fashion. Yet, its applicability to the " falling " of the moon and the falling of a terrestrial object gives it physical overtones and makes it imply more than the mathematical terms can strictly convey. Only as a conditional expression (of the form: if A, then B) is it mathematically true.

As we contemplate such a theorem, like Newton, we are concerned to know about its physical " truth " or its usefulness in ordering or explaining the phenomena of the external world: we want to find out whether homogeneous spherical bodies act gravitationally as if their masses were concentrated at their respective centers. This theorem is an example of the problem of interpreting or critically evaluating Newton's *Principia*. The job is not merely to check the mathematical derivations. We must examine the validity of the expressed and unexpressed assumptions made by Newton about the nature of the world, and explore the degree to which the final results accord with the data of observation and experiment. We must carefully study whether the mathematical statements are still valid when the symbols or concepts are correlated with observable entities or quantities derived from them. It is well known that the Newtonian dynamics fails in certain ranges of experience: e.g., it cannot give a satisfactory explanation for the advance of the perihelion of Mercury; it cannot—without serious alteration—be applied in its original form to the motion of small particles whose speed is appreciable compared to the speed of light. Nor can Newton's assumptions of an absolute time and an absolute space, the latter identified with the " sensorium " of God, pass the muster of experimental test. These questions, however, have arisen in a significant way only in fairly recent times and need not concern us here. They were not the major questions which stimulated productive research in the first century and a half following the publication of the *Principia*.

On the other hand, even in Newton's own time, it was plain— and to Newton himself—that his formulation of the dynamics of the solar system was ever so much more successful than his fluid mechanics, to which a third of the *Principia* was devoted. And once we leave the logical niceties of the " Mathematical Principles of Natural Philosophy " to examine Newton's experimental inquiries we sense a tentativeness and an obvious incompleteness. No longer are there experiments, theorems, and proofs but bold and ingenious hints, questions, and hypotheses of the various mechanisms that might explain the occurrence of natural phenomena. The *Opticks* ended in a set of " Queries," the nature of which will be discussed in Chapter Six. But here we may note that a series of questions asked, though not fully answered, by Newton constituted a challenge set by Newton for the scientists in the ages to follow. Who could doubt that a man of Newton's insight knew what questions should be studied! Fame awaited any investigator who could find an answer to a question that had baffled the Master.

Thus to understand the growth of scientific thought in the eighteenth century, we must pay as much attention to Newton's failures as to his successes. What leads, we must ask, did Newton give to others whose research proved fruitful? In this sense, the present monograph challenges Pope's couplet by asking how much light had actually been cast by Newton and how much he had left in darkness, or at least in semi-obscurity. How does the light cast by a single man brighten new areas of productive research? Such triumphs of eighteenth-century science as Hales's physiology, Franklin's theory of electricity, or Lavoisier's system of chemistry were not cast in the same form as Newton's *Principia*, although produced in the age of Newton; were they in any sense under the sign of Newton and influenced by him? These examples indicate the need of examining carefully the documentary material of the eighteenth-century scientists, those who lived and worked in the " age of Newton," not only the writings of Newton himself and modern commentaries.

Any study of the influences of one man's work on another must depend on what men say about their work as much as on their work itself. One of the aims of this monograph is to try to find, in a particularly active period of scientific innovation, the relation between what men say and what men do—at least in science. In displaying the development of one important field of physical science, electricity, this study is an attempt to see what actually happened to the "status quo" in the decades following Newton.

The Empirical Basis of Scientific Theories

This book is an inquiry into an aspect of the growth of science during the eighteenth century that has not been amply explored. In it two great names in the history of physical science are linked together: Isaac Newton and Benjamin Franklin. Newton's major scientific works, which had been published by 1704,‡ influenced the growth of thought in physical and biological science throughout the century. Hence, the ground of any investigation of eighteenth-century science must be a contemplation of the Newtonian view of science as expressed by Newton himself and as understood by the

‡ The first edition of the *Principia* appeared in 1687, and the first edition of the *Opticks* in 1704. Newton prepared revised versions of both books that contained new and stimulating material of importance (*Principia*: ed. 2, 1713; ed. 3, 1726; *Opticks*: Latin ed., 1706; English ed. 2, 1717; ed. 3, 1721; ed. 4,1730) .[4]

creative scientists during the decades following his work. Franklin was considered by his contemporaries to be one of the foremost experimental scientists of the " age of Newton "; he was likened to Newton during the eighteenth century in terms of admiration which the twentieth century is at pains to understand.

Benjamin Franklin was an experimental scientist and no mathematician. Hence any study of Franklin and Newton implies an exploration of the currents of a Newtonian experimental science, not the more familiar Newtonian mathematical science. The eighteenth century, " the age of Newton," was the time of the first full flowering of an experimental science: not merely the uncovering of a wide range of new empirical phenomena in all branches of science, but their correlation in theories founded on concepts that tended to express the actual manipulations in the laboratory.

Although the science of the seventeenth century had been marked by a considerable empiricism, the degree to which actual experiments and observations formed the basis of scientific thought has often been exaggerated, especially by those who have attributed to pre-Galilean science an almost total lack of empiricism. A careful study of the documentary evidence has shown that before Galileo science was not completely divorced from experience, as had been so often assumed, and that Galileo himself was not primarily an experimenter. Ernst Mach and the philosophical school of logical empiricism have attempted to see in Galileo the creator of experimental science, but modern scholars have found in Galileo a propensity for the " thought experiment." Many of the supposed experiments Galileo described were performed only in imagination and others could not have yielded the results he stated—be it noted, without giving the supporting data of actual trials.[5] In the spirit of his age, Galileo believed that a " true " theory was more important than any particular fact of experiment or observation. Galileo, therefore, admired Copernicus all the more because he had held to the heliocentric hypothesis even though some of the observations had seemed to contradict it.[6] At one crucial point in his *Dialogue on the Great World Systems*, Galileo discussed the experiment of a weight let fall from the mast of a moving ship. " Salviati "—speaking for Galileo—asks the Aristotelian whether he has actually performed this experiment in order to find out whether the weight will fall at the foot of the mast, in front of it, or behind it. Into the mouth of the Aristotelian—" Simplicio "—Galileo puts this reply: " I have not." But he allows " Simplicio " to state his conviction that the authors he has cited must have made the experiment and must have done so " accurately." " Salviati " counters with the statement that they " obviously " have not made the experiment since they give an absurd conclusion. But at this point Galileo, the good author, allows " Simplicio " a normal bewilderment, and has him ask " Salviati " in turn how he can be so positive since " you have not made a hundred tests; no, not even one test." That is quite true, Galileo proudly replies through " Salviati," he has not made a single test—there is no need of one, " I am sure, without experiment, that the effect will ensue as I tell you, for it is necessary that it should." [7]

Curiously enough, Galileo had tried such an experiment and almost certainly knew that Bruno had mentioned one.[8] In his book, nevertheless, he did not stake the conclusion on empirical evidence, preferring to rely on what is " necessary " as a conclusion from correct principles. Even in his " Two New Sciences," often hailed as the founding work in modern experimental science, Galileo was more concerned with necessary conclusions than proof by experiment. His " report " of the test of the law of uniformly accelerated motion, in which he claimed to observe the time taken by balls to roll down inclined planes, leads us to believe that he had made at most a rough check: a somewhat unnecessary one at that, since he was convinced of the correctness of his theoretical conclusions. We can easily, therefore, understand Mersenne's perplexity when he tried to duplicate Galileo's supposed trial and we can appreciate Mersenne's comment that evidently Galileo had not performed this experiment at all, or had not reported exactly what had occurred.[9] Of course, although Galileo did not rely on experiments as much as has often been supposed, and even if his experimental technique was often faulty, he was aware of the need of recourse to experience in order to show that a theory—such as the one about uniformly accelerated motion on an inclined plane—does truly apply to events in nature.

By the latter part of the seventeenth century, physical scientists were becoming wary of " thought experiments." Boyle, Hooke, and Newton—major exponents of the British empirical school—took pains to describe in detail all aspects of their experiments: the nature and construction of their apparatus and instruments, the very steps taken and the minutiæ of observation, and the actual measurements or other numerical data. Boyle found it easy to criticize Pascal's treatise on the equilibrium of fluids because it contained the description of an " experiment " in which a man sat under water for a full twenty minutes.[10] Yet we shall see that even Boyle accepted uncritically many supposed observations made by others, without any thought of testing them himself, so long as they appeared to be reasonable or provided data that were useful to his own theories. Such an attitude may be contrasted with Du Fay's approach to investigation toward the middle of the eighteenth century, typical of the new experimentalism. Having read, in the *Philosophical Transactions* of the Royal Society of London, about the experiments of Stephen Gray, his first step was to repeat Gray's experiments step by step and only then to proceed with his own.

The eighteenth century was characterized by the rise of a genuine empirical science. To some degree this development in science may be related to the growth of skepticism and a tendency to insist on facts and not fancies. But we must be careful to avoid exaggeration: the men of the eighteenth century were no less credulous than men had been in any previous period. The *Philosophical Transactions* published accounts of mermen as well as exact experiments on electrical conduction, and observations on the vegetable character of mussels as well as precise numerical data on celestial phenomena.[11] A whole array of first-rate men in the eighteenth century were believers in a supposed cross between a horse and a cow—an offspring called the "jumar"—and among the believers was the credulous Voltaire.[12] Even Linnæus believed, as did many others, that swallows hibernate under water.[13] The *Systema Naturæ* came to include the "jumar" in its proper classification and Linnæus wrote about the rabbit-chicken hybrids, supposedly produced by Réaumur, describing them as "chickens which were exactly like ordinary fowls except that they were covered, not with feathers, but with fine hair."[14] When we find men of the eighteenth century believing in phenomena that are utterly incredible to us, and in theories that seem wholly unwarranted by observation and experiment, we have brought home to us in a striking way the need for studying that age—or, indeed, any other—in its own terms. We may see at once why we cannot apply to the past our own canons of credibility and reasonableness, or our own preconceptions of experimental standards and the adequacy of scientific theories.

The eighteenth century holds a crucial position in the development of physical thought. Not only did experimental inquiries then open up many new fields of exact science, but also the rapid growth of concepts and theories controlled by experiment brought traditional fields to a new high state. The twentieth-century revolution in physics—inaugurated by the quantum theory, the discovery of radioactivity, and the theory of relativity—is now sufficiently advanced to enable us to view the physical science of the nineteenth century in historical perspective and justly to evaluate its magnificent achievements. We no longer need to begin every discussion of modern physics with an attack on the classical science of the nine-

teenth century. So we may turn to the eighteenth-century background of the concepts and theories of that classical nineteenth-
century physics in a spirit that was not possible earlier in our own
century. We may also escape the results of the excess of nineteenth-
century pride, which sought chiefly in the past for congruities between earlier concepts and its own.§ Such key notions for the understanding of nineteenth-century physics as field, atom, molecule,
charge, element, potential, action-at-a-distance, æther, attractive force,
repulsive force, heat, "fluid," energy, medium and wave were either
invented in the eighteenth century or then took a particular form
that influenced the course of physical thought during the next century, or arose in the course of explaining phenomena that were
prominent in eighteenth-century science.

Since one of the primary characteristics of nineteenth-century
physics, and also chemistry, was the production of mathematical
theories encompassing more and more varieties of phenomena, it is
of particular interest to study the non-mathematical forms in which
the antecedents of such theories first appeared. Hence, any study of
eighteenth-century physical thought must include considerations of
the relations between physical principles established by experiment
and their embodiment in later mathematical theories of increasing
generality. The coupling of the names of Benjamin Franklin and
Isaac Newton by the writers of the eighteenth century takes on an
added significance from the very fact that Franklin the experimenter
was ignorant of higher mathematics and was unable to read Newton's
acknowledged masterpiece, aptly entitled *Mathematical Principles of
Natural Philosophy.*[*] How then could Franklin be considered in
any sense a " Newton " and a major representative of the Newtonian
natural philosophy? This is one of the primary questions to be explored in this book. Its answer reveals at once some major characteristics of the science in the age of Newton not generally appreciated
by commentators on the eighteenth century and provides a background against which may be exhibited the role of Franklin in the
growth of physical thought from Newton to Clerk Maxwell.

§ For example, having witnessed the overthrow of the fluid theory of heat, or caloric
theory, and the establishment of the theory of heat " as a mode of motion," the men
of the nineteenth century were unable to find any virtue in the older theory, or to
see how it had served nobly in the advance of science. Even at the middle of the
twentieth century, one can find reference being made to the caloric theory as a " now
discredited " theory of heat, although such an attitude is less common today than it
was a hundred years ago.

* Franklin's knowledge of mathematics and his reading in the works of Newton are
discussed in Chapters Seven and Eight.

Effects and Influences of Scientific Theories

There are at least four major types of source material about the scientific thought of the eighteenth century. First, there is the large body of what scientists, philosophers, and historians have written, during the nineteenth and twentieth centuries, about Newton and the science produced in the century following his work. Second, the vast literature of what the non-scientists of the eighteenth century—such as philosophers, literary men, " social scientists," and vulgarizers—said about the science of their own day. Third, there are the statements by the eighteenth-century scientists about the methods used in their research and the aims and scope of their own work and that of their scientific colleagues. Finally, there is the actual body of scientific work itself, the particular theorems, methods of proof, choice of experiments, and subjects of investigation, which collectively give the character of the age. The four sources do not present a uniform view. Very often, the statements of nineteenth- and twentieth-century writers—whether scientists, historians, or philosophers—are apt to be overly influenced by a projection into the past of their own currents of scientific thought. It is difficult to avoid emphasis on special topics, or aspects of scientific research, that are of significant importance at the time of writing and that may be only distantly related to the character of eighteenth-century science as revealed by the documents of that age. Newton's theory of light, for example, was a corpuscular theory that included undulatory aspects. Many writers of the nineteenth century, witnessing the successive triumphs of the wave theory, often found it necessary to apologize for Newton's failure and found it all but impossible to approach Newton's theory on its own terms; while some writers of the twentieth century, all too aware of the current dual view of light as waves and corpuscles, have tried to view Newton's theory as the first form of their own kind of physics. But, however irrelevant such judgments may be for the understanding of Newton, the actual scientific research of the nineteenth and twentieth centuries, recorded in journal articles, monographs, and general scientific treatises, gives us a valuable clue to those elements of eighteenth-century science that were fruitful for the advance of science and those that possibly restrained an otherwise more rapid scientific progress. Whether or not those elements were of central importance in the scientific thought of the eighteenth century is another question and one that must be studied separately.

The contributions of eighteenth-century physical scientists to the advance of science during the nineteenth and twentieth centuries comprise concepts, laws, principles, and theories, and also observations and experiments, and particular effects. Some are obvious in their importance: the discovery of oxygen and Lavoisier's explanation of combustion, Franklin's law of conservation of charge and his electrical convection experiment, the discovery of pyro-electricity in tourmaline crystals by Æpinus and Wilcke, the concepts of latent and specific heat. But the theories, conceptual schemes, and grand hypotheses of the eighteenth century cannot be so simply evaluated. What about that "erroneous" ("now discredited") theory of heat based on a supposed "caloric fluid," a concept which grew up in the eighteenth century to "plague" the nineteenth? Or Galvani's theory of muscular contraction being due to the action of an "animal electricity" *sui generis?* Or even Franklin's theory of electrical action based on a single "subtle and elastic" fluid? It is fashionable today to dismiss certain older theories as simply wrong and outmoded, but the historian must evaluate them in terms of their positive accomplishment at the time of their invention and during the remainder of their life in science. The record is, I believe, plain that the classic idea of a luminiferous æther, stemming from Newtonian concepts of the eighteenth century, produced some of the major scientific advances of the nineteenth century, including the electromagnetic theory of Clerk Maxwell. The fluid theory of heat led to the principles of heat flow and conduction, the concepts of latent and specific heats, new and important kinds of measurements, and applications to the theory of chemical reactions—all of the greatest consequence to the advance of science. "Animal electricity," as expounded by Galvani, may be in a somewhat different category. Although the experiments which Galvani hoped would prove the existence of an electric nervous fluid, did lead to evidence of the existence of electrical potentials in cut muscle, his own theory was short-lived. Its major immediate effect on the advance of physical science was to stimulate Volta to attack it and to produce the electric battery and the theory of contact electricity, thus inaugurating a new era in physics and chemistry.

Even though one important result of Galvani's theory was to incite a better explanation of the observed phenomena,[15] such a statement cannot be generalized to imply that every theory in science can have a beneficial influence, even though in a negative sort of way. It would be difficult to find any useful product of the eighteenth-century theory of the Abbé Nollet, who tried to explain electrical phenomena by the simultaneous "effluence" and "affluence" of a mysterious substance that enters a body through one set of pores and leaves it through another. This theory did not coordinate the observed data particularly well; it led to no predictions of new phenomena nor to practical applications in important devices; it did not even challenge scientists to produce a better theory to explain the phenomena which it was designed to serve. So far as the growth of scientific ideas is concerned, this theory might just as well never have existed at all.

One reason why the theory of Nollet did not stimulate anyone to the attack was the existence of a much better theory produced independently at about the same time: Franklin's. We no longer use Franklin's theory exactly as he expounded it, but for at least three-quarters of a century it was—with the revisions of which it was capable—productive of continual application to new discoveries. We may legitimately say, therefore, that the rapid advance of electrical science during the late eighteenth and early nineteenth centuries was possible because of his creation. At the very least, this advance was easier and more secure because of the discoveries Franklin had made and the concepts he had employed so fruitfully to coordinate and explain the observed electrical phenomena and to predict new ones. Furthermore, the principle of conservation of charge, developed in Franklin's work, is still a fundamental principle in electrical science, and his explanation of how charges may be produced by electrostatic induction and how a condenser is charged are still to be found—with only minor changes in language—in every elementary textbook on electricity.

The apparent longevity of some of Franklin's results is independent of what may be termed the " lasting influence " of his scientific research considered in its entirety. However important some of his concepts, principles, and explanations may be today, we have no assurance that in fifty or one hundred years physical theory will continue to find them useful or in any way fundamental. There is probably more justification, therefore, in applying the word " lasting " to the influence of Franklin's research on the physical thought of his day, and the following half-century, than to any particular result which happens to accord with our current scientific conceptual schemes. Here, incidentally, we may see one of the weaknesses in attempting to reduce the history of science to a chronology of " important " discoveries. Scientific ideas change so rapidly that we would have to add the qualification: important to whom—to us? to our children? or to our fathers? But if we choose to trace out the growth of scientific thought, we are forced deep into the background of each age of discovery and must give earnest consideration to matters that are of less interest for the interpretation of specific natural phenomena than for our understanding of how ideas are formed, are related to the general " climate of opinion," filiated with other ideas, and productive of new forms of experience.†

Franklin was a leading exponent of the Newtonian school of experimental Newtonian natural philosophy. Thus, to appreciate Franklin as a scientist, we must study Newton as Franklin and the other scientists of the eighteenth century saw him. We cannot then help becoming more interested in the research that Newton stimulated than in his successful experimental analysis of white light and color and his explanation of the rainbow, and even his celestial mechanics. Newton's positive achievements were thought by many of the eighteenth-century scientists to be closed chapters of the history of science; the work was completed and the last word had been said. But the experimental scientists, like Franklin, were concerned with the chapters for which Newton had only given the title and which were yet to be written, and they quite properly hoped to see these chapters written in terms of their own discoveries. A study of Newton from the point of view of the eighteenth-century scientists reveals their intense interest in those very areas in which Newton had had no success in his explorations, topics which offered hope for future investigators with new experimental techniques that might enable them to see further than Newton. The scientists of the eighteenth century, in other words, saw Newton in two separate roles: as one who had provided answers to fundamental questions and as one who had indicated paths of research for the future. From the point of view of the growth, rather than the dissemination, of scientific ideas we share the excitement that was aroused in these experimental scientists by Newton's bold speculations about the æther and the nature of atoms, the construction of matter and the relation of the properties of the several varieties of matter to the characteristics and arrangements of their constituent parts, and even the exploration of " final causes " and the origin and ultimate destiny of the universe. Thus, following the trail of the influence of Newton's speculations leads us far afield from optics (as such) and mechanics into realms of chemistry, physiology, medicine, electricity, heat, and even psychology.

† The critical reader will, of course, observe that no historian can ever wholly divorce himself from his own age, however much he tries to disassociate himself from its preconceptions and to recapture the spirit of the past. The historian may steep himself to the limit in the literature of a previous century, but he cannot help but emphasize certain features which his own training has shown him are important. Such a reflection of the scientific values and point of view of the historian's own times becomes apparent chiefly with the passage of time. Thus we can easily recognize the prejudices of a nineteenth-century writer who deals with the Middle Ages, even if we can less easily see the effects of our own predilections; in the same way, an eighteenth-century copy (or forgery) of a Renaissance painting has for us some immediately perceivable eighteenth-century stylistic aspects, whereas in the eighteenth century it might have seemed a genuine creation of the fifteenth century.

Electricity: a Speculative Newtonian Experimental Science

In this book, I have chiefly sought to follow the rise of electrical theory as an example of what may be called speculative Newtonian experimental science, although some correlative material is presented on the Newtonian influence in other non-mathematical areas of scientific investigation. The choice of electricity as the major subject to provide a cross-section of physical thought in the age of Newton was dictated by a number of considerations. Electricity rose to the status of an exact science only after the death of Newton, and its entire history, therefore, can practically be written in a post-Newtonian frame of reference. Although Newton reported one curious electrical experiment to the Royal Society of London, he made no direct contributions to the subject. Neither he nor his contemporaries knew many of the simplest aspects of the electrical properties of matter. For instance, the two kinds of electrification (vitreous and resinous) had not yet been discovered, nor was any hint available about charging by induction; even the bare distinction between conductors and non-conductors had not yet been made. Newton had, to be sure, offered certain hints about electrical attraction being related to the same elastic æther which might be responsible for gravitational attraction, but he had not particularly illuminated the subject.

By studying the development of electrical theory in the eighteenth century, then, we may encounter the birth and growth of a " Newtonian science " whose whole existence post-dates Newton's own achievement. We may see in a concrete example just how the Newtonian influence acted to temper the progress of science and we may —during the process—clarify what can be meant by a " Newtonian science " and appreciate the fertility of Newtonian concepts and methods, and the qualities of his thought.

Electricity was in many ways a science characteristic of the eighteenth century. The apparatus for making experiments was simple and could be easily obtained by anyone who might be interested. For those with more courtly taste, there were elegant "electrical machines" capable of producing effects on a large scale. These were whirling cylinders, spheres, or plates of glass, mounted in wooden frames, and were to be found in every gentleman's "cabinet de physique." Accompanied by sparks and cracklings, electrical experiments could be simple and mysterious or large-scale and startling: having a natural appeal to the sense of the curious and the wonderful for which the century was noted. In the 1740's the Leyden jar increased the scale of electrical demonstrations and, in France at mid-century, large shocks were given simultaneously to 180 soldiers of the guard, and later to " the whole community of Carthusian monks of the Couvent de Paris.[16] Electricity was truly the wonder of the age, and showmen made their fortunes by offering an evening or so of electrical entertainment and instruction as they traveled about the country in Europe and even in far-off America. In the fashion of the age, there were demonstrations or electrical games bearing such names as " beatification," the " electrical kiss," and " conspirators," and even " treason."

Electrical research produced a vindication of the popular eighteenth-century Baconian belief that advances in science would always lead to useful applications. The attempts to cure paralyses, by producing contractions in the affected limbs by an electric shock, were probably not very useful, but no one could deny that the lightning rod—invented by Benjamin Franklin in an application of a multitude of his discoveries—was of great benefit to mankind. For the first time, man had the means to protect his buildings and his ships from the destructive effect of the lightning discharge.

The key figure in the production of the Newtonian science of electricity was Benjamin Franklin, and the very act of placing together the names of Franklin and Newton indicates—as we have seen earlier—the need for revision of some commonly held notions about what a Newtonian science might be. If we take the *Principia* of Newton as our exclusive model of Newtonian science, then Franklin's electrical theory can in no sense be considered Newtonian, despite Franklin's obvious adherence to the program of inquiry and speculation set forth in Newton's other works. Even in the late eighteenth century, Franklin was attacked for having departed from the strict method of geometrical deduction of the *Principia* [17] and for not having adopted the famous motto of that book: " Hypotheses non fingo." We will have to turn to other writings of Newton that Franklin read, and that were studied so extensively by the experimental scientists of the eighteenth century, in order to discover how the non-mathematical Franklin, with his expressed weakness for framing hypotheses, could possibly have been a Newtonian scientist. And it is just at this point that we will have to inquire into the difference between what Newton said and what he did. In the *Opticks* and the *Principia*, for example, he had much to say about the method of pursuing scientific inquiries. Historians have often quoted such statements as accurate descriptions of what Newton did. In such a view, Franklin's science might seem to represent the antithesis of Newton's. But if we disregard Newton's methodological precepts and study, instead, the way in which he actually proceeded in his scientific investigations or musings, we gain a different picture of Newton and of Franklin in relation to him. In general, methods of research are not learned from precepts on scientific method so much as from a close look at the actual research which produced important results. There is a great contrast between what Newton said about method and what Newton did in science. If we wish to gain a balanced perspective on the character of Newtonian scientific thought and on Newton's influence on the growth of science, we must go back to the writings of the eighteenth-century scientists. We must re-examine the textbooks that they studied, with the view of finding out the terms in which they conceived the Newtonian experimental philosophy to have been expressed. We cannot simply take Newton's statements at their face value.

There can be no question about the choice of Benjamin Franklin as the major investigator to be considered as a speculative Newtonian experimental scientist, once we have adopted electricity as the science to provide a cross-section of eighteenth-century physical thought. No one who makes even a superficial examination of the literature of electricity during the eighteenth century can escape the recognition of the commanding role of Franklin after the mid-century and the eventual universal adoption of the concepts and even the language that he introduced into electricity for the first time.

Empirical Science in the Age of Newton

The course of physical thought in the century following Newton reveals two separate patterns. One may be described as the analytical extension of the dynamics of the *Principia*, including the construction of a satisfactory rational fluid mechanics and the theory of perturbations by such men as Clairaut, d'Alembert, Laplace, the Bernoullis, and Euler.

Newton had devoted the whole of " Book Two " of the *Principia* to the subject of fluid dynamics and had produced a number of very original results, almost all of which are incorrect. This subject has been studied recently by C. Truesdell,[18] and it provides a striking example of how the work of one man influences the research of others. The success of Newton's formulation of celestial dynamics led naturally to a close study, theorem by theorem, of the whole *Principia*. In this process it was seen that the Newtonian fluid mechanics was far from satisfactory and attempts were made to supplant it, culminating in Euler's establishment of modern rational fluid mechanics. The theory of perturbations was particularly important because it showed that certain observed departures from predicted planetary motions could be explained by taking account of the gravitational influence of one planet on another. Thus Newton's theory was extended and was shown to be more accurate than Newton himself had believed, indicating that the universe might function as a machine without requiring occasional regulation by the " watchmaker."

The other pattern of scientific development in the " age of Newton " was empirical, characterized by the rapid accumulation of knowledge in such fields of physical science as optics, heat, electricity, magnetism, and the many aspects of chemistry. Students of eighteenth-century science are beginning to recognize that the latter group were as much under the sign of Newton as the former, although—and we must insist on this point again and again—not the traditional Newton exemplified by the *Principia*. Newton's influence on chemistry, by the way, is not as yet fully understood and the present essay might equally have been devoted to chemistry as a speculative Newtonian experimental science—had the author been a student of chemistry rather than of physics.[19]

Newton influenced the growth of electricity, even though that science was beyond his ken and created after his death. Although Franklin worked primarily in electricity, to some degree he in turn influenced the whole Newtonian tradition of the eighteenth century. His research may be considered typical of the non-mathematical approach to nature at its eighteenth-century best: the advance of scientific knowledge by simple, ingenious experiments that led to concepts closely allied to laboratory operations. The theories that rose from these experiments were tested by new experiments, producing a continual stream of new phenomena which broadened man's view and understanding of nature. An investigation of the general reactions of Franklin's contemporaries to his achievement—in Britain, France, Germany, Italy, Holland, Russia, the Scandinavian countries; i. e., wherever science flourished—demonstrates Franklin's role in the enlargement, and extension to new areas, of the kind of physical thinking that derived from Newton. A study of the growth of physical thought, therefore, shows Franklin as a major transitional figure between the physics of Newton and the physics of Faraday and Clerk Maxwell: the first man to show that a Newtonian science need not slavishly follow the details of Newton's every thought, but must be altered when applied to new problems and new subjects.

The importance of Franklin's contribution to physical thought is aggrandized by the significance of electricity—the subject of his scientific research—in the physical science of the nineteenth century. The unification of electricity and the cognate subject, magnetism, in the first half of the nineteenth century prepared the way for the relation of both to theories of light and radiant heat in the electromagnetic theory of Clerk Maxwell, which itself marks the zenith of classical or pre-quantum physics. Franklin thus stands at the beginning of a line of research that reaches out through the whole course of the theoretical physics of the nineteenth century. No one can trace the genesis, growth, and application of the key concepts for understanding modern physics without encountering the effect of Franklin's ideas on the primitive Newtonian formulations. And it is not without interest that three of the major twentieth-century pioneer investigators of the atomicity of electricity and the electrically charged fundamental constituents of matter—Thomson, Rutherford, and Millikan [20]—delighted in acknowledging the major contribution of Franklin in the growth of our understanding of electricity and the composition of matter.

Can a Non-Mathematical Theory be Exact?

Those who are accustomed to view in a mathematical expression the highest form of physical principles may see with a special interest the apparently non-mathematical development of ideas by Franklin in the important eighteenth-century tradition of speculative Newtonian experimental science. During the eighteenth century, this tradition was almost wholly separate from the mathematical tradition associated with the *Principia*. Yet we may observe that very often in the history of physical science a line of development that seems wholly outside of the range of mathematics may later become susceptible of a higher mathematical expression. "Maxwell's equations" may be considered a translation into mathematical language of the non-mathematical theories of Faraday, and there can be no question but that the permanent value of Faraday's theories has come in large measure from their having been translated into the language of mathematics. One is even tempted to say that Faraday thought along intuitive mathematical lines, although—like Franklin—he remained ignorant of higher mathematics throughout his life. Franklin, too, conceived his ideas in such a fashion that they could become embodied in a mathematical expression in the minds of Cavendish and Æpinus. No higher tribute can be paid to an experimental physicist than to show that his bold physical speculations can become part of a system of mathematical equations; those "qualitative" physical theories that cannot be reduced to mathematics are usually doomed to as chimerical an existence as the concepts on which they are founded. So Franklin's results turned out to be in a sense independent of any proof of existence of that electric fluid he postulated, and Faraday's did not depend on a demonstration that there *is* an all-pervading æther and that in it there *are* set up strains or actual lines of force. We have come to appreciate that hypothetical " fluids " and " lines of force " are of less importance than an equation, or a system of equations, whose variables relate to concepts founded on observation, and which may lead mathematically to another equation, or set of equations, which, like the first one, is an accurate description of observable events. Hence, in any critical evaluation of the science of the past, we are apt to place a high value on those concepts and theories that have lent themselves to the production of mathematical systems of nature.

There have always been times in the history of modern physical science—whether the sixteenth century, the seventeenth, the eighteenth, the nineteenth, or even the twentieth—when whole areas seemed to be outside the construction of mathematics and only later on became mathematical. These are usually periods of intense experimentation, when new results accumulate in such a bewildering array of phenomena and counter-phenomena that it almost seems as if no theory can be devised to correlate and explain all the observed data. Such was the situation in most of the experimental sciences at the time of Newton's death. Newton wrote in the preface to the first edition of the *Principia* that with regard to phenomena other than " the motions of the planets, the comets, the moon, and the sea," he suspected that they might be derived from " the same kind of reasoning from mechanical principles," but he could offer no evidence to support his opinion, which is thus seen to be only a kind of pious expression of a belief in the uniformity of nature. The way was clearly open for clever experimental scientists to wrestle with these " other " phenomena and discover new ones, and it was at this point that Franklin—unhampered by a thorough study of the *Principia*—produced out of the scattered and apparently unrelated phenomena of electrification the first stage in the formulation of a new exact science.

Although Franklin's theory was not mathematical, it was exact. This statement may seem a contradiction in terms because exact physical science is customarily presented in mathematical language, and Franklin's was not. Yet Franklin devised a complete conceptual scheme for the known facts about electrification in his day, one that worked. Given a description of a set of operations performed on conductors and non-conductors, a Franklinist could make an unambiguous prediction of the electrical states of all the objects at every stage of these operations; in practically every case the predictions were verifiable by actual test. Here was no mere qualitative mask of ignorance with an *ad hoc* explanation after but not before each electrical event, but a definite statement that could pass the muster of experiment. The theory was exact, furthermore, in that it was based on the comparison of magnitudes even though Franklin had no absolute basis for assigning numbers. And by being able to tell whether one charge was greater or less than another, or equal to it, even if the two were of opposite sign, Frankin was able to show in a large variety of examples a new principle: the law of conservation of charge. When numbers were assigned to electrical magnitudes, the fundamental concept to be quantified was electric charge, a concept that was first made precise by Benjamin Franklin. The Franklinian theory can, therefore, be described as the first stage of exactness in electrical science (preliminary to quantification and mathematical treatment) in which order was established out of a chaos of unrelated experimental facts.

Evaluating Scientific Theories of the Past

The work of any of the scientists of the past can be studied in two wholly different ways. One of these, applied to Benjamin Franklin, would be to examine carefully the experiments he devised and the conclusions he drew from them, and then to draw up a list of every effect, concept, and principle that was used by later physicists, giving special emphasis to those which are still of any use in the conceptual schemes we employ today. Franklin would come out well in such an analysis and we might even go to the extreme of assigning to him the " precursorship " of the concept of the electron, as Millikan once did,[21] because Franklin held that the matter of electricity, or the " electric fluid," was composed of particles that repel one another. Applied to Newton, this method would assign to him the " precursorship " of Einstein's theory of photons, or the concept of the duality of light, because the Newtonian theory of light invoked the action of light-particles whose particulate properties are governed by waves that they excite in the æther. In this kind of history special credit would be given to any man who held at an early time a view that was in some way similar to later or current views, even though that man might have had no direct influence whatever on the later development of the subject.

A case in point might be the statement of the lesser or minor circulation (more properly, pulmonary transit) of the blood long before William Harvey's discovery of the major circulation, or complete circulation. The discovery of the lesser circulation is usually attributed to the sixteenth-century Spanish heretic and mystic, Miguel Servetus, but historical research has disclosed that an Arab physician of the thirteenth century, ibn an-Nafīs, had advanced a similar concept much earlier.[22] Ibn an-Nafīs is plainly a " precursor " of Servetus, although wholly without influence in this regard since the only work of his that was known in Europe (prior to the investigations of twentieth-century historians) was a book on pharmacy which did not mention the lesser circulation at all. No one who is interested in the scientific thought of Islam, or in the occasion of the creation of scientific ideas, can fail to be fascinated by the wholly unexpected " discovery " of the lesser circulation in the twelfth century. But so far as the actual advance of physiology was concerned, this was no " discovery " at all; at least, it made no difference whatever to the growth of our knowledge of the circulatory system. This admittedly extreme example may serve as a warning that " precursorship " should be sought only in cases in which the discovery was disseminated. Yet a consideration of Newton's theory of light will tell us that even this restricted view of " precursorship " may be misleading.

When Einstein presented his views on light in 1905,[23] at a time when the wave theory of light reigned supreme, and suggested that it might be useful (at least from an " heuristic " point of view) to consider that light-energy is always particulate, he was not consciously returning to the point of view of Newton's *Opticks*. Although the *Opticks* had been issued in a German translation in the series of " Ostwald's Klassiker " in 1898, Einstein had not read it and knew about Newton only what was to be found in every book on physical optics. The most famous textbook on the subject in 1905 in Germany was Professor Paul Drude's *Lehrbuch der Optik*, published in Leipzig in 1900, and issued in an English translation made by G. R. Mann and Robert A. Millikan two years later. Section 2 of Chapter Two is devoted to " Hypotheses as to the Nature of Light " and contains some reasons why " Newton supported the emission theory of light, according to which light consists of material particles which are thrown off with enormous velocities from luminous bodies and move in straight lines through space." Like most textbooks of that day, Drude's *Lehrbuch* did not even mention the fact that Newton's view of light as corpuscular also embraced ancillary wave effects.‡ Since Einstein did not remember having known more about Newton's optical theories than was found in books such as Drude's, he could hardly have been suggesting a revival of them. But

‡ A few British textbooks, notably Preston's *Theory of light*, indicated that Newton had written of waves as well as particles, but this seems not to have been the case in German textbooks on optics. Preston, as a matter of fact, tried to reinterpret Newton's writings on light so as to dispense with the corpuscular aspects of his theory, and so place Newton among the founders of the undulatory theory of light.[24]

in a wholly different sense, we may be sure that Newton was not without influence on the development of theories of light up to 1905, and that in this way there is a direct line of descent from Newton to Einstein.

This discussion brings us back to what was, earlier in this chapter, called the " lasting " influence of scientific work. The wave theory of light—extended into the electromagnetic theory of Clerk Maxwell, radically altered by Planck in the quantum theory, in turn severely modified by Einstein's theory of photons of 1905—was brought to the attention of physicists at the opening of the nineteenth century by Thomas Young. Young's ideas derived in part from the seventeenth-century treatise on light by Huygens, from Hooke's writings, but also from Newton's *Opticks*.§ Newton had established the periodicity of light phenomena: the *sine qua non* of a wave theory. His research on color and on a large class of " interference " phenomena provided a major contribution to Young's theory; Young even used Newton's careful measurements to compute the wave-lengths of the several colors. Whatever the fate may be of our present view of the nature of light, whatever theories may be advanced to account for optical phenomena during the next century, nothing can ever alter the facts: Newton's researches in optics established the periodicity of light in the range he investigated; Newton greatly advanced (and practically opened up) the study of what we call " interference " phenomena; Newton's optical measurements, his suggestions about æther waves, and his explanation were acknowledged by Young to have been of the greatest importance in the creation of the wave theory of light which he presented to the scientific world in 1800—and which was developed, modified, and radically altered during the next century and a half. In this sense, Newton's contribution is a " lasting " one; it will stand forever as a stage in the development of our understanding of light that was of major importance for the progress of that science in the succeeding two centuries.

We can form a crude estimate of the importance of Newton's

§ Young held that Newton " was in reality the first that suggested such a theory as I shall endeavour to maintain." Furthermore, he said that his main contribution to the wave theory, the so-called principle of interference, was discovered " by reflecting on the experiments of Newton," and that its only antecedents were some hints written down by Hooke and " the Newtonian explanation of tides in the Port of Batsha." In defending his theory, Young observed that Franklin, too, had believed in the wave theory of light: " The opinion of Franklin adds perhaps little weight to a mathematical question, but it may tend to assist in lessening the repugnance which every true philosopher must feel, to the necessity of embracing a physical theory different from that of Newton." [25] (Newton's views on light will be discussed, below, in Chapters Five and Six; Franklin's in Chapter Eight.)

research in the history of optical theory by trying to envisage what that history might have been like if he had never lived, or if he had never been attracted to the investigation of optical phenomena. And so we are led to the second way of studying the work of any scientist of the past, which is to consider it in its full historical context. Applied to Franklin, the methods of proper historical investigation demand that we begin by analyzing the currents of scientific thought, and the state of knowledge in the areas in which he worked, during the decades just prior to his period of research. Only then can we examine what he actually did in science and evaluate his results in the light of the contemporary scientific scene. In this way we shall find it easy to understand the high praise given to his publications by his fellow scientists. Next we must explore the extent to which Franklin's research influenced the progress of science during the following decades, seeking evidence in the writings of his contemporary scientists and their immediate successors. Finally, we must look briefly into the growth of scientific ideas in the nineteenth century, in order to test whether the observed influence during the eighteenth century had conditioned patterns of physical thinking and directions of research that continued to be profitable for the new forms of science in the next century.

SOURCES

Immediately following each chapter there is a section of Sources and References. All books and articles are referred to, in this section, by author and date. Thus Fulton (1934) indicates the article in the Bibliography:

FULTON, JOHN F. 1934. The principles of bibliographical citation. *Bulletin of the Medical Library Association* **22**: 183-197.

All references to Newton's *Principia* and *Opticks* indicate a page in a particular edition, but I have also included the Proposition number (or Query number), so that the reference may be found in any edition. Similarly, every article or letter in Franklin's book is identified completely, so that it may be located in any edition of his writings, but reference is also generally made to the page of the first complete edition of his book on electricity and the modern reprint, Franklin (1769) and Franklin (1941) respectively. Newton's letters are to be found in various places, e. g., Birch (1756-1757), Newton (1779-1785), Brewster (1855), and More (1934); to render their location as simple as possible I have generally included in the references to them the date of the letter and the name of the addressee. In neither the case of Newton nor of Franklin have I always indicated which letters or other communications were read at the Royal Society or published in the *Philosophical Transactions*, although I have tried scrupulously to keep distinct such writings as were made public when written and those that remained in manuscript until a later date.

The section of Sources for each chapter contains the main secondary works which I have found useful; but these lists should by no means be considered exhaustive. In some cases, the lack of useful secondary sources is indicated. Every scholar finds some errors in fact and in interpretation in the writings of his predecessors. I have not made a parade of such errors in this book, preferring to present my own views without calling attention to the fact that they may differ from the statements of others. I believe it true that every book and article I have used has taught me something I would not otherwise have known; it has seemed to me more important to acknowledge my indebtedness than to show a lack of gratitude by citing works only to indicate minor slips. From time to time, however, it has been necessary to challenge accepted opinions.

The views of the history and nature of scientific thought presented in this chapter have been influenced chiefly by the writings of P. W. Bridgman, Crane Brinton, Léon Brunschvicg, Ernst Cassirer, Marshall Clagett, A. C. Crombie, Pierre Duhem, Albert Einstein, Henry Guerlac, Alexandre Koyré, Ernst Mach, Hélène Metzger, Perry Miller, Henri Poincaré, Joseph Priestley, Ferd. Rosenberger, George Sarton, Paul Tannery, Owsei Temkin, Hermann Weyl, Alfred North Whitehead, Sir Edmund Whittaker, Harry A. Wolfson.

Some general aspects of method in the history of science are to be found in Sarton (1936 and 1952), the latter containing a useful list of books on all aspects of the history of science, a list which may be supplemented by Russo (1954). A useful outline guide to the subject is Guerlac (1952). For views on the current status of work in the field see Guerlac (1950), Cohen (1954a and 1955b).

REFERENCES

1. Weyl, 1949: 134; Einstein's statement is quoted *ibidem*.
2. See Child, 1927: 121; Ball, 1915: 327; Turnbull, 1945: 12.
3. Cajori, 1928a; see also Cajori, 1922b and 1922c.
4. See Babson Collection, 1950: 9-12, 66-69; Gray, 1907: 5-22, 35-40.
5. See Koyré 1939; 1943a; 1943b; Cohen, 1950b: 347-348; also Olschki, 1927; 1942; 1943.
6. Galileo, 1953a: 343, 347; 1953b: 335, 339.
7. Galileo, 1953a: 158-159; 1953b: 144-145.
8. Galileo, 1953a: 140, note by G. de Santillana.
9. See Koyré, 1953.
10. See Pascal, 1937: 20, also fig. IX; Conant, 1950.
11. See Hill, 1751.
12. See Zirkle, 1941.
13. See Brett-James, 1926: 187 ff.
14. Réaumur, 1750, Memoir X, " Containing a view of the philosophical amusements the birds of a poultry-yard may afford." Linnaeus's statement is quoted in Hagberg, 1952: 199.
15. See Galvani, 1953: introduction.
16. See Needham, 1746: 256, 261.
17. See Franklin, 1941: Appendix II.
18. Truesdell, 1954.
19. See Metzger, 1930; Duhem, 1902; Guerlac, 1951.
20. Thomson, 1936: 249-258; Rutherford, 1906; Millikan, 1947: 11-15; 1950: 77, 69.
21. See Millikan, 1948.
22. Fulton, 1953a, and Bainton, 1953, contain guides to the earlier literature; see Fulton, 1953b, for complete bibliography.
23. Einstein, 1905.
24. See Preston, 1890: 21.
25. Young's early major statements of the wave theory of light were made in two Bakerian Lectures, read 12 Nov. 1801 and 24 Nov. 1803; his account of the origin of his ideas was written in 1804 in reply to an attack on the previous papers which was published in the *Edinburgh Review*. These are reprinted in Young, 1855: 1, Nos. VII, IX, X. For a discussion of Newton's explanation of the Batsha tides, see Cohen, 1940.

CHAPTER TWO

FRANKLIN'S SCIENTIFIC REPUTATION

Historians relate, not so much what is done
as what they would have believed.
—POOR RICHARD'S ALMANACK (1739)

THE TREATMENT of Franklin's scientific work by Americans presents a paradox to the historian of science. There is a vast array of books and monographs dealing with almost every aspect of Franklin's career and thought—his economic views, his political ideas, his literary style, his vocabulary, his service as postmaster, his diplomacy, his travels, his activities as printer, and so on—but no full-length work devoted exclusively to Franklin's scientific research. Until a decade or so ago there had never been an American edition of his book on electricity. Some excellent articles have presented information on specific aspects of Franklin's research, e. g., his contributions to meteorology, his studies of the Gulf Stream, or the date of his kite experiment, but the few general articles about his science have tended to link together his practical inventions and his contributions to electrical theory. Much has been said of Franklin the gadgeteer, and his " common sense." Many authors have pointed out that even in pure science he was more interested in knowledge for the sake of a possible application than for an understanding of nature, that his mind " turned ever by preference to the utilitarian and away from the theoretical and speculative aspects of things." [1] Some warrant for this latter point of view has been found in Franklin's own words. He once wrote, " What signifies philosophy [i. e., natural philosophy, or science] that doth not apply to some use? " [2] And he also declared, " Nor is it of much importance to us to know the manner in which nature executes her laws; it is enough if we know the laws themselves. It is of real use to know that china left in the air unsupported will fall and break; but *how* it comes to fall, and *why* it breaks, are matters of speculation. It is a pleasure indeed to know them, but we can preserve our china without it." [3]

Such quotations raise once again the question of the difference between what men say and what men do. We shall see in Chapter Four that removing these quotations from their contexts, and reading them without a due regard for the sentiments of the age, may give

27

them a character wholly out of keeping with the aims and scope of Franklin's scientific research as revealed by an analysis of his actual contributions to science. In other words, an adequate interpretation of Franklin's (or any man's) scientific research can be obtained only by considering it in its entirety, by viewing it in the light of the thought of his times. Be that as it may, the fact remains that the best discussions of Franklin's contributions to science have not been produced by Americans but by European writers, notably the British and Germans.[4]

I believe that one of the reasons for the neglect of Franklin as a scientist by American scholars, for the distorted view of his scientific career in American history books, may be found in the values which American society has placed on scientific research. It is a fact that during the first century and a quarter of national existence, America was not the birthplace of those leading scientific ideas and theories that revolutionized man's thoughts about the external world. But during this period, America produced a vast number of practical inventions, including the reaper, the sewing machine, the telegraph and telephone, and many others which radically altered the conditions of daily living, means of transportation and communication, and the methods of manufacturing and agriculture. Americans might well be proud of their achievements in technology during the nineteenth century. But among the names of truly great men of nineteenth-century science—Pasteur, Claude Bernard, Helmholtz, Faraday, Clerk Maxwell, Kelvin, Fresnel, Darwin, Koch, Cauchy, Gauss, Weierstrass, and Poincaré—there is but one American. Only Willard Gibbs * achieved a scientific stature equal to that of the European giants. The century did see the appearance of notable scientific research by Americans here and there—Beaumont, Silliman, Henry, Hall, Asa Gray, and Rowland—but a comparison with Britain, France, or Germany would not place nineteenth-century America in the status of a major nation for its contributions to pure science. The most important scientific innovation to cross the Atlantic eastward was the introduction of surgical anæsthesia, but this revolutionary development, despite its profound significance, is in the area of practical innovation. I shall not explore the possible causes of the low state of scientific research in nineteenth-century America, but the fact itself must be noted because it is related in at

---

* Gibbs [5] was a giant in the science of the nineteenth century, one of the greatest scientists the world has produced; perhaps as such he is atypical of his culture. We know so little about the occurrence of such extraordinary men that the comparison between Europe and America might be made more meaningful if we dealt with first-rate men who were not quite in the Gibbs-Clerk Maxwell-Pasteur category. Even so, the result of the comparison would be the same.

least two ways to the view held by Americans concerning Franklin as a scientist.

In the first place, American historians of the nineteenth century, and those of the twentieth century who were influenced by them, were keenly aware that technical progress was a characteristic aspect of the growth of America and they consciously or unconsciously sought out roots of American inventiveness in the colonial period. Naturally enough, they were pleased to find Franklin producing useful inventions and household gadgets—the " long arm " (grandfather of the gadget used by grocers to take small boxes down from shelves), a stool that opened up into a ladder, a rocking-chair that fanned the reader while he rocked, a letter press, the " armonica," bifocal glasses (badge of many a library scholar), the lightning rod, and an improved form of stove which posterity has named in honor of the inventor the " Franklin stove," but which he called the " Pennsylvanian fire-place." An undue emphasis on such practical achievements has caused historians to neglect Franklin's contribution to pure or " useless " science.

The state of nineteenth-century American science produced a second effect on estimates of Franklin as a scientist, because the major American scientists of the late nineteenth and early twentieth centuries learned their science from European sources—chiefly German, British, and French—either by studying abroad or reading European works. Even the outstanding contributions of Willard Gibbs, though made in America, were introduced to American scientists through the medium of European commentators; Gibbs, furthermore, studied abroad before he made his great discoveries. The American scientific research of the twentieth century is, therefore, almost entirely built on the monumental achievements of nineteenth-century European science. Looking backward to the roots of their own scientific tradition, American scientists have seen only their immediate European masters. They have never found a direct chain leading back to the colonial period in America. Benjamin Franklin has not appeared to be a founding father of the scientific tradition of American scientists. In point of fact, most American scientists do not even appreciate Franklin's major stature in the development of physical thought and would be hard pressed to explain how Franklin could ever have been considered a " Newton," save in jest.

Franklin as a Scientist, according to American Physicists

The recognition and support of pure science in America has been attained only by slow degrees and even today the victory is far from complete. A great majority of Americans, for example, still find difficulty in understanding why public funds for scientific research should not be used exclusively for investigations that will have "obviously" practical implications for medicine, for military purposes, or our economic well-being. Some shift in public opinion on the value of "pure" scientific research probably began after the Civil War. In 1875, at any rate, Joseph Henry optimistically reported a "great change" that "has taken place in the public mind as to the appreciation of the importance of abstract science as an element in the advance of modern civilization." [6] What he had in mind was the "general" acceptance in 1874 of the character of the Smithsonian Institution, of which he was the founding Secretary, as an agency doing scientific research, whereas at the time of James Smithson's bequest (1835) "to the United States of America, to found . . . an establishment for the increase and diffusion of knowledge among men," the distinction between "original research and educational instruction in science and literature was scarcely recognized."

Two years after the end of the Civil War, Henry had written that the creation of a National Academy of Sciences during the war years † marked the first recognition by the American government "of the importance of abstract science as an essential element of mental and material progress." A new means of acquiring "distinction" had been established; the "acquisition of wealth and the possession of political power" and "renown for successful military achievement" were—he thought—to be supplemented by scientific achievement. [8]

By the end of the century, however, Joseph Henry's aspirations for science had not been fully realized. At the fiftieth anniversary meeting of the American Physical Society, held in Cambridge, Massachusetts, in June, 1948, a reprint of Henry A. Rowland's "Presidential address delivered at the second meeting of the society, on October 28, 1899," was distributed. This memorable document, entitled "The Highest Aim of the Physicist," [9] is largely devoted to a defense of the ideal of "pure science" and an expression of hope that the future may witness an end to the deplorable condition, in which "much of the intellect of the country is still wasted in the pursuit of so-called practical science . . . and but little thought and money . . . given to the grander portion of the subject which appeals to our intellect alone." Looking in the past for names of Americans

† The abortive efforts to form a National Academy of Sciences prior to the Civil War provide an index of the place of science in the American national life in the first century of our republic; even after the Civil War, the role of the National Academy of Sciences in relation to national policy was inconsequential. [7]

whom "scientists throughout the world delight to honor," Rowland found only four, despite the fact that he had searched the record for a period of more than a hundred years:

Franklin, who almost revolutionized the science of electricity by a few simple but profound experiments. Count Rumford, whose experiments almost demonstrated the nature of heat. Henry, who might have done much for the progress of physics had he published more fully the results of his investigations. Mayer, whose simple and ingenious experiments have been a source of pleasure and profit to many.

We may note that three of the four men on Rowland's list—Franklin, Rumford, Henry—were in the "almost . . ." or "might have done . . ." category, while the fourth (whose name is just about completely unknown today) had produced experiments which Rowland assumed were well enough known to his auditors to require no further description. While Rowland appreciated that Franklin's work was of some importance, he obviously did not consider it of major rank.

Rowland's remarks formed the text for another address delivered before the American Physical Society at Cambridge, at the meeting of April, 1946. It was entitled "Fifty Years of Physics—A Study in Contrasts," [10] and the speaker ‡ expressed the following judgment concerning the place of Benjamin Franklin in Rowland's list:

The many-sided Franklin, a legendary figure, had won fame along various lines. Had he not been famous as a publisher and a statesman, he might never have been heard of as a scientist. Balzac described him

‡ A half-century after Rowland, Mayer's contribution was apparently unknown to American physicists. The address given in April, 1946, later printed in *Science*, contained a question of ". . . who was Mayer?" The speaker had found only one physicist, Henry Crew, who had known of Mayer, and he concluded: "A. M. Mayer (1836-1897) was professor of physics in Stevens Institute [Hoboken] and was the co-author of a very modest text (112 pp.) on Light. His contribution to physics has not been recorded in any history of physics with which I am acquainted." Now it should be pointed out that one set of Mayer's "simple and ingenious experiments" consisted of placing floating needles in a strong magnetic field. As one needle was added after another, Mayer found that the needles formed regular patterns, and that each additional needle produced a new pattern. These experiments were used by J. J. Thomson to "investigate the equilibrium of corpuscles in one plane by experiment as well as by analysis, using a method introduced by a different purpose by an American physicist, Professor Mayer." [11] Since the magnets show "how a number of bodies which repel each other with forces inversely proportional to the square of the distance between them will arrange themselves when under the action of an attractive force tending to drag them to a fixed point," J. J. Thomson saw a clear analogy with possible configurations of "corpuscles" (electrons) within atoms, in stable shells. He found these configurations: "three needles at the corners of a triangle, four at the corners of a square, five at the corners of a pentagon, . . ." but with six, a hexagon with one at the center . . . ." Thomson's application of Mayer's experiments marks the beginning of our knowledge of the internal structure of atoms; who will deny that these experiments were, as Rowland said, a "source of pleasure and profit to many"?

as " the inventor of the lightning rod, the hoax, and the republic." It has been maintained that there is no clear evidence that he ever performed the kite experiment, and it is certain that the experiment was performed elsewhere before Franklin wrote of it as a possibility. In any event, Franklin's work in science did not lack for publicity.

This statement is cited § because it is typical of the sentiment of many American scientists concerning Franklin's place in the growth of modern physics. All too many physicists know of Franklin as a scientist only that he once flew a kite during a thunderstorm (an experiment apt to be chiefly remarkable because " Franklin was not killed at once ") and that Franklin invented the lightning rod. Some few know, furthermore, that the designations used in electricity— " plus " and " minus " or " positive " and " negative "—are owed to Franklin, but this fact is sometimes mentioned in a derogatory fashion, since we would be better off if Franklin had reversed the names. If the lighting rod is an invention rather than a discovery, as Joseph Henry said,[13] then Franklin's legacy to pure physics would seem to comprise the kite experiment and an error in nomenclature that is at present a source of unfortunate confusion.

Since the physicist's knowledge about Franklin as a scientist is so often limited to the kite experiment, the denial that he ever made this experiment (like the statement that the experiment was not original with Franklin) strips him of his only apparent claim to the high place given him by Rowland. Franklin does not, in these terms, seem to have a sufficient stature to warrant his being mentioned in the same breath with Newton.

Franklin as a Scientist, according to the American Historian

One further consideration is certainly relevant in a discussion of the treatment of Franklin by historians. When historians look back on the personalities of past ages, they cannot help but envisage reasonable types. A " universal genius " is not such a " reasonable type "; when one is supposedly encountered, as in the case of Lio-

§ It may be observed that only the first sentence is true. (Balzac's statement may have been made, but he too was wrong; we need not discuss the merits of a novelist's statement in an historical argument.) Franklin's fame as scientist began when he was awarded the Copley Medal of the Royal Society of London in 1753, long before the world knew him as a statesman. The evidence about the kite experiment is provided in a letter of Franklin's, published in the *Philosophical Transactions* of the Royal Society and reprinted in all the editions of his book on electricity, and in the account he gave Priestley for his history of electricity; " the experiment " that " was performed elsewhere " was hardly antecedent to Franklin's writing " of it as a possibility," since that other experiment had also been devised by Franklin, published by him, and carried out in France according to his specifications—and, be it noted, by the translator of Franklin's book on electricity.[12]

nardo da Vinci, great stress is apt to be laid on his failures: his unfinished paintings, the treatises never completed for publication. No man is allowed by history (or, perhaps, by historians) to accomplish too much. Now Benjamin Franklin was a man whose appeal lies in the fact that he seems so human and alive, even after the passage of two centuries. He has been described as the only one of the founding fathers whom we might have wanted to greet by shaking his hand. Such a man might well do the things that other Americans do, and might even do them very much better. We are not particularly astonished to discover his wit and literary style, his skill as printer and newspaper editor, his sagacity in politics and diplomacy, and his efficiency in public service. As a trained craftsman, he was obviously talented at doing things with his hands, and it is completely reasonable that he was a talented inventor. Did not Jefferson too produce a variety of ingenious gadgets and inventions, like the improved plow? [14] It was characteristic of the "age of enlightenment" for men to be interested in science. Jefferson's hobby of palæontology is almost as well known to historians as Franklin's kite experiment. So far and no farther does the "reasonable type" extend. No one would ever think of coupling the names of Jefferson and Darwin. The average historian would never conceive—much less understand—a similar coupling of the names of Newton and Franklin.

As the figure of a Newton is far removed from that of a "founding father" of the American republic, so the full measure of Franklin's importance in the growth of physical thought removes him completely from the simple, plausible human beings that we tend to re-create in the past. It is far easier to reduce Franklin's supposed "hobby" to its "proper" place. Evidence to support this reduction is available; historians point to the relatively few years Franklin devoted to intensive scientific research. Mention of the short time Franklin spent as a scientist is repeated in the secondary literature *ad nauseam*; but who else in the history of science has ever had the importance of his scientific achievement judged by the measure of time it took to do the research? Euler wrote so many books and articles [15] that it seems as if a lifetime were too short for him to be able to write them all, much less revise them: but I know of no historian or scientist who has depreciated a single contribution of Euler's because it took so little time. No one would think of demoting Newton's scientific work to a minor position in the theory of thought because he abandoned science to work in the Mint and because even while he held his professorship in Cambridge he devoted a major part of his intellectual resources to the study of Biblical history, theology, and alchemy.

Franklin as a Scientist, according to the Historian of Science

One final consideration—perhaps the most important of all—that must be given its due weight in a discussion of modern views of Franklin as a scientist is the extreme youth of the history of science as a scholarly academic discipline. Historians of literature, philosophy, theology, political theory, and economic doctrine do not generally have much scientific training and experience; only in extremely rare instances is there an historian who has, say, studied any branch of science on the graduate level. Thus, even if the historian develops some interest in the history of science as it relates to his own research and teaching, all too often he is limited—especially in the science of the last 250 years—to whatever may be revealed by secondary works. The great primary documents of modern science— in physical science such works as Newton's *Principia Mathematica*, Laplace's *Mécanique Céleste*, Fourier's *Théorie Analytique de la Chaleur*, Clerk Maxwell's *Treatise on Electricity and Magnetism*—are written in a mathematical language that most historians cannot read. Students of intellectual and cultural and social history are often eager to use the results of research in the history of modern science, but they cannot usually do such research themselves. Considering the lack of adequate and accurate interpretive works produced by competent, professional historians of science, one cannot but applaud the historians for the brave efforts they have made.

Few scientists today have the time, energy, or inclination to read the original documents in the history of science. There was a time, now passed, when it was held that such a study might have immediate practical value for the research scientist. The most vocal exponent of this view was the great physical chemist, Wilhelm Ostwald, and his famous series of *Klassiker der exakten Naturwissenschaften* was produced as part of his program to improve research technique, and eventually to establish a new science of discovery, based on the study and analysis of great scientific works of the past.[16] No one, to my knowledge, holds with Ostwald's argument today, although in the past decades a number of scientists have come to appreciate the unique value of the study of the history of science for understanding the role of the scientific enterprise in our society.

Yet scientists often attempt to study the scientific documents of the past, despite their lack of historical training. Scientific books of two hundred years ago or more are written in a language that is different from that used in scientific books today. In order fully to understand and to evaluate the scientific writings of the time of Franklin, a knowledge of present-day electrical theory may be necessary but it is hardly sufficient. What is required is an appreciation of what other scientists were trying to do at that time, what the general scientific background of the era was: how the work in question was—in other words—related to the state of science itself at that time. To ask the scientist to steep himself in the science of the past is nothing other than to ask him to forego his scientific career and to become an historian of science. Clearly, the scientist, just like the historian, is hindered in his attempt to understand and evaluate the work of a man like Franklin by the lack of informed secondary works which would make the task feasible.*

In the light of the important place of scientific enterprise in the making of modern civilization, many otherwise well-informed persons find it difficult to believe that the history of science is actually so young a discipline that scholarly research in this field has barely been initiated. A few examples will quickly show how true this is. The greatest scientist of the modern period—Isaac Newton—cannot be studied easily, because there has been no modern edition of his collected works; that made by Horsley in the eighteenth century is woefully incomplete, and does not include even a significant part of Newton's writings, or of his correspondence. Furthermore, there exists no critically annotated edition of any of Newton's major works; the two greatest of these, the *Principia* and the *Opticks*, although in print, are difficult to use even for the specialist.† The same remarks apply to Lavoisier, the editing of his correspondence being only in the beginning stage. Innumerable other major figures lack biographies, critical editions, or published correspondence. There are, lastly, all too few studies on the growth of science in America.

Once we recognize that serious study of the history of science has barely been initiated, we begin to appreciate why Franklin the

---

* It should be observed, however, that there are always notable exceptions to generalizations of this kind.[17] Furthermore, the deep insight into his field of a research scientist can never be equalled by an historian of science; hence, the scientist will in many cases be able to discern significant aspects of earlier scientific work that would always escape the historian of science.

† For example, no edition of Newton's *Principia* has ever been issued in which the variations between the successive editions are indicated, a matter of some importance, to be discussed in Chapters Five and Six. The standard edition of today, edited by the late Florian Cajori, contains neither an index nor an adequate table of contents; to locate Newton's thoughts on a given subject, or his treatment of some given topic (in a theorem, corollary, or scholium), the student must read through the whole book, or consult the outline made by Rouse Ball.[18] The *Opticks*, likewise, does not exist in a " variorum " edition, and has only recently been issued with an analytical table of contents, although without an index.[19] The Royal Society of London is currently sponsoring an edition of Newton's correspondence, to be published under the able editorship of Professor Turnbull, but there appears to be no immediate prospect of an edition of Newton's published works, even the scientific ones, or of a complete edition of his unpublished manuscripts.[20]

physicist has been largely a neglected figure. Until now, it has been chiefly the historians, rather than the scientists, who have been interested in Franklin's experiments and theories. These historians have had to work without the guides and scholarly monographs to be found in all fields of learning save the history of science. No wonder that they have not been able to do justice to this aspect of Franklin's career! The stress often laid on the practical rather than the theoretical aspect of his work, the confusion of Franklin's inventions with his efforts in pure science, have produced an emphasizing of the " Franklin stove " and the lightning rod at the expense of the place of Franklin's thought in the age of Newton. But some historians would even have us believe that Franklin " directed " his scientific work so that it would have a practical outcome, or was interested only in aspects of science that would prove practical—thereby betraying nothing less than a woeful ignorance of the nature of scientific enterprise.

It has been mentioned earlier that some more or less adequate account of certain aspects of Franklin's research in electricity may be found in modern European books on the history of science. No one, who reads the material on Franklin in the books of Rosenberger, Hoppe, Whittaker, or Wolf, would categorize Franklin as a " practical " man or inventor at the expense of his contribution to experimental knowledge in electricity and to " pure " theory. Nor would any such reader reduce Franklin's impressive additions to electrical science to a single experiment (the lightning kite) and a new terminology.

Franklin as a Scientist, according to the Eighteenth-Century Scientists

The author of every book on electricity in the latter half of the eighteenth century either referred to Benjamin Franklin by name—and not alone for his lightning kite and rod—or employed the concepts which he introduced into electrical science.‡ His book on electricity was one of the most widely read and admired treatises of its kind in the eighteenth century. Five editions were published in English, one in Italian, one in German, and a French translation went through two editions before a new and better translation appeared. Here is a genuine index of his scientific reputation, because these ten editions in four languages all issued from the press before the American Revolution.[21]

‡ By this I mean that even those authors who believed in a two-fluid theory of electricity, based their ideas on a pair of Franklinian fluids; this topic is explored further in Chapter Eleven.

In 1753 Franklin was awarded the Sir Godfrey Copley Gold Medal of the Royal Society of London for having " deserved well of the philosophical [i. e., scientific] world . . . [for] the experiments he has made . . . [and] the conclusions which he imagines may be deduced from them." [22] Franklin was told he was " the first person out of the nation [England] that has had that honour conferred." [23] In April, 1756, he was elected a Fellow of the Royal Society and given the unusual privilege of having his name " inserted in the lists before his admission [i. e., the admission ceremony], and without any fee, or other payment to the Society. And that such name be continued in the lists, so long as he shall continue to reside abroad." [24] In 1772, Franklin was elected *associé étranger* of the Académie Royale des Sciences, Paris, a particularly significant honor since, by the governing statutes of that society, there could be but eight such foreign associates at any one time; for one hundred years no other American was so honored. Evidence is abundant of the esteem in which his work was held by contemporaneous scientists.

Celebrated as a leader in the world of science from one end of Europe to the other, Benjamin Franklin's principles " bid fair to be handed down to posterity," as Joseph Priestley wrote, " as expressive of the true principles of electricity; just as the Newtonian philosophy is of the true system of nature in general." [25] The " American Newton " [26] was, even then, better known as a scientist in Europe than in America. Such words as " Franklinism," " Franklinist," and the " Franklinian system," it was said, occurred on almost every page of some Continental books on electricity.[27] Silvanus Thomson noted in 1898 that electrophysiologists and electrotherapists " still indulge in the jargon of ' franklinization.' " [28]

The facts concerning the reception of Franklin's electrical ideas in Europe show clearly that his reputation as a scientist was independent of his own activities as printer and actually antedated his career as a statesman. Franklin never printed his own electrical writings during the period of his most intense creativity; their partial publication in the *Philosophical Transactions* and *The Gentleman's Magazine* was entirely the result of independent action by his British admirers, who also arranged for the publication in England of his book. So, too, the translation of that book into French, at Buffon's suggestion, was undertaken wholly on merit and without any personal intervention on Franklin's part; in fact, Franklin was pleasantly surprised by the news that a French translation had been made and published. To say, therefore, that had Franklin " not been famous as a publisher and a statesman, he might never have been heard of as a scientist," is absolutely wrong. Just the opposite is more nearly the case; his international fame and public renown as a scientist was in no small measure responsible for his success in international statesmanship. When Benjamin Franklin arrived in England in 1757 and again in 1764, or in France in 1776, he was not merely a representative of some provincial group, but a well-known figure with a commanding international reputation as a scientist. When Lord Chatham referred to Franklin's political ideas in Parliamentary debate, he compared him to " our Boyle " and " our Newton." The invention of the lightning rod, providing a device for preventing the destruction that had plagued mankind since time immemorial, of course made his name known on all levels of society, and it brought him a measure of fame among vast multitudes who could never hope to grasp the significance of theoretical physics. The demonstration that the lightning discharge, nature's mysterious and terrifying thunderbolt, was nothing other than the common laboratory spark discharge on a larger scale was particularly pleasing to the rationalist spirit of the day. It showed that experiment could eliminate common superstitions and fears. In an age in which kings, lords, and commoners were interested in science to a degree never before encountered in human history, Franklin, as one of the leading scientists of the age, met with a reception abroad that none of his American diplomatic colleagues could hope to command.

Comparing Science Past and Present

As we contemplate Franklin's scientific research in the age of Newton, we must keep in mind that the time in which he worked at electricity—the late 1740's and the '50's—was very long ago. A span of two centuries in modern science is difficult to bridge, even with a sympathetic eagerness to reach back to that state of knowledge and thought. In one sense, the physical science of antiquity or of the Middle Ages may be easier to grasp than that of the seventeenth and eighteenth centuries. Many of the concepts and postulates of distant ages are so totally different from ours that we can approach them freshly in their own terms without the encumbrance of our own preconceptions. But the physical science of the seventeenth and eighteenth centuries is largely our own science in its nascent form, and we cannot read any discussion written in those periods without attempting a translation of the ideas into our own more precise conceptual language and without making a comparison with our own more advanced state of understanding. It is difficult for us to appreciate the mighty effort required then to establish simple fundamentals that are taken for granted as " obvious " today. Yet, to make the achievements of the seventeenth and eighteenth centuries esteemed, we have only to see how many first-rate men struggled with them before a satisfactory result was obtained, however simple it may all seem in retrospect.

The fundamental postulate of the history of science is that the scientists of the past were just as intelligent as we are and that, therefore, the problems that baffled them would have baffled us too, had we been living then. Newton or Archimedes would have been a genius in any age. Yet since knowledge in science is cumulative, every college senior majoring in physics knows more about physics than Newton, just as Newton knew more physics than Archimedes. Archimedes could not have written the *Principia* because he lived too early, and Newton would not have written it had he lived in the twelfth century. But the average college senior majoring in physics would have written neither the *Principia* nor the works of Archimedes, no matter when he might have lived. And only a scientist of the first rank would ever have devised the experiments that Franklin performed, would have drawn from them the theoretical conclusions Franklin drew, and would have built thereupon the conceptual scheme which shall be described in the following chapters.

SOURCES

The literature concerning Franklin is so vast that a complete list of all the books and articles dealing with him would undoubtedly be much greater than the bibliography of his own writings, even if the latter included all printings, reprintings, translations, and collections. Such a bibliography of Franklin's writings, prepared about a half-century ago, is still useful although inadequate: Ford (1889). A selective guide to the secondary literature, of the greatest value to the student of Franklin, may be found in Mott and Jorgenson (1936: cxlii-clxxxviii), supplemented by Van Doren (1938: 786-807). Wechter (1941) contains an exemplary discussion of Franklin's reputation in America, exclusive of his scientific reputation; I have presented Franklin in the American tradition in Cohen (1953). The degree of practicality in Franklin's research is discussed in Cohen (1945b), and the whole question is placed in the larger perspective of American history in Shryock (1948); see also Fulton (1951), Kilgour (1949).

An examination of some first-class books on American history—it would not be of much value to discuss any that were not first-class—shows the curious state of opinion concerning Franklin's science. Greene (1943) reduces Franklin's whole career in science to the bare statement that he made " electrical experiments." Hockett (1943) mentions " experiments " which brought him fame and honorary degrees for " improvements in the electric branch of natural philosophy "—and no more. Parrington (1927) tells us of Franklin's science only that " his experiments in natural philosophy won the approbation of the gentry," and that he established " a reputation as a natural philosopher." Nettels (1946) contains a statement that Franklin " directed his scientific thought to the improvement of material conditions," calls him one of a number of " correspondents " of the Royal Society of London (but does not indicate his membership or the award of the Copley Medal for his research), mentions the lightning experiment and some inventions (stove, clock, lightning rod) but not his contributions to electrical theory. In Morison and Commager (1942) I found no word on Franklin as a scientist.

In Curti, Shryock, et al. (1950), " Franklin's work on electricity " is described as " outstanding "; it is a pleasant relief to find a statement that Franklin " started his investigations of electricity with no thought of their possible usefulness," but I regret that nothing is said about his theory of electricity. There is no indication that he proposed an original theory of electrical action, the first theory which actually unified the subject and enabled scientists to predict the outcome of so many experiments. Certainly no reader would guess that Franklin's contemporaries might have called him a " Newton," and that this appellation might have been deserved.

Although there are no adequate general surveys of science in America, several works contain valuable information on particular aspects of the subject. Scientific instruments and the teaching of science in Colonial America are discussed in Cohen (1950*a*); Hornberger (1945); and Morison (1936); American scientific institutions in Bates (1945); Cohen (1945*a*); Hale (1913-1915); and Pickard (1946); attitudes towards science and scientific research in America in Bush (1945); National Resources Committee (1938); Perazich and Field (1940); Steelman (1947); Shryock (1947). An historian's views of the whole problem may be found in Schlesinger (1946). A suggestive outline is presented in Guerlac (1952: 182-187).

REFERENCES

1. See Mott and Jorgenson, 1936: clxviii.
2. Letter to Polly Stevenson, 20 Sept. 1761, Franklin, 1941: 386; 1769: " 466 " [477].
3. " Opinions & Conjectures," §19, Franklin, 1941: 219; 1769: 62.
4. Thomson, 1936: 249-258; Hoppe, 1884: 27-41; Rosenberger, 1898: 16-21; Whittaker, 1951: 46-53; Wolf, 1952: 227-235; Priestley, 1775: *passim*.
5. Wheeler, 1951.
6. Henry, 1874: 8; see Coulson, 1950.
7. Hale, 1913, 1914, 1915; True, 1913.
8. Quoted in True, 1913: 15.
9. Rowland, 1899.
10. *Science* 104: 238, 1946.
11. Thomson, 1907: 110.
12. This whole question is treated at length in Cohen, 1952*b*, which contains bibliographical references to the earlier literature on the same subject.
13. Henry, 1886-1887: 320.
14. See Martin, 1952.
15. Eneström, 1910-1913.
16. Ostwald, 1910.
17. An example of extraordinary historical research by a scientist is Whittaker, 1951; of historical editing, Clerk Maxwell's Cavendish, 1921; of the study of an individual scientist, Dubos, 1950.
18. Newton, 1934; Ball, 1893: 74-112.
19. Newton, 1952.
20. Newton, 1954*b*; see Dreyer, 1924.
21. See Franklin, 1941: intro., pp. 141-148.
22. *Ibid.*, 127.
23. *Ibid.*, 128n.
24. Stearns, 1946: 244-246.
25. Priestley, 1775: 1: 193.
26. Kraus, 1949: 184.
27. Priestley, 1775: 1: 193.
28. Thomson, 1898: 137.

CHAPTER THREE

THE SCIENTIFIC PERSONALITY OF FRANKLIN AND OF NEWTON

> Like its literary and artistic counterparts, the process of scientific creation is a completely personal experience for which no technique of observation has yet been devised. Moreover, out of false modesty, pride, lack of inclination or psychological insight, very few of the great discoverers have revealed their own mental processes; at the most they have described methods of work—but rarely their dreams, urges, struggles and visions.
>
> —RENÉ DUBOS (1950)

MOST BIOGRAPHIES of men of science inform their readers about the main events of the particular subject's life, his family background, his religion, his schooling, his friends, his successive positions, his discoveries and his ultimate recognition or his failure to obtain it. Commonly, the subject's personality and the conditioning factors in his life are portrayed in total divorce from his creative activity. In extreme cases, the biography may have two wholly separate parts, one devoted to the " life " and the other to the " science "; [1] or two authors may collaborate, one relating the events in the subject's life and the other evaluating the contribution to science.[2] Underlying this conventional approach is an undeclared thesis that science has a life of its own and that every scientific discovery—whether a new phenomenon, a law or a theory—is independent of the personality of the discoverer because of the objective quality of science: the facts of nature, or relations between facts of nature, or conceptual schemes that accurately predict observed facts of nature. Science from this point of view is often contrasted with the arts. A symphony of Beethoven, a poem by Milton, or a drawing by Blake are obvious expressions of the creator's personality, and we may even recognize the author of the creation by paying educated attention to the style. By contrast, a phenomenon—for instance, the horizontal rotation of a magnetic needle, when a wire parallel to the needle carries an electric current of sufficient intensity—betrays nothing whatever of the personality of the discoverer, who might equally well have been any one of a number of investigators. The impersonal character of scientific knowledge is given added emphasis by the well-known fact that many important discoveries are made simultaneously by independent investigators of wholly different backgrounds and distinct personalities. Learned heads, therefore, are apt to nod in agreement when the statement, attributed to Einstein, is quoted to the effect that even had Newton or Leibniz never lived, the world would have had the calculus,[3] but that if Beethoven had not lived, we would never have had the C-Minor Symphony.*

Like all general truths, the propositions just stated need many qualifications. Certainly the form of a theory, and even the type of concepts employed, may reflect the personality of the creator. Why do the thoughts of one scientist appear as mathematical equations while those of another do not? In some cases the answer to this restricted question may seem to lie only in the previous mathematical training of the men, or even the degree of advancement of the subject at the time of their work, but this cannot tell the whole story; men think differently from one another. To take another example, how many scientists in 1905 would have described, or even have conceived, a theory as " heuristic " ? It is greatly to be doubted whether more than a handful of scientists were then even acquainted with the word. So we may guess that Einstein's concept of the photon, formulated as something of " heuristic " value,† was conceived and presented in a form peculiar to his own special kind of genius. The experimental facts about induced currents might possibly have been found by anyone, but surely the concept of " lines of force," or " tubes," reaching out through a full space from charged bodies and magnets, have certain characteristic qualities that seem uniquely related to the individual personality of their inventor, Faraday.

The historian, furthermore, cannot help exploring problems of personality whenever he studies the lifetime program of research of

* Professor Philipp Frank informs me that Albert Einstein was willing to admit this hypothesis in respect to only the early special theory of relativity, but not the general theory of relativity, a view also attributed to Einstein by his most recent biographer.[4] Einstein actually wrote that if he had not discovered the special theory of relativity Paul Langevin would have.

† A classic description of Einstein's " heuristic " presentation has been given by Karl K. Darrow as follows: " Where Planck in 1900 had said simply that bound electrons emit and absorb energy in fixed finite quantities, and shortly afterwards softened his novel idea as far as possible by making it apply only to the act of emission, Einstein in 1905 rushed boldly in and presented the idea that these fixed finite quantities of radiant energy retain their identity throughout their wanderings through space from the moment of emission to the moment of absorption. This idea he offered as a ' heuristic ' one—the word, if I grasp its connotation exactly, is an apologetic sort of word, used to describe a theory which achieves successes though its author feels at heart that it is really too absurd to be presentable. The implication is, that the experimenters should proceed to verify the predictions based upon the idea, quite as if it were acceptable, while remembering always that it is absurd. If the successes continue to mount up, the absurdity may be confidently expected to fade gradually out of the public mind. Such was the destiny of this heuristic idea." [5]

any scientist. The most casual reading of the diary and letters of Michael Faraday reveals his firm conviction of the unity of natural phenomena; his expressions of this point of view show an intense religious kind of flavor matched only by the lofty and occasionally lyrical quality of his general statements about " nature," which he personified as " our friend." Faraday's research program of showing the identity of the effects produced by electricity of different kinds (frictional, galvanic, pyro-, chemical, etc.) and of proving the convertibility of forces of one sort into another (electrical, magnetic, gravitational, etc.) was certainly inspired by a fundamental outlook on the world as a whole that was related to his personality and, without doubt, to his deep religious convictions. He was a Sandemanian, a member of a dissenting Protestant sect founded in the eighteenth century. Those who knew Faraday were impressed by his religious simplicity and the spiritual exaltation that he derived from the contemplation of nature. " His religious feeling and his philosophy," Tyndall wrote, " could not be kept apart; there was an habitual overflow of the one into the other." Science was " so glorious " according to Faraday that research " rejoices and encourages the feeblest; delights and enchants the strongest." [6] To understand the creative life of such a man, we must know those qualities of his personality that led him into the paths he followed. In the case of Newton, as we shall see, his personality so influenced his thought, writings, and scientific behavior that the mark remained on the life of science as a whole for more than a hundred years. In general, then, I believe that to gain an insight into the ways discoveries are made, and the genesis of ideas in science, we must appreciate certain personal qualities of the scientists, even though their actual contributions to science may be evaluated in the main stream of scientific thought on a higher level of abstraction.

Even if we grant that the personality of a scientist may influence the course of his research, we have still to face the question of how to study the personality of figures of the past. From the point of view of the psychologist, letters, diaries, and works prepared for publication may be more significant for what is omitted than for what they contain.‡ The reminiscences of friends, relatives, and

‡ The testimony of scientists themselves about their own discoveries is apt to be misleading if not downright false. An eminent scientist with whom I have discussed this question has written to me: " In the course of my own scientific life, I have had the good luck of witnessing, at very close range, the making of several important discoveries. I have also read the account of these discoveries, at times by the discoverers themselves, more often by others—scientists or laymen. And in practically all cases, I have been awed by the discrepancy between actual happenings and published accounts of them. I am convinced that in order to provide raw material for the historian of the future (and of the present), it would be most desirable to obtain

acquaintances are helpful, but it is generally true that information is scantiest for the most important formative periods: childhood and early youth. Modern methods of studying personality are not always helpful in studying figures of the past. Psychoanalysis is difficult to apply because the records of dreams and fantasies are incomplete. Although Freud himself made a " psycho-sexual " study of Leonardo da Vinci, based chiefly on a single infantile fantasy-image, he advised the greatest caution in such matters. When Freud was asked by Maxim Leroy to interpret the dreams described by Descartes, he pointed out that the analyst can tell little about dreams unless he has the cooperation of the dreamer.[7] Until now, only one known scientist of the highest rank was ever the subject of a psychological examination which was later published.§ Henri Poincaré, one of the greatest mathematicians of all times, allowed himself in old age to be the subject of a variety of psychological tests, administered by Dr. Henri Toulouse. The results are embodied in a disappointing book, which tells us very little about Poincaré's personality or the qualities of his creative genius; it is chiefly notable for the deficiencies of the exploratory methods of the investigator, who applied in a rather mechanical way the " intelligence " tests that had been devised for purposes far removed from the analysis of scientific genius.[9] We may nevertheless hope for a day when the dark majestic reaches of Newton's unconscious may be revealed by a new technique that will probe its depths by using, in a new way, Newton's letters and manuscripts and the anecdotes about his behavior.* How wonderful it

now very factual accounts of the accidents, chance circumstances, and blunderings, which play such an essential part in the making of discoveries. Only thus could be made clear the part played by the great and deep trends of thought in the progress of science. Unless I am mistaken, it is the discoverers themselves who should write the accounts. And it will not be easy to obtain from them the real truth. Scientists, just like other men, like fiction far more than truth, in particular when dealing with their own life and achievements. And then, it is so easy to forget, especially when forgetting contributes to increasing one's stature in society. Although it will be very difficult to obtain factual and honest accounts, trying is well worth the effort. Moreover, it is probable that with time a technique for obtaining true stories will emerge. Intelligent guidance may teach scientists the art and science of intelligent confessions."

§ The explorations of Anne Roe are intended to reveal some aspects of the psychological profile of a number of anonymous scientists, but she makes no attempt to relate the personality of those whom she has studied to their particular creative life. More recently, Lawrence Kubie has published a plea for scientists to write to him about their personality problems; it would seem that the major emphasis is a kind of preventive psychiatric therapy for scientists rather than an illumination of scientific creativity. The " occasion " of mathematical invention, based on example, has been studied by the French mathematician, Jacques Hadamard. An important essay on the whole subject of personality and science has been written by John K. Wright.[8]

* For example, Newton laid the foundations of the science of color analysis; yet he had a predilection for a single color, red. Colonel de Villamil, who discovered the " inventory of all and singular the goods, chattels and credits of Sir Isaac Newton at

would be to understand the mind and the whole personality of Newton.

Even though we have no technique at present available to us to permit an adequate exploration of the whole personality of scientists who lived long ago, we often find in the records rewarding information about the working habits, and quirks of character related to the scientific thought, of men like Newton or Franklin. We can explore the scientific personality of Newton and of Franklin chiefly in relation to the quite different kinds of veneration accorded these two scientists during the eighteenth century. The two divergent images of a scientist that they present are related to the feelings each one aroused and, in this way, to their respective places in the growth of scientific thought. An analysis of their personalities as reflected in their scientific stature is a necessary condition to an understanding of their influence throughout the century.

Aspects of Newton's Personality

It would be difficult to conceive two personality types as different as Franklin and Newton. One was a happy extrovert, with a wife and three children, who loved the company of women and was gregarious and self-assured. The other was a tortured introvert, who remained a bachelor all his life, and had—at the height of his powers—what we would call today a " nervous breakdown." Of " Newton, the Man," the late Lord Keynes has written:

For in vulgar modern terms Newton was profoundly neurotic of a not unfamiliar type, but—I should say from the records—a most extreme example. His deepest instincts were occult, esoteric, semantic—with profound shrinking from the world, a paralyzing fear of exposing his thoughts, his beliefs, his discoveries in all nakedness to the inspection and criticism of the world. " Of the most fearful, cautious and suspicious temper that I ever knew," said Whiston, his successor in the Lucasian Chair. The too well-known conflicts and ignoble quarrels with Hooke, Flamsteed, Leibnitz are only too clear an evidence of this. Like all his type he was wholly aloof from women. He parted with and published nothing except under the extreme pressure of friends. Until the second phase of his life, he was a wrapt, consecrated solitary, pursuing his studies by intense introspection with a mental endurance perhaps never equalled.

the date of his decease . . . ," observed that " nearly everything in his house is . . . of ' crimson '—crimson mohair curtains nearly everywhere. Newton's own bed was a ' crimson mohair bed,' with ' crimson harrateen' bed-curtains. The beds all had ' calico quilts,' which were, I fancy, what are called in India *rezais*—red cotton printed with Cashmere patterns. Newton's own room also had ' crimson mohair hangings,' lined with canvas, and in his dining-room there was a crimson sattee.' In fact, there is no other colour referred to in the ' inventory ' but crimson." [10]

FIG. 1. Sir Isaac Newton. Mezzotint by James MacArdel, after the painting by
Enoch Seeman. *Courtesy of the Burndy Library.*

FIG. 2. Benjamin Franklin. Engraving by E. Fisher, after the portrait by
Mason Chamberlin.

Lord Keynes also has said that Newton was " not the first of the age of reason," but " the last of the magicians ":

Why do I call him a magician? Because he looked on the whole universe and all that is in it *as a riddle,* as a secret which could be read by applying pure thought to certain evidence, certain mystic clues which God had laid about the world to allow a sort of philosopher's treasure hunt to the esoteric brotherhood. He believed that these clues were to be found partly in the evidence of the heavens and in the constitution of elements (and that is what gives the false suggestion of his being an experimental natural philosopher) , but also partly in certain papers and traditions handed down by the brethren is an unbroken chain back to the original cryptic revelation in Babylonia. He regarded the universe as a cryptogram set by the Almighty—just as he himself wrapt the discovery of the calculus in a cryptogram when he communicated with Leibnitz. By pure thought, by concentration of mind, the riddle, he believed, would be revealed to the initiate.[11]

In Part Two of this book, we shall have occasion to investigate in some detail the relations between what Newton said about science and the science his own technical writings display: this is part of that fundamental question to be explored, the difference—in science —between what men say and what men do. In the case of Newton this problem is made especially difficult for the interpreter because Newton's general statements about science, or about the proper kinds of scientific explanation (such as that he framed no hypotheses) , are apt to be at considerable variance with his actual practice. In attempts to harmonize the obvious discrepancy, many commentators have produced a tortured exegesis which requires the omission of many of Newton's major writings. The task of reading this secondary literature is often made even more complex by the practice of attempting to explain Newton's writings on one subject by those on another subject, as to use the *Opticks* to explain the *Principia,* even though Newton apparently kept the two quite distinct. Or, there is a practice of lumping together all of his writings on optics, as if there had been no change of mind between that youthful communication to the Royal Society in 1671 (when Newton was a young man of twenty-nine) [12] and the set of " Queries " in the *Opticks,* written forty-six years later for the edition of 1717. Yet another source of confusion is the presentation of Newton's single works—e. g., the *Opticks,* but more notably the *Principia*—without taking account of the development of ideas which was reflected in the major alterations or additions which were introduced by Newton in the successive editions he produced during his life-time.

Some of the changes introduced into the revised editions of Newton's works were made in response to criticism or were reflections of those familiar controversies referred to by Lord Keynes, which are as characteristic of Newton the scientist as his penetrating insight and his fabulous powers of concentration. It was a clearly marked trait of Newton's personality that he should resent criticism and be a continuous storm-center of controversy: both concerning the nature of his discoveries and their interpretation, and even his priority in the discovery itself. Although he entered the lists in his own behalf and encouraged others to take his part, he often declared a constant aversion for controversies. He wrote to Leibniz: " I was so persecuted with discussions arising out of my theory of light, that I blamed my own imprudence for parting with so substantial a blessing as my quiet to run after a shadow." [13]

Having been burnt by the fire of controversy at the time of his first publication, we are told, Newton became more cautious—at least about allowing his later writings to get into the hands of a printer. Yet he submitted a daring hypothesis to the Royal Society where it was read and discussed and entered into the archives.[14] It is said that he withheld the *Opticks* from the publisher until the last of the objectors to his first optical publications was dead. At any rate we know that the book had been as good as ready for the press for about a decade prior to its publication in 1704,[15] and that Hooke— with whom Newton had had many an unpleasant encounter—had died in 1703. Knowing something of Hooke's pugnacious temperament, we can appreciate this course of action and sympathize with it.†

The mature Newton was certainly never one to rush into print, or even to get himself into print at all. De Morgan once wrote that every discovery of Newton's had two aspects: Newton would discover something but it was a harder job for his contemporaries to discover that he had done so. Most of the *Principia* is said to have lain complete in notes and in the mind of the author when Halley came to ask him a question about celestial dynamics. The story of how Halley got Newton to write that great work is too well known to need any retelling here, but we may recall that Halley undertook to prepare Newton's masterpiece for the press, read the proofs, and— although far from wealthy—paid the costs of publication. Even though we accept the fact of Newton's caution in publishing, we

† David Gregory recorded, under the date of 1 March 1703/4, the immediate occasion of the publication of the *Opticks*: " Dr. Hook's remains are printing & by this time M. de Moivre's book against Dr. Cheyn[e] is out. The *Astrologos & Ephemeridum Conscriptoribus* in Dr. Cheyn[e']s Appendix to his book is intended against Mr. Halley. Mr. Newton was provoked by Dr. Cheyn[e']s book [*Fluxionum methodus inversa* (1703)] to publish his *Quadratures*, and with it, his *Light & Colours*, etc." [16]

Gregory also recorded, 16 Oct. 1695, " To give my most humble service to Mr. Newton, & to assure him that I'l put his Optics in Latin."

must use the utmost care to avoid the common exaggeration that Newton never published anything willingly or that he had no interest in having the world know of his discoveries. To imply that Newton would never have published his *Principia*, or even that the book would not have been written, but for Halley, seems to me idle guesswork and a case of confounding an occasion and a cause. Had Halley's visit to Newton occurred ten years earlier, he would not have come away with a promise of a *Principia* because Newton would not yet have solved some of the major problems. Halley arrived at an auspicious moment. Many of the most difficult questions had been resolved to Newton's satisfaction, and what lay ahead was the systemization, the proofs, and the details, knotty though they might be. After the stimulation of Halley, Newton was able to leap over the last hurdles. Not having the sixth sense of prophecy, I am frank to admit that I have no way of telling whether Newton would ever have produced a *Principia* without the occasion of a Halley. On the other hand, it is a matter of record that Newton required very little urging from Halley and that his other contributions to physical science (but not to pure mathematics) ‡ were produced and published without much pressure from the outside.

Looking backward we find it obvious that Newton wanted fame and the applause of the learned for what he knew to be his extraordinary contributions to science, as much as he supposed he wanted to preserve his " quiet." This is one of the fundamental ambivalences that marked his personality and which must be taken into account whenever we seek to understand his conduct.

The Growth of Legend: Newton and Barrow

The common account of Newton—a man who had no interest whatever in having anyone know about his discoveries—derives from reading certain statements of his out of the context of events, and is based on a curious interpretation of his relations with his old teacher, Isaac Barrow, Master of Trinity. Barrow was so devoted to Newton that he resigned his own professorship at Cambridge in 1669 so that Newton might have it. During that same year Barrow published his *Lectiones Opticæ*, and in the preface thanked his former

‡ Newton's major contributions to physics were embodied in the *Principia* and the *Opticks*. The latter was apparently prepared for press by Newton himself; although Samuel Clarke made a Latin version for Newton, the second and third editions were revised by Newton without the aid of a collaborator. We shall see, below, that his first contributions to physics, the papers on the telescope and on light and color, were submitted freely by Newton to the Royal Society. Although he did not publish his *Optical lectures* which were ready for the press some thirty years or more before the printing of the *Opticks*, his papers in the *Philosophical Transactions* and the *Opticks* itself contained practically the whole of his physical doctrine concerning light.

pupil and present successor for his kindness in having revised the copy and for having made valuable suggestions for the book's improvement.§ But this book contains no hint whatever of the character of Newton's own fundamental discoveries in optics, " although from his own pen we know that he had already made many of them." [18] The nature of these discoveries was such as to make Barrow's discussion of color appear to be so much nonsense. It is generally agreed that Newton's actions are in keeping with his general character in so far as publication was concerned. His customary reticence to make known his discoveries is offered as a lame excuse for Newton's withholding the information from Barrow. Yet I see no reason why Newton should have announced his first major discovery in someone else's book. Even so, does it not seem strange that Newton had so little sense of gratitude that he did not tell Barrow to hold up publication of the book until announcement of his own new discoveries? Should not Newton have told Barrow at least to suppress the section on colors, with its crude notions that Newton knew to be wide of the mark? So strange has this action seemed to scholars, who try to conceive Newton in their own image, that they have admitted a perplexity in understanding it, and one has gone so far as to describe Barrow's theory of light as an obvious " parody " on contemporaneous theories.[19]

Perhaps, in 1669, when Barrow showed Newton the sheets of his lectures, Newton was not yet ready to bring out the results of his own research. Barrow's book contained the lectures he had given at Cambridge as Lucasian Professor; presumably they had been well received and contained some useful information—should they have been suppressed because eventually they would become wholly or partly out of date? Hardly! I believe that the most significant conclusion to be drawn from this story may be only that in 1669 Newton may not yet have contemplated an early publication of his discoveries on light and color. This possible reticence at rushing into print may have been due to shyness, but Newton could very well have thought of waiting until he had completed a whole treatise on the subject. In this case, his own book would have replaced not only Barrow's,

§ Barrow wrote: ". . . when I resolved to publish [my optical and geometrical lectures], I could not bear the pains of reading over again a great part of these things; either from my being tired with them, or not caring to undergo the pains and study in new modelling them. But I have done in this as weakly mothers, who give up their offspring to the care of their friends, either to nurse and bring up, or abandon to the wide world. One of which (for I think my self bound to name them) is Mr. Isaac Newton, my collegue, a man of great learning and sagacity, who revised my copy and noted such things as wanted correction, and even gave me some of his own, which you will see here and there interspersed with mine, not without their due commendations." [17]

but also every other book on light and color that had ever been written. In Newton's day, unlike ours, scientific discoveries were not usually published in journals, but in books. In the strict modern sense of the phrase, there was no scientific journal in those days. It it said that the eventual publication of Newton's letter on light and color in the *Philosophical Transactions* of the Royal Society of London was the first time that a major scientific discovery was announced in print in a periodical.

All discussions of Newton's relations with Barrow are based largely on conjecture rather than documentary evidence. The only " facts " in the case are: (1) Newton had made his optical discoveries before 1669 when Barrow published his lectures, (2) Barrow's published lectures do not indicate any awareness of those discoveries, (3) Barrow's *Epist. ad Lectorem*, in the original Latin edition, contains this statement, " Verùm, quod tenellæ matres factitant, â me depulsum partum amicorum haud recusantium nutriciae curæ commisi, prout ipsis visum esset, educandum aut exponendum, quorum unus (ipsos enim honestum duco nominatim agnoscere) *D. Isaacus Newtonus*, collega noster (peregregiæ vir indolis ac insignis peritiæ) *exemplar revisit, aliqua corrigenda* monens, sed et de suo nonnulla penu suggerens, quæ nostris alicubi cum laude innexa cernes." *
From these three " facts " the conclusion has been inferred that since Newton had criticized Barrow's manuscript and had suggested some revisions he must have withheld the new discoveries from Barrow. Otherwise, would Barrow have published " the accepted and erroneous explanation of all those subjects "? [20]

The readiness with which commentators on Newton have assented to this story seems to me to be chiefly notable as evidence of the universal agreement as to the strangeness of Newton's personality. But I must admit that the story is susceptible of a wholly different explanation. It is possible that Newton *did* tell Barrow about his new discoveries. Barrow was just terminating his scientific career to devote himself to theology. For the record, he was publishing his optical lectures more or less as they had been read to the Cambridge students.† To have accepted the fundamental revisions required by

---

* This statement comes from Barrow's preface (1669) to his optical lectures. To " vindicate " Newton's character, it has sometimes been supposed that this preface was intended to apply only to the geometrical lectures, an error that might easily arise from the fact that the preface in question was printed in the English translation of the geometrical lectures. The title page contains a statement that the lectures had been " revised, corrected and amended by the late Sir Isaac Newton," but the preface was plainly marked: " The author's preface to his optick and geometrical lectures."

† Barrow, in the preface, apologized for this very fact: " I desire you, who are well versed in matters of this kind, to remember what those things are which you are

Newton's discoveries would have implied the discarding of part of the manuscript or a complete rewriting of it. Very few persons in Barrow's position would have been willing to embark on such a course, especially at the time of quitting the field of science. Furthermore, the implications of Newton's discoveries for a complete theory of color were not plain. Can we not imagine Barrow saying to himself that he will publish the book as it is and let the ideas fend for themselves until revised at some future time by Newton's work and that of others too? It is all the more likely that Barrow would have felt this way if he had not fully understood what Newton had told him—that is, of course, if Newton had told him anything.‡

To More, it was "quite inconceivable that Barrow would have permitted his book to be published if he had known about Newton's work." The reason is that Barrow "was too able a scientist not to have recognized its importance and at least to have alluded to it." [22] But if scientists of the stature of Huygens and Hooke did not give immediate assent to Newton's claims, why should we suppose that Barrow would have done so? To us, looking backward at the seventeenth century, it is clear that what Newton had done was to make all previous writings on color obsolete, but this implication was far from obvious to Newton's contemporaries,[23] as the controversy attendant on the publication of Newton's paper amply demonstrates. Furthermore, it is a matter of fact that no one has ever found a trace of an unfriendly reaction by Barrow to Newton, even after Newton's discoveries had been published. It was Barrow who proudly carried Newton's telescope to the Royal Society in 1671.[24]

Newton never made a secret of his optical discoveries. His own

perusing; not such as were designed for you alone; not published of my own accord; nor containing the exquisite thoughts of a mind wholly employed upon the subject; but that they are school lectures, read by duty, and sometimes spoken too hastily," The reader was not to "expect here any thing accurately performed, or beautifully digested." Had Barrow been able to satisfy this type of expectation, he would have had "to curtail many things, and substitute better [!] in their room; and to transpose the greater part, and to correct and reform the whole." He had neither inclination nor leisure for such a task nor the "power to execute" it. Therefore, he had chosen "rather to publish them [the lectures] *in puris naturalibus*, or as they were produced at first . . . ."

‡ In the twelfth optical lecture, Barrow rejected Descartes's views on color, and then offered his own views: "*Quoniam colorum incidit mentio*, quid si de illis (etsi præter morem ac ordinem) paucula divinavero?" He was only offering guesses, and not stating firm conclusions about color. Interestingly enough, these suggestions contain several points which Newton used in his *Opticks*: the suggestion that the ability of some bodies to reflect "whiteness," and appear white or transparent, and the appearance of "blackness" in other bodies, are related to their constitutions, their abundance of pores and the relative size of the "pores"; and the observation that in this way may be explained the property of black bodies (as compared to white ones) to "catch fire more readily, become hot, and burn." [21] We shall encounter Newton's discussion of these topics in Chapter Six and Chapter Seven.

lectures on optics, delivered in Cambridge in 1669, contained an account of what he had done, and a statement that they were to be considered a supplement to the section of Barrow's earlier lectures respecting refractions: " I judge it will not be unacceptable," said Newton, if I " subjoin what I have discovered in these matters, and found to be true by manifold experience, to what my reverend predecessor has last delivered from this place." [25] Whatever may be our opinion of Newton's attitude toward publication, we know that he was willing to talk to friendly auditors about what he had done, as in the case of the lectures on optics read in 1669,§ or the work on gravitation which he communicated freely to Halley on the occasion of that famous visit.

This story of Newton and Barrow shows how little we really know about crucial episodes in Newton's life, the circumstances of his discoveries, and even his whole personality. We can, therefore, understand why so many divergent views about almost every aspect of Newton's life in science have been produced by the scholars who have attempted to understand Newton and his influence.

The Publication of Newton's Ideas

Some time after the appearance of Barrow's book, Newton published in the *Philosophical Transactions* his own theory of light and colors based on his new experiments, and that great first controversy was on.

" The warm opposition his admirable discoveries met with, in his youth," wrote his disciple, Colin Maclaurin, " deprived the world of a full account of them for many years, till there appeared a greater disposition amongst the learned to receive them; and [this opposition] induced him to retain other important inventions by him, from an apprehension of the disputes in which a publication might involve him." [26] So seriously did Newton contemplate abandoning the career of an active scientist that he announced to the Secretary of the Royal Society, " I intend to be no farther solicitous about

§ The preface to the English edition of the *Optical lectures* (1728) begins: " It was as long ago as the year 1666, when Sir Isaac Newton first found out his theory of light and colours. Upon Dr. Barrow's resigning to him the professorship of the mathematicks at Cambridge, he made A. 1669, this discovery the subject of his publick lectures, in that University. In 1671 he began to communicate it to the world, as also a description of his reflecting telescope, in the *Philosophical Transactions*. About the same time he intended to publish his *Optical lectures*, wherein these matters were handled more fully. . . . But the disputes, which were occasioned by what he had already suffered to come abroad, deterred him from that design. . . . [These] *Lectures* . . . were deposited, at the time they were read, amongst the archives of the University. From whence many copies have been taken, and handed about by the curious in these matters."

matters of philosophy; and therefore I hope you will not take it ill if you never find me doing anything more in that kind." Yet the creative urge was in him so strongly that any disappointment about the reception of his work could not prevent him from going on in science. With Halley's urging, the *Principia* appeared in 1687. Eventually with Cotes's aid a second edition was published in 1713, and a third edition was prepared with the help of Pemberton. We might be led to expect that with increasing age and as a result of experience in controversy that had been avowedly painful to him, there would have been a greater caution. The famous statement about not framing hypotheses would seem a step in avoiding any dispute about mechanisms and first causes. But even in the General Scholium to Book Three, written for the edition of 1713, in which that famous statement first appeared, Newton gave a hint of an hypothesis on the grandest scale imaginable: it was centered on the concept of an all-pervading "spirit" with special properties to make the particles of bodies attract one another and cohere, to produce electrical attraction, the properties of light and radiant heat, and the action of the nerves in conveying sensation to the brain and the commands of the will to the muscles.* Furthermore, the successive editions of the *Opticks* contained more and more daring hypotheses which eventually embraced practically every aspect of nature's operations and which show little sign of the caution we might again have been led to expect, knew we not Newton.

As I shall have occasion to emphasize and to document in the next section of this book, when Newton wrote apropos of gravitation that he framed no hypotheses, he knew, and his readers knew, that years ago he had framed a rather elegant hypothesis of this sort. It had been first published in the second edition of the *Opticks* printed in 1717, reprinted 1718.† Although this particular hypothesis, like some of the others in the *Opticks*, had been presented in the guise of a "Query," Newton's contemporaries must have been aware that the "Queries" were imperfect answers rather than genuine questions, and the nature of the hypotheses as such was plain to many scientists of the eighteenth century.‡

So disappointed was Newton by the lack of universal applause for his earliest published research in optics, that his whole personality was altered; or, perhaps, certain traits of personality were accen-

---

* These conjectures will be discussed more fully in Chapter Five and Chapter Six.

† The older men of science might have remembered Newton's "hypothesis" on the nature of the æther which had been read at the Royal Society in 1675, and which presumably was available in the Royal Society's archives.

‡ The character of these "Queries" will be described in Chapter Six and in Chapter Seven.

tuated and brought to the fore. He suffered a deep blow to his pride when his fellow scientists, including Huygens whom Newton admired more than practically any other of his contemporaries,[27] refused to see the discovery that was clearly indicated by his experiments. Newton believed that the facts of experience or observation were being rejected either because of the prior hypotheses held by others or because of antipathy to an hypothesis supposedly advanced by him. Debate is endless as to whether Newton had actually advanced an hypothesis or a theory, and as to whether Newton's results were independent of his preconceptions.[28] This question, however interesting, need not detain us, because we are chiefly concerned to note the effect of the dispute on Newton's later publications in science, and not to evaluate the claims of Newton or his advocates or those of his disputants. The fact remains that Newton thereafter alleged that his scientific results were being presented in a form that was free—or as nearly free as possible—from any hypotheses. The view of science that he tendered, has been described as one in which " hypothetical particles, and hypothetical relations between them, should be eschewed in science, and that science should consist only of laws embodying the results of measurements produced by observation and experiment." [29] This traditional view will be subjected to a closer scrutiny in Chapters Five and Six.

To assume, however, that Newton had produced his results without ever a recourse to hypothesis would be to take Newton's word rather than his deed. Any description of Newtonian science as science without hypotheses is a gross parody—and not only of Newton's own work,§ but of any creative scientific research save the rudest empiricism. Franklin admitted freely his natural inclination to invent hypotheses and indulged it to the extent that control by experiment allowed. Hence if we are to consider Franklin as in any way a representative of a Newtonian tradition, we must take care to avoid the pitfalls of accepting—as a fundamental or even defining quality of mature Newtonian science—a point of view that arose from a reaction to dispute and that may be no more than a characteristic expression of Newton's distinguishing personality.

The Development of Newton's Personality

The bare recital of some of the facts of Newton's childhood prepares us for the unusual personality he later developed. He grew up deprived of mother and father; his father died three months before Newton was born, and his mother married again within

§ The senses in which Newton used the word " hypothesis " will be presented in Chapter Five and Appendix One.

two years, leaving her first son in the care of a grandmother and an uncle. He had been born prematurely and had for some time to wear a bolster around his neck, since he was too feeble to hold his head upright without external aid. Significantly, he was fond of relating stories of his childhood and loved to repeat how his mother had often told him that at birth he had been tiny enough to have been put into a quart mug. When Newton was sixteen, his mother, widowed for the second time, brought him home from school to run the farm; he had given as yet no signs of genius. But he was an absent-minded farmer and his mother wisely decided to send him on to the university. Practically only two years—and those adolescent years—were spent with his mother, and she had then three children from her second marriage who demanded her attention.

We can readily understand, then, how this shy and introspective youth, deprived of the normal familial surroundings, turned to books for company and later became absorbed in drawing and in the design and construction of a variety of gadgets and mechanical toys. One who knew him well in his youth described him as " always a sober, silent, thinking lad " who " was never known scarce to play with the boys abroad, at their silly amusements." He was much happier to be at home, " even among the girls," and he would " frequently make little tables, cupboards, and other utensils " for the girls " to set their babies and trinkets on." [30] The late Dean More called attention to two influences on young Newton's character which had escaped previous biographers. One was the temper of the times in the countryside just recovering " from the terrors of a protracted and bitter civil war." Newton had no protection from the frights of his imagination except what might be afforded by " his grandmother and such unreliable labourers as could be hired," and he had no sympathy with the rough play of the neighboring children, "made still rougher by imitation of the lawless deeds of the soldiers." Being physically weak, he was probably unable to compete with them in their games and contests * " and the only recourse of such a boy to escape the humiliation of being taunted as a weakling, and to avoid the physical torments inflicted by childish bullies, was to isolate himself." [32]

A solitary and lonely boy, he grew to manhood without either

---

* We must observe, however, that at school at Grantham he was strong enough to beat up a school bully, which was the occasion of his becoming a top student: " Sir Isaac used to relate that he was very negligent at school, and very low in it, till the boy above him gave him a kick on the belly, which put him to a great deal of pain. Not content with having thrashed his adversary, Sir Isaac could not rest till he had got before him in the school, and from that time he continued rising till he was the head boy." [31]

intimate friendships or a close family circle. Dean More describes him in terms of

a morbidly suspicious and secretive mind which must have had its source in a form of vanity, or in an exaggerated sensitiveness of personal honour. In spite of a strong will and the exercise of self-discipline, he was subject to peevish outbreaks of ill-temper, and of suspicious injustice even towards those who were his best friends. On such occasions he stooped to regrettable acts which involved him in a succession of painful controversies that plagued his life, robbed him of the just fruits of his work, and disheartened his sincere admirers.[33]

Locke wrote, in 1703, " that Newton was a nice man to deal with, and a little too apt to raise in himself suspicions where there is no ground." [34] The word " nice " here means " difficult " or " overprecise," as Andrade has pointed out,[35] and this judgment is confirmed by Flamsteed's opinion: that Newton was " insidious, ambitious, and excessively covetous of praise, and impatient of contradiction." Even after the total breach of their friendship, Flamsteed could admit of Newton, " I believe him to be a good man at the bottom; but, through his natural temper, suspicious." [36]

Newton combined qualities of " timidity and diffidence " with a " hatred of cruelty " and a noted " sympathy and generous aid to those who might be in trouble." [37] Yet in his relations with others he was " cold and formal " and unable to give anything of himself, save to problems of the mind. Newton tended, I believe, to associate himself more closely with the job at hand than most people are wont to do. While employed at the Mint in later life, he was careful to avoid any semblance of occupying himself with scientific or any other non-administrative affairs during working hours—while on the King's time,† as he put it. During his professional days, he lived in his own creations, his real life having been his research and contemplation rather than the external contacts with others. Hence it was that any attack on his ideas, his experiments, his theories, or even his hypotheses, did not seem like a scientific dispute on an abstract plane, but was a threat to his very life in the terms in which he had conceived it. So we can, by appreciating the qualities of Newton's personality, understand why the disputes about his early work on light and the later controversies with Hooke, Flamsteed, and Leibniz, must have affected him more deeply than most men.

It was wholly in character, therefore, for Newton to seek to

---

† Newton's words are: " I do not love to be printed upon every occasion, much less to be dunned and teased by foreigners about mathematical things, or to be thought by our own people to be *trifling* away my time about them, when I should be about the King's business." [38]

present his science in a way that would arouse a minimum of dissent and criticism. A mathematical derivation of one proposition from another is either right or wrong and not a proper subject for argument; either a mathematical method may be applied to solve problems or it fails in the application. Experiments can easily be repeated to test whether or not the experimenter has reported his results accurately. If in the *Principia*, Newton could have confined himself to the "mathematical principles of natural philosophy," without having to introduce their application to the situations of the external world, there would probably have been little ground for discussion. And, indeed, we may observe that the earliest criticism of that great book was directed to the physical suppositions (like the nature of the gravitational force) rather than the mathematical derivations: to Book Three rather than Book One. Had the whole of the *Opticks* been kept to the avowed aims of Book One—to " propose and prove " the " properties of light " by " reason and experiments " and " not to explain the properties of light by hypotheses "—there could have been little objection to it. But Newtonian science was not so limited as Newton alleged and a study of his own writings showed that there were conjectures, hypotheses, and all the other non-demonstrable aspects that are found to underlie the discussion of any scientific investigation.

Newton's Scientific Behavior

The two common myths about Newton that tend to distort our view about his conduct in science are that he did not really care about science and that he had no interest in having others know about his discoveries. Since both derive from an uncritical acceptance of Newton's own testimony in words about himself, a careful analysis of his conduct is required if we wish to understand the man Newton. Surely, no man who worked as intensely as Newton did can be described as one who really did not value his studies. Let us examine the testimony of Humphrey Newton (no relation), who served as amanuensis while Newton held the Lucasian Professorship at Cambridge. " I never knew him to take any recreation or pasttime either in riding out to take the air, walking, bowling, or any other exercise whatever," he wrote, " thinking all hours lost that was not spent in his studies, to which he kept so close that he seldom left his chamber except at term time, when he read in the schools as being Lucasianus Professor. . . ." He was so intent and serious upon his studies, that he ate sparingly and often forgot to eat altogether. Many times when going into his chamber Humphrey found Newton's meals untouched. He would remind Newton about his meal and ask whether he had eaten. Humphrey says that Newton would reply, " Have I? " Then, according to Humphrey, Newton would go " to the table, would eat a bite or two standing, for I cannot say I ever saw him sit at table by himself." During this time, Newton usually went to bed at about two or three o'clock in the morning, but sometimes not until five or six, sleeping only about four or five hours.

" He very rarely went to dine in the hall, except on some public days, and then if he has not been minded, would go very carelessly, with shoes down at heels, stockings untied, surplice on, and his head scarcely combed." Humphrey added: " At some seldom times when he designed to dine in the hall, [he] would turn to the left hand and go out into the street, when making a stop when he found his mistake, would hastily turn back, and then sometimes instead of going into the hall, would return to his chamber again." " I can't say I ever saw him wear a night gown, but his wearing clothes that he put off at night, at night I do say, yea, rather towards the morning, he put on again . . ." " In a morning, he seemed to be as much refreshed with his few hours' sleep as though he had taken a whole night's rest." " . . . the old woman his bedmaker . . . has sometimes found both dinner and supper scarcely tasted of, which the old woman has very pleasantly and mumpingly gone away with." [39]

These extracts reveal Lord Keynes's " wrapt, consecrated, solitary " Newton, rather than the man who regarded science " for its own sake as of little more value than an intricate game of chess," described by Dean More. To be sure, while Newton was in Cambridge before going to the Mint, his studies were not confined to science, but embraced theology, history, mystical philosophy, and Biblical criticism. This combined activity, however, would have seemed less strange to Newton's contemporaries than to us, since in those days theology and natural philosophy were closely linked. Boyle wrote a *Christian Virtuoso* as well as a *Sceptical Chymist* [40] and even Franklin referred more than once to the divine providence.

One possible reason for supposing that Newton did not find scientific inquiry congenial is the alleged reluctance of Newton to publish his discoveries. Yet the willingness to bare the results of research to the world does not, it seems to me, have too much relation to the passion a man may have for inquiry into the operations of nature. Can anyone who has examined the notebooks of Leonardo da Vinci, to take one example, doubt for even a fleeting second his consuming passion to understand how nature works? And yet Leonardo never published even a short tract, nor did he complete a single one of his projected books. Or, take that strange man, Henry Cavendish, whose intense powers of mathematical analysis were combined with a gift for experiment reminiscent of Newton himself. Cavendish published only one paper of importance in physics during his lifetime; yet his notebooks contained a record of experiment and theory in physics that embraced an extraordinary number of the laws and concepts discovered anew during the next half-century.[41] Despite his aversion to publication, Cavendish was wholly devoted to science: research, in fact, was his entire life even to a greater degree than in the case of Newton. In any event, the general opinion about Newton, " that it was as difficult to force his mind to divulge his ideas as it had been for him to create them," seems to me to be much too literal an interpretation of Newton's sentiments. Let us look further at the record.

Some time prior to 1668, Newton devised a reflecting telescope. A rumor about the new instrument reached the Royal Society, whose members recognized its merits at once, and asked for one. Newton constructed a telescope for the Society, and sent it on to them, whereupon he was proposed for membership in the Society and elected a Fellow on 11 January 1671/2. Newton wrote to Oldenburg on 6 Jan. 1671/2 that he was grateful for the esteem of his invention " of which I have hitherto had so little value." Had not the Royal Society asked him about it, he " might have let it still remain in private as it hath already done some years." He added that he would " endeavour to testify my gratitude by communicating what my poor and solitary endeavours can effect toward the promoting your philosophical designs." [42]

Then, on 18 January 1671/2, he asked when the Society met, so that he could give them an account of a scientific discovery, the very one which had induced him to make the telescope, " and which I doubt not but will prove much more grateful than the communication of that instrument, being in my judgment the oddest, if not the most considerable detection, which has hitherto been made in the operations of nature." [43] Plainly, Newton was so delighted by the reception accorded to his telescope that he was eager to present his discoveries concerning dispersion and the composition of white light, so that they too might win him the applause of the London virtuosi. It is easy for us to understand Newton's feelings: a lonely man with no intimate companions, he had at last found a group of experts who appreciated his creations and he eagerly sought their praise. His immodest evaluation of his discovery indicates the judgment he hoped would be confirmed by the experts of the Royal Society and the scientists throughout the world.

The controversy that arose upon the publication of Newton's paper on light and color was hardly the universal praise and acclaim that Newton had hoped would be aroused by his "detection." Objections were raised by great men and lesser ones: Huygens, Hooke, Pardies, Linus, Lucas, Gascoines.[44] Pushed by Oldenburg, Secretary of the Royal Society, Newton wrote an answer to each letter that his paper occasioned. He was so annoyed at having to sustain the controversies that he declared to Oldenburg, in a kind of state of desperation, on 18 November 1676, that he had made himself "a slave to philosophy," and that he planned "resolutely [to] bid adieu to it eternally, excepting what I do for my private satisfaction, or leave to come out after me; for I fear a man must either resolve to put out nothing new, or to become a slave to defend it." [45] And so the legend began. As Dean More puts it, Newton's "naïve expression of pleasure changed to disgust, and he accused nature as well as men of being litigious; to enjoy peace of mind, he resolved in future to meditate, but not impart his cogitations to a carping public." [46] But from Newton's own statement we learn that his chief resolve was to leave the papers describing further research to be published after his death: he obviously wanted them to be made public, but he did not want to be in a position to have to hear what might be said against them or to have to defend them. We must observe, furthermore, that what Newton probably objected to was the criticism, not the controversy. He could have escaped the latter by refusing to be drawn into it, merely allowing the fate of his writings to be judged by posterity or by others who might try to improve upon what he had said.‡ But he could not avoid criticism and, because there was bound to be criticism of so novel a series of results, Newton—being Newton, being sensitive to any adverse comment—could not help but reply to his critics and so could not escape controversy. Yet he continued his scientific work and, after Halley's visit in 1684, he wrote his *Principia* for the Royal Society to publish.

Newton needed little urging to write the *Principia*. All that was required, apparently, was a little praise from Halley and the knowledge that the Royal Society admired the work. I have read again and again the story of Halley's visit and the events that followed it, and I find little or no reluctance on Newton's part to compose his great work and to have it make its way in the world. Indeed, the only possible basis for any statement that Newton was hesitant about publishing his system of terrestrial and celestial dynamics is

‡ This point is crucial in any attempt at differentiating what Newton said from what Newton did. At any time in the first controversy over his theory of light and colors, Newton could have written to Oldenburg that he would answer no more public letters addressed to the Royal Society, nor reply to any criticism. Whatever may be said of Newton's horror of controversy, the fact remains that Newton shares the responsibility for keeping the controversy going.

that he did not write out his system until after Halley's visit. Newton wrote an autobiographical statement, perhaps in 1714, in which he said that in 1665 or 1666, he had discovered the inverse-square law of gravitation, or had " deduced that the forces which keep the planets in their orbs must [be] reciprocally as the squares of their distances from the centres about which they revolve." [47] But why did Newton keep this result to himself? Was it only the fear of controversy? One of the reasons alleged for the delay in the announcement of the law of gravitation is that when Newton tested the law in the case of the earth and moon, he used a poor value for the earth's radius. But a considerable research, chiefly by Florian Cajori, has indicated that what bothered Newton was also his inability to prove that the earth, or any other body that was " more or less " homogeneous and spherical, would act gravitationally as if all of its mass were concentrated at its center. Newton had made calculations in 1666 and again in 1671 or 1672. These calculations showed only a rough agreement between the predictions of theory and the results of observation; he found that the " proportion of our gravity to the moon's conatus recedendi a centro terrae," as he wrote in 1686, had not been calculated accurately enough.[48]

Cajori laid great stress on the three words: " not accurately enough." [49] To be sure, Newton wrote to Hooke in 1679 that he " had for some years last been endeavouring to bend myself from philosophy to other studies in so much that I have long grutched the time spent in study unless it be perhaps at idle hours sometimes for a diversion." [50] Whatever his views on philosophy, and the time it had occupied, he was bothered by difficult technical scientific aspects of gravitation theory. There was that vexing matter of the variation in gravity with latitude, due to the earth's rotation, which he described as " a thing of far greater difficulty then I was aware of." [51] In 1671 there were not even any experimental values for the distance a body would fall in unit time from rest in different latitudes. But of far greater importance, apparently, was Newton's inability to deal with that seemingly " simple " problem of exactly how a sphere attracts an outside particle. Unless he could give a clear statement of this attraction, and prove it, he had only an approximate theory and his test came out " not accurately enough." According to the conclusions of Cajori, " Not until 1685 did Newton settle this mathematical question to his satisfaction." The effect of Halley's visit in 1684, in this view, was to stimulate Newton " to return to the whole question of gravity which had been intermittently in his thoughts since he saw the apple fall in the autumn of 1666." [52] Within the year he had solved the problem and had shown that gravitation is actually universal, applying to every particle of matter.§ Newton, in other words, wrote out his *Principia* and submitted it for publication only after he had solved to his own satisfaction the scientific problems connected with the theory of gravitation. Whatever his attitude may have been during the years between the controversy over light and the completion of the *Principia*, we know that the problems of gravitation were in his mind and that he had not solved them. Newton showed no particularly great reluctance to publish his *Principia* once it was written, but he obviously could not write it until he understood and could prove the important things that were to go in it.*

There is, in the light of Newton's personality, one further remarkable issue concerning his actual publication of the *Principia*. There had been a clash with Hooke at the time of the appearance of Newton's first paper on light, in 1672; a second one occurred in 1679. Newton had congratulated Hooke in 1677 on his election as Secretary of the Royal Society, and, in 1679, Hooke wrote a friendly note to Newton asking him to resume his communications to the Society of "what shall occur to you that is philosophicall." But Hooke said explicitly in this letter that Newton might " be assured that whatever shall be soe communicated shall be noe otherwise further imparted or disposed of than you yourself shall præscribe." [54]

§ This result has been described beautifully by H. H. Turner: In the problem " of linking up the attraction of the earth on a body so far away as the moon with its attraction on the apple close to its surface," Newton saw " grave difficulties " in the application of the inverse-square law " of which lesser minds were unconscious." In the case of the attraction of the earth on the moon, " the various particles composing the earth (to which individually Newton hoped to extend his law, thus making it universal) are at distances from the moon not greatly different either in magnitude or direction; but their distances from an apple differ conspicuously in both size and direction. How are the separate attractions in the latter case to be added together or combined into a single resultant? and in what ' centre of gravity,' if any, may they be concentrated? The beautiful theorem which he discovered, showing that the total attraction of a sphere on an apple at its surface, just as on a distant satellite, is accurately concentrated at the centre of the sphere, came as a complete surprise to him and must have given him great joy. It put the law of gravity on an entirely new footing, converting what had been possibly only a crude approximation for planetary bodies into an accurate and universal law." [53]

* In an article on " The Letters of Isaac Newton," in *The Manchester Guardian Weekly* (Thursday, 8 October 1953), Professor H. W. Turnbull, editor of the forthcoming Royal Society edition of Newton's correspondence, writes: " Another newly found manuscript on gravitation consists of rough notes written on the blank spaces of an old and torn legal document. . . . The notes contain his calculations of the gravity of the moon, and belong to the period of 1665-6, when students from Cambridge were sent down on account of the plague, and Newton went home to Lincolnshire. It is a well established supposition that after finding a discrepancy between the calculation of lunar gravity and the facts, Newton threw aside his early work and did not return to it for twenty years. This is borne out by the notes themselves—the mistake was due to taking the radius of the earth to be 3,500 miles."

Yet when Newton sent Hooke such a philosophical letter as had been requested, Hooke did not treat it as he had promised he would, but immediately presented it to the Royal Society (on 4 December 1679) and one week later (on 11 December 1679) Hooke read his answer to Newton, a letter to Newton dated 9 December 1679, in which he pointed out a serious blunder that Newton had made. Newton was furious, not only at having to be corrected by Hooke, but also because Hooke had "exposed his blunder in public," [55] despite the earlier statement about the correspondence being private. On the basis of these two earlier collisions, Newton certainly must have known that the *Principia* would inaugurate a further disagreeable controversy with Hooke, and indeed it did.

No sooner had the early part of the *Principia* been presented to the Royal Society and approved for publication, than Halley wrote to Newton about Hooke's claim to the discovery of the inverse-square law of gravitation. Newton was disgusted, as we might expect. He defended his own claims to discovery in letters to Halley, but he was seriously concerned. On 20 June 1686 he wrote to Halley that he had planned the *Principia* in three books:

The third I now design to suppress. Philosophy is such an impertinently litigious Lady, that a man had as good be engaged in lawsuits, as have to do with her. I found it so formerly, and now I am no sooner come near her again, but she gives me warning. The two first books, without the third, will not so well bear the title of *Philosophiæ Naturalis Principia Mathematica*; and therefore I had altered it to this, *De Motu Corporum libri duo*. But, upon second thoughts, I retain the former title. 'Twill help the sale of the book, which I ought not to diminish now 'tis yours.[56]

Did Newton really intend to suppress the third book? † We have

---

† More was aroused by this letter to a passionate attack on Newton: "No one could blame him for being thoroughly angry. But one can not excuse him for his decision—to suppress the third book simply because one man, with a mind diseased by jealousy and vanity, had foolishly made a scene. What manner of a man was Newton, who could thus contemptuously cast off his own intellectual child; there is certainly no parallel to the incident in all history. Did any other man ever show a deeper jealousy and vanity than Newton, who could let the personal criticism of another, and a slight reflection on his own character, outweigh the work of his life and the fruit of his genius? Since the book, thus mutilated, would be greatly restricted in its scope and value, he decided to change the title of *System of The World* to the colourless one of *On the Motion of Bodies*. Then it occurred to him that Halley had a financial interest in the book, however unimportant it might be to himself, so he decided to retain the catch-sale title even though it were misleading because, forsooth, ' 'Twill help the sale of the book, which I ought not to diminish now 'tis yours.' This incident, I confess, shocks me. It is not inspiring to see a work of genius carelessly chaffered as might be a second-hand piece of furniture, even if the advantage be ostensibly sought for a friend's purse. If gratitude had really been the motive it would have shone with a brighter lustre if he had refused to let his personal annoyance overweigh his duty to make public his work." [57]

no way of telling. But the fact of the matter is that a tactful letter from Halley, explaining the matter in detail, was all that was required to change Newton's mind and to make him wish he " had spared the postscript " to his last letter. More than once Newton was given to an impetuous expression in a letter which he would later regret. I doubt that we need take too seriously Newton's statement about the proposed mutilation of his masterpiece.

Once the *Principia* had been published, Newton was anxious to correct or perfect it, and he carefully noted errors and misprints, and made a variety of significant improvements. In 1706, two years after the publication of the *Opticks*, David Gregory recorded: " Sir Isaac Newton shewed me a copy of his Princ. Math. Phil. Nat. interleaved, and corrected for the press. It is intirely finished as farr as Sect. VII Lib. II, pag. 317." Gregory's memorandum indicates that although the rest of the revision was not " intirely finished," Newton had already made some revisions in Book Three.[58] More than half of the *Principia*, in other words, had been revised by Newton for a second and corrected edition long before the collaboration with Cotes.

Newton, it may be observed, not only brought out two revised editions of the *Principia* but also a number of revised editions of his *Opticks*. We are apt to make too much of the fact that the *Opticks* had been ready for the press for at least a decade before he published it. We must keep in mind that this was not an extraordinary delay for those days. Huygens' *Traitè de la Lumière*, the rival work on this subject, had been written in 1680, but it too was not published until a decade later.[59]

It has never been shown that in any field of physical science Newton made great discoveries which he did not publish during his lifetime. He was not, however, as ready to make public his mathematical discoveries as those he had made in physics. Much of that dreadful controversy with Leibniz could have been avoided had Newton been at all willing to publish, or even divulge, his work in mathematics.‡ His reluctance is difficult to explain, but one reason

‡ Newton's attitude in respect to his unpublished discoveries has been well described by More: " Where he felt his exclusive rights of discovery to be involved, no one could be more determined to assert himself. He held jealously to the conviction that if he had made a discovery, it was his personal property for all time, even if he kept it locked in the secret chambers of his own mind. If another should later make the same discovery and publish it first, he held to the opinion that no rights were attached to priority of publication; the author had merely trespassed unwittingly on Newton's property and should receive no credit." [60]

It is an interesting measure of Newton's genius that during the years prior to the publication of the *Principia*, no one else had advanced toward the results of that work to jeopardize its originality; Hooke claimed to have " proved " that the inverse-

may be that perhaps he did not really like his own creation. Newton preferred the methods of the ancients to those of the moderns and chose to present his mathematical theorems and proofs in the *Principia* in the geometric style of Euclid and Apollonius rather than the algebraic style of Descartes. It is often supposed that Newton worked out his theorems analytically, using the method of fluxions (or the calculus) that he invented, and then translated the work into the older geometric language; but whether he made his discoveries by using the calculus or not, the fact remains that no fluxions appear as such in the *Principia*. David Gregory noted that Newton once said: " Algebra is the analysis of the bunglers in mathematics." [61]

Changes in Newton's Scientific Behavior

Newton's behavior in scientific matters is not always clear. In the revised (second and third) editions of the *Principia*, he actually removed the word " hypothesis " in many cases and added the final scholium in which he said that he " framed no hypotheses " whatever. Surely this procedure was part of his program to avoid controversy and to prevent his " hypotheses " from being generally known. But Newton was always ambivalent about wanting the world to know his thoughts and trying to hide them. As has been mentioned earlier, that very same general scholium containing the phrase *hypotheses non fingo* terminated in a hint of a most extravagant hypothesis.

Newton seems often to have acted as if he had a set of secrets, of which he felt a compulsion to give the world a hint, but no more than a hint. Of course, Newton had one real secret, and concerning it he did his best to keep the world in ignorance: this secret was his " Unitarianism," his anti-Trinitarian religious belief which has been likened to a Judaic monotheism " of the school of Maimonides." §

---

square law of gravitation followed from Kepler's work, but no one has ever seen the " proof," nor was he a good enough mathematician to have solved the problem of the attraction of a sphere and a particle. The same situation held with regard to Newton's *Opticks*. He was, in other words, so far ahead of any possible rival in physics that there was no urgency in publication. In mathematics, on the other hand, Leibniz was a formidable rival and partially scooped Newton: a fact which explains the acrimony of the controversy with Leibniz and which provides a testimony to Leibniz's genius—he was a man who could actually be a genuine rival and could make Newton suffer in his pride.

§ The phrase comes from Lord Keynes, who had collected and studied a vast quantity of Newton's unpublished manuscripts, most of them dealing with theological subjects. Lord Keynes concluded: " Very early in life Newton abandoned orthodox belief in the Trinity. . . . He was persuaded that the revealed documents give no support to the Trinitarian doctrines which were due to late falsifications. The revealed God was one God. But this was a dreadful secret which Newton was at desperate pains to conceal all his life. It was the reason why he refused Holy Orders,

In the generations immediately following Newton, his word was apt to be taken at its face value. Serious men of science, unaware that Newton's warnings against speculations and hypotheses were the result of his personality and not his method, echoed Newton's sentiments uncritically. W. J. 'sGravesande declared that hypotheses were a scientific abomination, and then proceeded to develop a theory of heat in which " fire " is represented—dare we say " as an hypothesis " —as a material substance. Those who, like Franklin, expressed hypotheses to be put to the test of experience, were apt to be castigated by men who said that this was never Newton's method.*

When the *Opticks* was published in 1704, all of the original objectors to Newton's first paper on light were dead. Furthermore in 1696 he had been given a kind of public recognition as a great man by his appointment as Warden of the Mint. In 1699 he was made an *associé étranger* of the French Academy of Sciences and a member of the Council of the Royal Society. In 1703 he was elected President of the Royal Society. He had, in other words, received so many tokens of his own worth that perhaps by 1704 he no longer feared criticism as much as he had earlier. Thus we can understand why he permitted some of his inner thoughts and speculations to appear in the " Queries " at the end of the *Opticks*. In 1705 he was knighted by Queen Anne, and in the following year even more daring speculations were published in the Latin version of the *Opticks*. In 1709 he began to prepare in earnest the second edition of the *Principia*, which was published in 1713. Secure in his position, the center of adulation of a vast company of learned men and public figures, he produced still further speculations for the second and third English

and therefore had to obtain a special dispensation to hold his Fellowship and Lucasian Chair and could not be Master of Trinity. Even the Toleration Act of 1689 excepted anti-Trinitarians. Some rumours there were, but not at the dangerous dates when he was a young Fellow of Trinity. In the main the secret died with him. But it was revealed in many writings in his big box. After his death Bishop Horsley was asked to inspect the box with a view to publication. He saw the contents with horror and slammed the lid. . . . It is a blot on Newton's record that he did not murmur a word when Whiston, his successor in the Lucasian Chair, was thrown out of his professorship and out of the University for publicly avowing opinions which Newton himself had held secretly for upwards of fifty years past. That he held this heresy was a further aggravation of his silence and inwardness of disposition." [62]

* Franklin's friend, Sir John Pringle, President of the Royal Society of London, attributed to Bacon the Newtonian warning against hypotheses. The occasion was the award of the Copley medal to Joseph Priestley, and Pringle spoke of Bacon, who " with that spirit of divination peculiar to exalted genius, assured his disciples that when men cease to trifle in framing *hypotheses*, and building hasty systems; and should, by a proper induction from sober and severe experiments, attain to the knowledge of the *forms* of things [their more intimate qualities and laws]; they should in the end command Nature, and perform works as much greater than were supposed practicable by the powers of natural magic, as the real actions of a Caesar surpassed the fictitious ones of the hero of a romance." [63]

editions of the *Opticks* in 1718 and 1721, and he prepared the third edition of the *Principia* with Pemberton's aid.

Yet it is interesting to observe that the title page of the first English edition of the *Opticks* (1704) did not bear an author's name, although an "advertisement" is signed "I. N." The contents, however, left no doubt as to the author. The second English edition (1717) and the Latin translation (1706) contained Newton's name. Another anonymous publication, according to a memorandum of David Gregory, was "The table of the degrees of heat in the Philos. Transact. for March & Aprile 1701 [which] is Sir Isaac Newtons, as he told me 25 Feb. 1705/6. . . ."

During these years there was yet another controversy, but of a somewhat different order from the earlier ones. The dispute with Leibniz did not center on hypotheses or experiments, but on that odious charge of plagiarism. But now Newton appeared no longer as an offended professor who might find nature and man litigious and hope to withdraw from the conflict. As a man of affairs, he acted according to the ways of the world, not appearing in person on the stage of the controversy, but skillfully manipulating each step from behind the curtain.[64]

Newton's position in the world at the time of publication of the *Opticks* was so vastly changed from what it had been when he had published the *Principia* that we can explain the difference between the two works. We shall see, in Chapters Five and Six, that this difference is of importance to our understanding of the strands of Newtonianism in the eighteenth century. The security and recognition that characterized the later years of Newton's life, it would appear, produced that dazzling set of speculative hypotheses that were the inspiration of experimental Newtonian scientists throughout the century and resulted in a great scientific tradition that can be traced to Newton's *Opticks*.

Franklin the Man

In contrast to Newton, Franklin provided a relatively large amount of information about himself, not only in his renowned "Autobiography," but in many autobiographical letters, reminiscences, and even youthful letters and literary compositions. We thus know a great deal about Franklin's life and the development of his ideas prior to his scientific research.

Any consideration of Franklin's scientific personality must take as its point of departure that when he began to study scientific problems in the 1740's, he was already a successful man in the world's eyes. As editor, publisher, book-seller and shop-keeper, he had made his mark, and within a few years would be able to retire in the fond but vain hope of dedicating himself primarily to science. He was already a leading member of the community, associated with the many projects of civic improvement for which Philadelphia was noted in the mid-century. His almanac, "Poor Richard," was read from one end of the country to the other, and his newspaper, the *Pennsylvania Gazette*, had a larger circulation than any colonial rival. A family man, he had two children, and he was in every respect one of the foremost citizens of Philadelphia and the colony of Pennsylvania. Franklin's childhood recollections were of a large closely-knit family, with all the love, rivalry, and jealousy that are concomitants of active family life. He played happily with boys his own age and was their natural leader. He respected his father and adored his mother. He had the normal childish ambition of going to sea, but his father insisted on a trade and Franklin was apprenticed to his brother James, a printer in Boston. Unlike Newton, Franklin had little benefit of schooling, but like Newton he developed great dexterity with his hands and a great ingenuity in devising mechanical contrivances. Both Franklin and Newton were fortunate in their manual skill, the necessary condition for a successful career in experimental science in a day when even the simplest kinds of laboratory equipment usually had to be made by the experimenter himself.

Franklin, in contrast to Newton, was physically strong, built like a wrestler.[65] Throughout his youth and early manhood he was glad to demonstrate his great strength and to exhibit his athletic prowess; once he almost succumbed to the temptation of a career as a swimming teacher. Like all active boys, Franklin was sensitive to the repressive influence of his older brothers, a situation that was aggravated by a bond of apprenticeship to his brother James. Franklin was able to exert his superiority over James by writing anonymous contributions to the newspaper, which James printed in ignorance of their true author.[66] They were easily better than anything James himself could have produced. When the occasion arose, young Franklin was able to escape from the confines of an unpleasant apprenticeship; his subsequent departure from Boston and arrival in Philadelphia are too well known to need any retelling. But the point is that Franklin is seen to have been a man who could face up to realities and so become master of his own destiny. From a penniless youth who looked for employment in Philadelphia, he rose to take his place as the leading citizen in the town. Able to meet experience on its own terms, he was sensitive to criticism and profited from it. Even had his essay into science been non-productive, he would have been—

by the world's standards and his own—a success in more kinds of different activities than a single life is usually allowed to encompass. We can, therefore, all the more readily understand why Franklin's reactions to science on every level of affective behavior were entirely different from Newton's.

Not only did Newton live in his science in a sense that he never did in the external world, but his very profession during the creative years was science; he was " employed " as Lucasian Professor of Mathematics at Cambridge. Franklin, in contrast, did his major scientific work in moments snatched from public and private business during the 1740's and '50's. Public alarms interrupted his research at the most creative instant. No sooner had he sent his first communication of results to England than French and Spanish privateers began to extend their operations to the very outskirts of Philadelphia.[67] Franklin took the lead in arousing his apathetic fellow-townsmen to the dangers and he produced his first political pamphlet, *Plain Truth* (published on 14 November 1747),[68] as part of the campaign. When the Peace of Aix-la-Chapelle brought a cessation of hostilities, he took measures to retire from business and public life, hoping to find " leisure to read, study, make experiments, and converse at large with such ingenious and worthy men as are pleased to honour me with their friendship or acquaintance, on such points as may produce something for the common benefit of mankind, uninterrupted by the little cares & fatigues of business." [69] As everyone knows, this dream was never realized, and his hand was applied to more and more important matters of state and society. But wherever he was and whatever he was doing, whether in London as colonial agent or in Paris as minister, Franklin's interest in science never flagged. He kept up with the literature, sought out scientific cronies, and continued to make what experiments he could. His philosophy in these matters was expressed in a letter of 1750, wherein he wrote: " Had Newton been pilot but of a single common ship, the finest of his discoveries would scarce have excused, or attoned for his abandoning the helm one hour in time of danger; how much less if she carried the fate of the commonwealth." [70]

Franklin's Scientific Personality

One of the features of Franklin's scientific writings that most appealed to his contemporaries, and that has been a source of esteem for all who have read his work ever since, is the frankness which characterized everything that flowed from his pen. In the " Autobiography," he freely admitted all sorts of *errata*, his spending money entrusted to his care and his attempts at seducing a friend's mistress.

In his scientific communications, he was always ready to admit error and to acknowledge the superiority of a better explanation than his. After sending his first two papers on electricity to Peter Collinson in London, he wrote that further experimentation had revealed some phenomena that his principles could not explain and he had, therefore, become " a little diffident" about his " hypothesis " and ashamed that he had expressed himself " in so positive a manner." " In going on with these experiments," he said, " how many pretty systems do we build, which we soon find ourselves obliged to destroy! If there is no other use discovered of electricity, this, however, is something considerable, that it may *help to make a vain man humble.*" [71]

After Franklin had written out a first possible explanation of the action of pointed conductors, he re-read his thoughts on this subject and admitted that he now had " some doubts about them," even though they had " appeared perfectly satisfactory " when they had first " floated " into his mind. Yet, he added, " as I have at present nothing better to offer in their stead, I do not cross them out: for even a bad solution read, and its faults discovered, has often given rise to a good one, in the mind of an ingenious reader." [72] When Franklin had first begun to submit his scientific papers to the inspection of the London scientists, he was more cautious than he was later on. In 1747, when he had found that his hypothesis would not adequately account for all the new phenomena he had discovered, he told Collinson: " I must now request that you would not expose those letters [describing that hypothesis]; or if you communicate them to any friends, you would at least conceal my name." [73] But by 1753 he was secure enough about his achievement, which had been given its just recognition, to write: " These thoughts, my dear friend, are many of them crude and hasty; and if I were merely ambitious of acquiring some reputation in [natural] philosophy [i. e., science], I ought to keep them by me, till corrected and improved by time, and farther experience. But since even short hints and imperfect experiments in any new branch of science, being communicated, have oftentimes a good effect, in exciting the attention of the ingenious to the subject, and so become the occasion of more exact disquisition, and more compleat discoveries, you are at liberty to communicate this paper to whom you please; it being of more importance that knowledge should increase, than that your friend should be thought an accurate philosopher." [74]

Franklin's book on electricity went through five editions in English, but Franklin was not at hand to supervise the first three, which were printed in England while he was in America. Yet he was in

England while the greatly expanded fourth edition (London, 1769) was going through the press, and he made a number of significant alterations in the previously published text. Apart from minor changes like the correction of misprints, and the addition of an introductory letter acknowledging his indebtedness to Peter Collinson (who had just died),[75] the changes made by Franklin were of two kinds. One comprised footnotes stating the respective contributions —devices, observed phenomena, concepts—made by his three co-experimenters: Ebenezer Kinnersley, Philip Syng, Francis Hopkinson.[76] The other consisted of a series of footnotes amplifying or correcting certain statements he had made before he had fully understood the matters under discussion. For example, Franklin had at one time been under the misapprehension that the process whereby metals are " melted " by lightning was a kind of " cold fusion," but a footnote showed the evidence to support the view that the " fusion " arose from the heat which was developed and which was sufficient to bring the metal to its melting point.[77] Another proposition, about conducting bodies, was " since found to be too general." [78] At one place, in a discussion of the production of positive and negative states of electrification, the reader was referred to the " discoveries of the late ingenious Mr. Symmer," who had invented a theory of electrification that stood in direct opposition to Franklin's.[79] Another note " rectified " an early opinion on where the charge " resides " in the Leyden jar; Franklin observed: " The [electric] fire in the bottle was found by subsequent experiments not to be contained in the non-electric [conducting material] but *in the glass. 1748.*" [80] Still another note offered an explanation for the observed phenomenon of candlelight discharging an electrified insulated ball whereas sunlight would not do so; the note pointed out that " this different effect probably did not arise from any difference in the light," but rather from the existence of " particles separated from the candle " during the burning; [81] and so on.

In one important experiment, in which a can on an insulating stand was electrified and then showed signs of electrification on the outside but not the inside surface, Franklin described the effect as " singular." [82] " You require the reason," he wrote to Lining in 1755, " I do not know it. Perhaps you may discover it, and then you will be so good as to communicate it to me." A footnote indicated that later he had found a " reason " which he recommended " to the farther examination of the curious." It was the " mutual repulsion of the inner sides of the electrised cann." Franklin's friend, Priestley, saw the logic of this explanation in relation to Newton's work on gravitational fields within spherical shells, and by analogy drew the proper implication that the absence of an electric field within a charged sphere indicated a law of force of the inverse square.[83]

Because of Franklin's simple admission of his mistakes, and the addition of better explanations to complement earlier and inferior ones, his book is more interesting to read than a conventional treatise. Its pages at once give the reader a sense of the growth of Franklin's ideas as well as an introduction to electrical science in Franklinian terms. The book served as a model of how to make delicate experiments and the best way to draw conclusions from the data of observation. Written in a warm and intimate style, its pages sprinkled with humor and almost every paragraph enlivened by wit, Franklin's book on electricity was as much an expression of his warm and vibrant personality as his editorials in the *Pennsylvania Gazette*, his satirical letters to the press when he was in England as colonial agent, his bagatelles, and even his letters to the ladies. Long after Franklin's book had ceased to be the source of up-to-date information on electricity, it was recommended as a model of the experimenter's art and of literary expression in science. In Franklin's " language," Sir Humphry Davy told his students, " science appears . . . in a dress wonderfully decorous, the best adapted to display her native loveliness " ; hence " the style and manner of his publication on electricity are almost as worthy of admiration as the doctrine it contains." [84] Joseph Priestley told his readers that he could not decide which pleased the world most: " the simplicity and perspicacity with which . . . [the book is] written, the modesty with which the author proposes every hypothesis of his own, or the noble frankness with which he relates his mistakes when they were corrected by subsequent experiments." [85] In 1753 Diderot recommended the book (which he had presumably read in the French translation just then published) as the highest expression of experimental science,[86] and David Hume called Franklin the " first author " and the " first great man of letters " for whom Europe could be beholden to America.[87] Surely there can be no question but that the immense popularity of Franklin's book was in some measure due to that literary style of which he was a master before he undertook a single electrical experiment. Style, as Franklin's friend, Buffon, observed, is the man himself. The happy style of *Experiments and Observations on Electricity made at Philadelphia in America* reflected Franklin's personal qualities just as much as the forbidding and austere aspect of the *Principia* afforded a glimpse of a Newton " with his cold and silent face, forever voyaging strange seas of thought, alone."

Franklin's ease in the world and personal security prevented him from having the fear of being attacked that characterized Newton and that produced the form of some of Newton's writings. Franklin willingly exposed his thoughts, speculations, and hypotheses to the world without either fear of ridicule or concern for their contradiction. "Suppositions, however ingenious," he observed, "are often mere mistakes." He found that in scientific matters "a frank acknowledgment of one's ignorance is not only the easiest way to get rid of a difficulty, but the likeliest way to obtain information, and therefore I practice it; I think it an honest policy." Anyone who is familiar with the scientific articles and monographs that are being published now-a-days, and who has the opportunity of reading Franklin's book, will be quickly convinced that current editorial and publishing practice in science, which divests every printed sentence of any personal quality, so that all articles and monographs are apt to read alike (impersonally and badly), is an abomination. If only the great men of science in our day could reveal themselves to us in their writings as Franklin did, and as Faraday, Kelvin, Helmholtz, and Clerk Maxwell were still able to do! The delight of enthusiasm and contemplation, the pursuit of false trails and the sudden revelation in a happy accident; all the personal joys of discovery are missing now, with a consequent loss of inspiration and illumination, to say nothing of reading pleasure.

I suspect that one reason why Franklin was less anxious than Newton about the possibility of a statement being incorrect lies in his having been a printer. Franklin was a good printer who knew every aspect of the craft from the casting of type to composition and presswork.[88] When he wrote his last will and testament in 1788, he began it: " I, Benjamin Franklin of Philadelphia, printer, late Minister Plenipotentiary from the United States of America to the Court of France, now President of the State of Pennsylvania. . . ."[89] So proud was he of having been a printer that he placed this title before his positions of honor. Every printer, especially if he is the publisher of a newspaper as Franklin was, is aware that he cannot help making errata. What counts is not so much the making of mistakes as the frank acknowledgment of them and the correction of them in a later issue. By training as well as by temperament Franklin was willing to admit that he made mistakes and was grateful to friendly critics who called his attention to *errata*.

Controversies arising from Franklin's Scientific Work

Although Franklin's personality allowed him to state freely his speculations and hypotheses, and even his ignorance, in a way that Newton never did, it does not follow that he was unmoved by attacks, that he never felt the blow of disappointment when his ideas were not appreciated or when they failed to win universal adoption. There was hardly a major contribution he made which did not arouse some kind of critical aspersion or controversy. Even the Franklinian theory of electrical action, while praised by Watson at the Royal Society and in the Society's *Philosophical Transactions*, was said to have been discovered independently and earlier by Watson himself. In France, M. de Romas boasted that he had invented the experiment of the lightning kite earlier than Franklin.[90] The Abbé Nollet insisted that he had " shown " that the lightning discharge is an electrical phenomenon long before Franklin began his electrical research. The electrical properties of pointed conductors were claimed as the discovery of a number of scientists. Father Diviš was supposedly an independent inventor of the lightning rod,[91] although perhaps this claim never came to Franklin's attention.

Franklin's experimental findings about the electrical properties of glass, as in the Leyden jar, were disputed by many French scientists. In England Benjamin Wilson disagreed with Franklin's explanation of the Leyden jar.[92] In France, and to some extent in England, the followers of the Abbé Nollet opposed Franklin's theory of electrical action and Nollet wrote a whole book, and a supplementary book which followed, to expose Franklin's supposed errors and to make clear his own place in the history of electricity.[93] The introduction of lightning rods was opposed by all manner and degree of prejudice;[94] and in England, where they were introduced, a bitter controversy arose as to whether Franklin had been correct in advising that rods end in points rather than balls.[95]

Franklin was somewhat embittered, though not undaunted, by claims of prior discovery or prior invention of the fruits of his creation. He wrote his friend Dr. Lining of Charleston in 1755:

The treatment your friend has met with is so common, that no man who knows what the world is, and ever has been, should expect to escape it. There are every where a number of people, who, being totally destitute of any inventive faculty themselves, do not readily conceive that others may possess it: They think of inventions as of miracles; there might be such formerly, but they are ceased. With these, every one who offers a new invention is deemed a pretender: He had it from some other country, or from some book: A man of *their own acquaintance*; one who has no more sense than themselves, could not possibly, in their opinion, have been the inventer of any thing. They are confirmed, too, in these sentiments, by the frequent instances of pretensions to invention, which vanity is daily producing. That vanity too, though an incitement to invention, is, at the same time, the pest of inventors. Jealousy and Envy deny the merit or the novelty of your invention; but Vanity, when the novelty and merit are established, claims it for its own. The smaller your invention is, the more mortification you receive in having the credit of it disputed with you by a rival, whom the jealousy and envy of others are ready to support against you, at least so far as to make the point doubtful. It is not in itself of importance enough for a dispute; no one would think your proofs and reasons worth their attention: and yet if you do not dispute the point, and demonstrate your right, you not only lose the credit of being in that instance *ingenious*, but you suffer the disgrace of not being *ingenuous*; not only of being a plagiary but of being a plagiary for trifles. Had the invention been greater it would have disgraced you less; for men have not so contemptible an idea of him that robs for gold on the highway, as of him that can pick pockets for half-pence and farthings. Thus through Envy, Jealousy, and the Vanity of competitors for Fame, the origin of many of the most extraordinary inventions, though produced within but a few centuries past, is involved in doubt and uncertainty. We scarce know to whom we are indebted for the *compass*, and for *spectacles*, nor have even *paper* and *printing*, that record everything else, been able to preserve with certainty the name and reputation of their inventors. One would not, therefore, of all faculties, or qualities of the mind, wish, for a friend, or a child, that he should have that of invention. For his attempts to benefit mankind in that way, however well imagined, if they do not succeed, expose him, though very unjustly, to general ridicule and contempt; and, if they do succeed, to envy, robbery, and abuse.[96]

Throughout his whole life Franklin resented the fact that his earliest communications, however applauded by the Royal Society, were not fully printed in the Society's *Philosophical Transactions* and that no attempt had been made in England to perform his lightning experiment before the news of the successful French experiments. His election as Fellow of the Royal Society had been marked by unusual tokens of esteem, he had been awarded the Copley Medal (the Society's highest honor), and had served on the Society's Council; even so, he could never forget that when his paper on lightning had been read at the Royal Society it had been " laughed at by the connoisseurs," and in 1788, in the third portion of his " Autobiography," he still felt the need of complaining that the letters read at the Royal Society " were not at first thought worth so much notice as to be printed in their Transactions."

Franklin was rather proud of his ability to accept criticism and to modify his opinion, especially since these were qualities he rarely found in others. During the course of a discussion with Kinnersley, a fellow experimenter of Philadelphia, he observed: " You see I am willing to meet you half way, a compliance I have not met with in our brother Nollet, or any other hypothesis-maker, and therefore may value myself a little upon it, especially as they say I have some ability in defending even the wrong side of a question, when I think fit to take it in hand. " [97] But he was unquestionably bothered by attacks upon his work. When Nollet tried to make a parade of Franklin's errors, Franklin lamented that the Europeans had such reluctance to " allow that they can possibly receive any instruction from us Americans." [98] Franklin read Nollet's books, " repeated all the Abbe's experiments in vacuo " and found them to " answer exactly as they should do on my principles." He decided to write a reply, since Nollet had " laid himself extreamly open by attempting to impose false accounts of experiments on the world to support his doctrine." [99] Poised on the brink of the precipice of controversy, he wisely changed his mind. He encouraged others who wished to enter the lists to do so, and arranged for the publication of David Colden's rejoinder to Nollet; but he himself refrained from writing, although he had " actually " begun an answer. He felt that his published writings contained full descriptions of all the experiments which " anyone might repeat & verify " ; if they could not be verified, they " could not be defended." The " observations offered as conjectures " were " not delivered dogmatically " and he was not, therefore, " under any obligation to defend them." He concluded, in a spirit that still evokes admiration as ideal conduct in scientific disputes, that he would let his papers " shift for themselves, believing it was better to spend what time I could spare from public business in making new experiments, than in disputing about those already made." [100] But he was human enough to rejoice later on that his own theory " was by degrees universally adopted by the [natural] philosophers of Europe, in preference to that of the Abbé; so that he lived to see himself the last of his sect, except Monsieur B———, of Paris, his élève and immediate disciple." [101]

In 1773, at the height of the controversy as to whether lightning rods should terminate in knobs or points, Franklin wrote to Jean B. Le Roy apropos of B. Wilson's article attacking pointed conductors, " I find it is expected from me that I make some answer to it, and I shall do so, tho' I have an extreme aversion to public altercation on philosophic points, and have never yet disputed with anyone who thought fit to attack my opinions." [102] Once again, however, Franklin's equilibrium and good sense won a mastery of the situation and he did not write an answer, " being averse to disputes." [103] Still concerned about the affair in 1777, he joked about Wilson being " as much heated about this *one point* as the Jansenists and Molenists about the *five*." [104] He boasted that he had " never entered into any controversy in defence of my philosophical opinions," but had left them " to take their chance in the world. If they are *right*, truth and experience will support them; if *wrong*, they ought to be refuted and rejected."

Having seen bitter controversies in science, with effects as deplorable as those that arose in political disputes, he sought to have others follow his way. When a "misunderstanding" arose between two of his friends, Ingen-Housz and Priestley, he begged Ingen-Housz to "omit the polemic piece" in the new French edition of his work, since "public altercation" makes "the ignorant . . . diverted at the expence of the learned." Ingen-Housz was told to "go on" with his "excellent experiments, produce facts, improve science, and do good to mankind." In this way, said Franklin, "Reputation will follow, and the little injustices of contemporary labourers will be forgotten. . . . You can always employ your time better than in polemics." [105]

In the realm of science, Franklin was as generous as he was in private life. Although Romas had claimed the kite experiment as his own, Franklin recognized the solid merit of his research and went out of his way to call attention to it.[106] Robert Symmer, whom Franklin knew in London, was the author of the "revived" two-fluid theory of electricity, the rival of Franklin's theory which was based on the action of a single fluid. Franklin's concern to find the truth, even if at the expense of his own concepts, led him to aid Symmer in his research in every way that he could. Symmer gratefully acknowledged that the apparatus, used by him to perform the experiments he believed would vindicate the two-fluid theory and show the inadequacy of Franklin's, had been provided for him by Benjamin Franklin.[107]

Franklin's Scientific Style

Wholly apart from the personal qualities of integrity and generosity that endeared him to his scientific colleagues, Franklin was respected in the world of science for the important new discoveries that he had made, for his theory of electrical action which had made a science of electricity, and for the splendid style of his scientific writings. His book is available for anyone to read and to make his own judgments as to its qualities; certain portions of it will be quoted in the following pages since a summary written by a pen inferior to his would be an injustice to the reader. But a few unpublished letters will give the reader some further glimpse of the scientific personality of Benjamin Franklin and an insight into the qualities that made his scientific writings so widely read and esteemed in the eighteenth century and ever since.

Franklin's letter to the Royal Society acknowledging the receipt of the Copley gold medal is a masterpiece of wit. This letter turns on a pun, of the sort for which he was famous, about the alchemists dream of making ("multiplying") gold. It is printed from the original in the archives of the Royal Society of London.[108]

Philad[a]. May 29, 1754

Gentlemen,

The very great Honour you have done me, in adjudging me your Medal for 1753 demands my grateful Acknowledgements, which I beg you would accept as the only Return at present in my Power.

I know not whether any of your learned Body have attain'd the ancient boasted Art of *multiplying* Gold; but you have certainly found the Art of making it infinitely *more valuable*.

You may easily bestow your Favors on Persons of more Merit; but on none who can have a higher Sense of the Honour, or a more perfect Respect for your Society and Esteem of its excellent Institution, than

Gentlemen,

Your most obliged
& most obed[t]. Servant,

B. Franklin.

Presid[t]. & Council of
the Royal Society

One of Franklin's most famous scientific letters deals with his experiments on the stilling of waves by pouring oil on the waters. Addressed to Dr. William Brownrigg, this letter was printed in the *Philosophical Transactions* and has been reprinted in the editions of Franklin's writings ever since.[109] The original letter, in the archives of the Royal Society, contains several introductory paragraphs that have never been printed and that are indicative of the warm personal feelings that marked even scientific communications from Franklin's hand.

London, Nov. 7, 1773.

Dear Sir,

Our Correspondence might be carried on for a Century with very few Letters; if you were as apt to procrastinate as myself. Tho' an habitual Sinner, I am now quite ashamed to observe, that this is to be an Answer to your Favour of January last.

I suppose M[rs] Brownrigg did not succeed in making the Parmesan Cheese, since we have heard nothing of it. But as a Philosophess, she will not be discouraged by one or two Failures.—Perhaps some Circumstance is omitted in the Receipt, which by a little more Experience she may discover.—The foreign Gentleman, who had learnt in England to like boiled Plumpudding, and carried home a Receipt for making it, wondered to see it brought to the Table in the Form of a Soup. The Cook declar'd he had exactly followed the Receipt. And when that came to be examined, a small but important circumstance appeared to have been omitted. There was no Mention of the Bag.

I am concerned that you had not, and I fear you have not yet found time to prepare your excellent Paper for Publication. By omitting it so long, you are wanting to the World, and to your own Honour.

I thank you for the Remarks of your learned Friend at Carlisle. I had when a youth, read and smiled at Pliny's Account of a Practice among the Seamen of his time, to still the Waves in a Storm by pouring Oil into the Sea. . . .

. . . I would wish you to communicate this to your ingenious Friend M^r. Farish, with my Respects; and believe me to be, with sincere Esteem,

> Dear Sir,
> 　　Your most obedient
> 　　humble Servt.
> 　　　　B. Franklin.

When the occasion required it, Franklin could, of course write the more customary formal note. When he received word that he had been elected one of the eight foreign associates of the Royal Academy of Science, he wrote the following letter, now published for the first time from a photostat of the original in the Académie des Sciences, Paris.

London, Nov. 16, 1772

Gentlemen,

A Place among your foreign Members is justly esteemed by all Europe, the greatest Honour a Man can arrive at in the Republick of Letters. It was therefore with equal Surprise and Satisfaction that I learnt you had condescended to confer that Honour upon me. Be pleased to accept my grateful Acknowledgments, and believe me with the greatest Esteem and Respect,

Gentlemen, your most obliged and most humble Servant

B. Franklin

Royal Academy of Sciences
at Paris

An unpublished letter in the library of the American Philosophical Society is of particular interest in that it displays Franklin's views that science and learning transcend national boundaries and political quarrels, even wars.

Passy May 4, 1779

Dear Friend,

I received your kind Letter of last Month, and I forwarded that Part of it, which related to Mr. Williams. Inclosed you have his Answer.

I shall be glad to see those Papers of yours which you tell me will be in the Transactions, or indeed any thing of your Writing. By the way, mentioning the Transactions puts me in mind that I have received none of the Volumes published since my Departure from England in March 1775. I do not suppose that Politicks have so far taken the Lead of Philosophy in the Society as to judge me unworthy of having them; and therefore request you would be so good as to take the Trouble of sending them to me, by the Stage to Dover, directed to the Care of M. Le Veux, Negociant à Calais. I believe that Carriage should be paid to Dover, which you will charge to my Account. That you may see I have not totally neglected Philosophy, though I have little time for it at present, I send you inclosed some of my Thoughts, occasion'd by seeing here one of the late Northern Lights. The paper translated into French was read in the Academy of Sciences and well received, and perhaps will be printed in their Memoirs; I cannot therefore properly propose your giving it to be read at the Royal Society; but after amusing yourself and your excellent Friends with it, I would wish you to deliver it to Mr. Benjamin Vaughan or to Dr. Priestley for him: And if you think such a Thing might not be judged improper under present Circumstances, I may perhaps show the Continuance of my ancient Respect for that Society by offering it soon a Paper on a more useful Subject.

With great and sincere Esteem, I am, my dear Friend,

> Yours most Affectionately
>
> B. Franklin

Dr. Ingenhause

P. S. May 5. Since writing the above, I have receiv'd yours of the 9th April, which I shall answer in my next.

Newton and Franklin: Some Differences and Similarities

The portrayal of the scientific personalities of Franklin and of Newton prepares us to understand the way in which the men of the eighteenth century were apt to revere Newton and to love Franklin. One was a man shrouded in mystery, a source of legend in his own life-time,† the other was a man of flesh and blood whom the world knew and understood. The Marquis de l'Hôpital could ask seriously whether Newton ate and slept like other men, but no one would have asked a similar question about Franklin. Both Newton and Franklin were elected, early in their scientific careers, Fellows of the Royal Society and, later on, members of the Society's Council, just as both won the coveted distinction of becoming one of the eight foreign associates of the French Royal Academy of Sciences. To Franklin as to Newton, the Royal Society

---

† For example, Newton was supposed to have been about to propose to a young lady, took her hand in his, and then—absent-mindedly tamped the burning tobacco in his pipe with her little finger instead of raising her fingers to his lips. This scene later became the subject of an illustration by Cruikshank, and the story was apparently widely circulated in Newton's day and after.[110]

made a generous gesture. When Newton asked Oldenburg to present his resignation to the Royal Society, Oldenburg apparently supposed the reason to be financial and recommended that his weekly dues be excused; the Council voted approval. When Franklin was elected a Fellow, the Council voted that his name " be inserted in the lists before his admission, and without any fee, or other payments to the Society." [111] Curiously enough, neither Franklin nor Newton was in such a bad financial state that the money would have made the difference between membership and non-membership.

Franklin and Newton, we have seen, were both skilled at making things with their hands; they had the talent to execute the experiments they conceived, and the skill to make the apparatus. Both Franklin and Newton were encouraged by the Royal Society in the early days of their scientific careers. Newton's early publications on light and color, and his later publication of the *Principia*, were visible tokens of the Society's patronage. Franklin, too, received the applause of the Society and was stimulated to produce more results. Both men received their first scientific recognition from the outside world from the Royal Society.

Newton's career was similar to Franklin's in that only a part of his life was devoted to scientific inquiry; he too had a variety of other consuming interests. Both were public servants during the later years of their lives. When Newton was a Member of Parliament, he spoke but once in the House—it was said—and then to request an usher to close a window.‡ Yet we know that he was busy behind the scenes, that he " undoubtedly supported steadfastly the Whig measures, and he zealously attended to the interests of the University." [113] His series of thirteen letters to the Vice-Chancellor of Cambridge, John Covel, More has concluded, show that he " played an important part in the Convention Parliament by acting as mediator and adviser to the University, and he, apparently, handled a difficult task with tact and success." [114] Franklin, too, was never a good public speaker and, during the Second Continental Congress and the Constitutional Convention, was effective chiefly on committees.[115]

As we explore more fully the quality of Newton's science, and the various interpretations of his work in the eighteenth century, we

‡ It is certainly a mistake to suppose that Newton was chosen to represent the University for any other reason than a presumed ability in politics. " This election to the Convention was a proof of high confidence in his power, out of science, on the part of members of the University: it may well be doubted whether such a constituency, at such a crisis, would have invested half their share of the settlement in a compliment to the author of the ' Principia,' which, it may be added, was little more than a twelvemonth old." [112]

shall see the legitimate sense in which Franklin's kind of scientific work—despite its adumbration of hypotheses and lack of mathematics—can be called " Newtonian." In other words, Franklin can be considered a speculative Newtonian experimental scientist in a way that an important segment of Newton's followers would have understood. It is, in fact, the purpose of this monograph to show that Franklin was a Newtonian scientist by displaying the many-sided character of Newtonian science in Franklin's day and by analyzing Franklin's own contributions to science in Newtonian terms.

Although in the eyes of his contemporaries Franklin seemed to be one of the foremost Newtonian scientists, he was a Newton only on a smaller scale than the original. This evaluation in no way belittles the grand stature of Franklin. The world, after all, has produced only one Newton, just as—to use the famous words of Laplace—there is only one law of the cosmos and Newton discovered it.[116] Of only Newton, and of no other scientist who has ever lived (with the possible exception of Archimedes), can it be asked meaningfully whether he has ever had a peer in the whole history of science. For creative ability in breadth and depth, Newton stands alone. The revolution in men's thinking that he wrought is without comparison in the affairs of men. Those of Franklin's contemporaries who called him a Newton were paying him the highest tribute in their power, and in this way we are provided with an index of the esteem in which they held him. To say that, of course, he was hardly the equal of Newton, is not to lessen in any way the importance of his contribution. There was but one Newton and his name was Isaac; even so, as we explore the growth of physical thought in the century following Newton's work, we shall find that Franklin held a primary position in the science of his day. Any survey of the growth of physical science cannot fail to reveal his Newtonian contribution. It is equally clear that, however pleased Franklin must have been when called a Newton, his modesty and honesty would have found some embarrassment in that compliment. Yet to have made an " exact science " of electricity was an achievement worthy of Newton and in this sense we can appreciate the designation without undue exaggeration.

SOURCES

The literature concerning Newton is as large as that concerning Franklin. Two Newton bibliographies, each making no pretense to completeness, contain some account of the secondary literature: Gray (1907), Babson Collection (1950). The standard biography is More (1934), which supplements but does not entirely replace Brewster (1855). For Newton's personality two recent essays are of paramount importance, Andrade (1947) and Keynes (1947), as are De Morgan (1885 and 1914); de Villamil (1931) is particularly valuable for the reconstruction of Newton's physical surroundings and his library. The Royal Society edition of Newton's correspondence, edited by Professor Turnbull, will be of the utmost value for our understanding of Newton. Andrade (1950a) is an informative and clear presentation of Newton and what he did, written in simple terms for all to understand.

Our difficulty in comprehending Newton the man comes from the quality of his own extraordinary personality. Newton, after three centuries, can still arouse strong passions and so the literature about him tends to become extremely partisan. A biographer of Newton is apt to quarrel with Hooke as Newton did, or even attack Einstein as it might be supposed that Newton would have done. Furthermore, there has been a tendency to make of the greatest English man of science a model of the great man in every possible sense: paragon of virtue, exemplar of moral conduct, defender of the true faith. There has never been produced a faithful account of Newton's religious views.

De Morgan reported that in the nineteenth century there was a popular jingle which indicates the degree of Bayardism concerning Newton:

> And, so you think that Newton told a lie;
> Where do you hope to go when you die!

So great was the hero-worship of Brewster that he, throughout his biography, called Newton the " High Priest of Science," Stukeley's phrase, which quite properly aroused an antidote in De Morgan (1914). More, taking a somewhat better balanced or more detached point of view, castigated Brewster for portraying his hero " without blemish intellectually and morally," and for conceiving " his duty to explain away whatever may mar the ideal he would create. He [Brewster] says of himself that, where he found evidence which confirmed facts known to reflect adversely on Newton's character, he published it; but if the facts were not previously known, he felt bound in honour to respect the privacy of his discovery. The irritation and suspicion which such a policy inevitably arouses in the mind of the reader defeated his purpose." Yet when More adds, " there is absolutely nothing in his [Newton's] life so serious that it should have been suppressed," we are apt to wonder about More's own qualities as a biographer; were something " serious " to have been uncovered, would More then have " suppressed " it? Furthermore, valuable as More's biography is, it contains no bibliography and is inadequately documented and indexed; the student of Newton still needs Brewster's two volumes for the wealth of information they contain which is not to be found in More.

More himself used Newton to attack the science and scientists of his own day. More scorned " such scientists as can recognize no phenomena and no laws except those of matter, space, and time," and he ridiculed " modern science " which " still debauches itself with hypotheses of æther [1934!], electronic structures, and fantastic cosmogonies," and he also referred to the best physical science of his day in such phrases as, " the pretensions of modern pseudo-science "—all in the name of Newton. " It is a notable fact," writes this biographer, " that . . . two works, probably the two most stupendous creations of the scientific brain, are now under attack—*Organon* by modern symbolists in logic [!], and the *Principia* by the relativists [!] in physics. But Aristotle and Newton will be honoured and *used* when the modernists are long forgotten." " Professor Einstein's Generalised Theory of Relativity " becomes for More the " boldest attempt towards a philosophy of pure idealism," which " is merely a logical exercise of the active mind "; ignoring " the world of brute facts," and departing from Newton, this new physics of Einstein " ultimately evaporates into a scholasticism " that " will cause the decadence of science as surely as the mediæval scholasticism preceded the decadence of religion."

Such statements show the extent to which we still lack an impartial view of Newton taken at his own measure; perhaps this will always be the situation. Thus the problem in evaluating the scientific personality of Newton is to try to disengage the statements made about him, during some three hundred years, from the respective personalities of those who knew him or who have written about him. One general weakness which dominates most of the Newton literature is that too many authors have taken his statements at their face value. For example, if Newton said he disliked controversies, they say that Newton disliked controversies—despite the evidence that Newton was the center of so many scientific altercations.

In contrast to Newton, Franklin presents a wholly different problem. So little adequate literature exists about Franklin as a scientist that we are not surprised to find practically no discussion in print on the subject of his scientific personality. There are a number of excellent works that deal with Franklin as a person, and that reveal his general character and his scientific interests. Van Doren (1938) is a splendid biography, and is supplemented by the collection of " autobiographical writings," Van Doren (1945). Ford (1899) contains a well-balanced view, often marked by keen insight. The introduction to Mott and Jorgenson (1936) is most valuable. The best view of Franklin's scientific personality is to be found scattered through the pages of Priestley (1775), since Priestley knew Franklin the man as well as his scientific work. Becker (1946) offers a stimulating and penetrating view of Franklin and his thought. I have attempted to portray the relation between Franklin's scientific empiricism and his general outlook in the introduction to Cohen (1953).

A brilliant analysis of Newton's " note-book," in Hall (1948), leads to " a revised time-scale " for Newton's discoveries: 1664 to spring 1665 for the early prismatic experiments, " winter 1666 for completion of the theory of colors and construction of the reflecting telescope."

REFERENCES

1. E.g., Olmsted, 1938.
2. E. g., Campbell and Garnett, 1882.
3. See Moszkowski, 1921: 99.
4. Vallentin, 1954.
5. Darrow, 1926: 116; cf. Einstein, 1905.
6. Tyndall, 1870: 186; Faraday, 1932-1936: *passim.*
7. Freud, 1934; *cf.* Galdston, 1944.
8. Roe, 1951; Kubie, 1953-1954; Hadamard, 1945; Wright, 1944.
9. Toulouse, 1910.
10. de Villamil, 1931: 14.
11. Keynes, 1947: 28, 29.
12. Newton, 1671/2; reprinted in Roberts and Thomas, 1934: 71-91, and reprinted in facsimile in Sarton, 1930.
13. Letter to Leibniz (9 Dec. 1675), Brewster, 1855, 1: 96.
14. Printed in Birch, 1756-1757: 1: 247-305; reprinted in Brewster, 1855: 1: 390-419.
15. See More, 1934: 506; see Wallis's letter to Newton, 10 April 1695, in Edleston, 1850: 300.
16. Gregory, 1937: 15.
17. Barrow, 1735, Preface, p. iv; translated from the Latin in Barrow, 1669, Epistola ad lectorem.
18. Andrade, 1947: 6; see Hall, 1948: 240n.
19. Vavilov, 1947: 44.
20. More, 1934: 81.
21. See Osmond, 1944: 129.
22. More, 1934: 81.
23. See Rosenfeld, 1927.
24. Osmond, 1944: 119; see Rigaud, 1841: 2: 126.
25. Newton, 1728a: 2.
26. Maclaurin, 1748: 13.
27. Pemberton, 1728; see Turnbull, 1945: 8.
28. E. g. Whewell, 1858; Rosenberger, 1895; Jourdain, 1915a; 1915b; 1915c; More, 1934; Roberts and Thomas, 1934.
29. Brown, 1950: 95.
30. See Stukeley, 1806: 179.
31. Conduitt, 1806: 159n.
32. More, 1934: 16.
33. *Ibid.,* 17.
34. King, 1830: 2: 37; reprinted in More, 1934: 490.
35. Andrade, 1947: 17.
36. More, 1934: 409.
37. *Ibid.,* 17.
38. Letter to Flamsteed, 6 Jan. 1698/9, More, 1934: 482.
39. More, 1934: 247, 250.
40. See Fulton, 1932b.
41. See Cavendish, 1879.

42. Rigaud, 1841: 2: 312-313.

43. *Ibid.*, 315.

44. See Rosenfeld, 1927.

45. Rigaud, 1841: 2: 405; reprinted in More, 1934: 91.

46. More, 1934: 80.

47. *Ibid.*, 290; but cf. Hall, 1948: 240n.

48. Letter to Halley, 20 June 1686, Ball, 1893: 157.

49. Cajori, 1928a: 177 ff.

50. Ball, 1893: 141.

51. Letter to Halley, 14 July 1686, Rigaud, 1838: 40.

52. Cajori, 1928a: 180, 186.

53. Quoted in Cajori, 1928a: 187, from the *London Times*, 19 March 1927.

54. The correspondence between Hooke and Newton at this time has been published in Ball, 1893; Pelseneer, 1929; 1939; and Koyré, 1952. For an excellent view of Hooke, see Andrade, 1950b, and Patterson, 1949-1950.

55. The phrase is Koyré's.

56. Ball, 1893: 158; partially reprinted in More, 1934: 310.

57. More, 1934: 311.

58. Gregory, 1937: 36.

59. Huygens, 1912: preface.

60. More, 1934: 196.

61. Gregory, 1937: 42.

62. Keynes, 1947: 30-31.

63. Pringle, 1783: 37.

64. See De Morgan, 1914: 187 ff.

65. Van Doren, 1938: 90-91.

66. "The Dogood Papers," Franklin, 1907: 2: 1-49; see Miller, 1953: 341-343, 361-362.

67. See Franklin, 1941: intro., pp. 5-7; Van Doren, 1938: 183-187.

68. Franklin, 1907: 2: 336-353.

69. Letter to Cadwallader Colden, Colden, 1919-1920: 4: 78-79.

70. Letter to Colden, Colden, 1919-1920: 4: 227.

71. Letter to Peter Collinson (14 Aug. 1747), Franklin, 1907: 2: 324-325; a corrected version in Franklin, 1941: 63.

72. "Opinions and Conjectures" (1749), Franklin, 1941: 219; 1769: 62.

73. Letter to Collinson (14 Aug. 1747); see note 71 above.

74. Letter to Collinson (Sept. 1753), Franklin, 1941: 279; 1769: 127.

75. See Franklin, 1941: 158-159.

76. *Ibid.*, 148 ff.; "Letter II" (to Collinson, 11 July 1747), *ibid.*, 171 ff.; Franklin, 1769: 3 ff.

77. "Letter V" (to Dr. John Mitchel, 29 Apr. 1749), Franklin, 1941: 211; 1769: 52.

78. Franklin, 1941: 247; 1769: 96.

79. "Letter X" (to Ebenezer Kinnersley, 16 Mar. 1752), Franklin, 1941: 255; 1769: 106.

80. "Letter III" (to Collinson, 28 July 1747 [printed as of 1 Sept. 1747]), Franklin, 1941: 180; 1769: 13.

81. "Letter II (to Collinson, 11 July 1747), Franklin, 1941: 173; 1769: 5.

82. Franklin, 1941: 336; 1769: 326.

83. Priestley, 1775: 2: 374.

84. Davy, 1840: 264.

85. Priestley, 1775: 1: 192-193.

86. Diderot, 1875a.

87. Hume to Franklin (10 May 1762), Franklin, 1907: 4: 154.

88. See Wroth, 1943.

89. Franklin, 1907: 10: 493.

90. See Cohen, 1952b.

91. See Hujer, 1952; Cohen and Schofield, 1952.

92. Franklin, 1941: intro., ch. iii (2, 3).

93. Nollet, 1764c.
94. See Cohen, 1952a.
95. See Franklin, 1941: intro., ch. iii (4).
96. Franklin, 1941: 337-338; 1769: 327-328.
97. Letter to Kinnersley (20 Feb. 1762), Franklin, 1941: 367; 1769: 407.
98. Letter to Cadwallader Colden (12 April 1753), Colden, 1919-1920: 4: 382-384.
99. Letter to Colden (1 Jan. 1753), *ibid.*, 358-359.
100. "Autobiography," Franklin, 1949b: 384.
101. *Ibid.*, 386.
102. Franklin, 1907: 6: 28-29.
103. Letter to Jan Ingen-Housz (30 Sept. 1773), *ibid.*, 141-143.
104. Letter dated 4 Oct. 1777, *ibid.* 7: 64-65.
105. Letter dated 2 Oct. 1781, *ibid.* 8: 314.
106. Franklin, 1907: 5: 422n.
107. Symmer, 1759.
108. See Cameron, 1952: 116n.
109. Franklin, 1907, 6: 153-165.
110. See Edleston, 1850: lxxx; More, 1934: 132. The Cruikshank illustration of "Sir Isaac Newton's courtship" is reproduced in Watson, 1954.
111. See Stearns, 1946.
112. De Morgan, 1885: 11.
113. More, 1934: 346.
114. *Ibid.*, 351.
115. See Ford, 1899: 453-455.
116. Laplace, 1821.

PART TWO

Newton:
The New Natural Philosophy

CHAPTER FOUR

PHYSICAL THEORY IN THE AGE OF NEWTON AND FRANKLIN

> Even mistaken hypotheses and theories are of use in leading to discoveries. This remark is true in all the sciences. The alchemists founded chemistry by pursuing chimerical problems and theories which are false. In physical science, which is more advanced than biology, we might still cite men of science who make great discoveries by relying on false theories. It seems, indeed, a necessary weakness of our mind to be able to reach truth only across a multitude of errors and obstacles.
>
> —CLAUDE BERNARD (1865)

IN THE previous chapter, some indication was given of the relation of the scientific thought of Franklin and of Newton to their respective personalities, thus preparing the way for an appreciation of the difficulties in interpreting Newton's thought, or even finding out exactly what it was, as contrasted to the relative simplicity of tracing the evolution of Franklin's ideas. But the full measure of a man's creation is obtained only by a consideration of the general state of mind when he did his work. In its simplest aspect, this consideration merely becomes a device to show how superior one man was to his contemporaries; but in larger terms an appreciation of the background to any man's thought clarifies and makes specific the problems to which he devoted himself and the very character of his ideas. The atomism of Newton, even as modified by Franklin, to take but one example, cannot be evaluated without giving due weight to the vogue of atomistic concepts as expressed in the writings of such of Newton's predecessors as Bacon and Galileo, or contemporaries like Boyle and Hooke. The temptation then arises to investigate the background of Bacon and Galileo, and so to trace the major concepts backwards through time to antiquity. We need not rewrite the history of ancient and mediæval science in order to understand the scientific thought of Franklin. Yet, to the extent that eighteenth-century scientific concepts were derived in part from, and were influenced by, the seventeenth-century reaction to scholastic physics we must take cognizance of the late mediæval physics. At the minimum, we must note how much of it had survived the seventeenth-century onslaught, was still being taught in Newton's day, and was a part of the academic curriculum even in Franklin's youth.

91

From the point of view of the history of science, the eighteenth century was a long time ago, despite the fact that the science of that day presents formal aspects that are easily recognizable to anyone who is acquainted with the science of the last one hundred and fifty years. We can often readily translate the best writing of the mid-eighteenth century into our modern precise scientific language, but we are apt to distort such writing by introducing senses that the authors could never have intended. The reason is, of course, that many of our major fundamental concepts are only refinements of those that were current two hundred years ago. But the differences as well as resemblances between that age and the present are significant to the historian of science. The historian, while pleased to note the degree of modernity, is apt to be more concerned with the equal degree of antiqueness, especially because this aspect of eighteenth-century scientific thought is an index of the actual aims of the scientists of that day. They obviously had no idea of the directions in which their work would take their successors a century or more later, but they were certainly conscious of certain trends in the science of their time which had to be attacked. These were vestiges of the scientific thought of a less modern age, like the electrical theories that were based on the concepts of a Cartesian physics. So it is that to approach the physical science of the age of Franklin we cannot limit ourselves to the modern masters who were revered (like Boyle and Newton) ; we must also consider the older writers who were still under attack, or who had only recently been vanquished and banished from experimental science, because the effects of the battle were a conditioning factor on the trends of scientific thought.

A striking example of the scars borne by eighteenth-century science from the battles of the seventeenth century is found in the history of biology. William Harvey's discovery of the circulation of the blood was one of the outstanding scientific achievements of the seventeenth century and it certainly marks the beginning of modern animal physiology. Curiously enough, Harvey was a great admirer of Aristotle, and even had a kind word to say for Galen. At the very time when Galileo and his pupils were constructing a physics on a non-Aristotelian basis, Harvey was eloquent in his veneration of Aristotle. In *De Motu Cordis*, setting forth the arguments for the circulation of the blood, no author is quoted as many times as Aristotle, and none is cited with more approval. Harvey also applauded Aristotle in his *De Generatione Animalium*, where he followed his Greek master in advocating a doctrine of epigenesis. In the eighteenth century there was a rather general adherence to a theory of animal generation called " evolution " or pre-formation, according to which tiny " preformed " individuals of each generation pre-exist in their parents, either in the spermatozoa or the ova according to the particular theory of each writer. The rejection of the Harveyan presentation of epigenesis [1] would seem to be part of the anti-Aristotelian character of the " new science " of the late seventeenth century. In other words, to understand the biological ideas held in the eighteenth century, we must take into account the effects of the war against Aristotelian science which had just been terminated.

The situation in physics in the eighteenth century was not very different from that in biology. Over and over again in the writings of both Franklin and Newton, we find an awareness of the need for avoiding any semblance of the older physics, a horror of " occult forces " and the consequent invention of ingenious conceptual schemes for eliminating the " action-at-a-distance " that seemed so obvious a conclusion—if it could have been tolerated. So, before displaying the Newtonian frame in which the physical concepts of Franklin and his contemporaries were set, we must inquire into the currents of thought that had been conditioned by a conscious rejection of the pre-mechanical physics. We must seek out, in other words, the influences of the past which, like unwelcome ghosts, still haunted the creative thought of the age of reason.

Vestiges of Aristotle and Descartes in the Early Eighteenth Century

When Franklin was born in 1706, the Royal Society of London (the oldest scientific society or academy still existing today) was only forty-six years old; its French counterpart, the Académie Royale des Sciences, was but forty years old. Galileo had been dead sixty-four years and Boyle had died fifteen years earlier. Isaac Newton, Master of the Mint, was sixty-four years of age, and had published his *Principia* only nineteen years previously and his *Opticks* but two years past. At that time, in British continental America, there were in existence only three colleges, Harvard, Yale, and William and Mary. The great scientific revolution of the seventeenth century was barely an accomplished fact. We may note that when the second edition of the *Principia* was published in 1713, seven years after Franklin's birth, it was still necessary to attack the Cartesian vortices. Roger Cotes wrote a preface to that end, and Newton added a General Scholium beginning: " The hypothesis of vortices is pressed with many difficulties."

While the Galilean-Newtonian system of physics was making progress against the system of Descartes, especially in England, the victory was not complete in the first quarter of the eighteenth cen-

tury. One of the chief textbooks in general use was Jacques Rohault's *Traité de Physique*, in the translation into Latin by Samuel
Clarke, published in 1697.[2] This work was strictly Cartesian, although the translator—who had studied the Newtonian philosophy
at Caius College, Cambridge, and had defended this subject for his
bachelor's degree in 1695—had added notes which mention Newton.
When a second edition appeared in 1702, four years before Franklin's birth, these Newtonian notes had assumed sufficient importance to be mentioned on the title page, which reads: *Jacobi
Rohaulti Physica: Latinè vertit, recensuit, & uberioribus jam adno-
tationibus, ex illustrissimi Isaaci Newtoni philosophiâ maximam
partem haustis, amplificavit & ornavit Samuel Clarke*, etc. (London,
1702). This work was later translated into English by John Clarke,
Samuel's brother, under the title, *Rohault's System of Natural
Philosophy, illustrated with Dr Samuel Clarke's Notes taken mostly
out of Sir Isaac Newton's Philosophy* (London 1723; reprinted 1729,
1735), and its continuing popularity was assured. Many generations
of students (at Yale until 1743) learned what Newtonianism they
did along with the Cartesianism of this " ambivalent " book which
presented one kind of physics in the text and another in the footnotes.

In Franklin's youth, the Newtonian philosophy was conquering
the Cartesian in England, although, be it noted, slowly. But on the
Continent, Newtonian ideas were not yet generally accepted. In
1728, when Franklin was twenty-two years of age, Ephraim Chambers, in the *Cyclopædia* from which Franklin was to reprint many
articles in his *Pennsylvania Gazette*, noted that " Notwithstanding
the great merit of this philosophy, and the universal reception it has
met with at home, it gains ground very slowly abroad; Newtonianism
has scarce two or three adherents in a nation; but Cartesianism,
Huygenianism, and Leibnitzianism remain still in possession." Voltaire's comparison of the Cartesian atmosphere of France and the
Newtonian atmosphere of England in the 1720's is well known.[3]
Furthermore, although neo-Aristotelian or scholastic physics may
have been dead in England and the colonies, it certainly had not
been dead very long. When Franklin was born, Harvard students
were still studying a transitional textbook between the old and the
new science, Morton's *Compendium* (in active use until the 1720's)
which was largely Aristotelian and Cartesian with some discoveries
and principles of the " new science " introduced here and there.[4] In
1726 Cotton Mather, who had earlier published some account of
Newtonianism and the new science in his *Christian Philosopher*,
extolled the virtues of experimental philosophy to candidates for

the ministry. He commended " the *Principles* of our perpetual dictator, the incomparable Sr. Isaac Newton," [5] and regretted that the new Science was not universally held—" O Monstrous! if I am not misinformed they do in some universities at this day foolishly and profanely . . ." continue to swear allegiance to Aristotle. Yet the older physics, to the extent that it survived on the Continent, was only a weak dying opponent of newer ideas and in France was being replaced by the new orthodoxy: Cartesianism.

The Attack on the Doctrine of " Forms " and " Qualities "

During Franklin's youth, the opponents of the " new science " could still be remembered. In the writings of Newton and of Franklin we can easily detect the overtones of a conscious anti-Aristotelianism. Paradoxical as it may seem, therefore, to mention Aristotelian physics in a book about Franklin and Newton, we cannot understand what Newton did, or what Franklin learned from Newton, without some indication of the currents of thought that the men of Newton's day rejected. In this way the gulf of time that separates us from the days of Franklin's youth is made clear. For despite the modern character of Franklin's sentiments and style, he was born a long time ago: less than a hundred years after Shakespeare's death, only thirty years after the siege of Vienna by the Turks.

The difficulty in understanding the age of Franklin and Newton stems in part from the now traditional point of view that Newtonian science means the science of the *Principia,* and that the men of the Enlightenment universally appreciated " mathematical principles of natural philosophy." There can be no doubt that the Newtonian formulation of the dynamics of terrestrial and celestial bodies, the discovery of the mathematical laws of the universe, was one of the truly momentous events in the development of science. It was, historically, such a " spectacular advance that other aspects of the revolt against Aristotle tend to be obscured." Such is the thesis presented by Miss Marie Boas in a recent investigation of the theoretical science of Robert Boyle in relation to the main principles of Bacon: an elucidation of Boyle's and Bacon's " enthusiastic espousal of the experimental, as distinct from the mathematical or rational approach to science." [6] The beginnings of modern dynamics may—in a sense—be dated from Galileo's *Two New Sciences*, published only about one hundred years before Franklin undertook research in electricity. The older science can be described as " pre-mechanical "; it sought for explanations of physical phenomena in terms of " substantial forms " and " real qualities." " Forms " and " qualities "

seem to the modern reader to be only names for various properties
of bodies, but the pre-mechanical science was postulated on forms
and qualities as the true cause of sense perception and they were
thought to have " a verifiable existence." [7] This theory of forms and
qualities had roots in Aristotle's famous association of the " qualities " of hot, cold, wet, and dry with the traditional four elements
of earth, air, fire, and water. Elaborated by generations of Aristotelians, the theory held that sense-perception was a process of " detection of certain entities intimately associated with matter." [8] While
" substantial forms " are perceived by us only in association with
matter, they can by suitable processes be removed from matter or
introduced into matter, and so may be considered as having a " kind
of independent existence of their own." [9] As an example, we may
note what happens when an iron poker is placed in the fiery flame;
it acquires the " form of heat " which is so plentiful in the fire, but
it does so " imperfectly " and so cools on being removed from the
fire. When matter is burned, or converted in " fire," there is a
" perfect assimilation " of the " form of heat "—thus " fire " may
be considered material in nature.

I have mentioned, earlier, the textbook of Charles Morton, still
in use at Harvard and Yale during Franklin's youth. It may be called
a " transitional " book because it presents the Aristotelian categories
and the doctrine of forms and qualities, but also the animadversions
against them by the atomists, such as Gassendi, and the sentiments of
Boyle and Descartes in favor of a mechanical philosophy. Thus, in
Chapter Two of the *Compendium*, Morton discussed " form " as a
" substantial (or rather essential) principle of natural body which
by active union with the matter doth constitute it in some species
of bodyes." As an analogy Morton offered the body of man and his
rational soul (" the form of man ") ; the soul, when united actively
with the body (" the matter of man "), makes the man, a " species "
distinct from other animals, but the soul when separated from the
body, is not man, and the body from which the soul has departed
is but a carcass. In physics, Morton said, form " is taken only for
the chief essential part that gives specifically being to a natural body,
and therefore also it is called substantial form. . . ." Form is not a
true substance because it is an " incomplete being in that it is but a
part; yet 'tis said to be substantial because it is an essential part of a
true substance, namely, body." Noting that some " latter men "
apply the term " substantial " to no " form but the soul of man,"
Morton referred his reader to " Mr. Boyles treatise of essential
forms." [10]

Confusing and even baffling as these concepts may seem to the twentieth-century reader, they must be considered here because they were still somewhat current, if under attack, during Franklin's boyhood. The great scientific revolution of the seventeenth century can be considered, in one very real sense, as an integrated movement to replace the neo-Aristotelian doctrine of " real qualities " and " substantial forms " by the " mechanical philosophy ": in which the " new science " of mechanics as explicated by Galileo was to be applied to explain the physical and chemical properties of bodies— of which so many new ones were being discovered in the latter part of the century. In this view, we find a unity of effort in such apparently diverse figures as Galileo, Descartes, Bacon, Boyle, and Newton.

Morton noted that gravity is a quality said by " the antients " to arise " from cold cheifly and causing bodyes to discend or tend towards the center "; it is called " gravitation or endeavour, or inclination to be as near the center as it can; and this without an impediment is alwayes in the strait perpendicular line." [11] But gravity, and levity, and all qualities arising from " substantial forms "—including heat, cold, color, fluidity, elasticity, taste, volatility, magnetism, specific gravity, impetus—were in the new philosophy to be replaced by mechanical concepts: the consistent application of mechanics to the atomic theory.

One of the chief advocates of this new philosophy was Francis Bacon, who " noted in *The Advancement of Learning* how much could be gained by the discovery of forms. By this phrase," Miss Boas points out, " Bacon meant the discovery of a general method of explanation for the observed properties of bodies. . . . The proper method of approach was clearly that of experiment; and the discovery of forms was to be at once the reward and the foundation of the new inductive science." [12] The method of the science of induction, occupying the second half of Bacon's *Novum Organum*, is largely devoted to such a study of " forms." After collecting miscellaneous observations and the results of genuine experiments with " fire " and the heat produced in chemical action, Bacon concluded that heat is merely a " mode of motion," thereby reducing one " form " to its mechanical explanation. Although this was the only " form " that Bacon studied thoroughly, he predicted that other " forms " could be accounted for in a similar fashion in terms of matter and motion, mentioning explicitly whiteness, putrefaction, magnetism, density, softness, liquidity, and even animation.

Bacon's influence on the development of science has long been debated, and historical opinion on this subject has varied greatly from scholar to scholar and from scientist to scientist and even from one generation to another. That Bacon understood the way in which abstract or pure science would produce practical innovations of great consequence for changing the patterns of men's lives is generally granted. Assent is given to his recognition of the need for organized research and scientific communication. His role as inspirer of the Royal Society of London, the first long-lasting major scientific society, is universally appreciated. But debate still rages as to whether Bacon influenced the growth of scientific thought as such, or whether modern science has been in any sense Baconian, or even whether any importance is to be given to those aspects of science that seem to be Baconian. Often it is said that Bacon preached about experiment but never experimented. In many a discussion, stress is laid on his strictures against Gilbert and Galileo and his failure to accept the Copernican system, and importance is given to the famous statement of Harvey that Bacon philosophized about science in the manner of a Lord Chancellor. No such considerations need detain us here, since our concern is neither to establish him as the *fons et origo* of our modern experimental science, nor to deny that place to him. We have merely to note his role in the attack on the pre-mechanical philosophy of " forms " and " qualities " and his program of reducing " forms " and " qualities " to principles of " matter and motion ": to be cognizant of his influence on Boyle, which has been amply demonstrated. This aspect of his role in the growth of science is significant because the tradition exemplified by Bacon and Boyle is essential to an understanding of the physical thought of the age of Newton, and without it we cannot begin to comprehend Franklin's creative research and its place in that age.

Boyle's " Corpuscular Philosophy "

The Honourable Robert Boyle is usually mentioned in the history of science for the discovery of the law of gases which bears his name; his improvement of the air pump and experiments in pneumatics; his supposed " clear " statement of the character of elements, compounds, and mixtures, and his experiments on calcination. Here we shall be more concerned with the way in which Boyle developed and illustrated a form of Bacon's mechanical philosophy which he christened the " corpuscular philosophy "—a mechanical atomism that had a wide influence and that has been described as " the connecting link between the seemingly quite unrelated experimental essays Boyle published so steadily year after year." [13] That Boyle is to be considered the heir of Bacon in the sense described above is clear from his own writings. He believed that the physical world was an integrated mechanism, the action of which could be explained in the

" corpuscular " terms of matter and motion. The universe was for him a " self-moving engine," as he put it, a " great piece of clock-work." [14] All things, according to Boyle, are to be considered in terms of those " two grand and most catholick principles of bodies, matter and motion," [15] a guiding principle that was also in large measure accepted by Boyle's junior contemporary and quondam assistant, Robert Hooke,[16] who was second in the experimental art (if at all) only to Boyle himself.

In every branch of physics and chemistry, Boyle sought for explanations of " forms " and " qualities " in terms of corpuscles and their mechanical action and he tried, " as Bacon had urged, to base his explanations upon experiment so that they should conform to the real world of nature." [17] To such an extent did Boyle subscribe to simple " corpuscular " explanations that on one occasion, he explained the supposed curative power of certain gems on the basis of material emanations coming from them. Boyle's advocacy of the corpuscularity of light, like Newton's doctrine of colors provides yet another example of the explanation of a set of physical phenomena by mechanical corpuscular action. Newton, in fact, stated explicitly that the result of his investigations was to show that " Colours are not *qualifications of light* " (as was generally believed) and that light itself is a " body." Furthermore, colors cannot be considered " the qualities of the objects we see," [18] but if anything, the qualities of light itself.* And we may note that even the rival undulatory theory of Huygens, though framed in opposition to the concept of optical phenomena as being caused by streams of light corpuscles or particles, was itself based on the mechanical action or motion of æther particles [19] and so was allied to the " new philosophy " exemplified by the British school. An important instance of an explanation in terms of " matter and motion " is found in Boyle's *Experiments and Notes about the Mechanical Origine or Production of Electricity* (London, 1675), which is, incidentally, the first book on electricity in the English language. Boyle begins:

That 'tis not necessary to believe electrical attraction (which you know is generally listed among occult qualities) to be the effect of a naked and solitary quality flowing immediately from a substantial form; but that it may rather be the effect of a material effluvium, issuing from, and

---

* Newton's statement that colors are " qualities " of light and not " qualities " of bodies was only another way of saying that the visible color of an object depends on the kind of light by which it is illuminated and the particular selectivity of color-reflection and color-absorption of the object. Color is not a " qualification " of light, but the result of an absorption and reflection process. From the point of view of this chapter, Newton's use of the older terminology of " qualities " is more pertinent than the correctness of his statement.

returning to, the electrical body (and perhaps in some cases assisted in its operation by the external air) seems agreeable to divers things that may be observed in such bodies and their manner of acting.[20]

Boyle, we may observe, did not take account of the fact that experiments with his vacuum pump can show that electrical attractions occur as well in vacuo as in ordinary air, and that the likelihood of " assistance " by the " external air " is small.† But he noted a variety of " differing hypotheses (and all of them mechanical, proposed by the moderns) to solve the phænomena of electrical attraction," and concluded that all of them exhibit agreement " in what is sufficient for my present purpose, namely, that electrical attractions are not the effects of a meer quality, but of a substantial emanation from the attracting body; And 'tis plain, that they all endeavour to solve the *phænomena* in a mechanical way, without recurring to substantial forms, and inexplicable qualities, or so much as taking notice of the hypostatical principles of the chymists." [21]

Boyle's concept of the mode of electrical action did not of itself constitute a notable advance in electrical theory, by which I mean only that he was not able to explain adequately the observed phenomena which baffled his contemporaries, nor was he able to predict any new effects which could then be uncovered by experiment. Yet the significance of his little book on electricity becomes apparent to us when we consider it in the light of the complete program of rejecting " forms " and " qualities " and of substituting in their place a new kind of explanation based on the mechanical corpuscular concepts, in this case a " substantial emanation from the attracting body " or " effluvia."

The Boyle-Bacon theory of heat, as arising from motion of the

---

† Boyle reported that a piece of Amber "warmed at . . . the fire, and presently after chafed . . . a little upon a piece of cloth " would become " excited " to a greater degree by " a very few rubbings . . . than many more would otherwise have done: As if the heat of the fire had put the parts into a general, but confused, agitation; to which 'twas easie for the subsequent attrition (or reciprocation of pressure) to give a convenient modification in a body whose texture disposes it to become vigorously electrical." Actually, the " fire " made it easier to electrify the piece of amber by removing from its surface the oil and water vapor. Boyle likewise missed the point in his discussion of why " weaker electricks [non-conductors] require to be as well wiped as chafed; and even good ones will have their operation promoted by the same means." This process " frees the surface from those adherences that might choak the pores of the amber, or at least hinder the emanations of the steams to be so free and copious as otherwise it would be." So, too, Boyle did not appreciate why the electrical attraction of a piece of rubbed amber was weaker on cloudy days than on clear days. For the historian of science, there is no phenomenon of greater interest than to see a man of the stature of Robert Boyle who has all the facts available to him, but who cannot help but see them in the light of his own times and his own preconceptions, and thus miss what later generations will call the " obvious " implications.

smallest parts of matter of which bodies are made, gave added sanction to the doctrine of effluvia, " which teaches the effects of electrical
[i. e., charged] bodies to be performed by corporeal emanations,"
Boyle wrote. " For ' tis known, that heat, by agitating the parts of
a fit body, solicites it as it were to send forth its effluvia, as is obvious
in odoriferous gums and perfumes, which, being heated, send forth
their fragrant steams, both further and more copiously than otherwise they would." [22] The application of a similar argument to
explain the increase in brightness of an iron poker that is heated
indicates a unity of conception applied to a large number of diverse
physical phenomena that is a kind of final test of any conceptual
scheme. Since Boyle's " effluvia " are little corpuscles that are put
into motion by "attrition" or friction when a body is rubbed,
electrical action was related to heat and both were included in a
kind of " atomic " dynamics.

One characteristic of the older science had been the constant
recourse to phrases and concepts of an animistic sort, including sympathy, congruence, and hatred or aversion. The science of pneumatics of the seventeenth century had replaced the animistic notion
that nature abhors a vacuum by a mechanical explanation in terms
of air pressure and the " spring " of the air which, according to Boyle,
arose from the particulate nature of air, although he was unwilling
to decide between the Epicurean and Cartesian notions about the
" springy " particles. Bacon had written that " what are called occult
and specific properties, or sympathies and antipathies, are in great
part corruptions of philosophy [i. e., science]." [23] Boyle echoed these
sentiments in his animadversions on the supposed *horror vacui*: " It
will not easily then be intelligibly made out, how hatred or adver-
sation, which is a passion of the soul, can either for a vacuum, or
any other object, be supposed to be . . ." in inanimate bodies, nor
to see how inanimate bodies such as air and water may " be so generous as to act contrary to what is most conducive to their own particular preservation for the public good of the universe." [24]

Boyle's final statement on the particulate nature of matter and
the mechanical action of corpuscles to explain the observed properties of bodies is to be found in a work entitled *The Origin of Forms
and Qualities, according to the Corpuscular Philosophy* (1666),[25]
a title which makes it clear that the new particulate doctrine of
" matter and motion " was to replace the older concepts of " substantial forms " and " real qualities." But, despite his enthusiastic
espousal of corpuscular explanations for all kinds of natural phenomena, Boyle was not too sure that light consists of a mere stream
of material particles. In his *Experimental History of Colours* (1663),
he had raised the question of whether " the corpuscles, that make up

the beams of light," are "solary effluviums, or minute particles of some ætherial substance"; [26] and in his *Essays of Effluviums* (1673), he mentioned that much dispute may be found "even among the moderns" as to light "being or not being a corporeal thing." [27] In his *Fire and Flame* (1673), he decided to put the question to the test of experiment: "I thought it worth the inquiry, whether a thing so vastly diffused as light is, were something corporeal or not? and whether, in case it be, it may be subjected to some other of our senses, besides our sight, whereby we may examine, whether it hath any affinity with other corporeal beings that we are acquainted with here below?" [28] Apparently, the British weather prevented him from a comparative experimental study of flame and sunlight,[29] and *Fire and Flame* contains only the results of his experiments on calcination by the action of fire. We shall see in Chapter Eight that Franklin was led to study the difference between sunlight and candle-light (flame) in their ability to discharge an electrified ball; the significant distinction he found may have been responsible for his doubts (similar to Boyle's) that light consists merely of a stream of corpuscles.

The problem posed and partially solved by Boyle, of how to account for the attraction of light bodies by electrified bodies without having recourse to "occult" forces or the doctrine of "qualities," has been a continuing source of concern to physicists ever since. Not only did it occupy some of the best minds of the nineteenth century, but also Franklin and Newton—and not alone in connection with electrical attraction, but also electrical repulsion, magnetic attraction and repulsion, chemical action, and gravitation. After the time of Boyle, scientists disdained any such explanation as might be couched in language like "the effect of a naked and solitary quality flowing immediately from a substantial form." Electrical attraction might be considered to have a satisfactory mode of operation through the action of a "material effluvium" that issues forth from rubbed (warmed) or electrified bodies, somewhat as steam arises from boiling water, on the supposition that such effluvia always return to the parent body and that, in doing so, they tend to carry along small bits of paper or straw. In the case of gravitation, however, the same type of explanation would not suffice. Gravitation does not require any rubbing and is like magnetic action, in that it seems to occur without any effort on man's part. Furthermore, in gravitational phenomena, the forces are enormous and extend over vast distances, as from the Sun to Saturn.‡

‡ Newton was fond of contrasting magnetic force and gravitational force. For instance, in his version of the "corpuscular philosophy," he invented short-range

Even though Newton had, in the *Principia*, established the Copernican system on a mechanical basis, in so far as he had shown that the inverse-square law of gravitation accounts for the observed celestial motions and the tides, he was not fully satisfied, since the mathematical formulation—even though agreeing with observation to a high degree—did not by itself provide the kind of mechanism invented by Boyle for electrical attraction.

Newton's Views on Scientific Explanation

Galileo had written in his *Two New Sciences* that " The present does not seem to be the proper time to investigate the cause of the acceleration of natural motion concerning which various opinions have been expressed. . . . At present [!] it is the purpose . . . merely to investigate and to demonstrate some of the properties of accelerated motion (whatever the cause of this acceleration may be) . . ." [30] We have no warrant, of course, to conclude from this statement that Galileo always restricted himself to " how " bodies fall without any concern as to " why " bodies fall. Galileo merely said that he did not want to investigate the " cause " of acceleration at this time. In any event he did not wish to express his thoughts on this topic in public. So, too, when Boyle discussed the " spring of the air," he did not wish to commit himself any further than a statement equivalent to the description of the air as an " elastic fluid." At least two explanations came to his mind: one was that the air near the earth might be conceived as " a heap of little bodies, lying one upon another, as may be resembled to a fleece of wool." Another was to follow the notions of Descartes and to suppose that the " elastical power " of the " particles of air " does not " depend upon their shape or structure, but upon the vehement agitation. . . ." When Boyle declined to declare " peremptorily " for either of these alternatives, he explained that he was not willing to meddle " with a subject, which is more hard to be explicated than necessary to be so by him, whose business it is not, in this letter [!] to assign the adequate cause of the spring of the air, but only to manifest, that the air hath a spring, and to relate some of its effects." [31] We may note that Boyle, like Galileo, was willing to forego any discussion of the actual cause of the phenomena described, but we cannot conclude that either Boyle or Galileo held no opinion on such subjects. Nor can we properly say that Boyle would *under no circumstances* express his belief.§

forces between near-by corpuscles, invoking the analogy to forces emanating from magnets and terminating on near-by pieces of iron.

§ Franklin stated a similar aversion to a discussion of " how " Nature executes her laws, being content to know and apply the laws themselves.

When Hooke objected to Newton's seeming advocacy of the corpuscularity or " corporeity " of light, Newton replied that although
he had indicated a preference for an atomic theory of light, " I do
it without any absolute positiveness," making it at " most but a very
plausible *consequence* of the doctrine, and not a fundamental *supposition.*" He was aware that the observed properties of light were in
some measure capable of being explicated " not only by that, but by
many other mechanical *hypotheses.*" This was his reason for choosing " to decline them all, and to speak of light in *general* terms,
considering it abstractly . . . without determining what that thing
is. . . ." [32] Presenting both the possibility of a wave theory and a
corpuscular theory, Newton nevertheless had strong predilections
for the latter, indicating evidence to support the view that the rays
of light are " very small bodies emitted from shining substances." [33]

Newton was in a similar position when he published the first
edition of his *Principia.* He did not address himself directly to the
cause of gravitation but rather indicated the kinematical results of a
dynamics based on the inverse-square law. The famous " General
Scholium " at the end of the third book of the *Principia,* devoted
primarily to the nature of the gravitational attraction between
bodies, which appeared for the first time in the second edition
(1713), included a short discussion of the nature of God. Roger
Cotes, who edited the second edition under Newton's direction, had
evidently been disturbed by a letter from Leibniz to Hartsoeker,[34]
especially the sentence in which Leibniz attacked the *Principia* for
having been " built upon miracles, and . . . occult qualities." * In
the light of our previous discussion, we can see that these must have
appeared as " fighting words." Newton's discussion of the nature of
God partially answered the charge concerning " miracles " and concluded with the famous sentence: " And thus much concerning
God; to discourse of whom from the appearances of things, does
certainly belong to natural philosophy." Then Newton admitted
that, although he had " explained the phenomena of the heavens
and of our sea [i. e., the tides] by the power of gravity," no assignment had as yet been made of " the cause of this power." He added:

But hitherto I have not been able to discover the cause of those properties of gravity from phenomena, and I frame no hypotheses; for whatever
is not deduced from the phenomena is to be called an hypothesis; and
hypotheses, whether metaphysical or physical, whether of occult qualities
or mechanical, have no place in experimental philosophy. . . . And to us
it is enough that gravity does really exist, and act according to the laws

---

* This point is discussed at length in the next chapter. The phrase occurs in a
note written on 18 March 1713 by Roger Cotes (editor of the second edition of the
Principia) to Newton,[35] describing Leibniz's recently published letter.[36]

we have explained, and abundantly serves to account for all the motions of the celestial bodies, and of our sea.[37]

Then follows the final paragraph, which was to stimulate speculation for at least two centuries, and which had a special significance in that (*i*) it hinted that electric attraction and repulsion were produced by the same mechanism as the attraction which makes particles cohere in bodies, (*ii*) the phenomena of mechanics, electricity, optics, heat, and animal sensation and volition (but not magnetism!) were to be explained on the basis of one unitary principle, and (*iii*) that to understand these matters, attention should be concentrated on what happens between, as well as within, bodies:

And now we might add something concerning a certain most subtle spirit which pervades and lies hid in all gross bodies; by the force and action of which spirit the particles of bodies attract one another at near distances, and cohere, if contiguous; and electric bodies operate to greater distances as well repelling as attracting the neighboring corpuscles; and light is emitted, reflected, refracted, inflected, and heats bodies; and all sensation is excited, and the members of animal bodies move at the command of the will, namely, by the vibrations of this spirit, mutually propagated along the solid filaments of the nerves, from the outward organs of sense to the brain, and from the brain into the muscles. But these are things that cannot be explained in few words, nor are we furnished with that sufficiency of experiments which is required to an accurate determination and demonstration of the laws by which this electric and elastic spirit operates.

Curiously enough, there is no mention in this paragraph of gravitational attraction between gross bodies.

The late Florian Cajori insisted that Newton had nowhere stated that gravity is an innate, inherent property of matter, even though such an interpretation was made by a number of readers.[38] Yet, in terms of the actual language of the first edition of the *Principia*, there was some justification for such a view, especially since Newton did not actually declare himself unequivocally on this topic. Newton, we know, did not believe gravity to be an innate property of matter any more than did his opponents. A letter to Boyle, dated 28 February 1678/9, prior to the publication of the *Principia*, contained Newton's speculations on the " cause of gravity " and an attempt to explain attraction by the operation of an " aether " consisting of " parts differing from one another in subtility by indefinite degrees," rather than attributing gravity to matter itself as an innate property. Since this letter was not made public for some decades,†

† In Franklin's day this letter was widely discussed and the principles it contains were being applied to the explanation of electrical phenomena. The implications of the letter are discussed in Chapter Five and Chapter Seven.

readers of the first edition of the *Principia* could not know Newton's true sentiments. Thus Richard Bentley, friend and admirer of Newton, and author of the first series of "Boyle Lectures" in which Newtonian dynamics was used to bolster the traditional arguments for the existence and attributes of God,[39] at first believed that Newton held the view we have described above. In a letter to him, Newton pointed out the error of Bentley's assumption: "You sometimes speak of gravity as essential and inherent to matter. Pray, do not ascribe that notion to me; for the cause of gravity is what I do not pretend to know, and therefore would take more time to consider of it." In a famous passage in another letter to Bentley, Newton wrote:

It is inconceivable, that inanimate brute matter should, without the mediation of something else, which is not material, operate upon and affect other matter without mutual contact, as it must be, if gravitation, in the sense of Epicurus, be essential and inherent in it. And this is one reason why I desired you would not ascribe innate gravity to me. That gravity should be innate, inherent, and essential to matter, so that one body may act upon another at a distance through a *vacuum*, without the mediation of any thing else, by and through which their action and force may be conveyed from one to another, is to me so great an absurdity, that I believe no man, who has in philosophical matters a competent faculty of thinking, can ever fall into it. Gravity must be caused by an agent acting constantly according to certain laws; but whether this agent be material or immaterial, I have left to the consideration of my readers.‡

This paragraph was one that Faraday loved to quote [41] and that he used to support his own position of concentrating on the medium between charged or magnetic bodies in terms of the "lines of force." Franklin too was stimulated by this attitude and could not accept the idea of bodies acting simply at a distance.

Newton's point of view in the General Scholium to Book Three of the *Principia* was not markedly different from that adopted in his first publication in physics, the account of his experiments on dispersion and the composition of white light. There he had indicated that it "is not so easie" to determine "what light is" and had declared that he would not "mingle conjectures with certainties," [42] although, as we have just seen, Newton became convinced that light probably consists of a stream of tiny hard bodies.

Newton's speculations on the nature of matter, light, the æther, and the mode of action of the gravitational force eventually took him far beyond the rigid limits of mathematical deduction or even direct observation of nature. His brilliant imagination produced a

‡ These letters were not published until the middle of the eighteenth century.[40]

series of physical concepts which were a continual source of inspiration to the experimental scientists of the eighteenth century and which were not without effect on the physicists of the nineteenth century. The rise of electrical theory in the two centuries after the publication of the *Principia* can be written largely in terms of the mechanisms of gross and subtle matter in imitation, contradiction, extension, or revision of Newton's ideas.§ Franklin's outstanding contribution to the theory of electrical action lay precisely in his clear grasp of the value of Newton's speculative ideas and in his understanding of the importance of following the spirit rather than the letter of what Newton said. Basing his own version of the " electric fluid " on Newton's views of the æther and matter and also on the ideas associated with the Bacon-Boyle revolt against " forms " and " qualities," Franklin achieved an original creation that may be considered a masterpiece in the revolutionary tradition of explanation of physical phenomena by the doctrine of " matter and motion."

Bacon, Newton, and Franklin

So far as electrical theory was concerned, the legacy of Bacon to the eighteenth century was the program of basing explanations of physical phenomena on the mechanical principles of matter and motion, with the correlative prohibition of " forms " and " qualities " and " occult forces." In chapter after chapter of this book, we will see consequences of this doctrine: in Newton, in Franklin, and in other scientists of the eighteenth and nineteenth centuries. The whole course of physical speculation during the latter eighteenth century was conditioned by a horror of any kind of " occult " force acting through empty space that was comparable only to nature's own *horror vacui* as postulated before Galileo and Boyle. Franklin's theory of " electrical atmosphere " was an elaborate contrivance, patterned after Newton's, to avoid " action-at-a-distance," and Franklin voiced Newton's own sentiments when he wrote, " I agree with you that it seems absurd to suppose that a body can act where it is not." [43]

Now Bacon was certainly not a scientist—at least not in the sense that Boyle, Hooke, Newton, and Franklin were—even though he did

§ There are two major trends in the history of electrical theory. One is the invention of mechanical models based on the motion of imponderable fluids (Franklin), lines of force or strains in the æther (Faraday), and vortical rotations of tubes within tubes in the æther (Clerk Maxwell). The other is the development of systems of mathematical equations that are independent of the particular mechanical model (Green, Gauss, Webber, Kelvin, Clerk Maxwell). That both trends culminate in Clerk Maxwell explains why his work can be considered the peak of classical physics, or of the pre-electron physics of electrical action.

perform experiments and even lost his life as a consequence of experimentation in the snow. A case can be made that the tradition that descended to Franklin from Boyle and Newton did not actually need a Bacon to inspire it; we may be certain that the ideas so forcibly expressed by Bacon were in the air and were not original with him. But the facts of history must not be denied. Bacon did write, and his books were read by Boyle who took them to heart. The Bacon-Boyle approach to natural philosophy did influence Newton's speculative experimental science, and Franklin admired and read both Boyle and Newton, and was acquainted with the writings of Bacon.

But Bacon was not esteemed in the eighteenth century merely as a supposed inventor of the "scientific method." He entered the scientific milieu in several other ways. The encyclopædic ideal certainly derived from Bacon's enthusiasm for the systematization of knowledge and the collection of "histories" of all sorts of natural phenomena and of trades. (In the eighteenth century, this view was productive of the many scientific dictionaries and the great *Encyclopédie* of Diderot [44] and D'Alembert.) The Royal Society of London had been conceived as a Baconian enterprise. Its founders generally had appreciated Bacon's vision of an organized company of scientists and learned men seeking out knowledge of the external world, gathering together and advancing such knowledge, and diffusing it. Sprat's *History of the Royal Society*, a seventeenth-century defence of the Society's aims and achievements, bore an elegant frontispiece depicting the President of the Royal Society on one side of the Society's patron, Charles II, and on the other Bacon as "artium instaurator." [45] To this day, the oldest scientific society in America, founded by Benjamin Franklin, bears the "Baconian" name: "The American Philosophical Society Held at Philadelphia for Promoting Useful Knowledge." The word "Baconian" is to be taken in the sense familiar to the eighteenth century of "useful."

Bacon's vision of science endowing man with new powers has caused him to be called "Philosopher of Industrial Science." [46] He preached that the roads to knowledge and to power are identical and that true science must produce a testimonial in the form of fruits—practical innovations consequent upon scientific discoveries. When Franklin asked, "What signifies philosophy that doth not apply to some use?" Bacon was speaking through his lips. The occasion was Franklin's discussion of the relative power of absorbing solar heat in materials of different colors, notably those that were black or white. The application he had in mind was the choice of clothing during hot weather, especially in the tropics. But we must not conclude that Franklin was a "practical" man in the sense that he always turned to the "utilitarian" aspects of things and scorned speculation or knowledge that was intended chiefly to illuminate the operations of nature. Bacon himself had pointed out that "fruits and works" were merely the "sponsors and sureties" for the truth of science; and although he did indicate a belief that "truth and utility are the very same things," he was careful to note that "works themselves are of greater value as pledges of truth than as contributing to the comforts of life." [47] Had Franklin restricted his scientific activities to those subjects that were obviously of utilitarian value, he would hardly have chosen electricity as his major field of research. Looking backward from the vantage point of the electrical age, it is easy for us to conceive of Franklin as a pioneer in an obviously practical area of inquiry; but looking at the subject as it existed in the 1740's, we may search in vain for much warrant that it would ultimately yield a practical issue save in a general Baconian outlook, a pious belief that all true knowledge of natural phenomena will at some future time produce something of value beyond itself.

Like all good scientific research, Franklin's was productive and fruitful; and like much research of consequence, it was useful. Here I intend "productive" to mean that it led to a host of important new phenomena which were linked together in a comprehensive theory of electrical action, one that led to the prediction of still further phenomena and a more comprehensive view of all aspects of the subject. It was productive, then, of increased knowledge, and a more penetrating view of the operations of nature than man had theretofore possessed. Franklin's research was "fruitful" in the sense that it led to wholly new kinds of investigation, chiefly in the important domain of atmospheric electricity. His discoveries about the action of pointed conductors, grounding, and the various phenomena of electrostatic induction and spark discharges, led him to devise an experiment to test the possible electrification of clouds; his investigations were thus fruitful in opening up a new subject, they were fruitful of a new form of experience. But Franklin's research was also "useful" in that he was able to embody his discoveries in a practical device for protecting man's structures from destruction: the lightning rod. So was the Baconian view of science fully vindicated.

Clearly, when Franklin began his research, he could not have had even the vaguest intuition of the actual character of the discoveries he would make; there was no possibility whatever of a prevision of a protective lightning rod. But once he had found out how electrical effects are produced, he did not hesitate to make an invention that would serve man's needs. Even before he had been able to demonstrate by empirical test that the lightning discharge is an electrical phenomenon, he was convinced that the lightning phenomena must follow the laws he had discovered to hold for pointed conductors in the laboratory. He had not yet been able to find a wholly satisfactory answer to the question of why the pointed conductors should follow the laws he had formulated, but he was anxious to apply these laws just the same. A knowledge of these laws, in other words, he concluded in 1749, " may possibly be of some use to mankind " even though we may never be able to explain " the power of points." Such was the tone of his first description of the lightning rod. In a spirit reminiscent of Galileo and Boyle, he declared that it " is of real use to know that china left in the air unsupported will fall and break; but *how* it comes to fall, and *why* it breaks, are matters of speculation. It is a pleasure indeed to know them, but we can preserve our china without it." [48] The sense of these lines is that the discovery of the laws of nature is the primary job of the scientist, that a knowledge of these laws constitutes a satisfactory issue of scientific research, and that causes of " *how* it comes to fall " and " *why* it breaks " are subject to speculation.* As to the " cause " of falling and breaking, the major author of the speculations being discussed in Franklin's day was Newton himself, chiefly in his *Opticks* and the letter to Boyle of 28 February, 1678/9. And when Franklin added that the aim of science is to " know the laws themselves " rather than " the manner in which nature executes her laws," he was merely echoing Newton's statement in the General Scholium to Book Three of the *Principia*, when he expressed his inability to assign the " cause " of the " power of gravity " which had sufficed to explain " the phenomena of the heavens and of our sea." " I have not been able to discover the cause of those properties of gravity from phenomena," Newton explained, but " to us it is enough that gravity does really exist, and act according to the laws which we have explained, and abundantly serves to account for all the motions of the celestial bodies, and of our sea."

It is certainly a curious paradox that a statement of Franklin's which is a paraphrase of Newton's sentiments should become interpreted, out of context, as a measure of his utilitarian view of science and his lack of interest in pure science as such. We may recall that famous anecdote about Newton in which a friend had borrowed a copy of Euclid's *Elements* and on returning it had asked Newton what use it might have; as the story goes, this was the only occasion on record when Newton was known to have laughed.

* Franklin, of course, did not question the value of studying " how it falls," but only " *how* it comes to fall."

SOURCES

The science of the seventeenth century must be studied in the actual writings of seventeenth-century scientists. Wolf (1950) is the only general survey of the subject and is particularly valuable for the material on scientific instruments, for which see also Boffito (1929) and Daumas (1953). In addition to the writings of Koyré and Olschki on Galileo, valuable information of the background of the seventeenth-century scientific revolution may be found in Crombie (1953a and 1953b). The subject of British science in the seventeenth century in relation to aspects of Protestantism is developed in Jones (1951), Merton (1938), and Stimson (1935); also in Pelseneer (1947). Miller (1954) contains a penetrating analysis of Protestantism and science in colonial America. Burtt (1932) is an indispensable classic and should be supplemented by Strong (1936).

For the scientific societies of the seventeenth century, see Brown (1934), Ornstein (1938), Stimson (1948), and Weld (1848). The textbooks of Newtonian science are described in Brunet (1926 and 1931), and Sarton (1948a); the American uses of these textbooks are discussed in Cohen (1950a), Hornberger (1945), and Morison (1936). See also Babson Collection (1950) and Gray (1907).

Masson (1914), More (1944) and Maddison (1951, 1952) present the life of Boyle, while Fulton (1932b) is an indispensable guide to Boyle's own writings and the secondary literature concerning him. The whole subject of Boyle's "natural philosophy" has been illuminated by the doctoral dissertation of Marie Boas, written at Cornell University under the direction of Henry Guerlac, (Boas, 1952). Special attention may be called to the masterly statement of Boyle's scientific programme in relation to Bacon, in Boas (1950). Valuable points of view may be found in Fisch (1953), Kuhn (1952), Fulton (1931; 1932a).

For a bibliography of Boyle, see Gibson (1950). For a stimulating point of view on Boyle and the corpuscular philosophy, see the articles by Hooykaas.

The literature concerning Bacon's place in the history of science is long and controversial. In addition to the two works of Miss Boas, referred to in the previous paragraph, the following may be consulted: Broad (1926); Cajori (1925); Dieckmann (1934); Farrington (1949); Fowler's introduction to Bacon (1878), Fowler (1881); Frost (1927); Liebig (1863); Roller (1953); Santillana (1941).

REFERENCES

1. See Cole, 1930; Meyer, 1939; Needham, 1934.
2. See Sarton, 1948a; Brunet, 1931.
3. Voltaire, 1909; 1926.
4. Morton, 1940.
5. Mather, 1938; for Mather's earliest use of this phrase, see Miller, 1953: 440.
6. Boas, 1950.
7. *Idem.*
8. *Idem.*
9. *Idem*
10. Morton, 1940: 10-11.
11. *Ibid.*, 39.
12. Boas, 1950.
13. *Idem.*
14. See Boas, 1952: 486.
15. Boyle, 1772: 3; 14 (Origin of Forms & Qualities).
16. Patterson, 1948: 151.
17. Boas, 1950.
18. Newton, 1671/2.
19. Huygens, 1912; 1937: ch. 1. See Ronchi, 1939: ch. 4, and Bell, 1947: ch. 11.
20. Boyle, 1675: 1.
21. *Ibid.*, 7.
22. *Ibid.*, 8.
23. Bacon, 1878: bk. 2, aph. 50.
24. Boyle, 1772 1: 75 (Spring of the Air).
25. See Fulton, 1932b.
26. Boyle, 1772: 1: 704.
27. Boyle, 1772: 3: 685.
28. *Ibid.*, 707.
29. Boas, 1952: 473.
30. Galileo, 1914: 166.
31. Boyle, 1772: 1: 11-12.
32. See Roberts and Thomas, 1934: 97.
33. Newton, 1952, qu. 29.
34. See Edelston, 1850: 153; Newton, 1952: preface, p. xxix.
35. Edleston, 1850: 153.
36. For details about this letter, see Newton, 1952: preface, p. liii, n. 21. Cajori quoted an extract from another contemporaneous version of the letter, Newton, 1934: 669.
37. General Scholium to Bk. III, Newton, 1934.
38. Newton, 1934: 633.
39. Bentley, 1838; facsimile in Newton, 1955a.
40. See Babson Catalogue, 1950: 111.
41. Tyndall, 1870: 83.
42. Newton, 1671/2.
43. Franklin, 1769: 258.
44. *Cf.* Dieckmann, 1943.
45. *Cf.* Stimson, 1948; Weld, 1848; Ornstein, 1938.
46. Farrington, 1949.
47. *Cf.* Schrecker, 1948.
48. "Opinions and Conjectures . . . 1749," Franklin, 1941: 219; 1769: 62.

CHAPTER FIVE

THE TWO MAJOR SOURCES OF THE NEWTONIAN PHILOSOPHY: THE *PRINCIPIA* AND THE *OPTICKS*

Newton, in his *Principia*, deduces from the observed motions of the heavenly bodies the fact that they attract one another according to a definite law. . . . In his *Principia*, he confined himself to the demonstration and development of this great step in the science of the mutual actions of bodies. He says nothing about the means by which bodies are made to gravitate towards each other. We know that his mind did not rest at this point—that he felt that gravitation itself must be capable of being explained, and that he even suggested an explanation depending on the action of an etherial medium pervading space. But with that wise moderation which is characteristic of his investigations, he distinguished such speculations from what he had established by observation and demonstration, and excluded from his *Principia* all mention of the cause of gravitation, reserving his thoughts on this subject for the " Queries " printed at the end of the *Opticks*.

—J. CLERK MAXWELL (1876)

IN THE preceding chapter, some indication was given that in the age of Newton, physical thought developed in a special direction of atomism that had as its aim to work out the detailed consequences of that mechanical corpuscular philosophy which had replaced the philosophy of substantial forms and real qualities. Franklin's atomistic concepts of matter and electricity were formed in a great tradition of masters whose work he esteemed, including Galileo, Bacon, Boyle, and Newton.

We need not concern ourselves with any of the quarrels between " Cartesians " and " atomists " (like Boyle), because the early years of the eighteenth century witnessed an almost universal acceptance of the Bacon-Boyle-Newton atomistic philosophy. Franklin only once encountered a survival of the Cartesian point of view: in the theories of the Abbé Nollet, which can be described as a modified form of the Cartesian philosophy in the physics of electricity. Yet we cannot side-step an exploration of the ways in which the atomistic concepts of Galileo, Bacon, and Boyle were used by Newton in his essays in experimental science, because this is the very ground of Franklin's scientific thought.

In such a discussion, we must keep in mind that Newton produced two major works in physical science: the *Principia* and the *Opticks,* and if we would understand the science of the age of Franklin, the *Opticks* must command our attention. Its place in the thought of the eighteenth century seems to be but little understood, probably because our historians have been so over-awed by the magnificent achievements embodied in the *Principia* that they have neglected the *Opticks* or have considered it a " lesser " work. Then, too, our scholarship in the history of science is still dominated by the point of view of the nineteenth century. The major surveys of the development of physics to which historians must refer were produced in the nineteenth century—notably those by Rosenberger, Gerland and Heller—and during the latter half of the nineteenth century the *Opticks* was conceived to have been the chief expression of the corpuscular theory of light. In an age that witnessed the triumph of the rival undulatory theory, and its amplification in the electromagnetic theory of Clerk Maxwell, Newton's *Opticks* was not considered to be the great work. British physicists conceived it to be a sort of national disgrace, the failure of genius. As late as 1909, Sir Arthur Schuster apologized for Newton's error, noting that " there is no doubt that Newton's great authority kept back the progress of the undulatory theory for more than a century." [1] While the *Principia* was being reprinted over and over again during the nineteenth century, the *Opticks* remained out of print save for an appearance in German translation in 1898 in " Ostwald's Klassiker." [*] General interest in the *Opticks* was revived chiefly after the suggestion of a sort of particulate theory of light by Einstein in 1905, confirmed in the Compton effect; and the extension in the '20's of the undulatory-particulate duality of light to a similar duality of matter by de Broglie, confirmed in the experiments of Davisson and Germer and those of G. P. Thomson.[†] While the *Principia* was supposedly rendered outmoded and " old fashioned " by Einstein's restricted theory of relativity of 1905, the *Opticks* came to be regarded as a symbol of the precursorship of genius, owing to Einstein's concept of photons proposed in the same year. In 1931 a reprint of the *Opticks* was issued with a foreword by Albert Einstein and a preface by E. T.

[*] See the discussion in Chapter One.

[†] Thomson viewed the doctrine expounded in Newton's *Opticks* in the new tradition of the " duality " of light and of matter which his own experiments had helped to establish: " After being regarded for generations as an artificial attempt to save a dying theory, we have proved this ' guess ' of Newton's to be a supreme example of the intuition of genius." [2]

Whittaker, and the continuing demand has been so great that an inexpensive paper-bound reprint was made in 1952 in an edition of 3,000 copies, which was exhausted in three years and was reissued in 1955 in an edition of 2,000 copies.[3] The history of the reputation of Newton's *Opticks* was used in an earlier chapter to illustrate the remarks about the historical and the non-historical approach to great scientific works of the past. The "lasting" importance of the *Opticks*, it was said, cannot be measured by either the views of nineteenth-century physicists or those of the twentieth, but rather by the influence it had on the immediate development of physical science: the way in which it stimulated men of science for at least a century, and led them to produce the developments that in the end made possible a wave theory in the nineteenth century which the twentieth century could partially reject. Nor is that all; for as we shall see, in this and succeeding chapters, Newton's *Opticks* established an experimental view of nature that conditioned the growth of many branches of science other than optics proper, including plant and animal physiology, psychology, heat, electricity and magnetism, and chemistry.

Two Newtonian Sciences: Mass Points and Varieties of Matter

The *Opticks* of Newton is, in one very important sense, markedly different from the *Principia*. In the latter, Newton was largely able to treat bodies as if they were deprived of every property save their " quantity of matter," by which expression Newton meant " mass." ‡ One of the few places in the *Principia* where Newton discussed different kinds of matter is the description of the beautiful experiments he contrived to test the proposition that at a given place on the earth

---

‡ The opening definition of the *Principia* states that " quantity of matter" is the product of density and volume, and this " quantity " is to be understood " hereafter everywhere under the name of body or mass." It is proportional to weight, as experiment shows. In Book III, cor. IV to prop. VII, Newton defined bodies of the " same density " as those " whose inertias are in the proportions of their bulks." The circularity of these definitions has been the subject of much comment. The late Henry Crew[4] observed that the traditional fundamental quantities of mass, length, and time (M, L, T) yield the derived quantity of density (M/L^3), but that the choice of density, length, and time (D, L, T) would yield mass as a derived quantity (DL^3). This notion could serve to account for the definitions at the beginning of the *Principia*, and would accord with the atomistic view that the fundamental property of a body is the number of corpuscles per unit of volume, or density, which might characterize a body in terms of the material, whereas mass would in this view be a measure of the total number of corpuscles in a given sample or body. The density would thus contain the information about the concentration of corpuscles and the volume would thence provide the number of corpuscles or mass. Unfortunately, Newton was discreetly silent on this question and such guesses as we may make cannot be confirmed by statements in the *Principia*. But we may observe that " densities " of bodies can be compared as readily as their " inertias."

the weight of a body is always proportional to its mass, no matter what the material or kind of matter. In modern terms, he tested by experiment the equivalence of gravitational and inertial mass for different materials.[5]

To be sure, a given mass may have or acquire motion and, hence, momentum (or kinetic energy), and Newton knew that the action of forces on bodies may produce deformations as well as accelerations. Galileo had, in his " two new sciences " comprehended local motion and the resistance of materials, but in the *Principia* Newton was more interested in motion, and the production of motion by forces, than in materials.§ Now the kind of deformation a body may undergo (i. e., twisting, stretching, compression, bending, or shear) depends not alone on the magnitude and kind of force or forces applied, but also on the particular structure of the body. When a body is moved by force, however, the ensuing motion (or acceleration) depends almost exclusively on the magnitude and orientation of the force, the initial state of the body (motion or rest), the mass or inertia of the body, and the nature and condition of the medium in which the body exists. In motion, then, the result of the action of a force may be related to the " local environment "—i. e., the friction between a body and the surface on which it rests, or the air resistance which depends on the body's speed and shape—but the ensuing acceleration is independent of the internal structure of the body and the kind of material of which it is made, say glass or steel. Thus Newton's " second law " is a relation between forces and the accelerations (or rates of change in momentum) produced by the forces. The constant of proportionality is the mass of the body acted on. This proportionality holds in complete independence of the sort of body it may be (whether brittle or elastic, soft or hard, etc.) and irrespective of what " kind " of mass may be involved (whether wood, iron, brass, or clay). Gravitation is " universal " not only because it is a force which draws together any two masses in the universe, but also because it acts between bodies without any relation whatever to the shape, size, structure, or composition of such bodies. To compute the gravitational attraction in any given situation, all that is needed is a knowledge of the masses of the two bodies and the distance between them.*

§ That is, Newton was not particularly interested in exploring in the *Principia* the materials out of which bodies are made, although Book II is devoted to the materials (kinds of medium) through which bodies may move.

* Newton did not have a means of determining the value of G (the constant of universal gravitation) and could only compare gravitational forces but not compute them in particular instances. Such computations were posisble only after the introduction of experiments, such as Cavendish's, which yielded the value of G, about a century after the publication of the *Principia*.

The last phrase above, " the distance between them," gives what seems to me to be a key to the essential character of the *Principia* as a physics of bodies. One of the crucial theorems in Newton's gravitation theory—the one that was a stumbling block in the way of completion of the *Principia* for about twenty years—dealt with this problem: in considering the gravitational attraction between the earth and a terrestrial object (or even the earth and the moon), what value is to be used for " distance between them "? If an apple is attracted by the earth, we might guess that " the distance between them " is measured from the bottom of the apple to the nearest point on the surface of the earth, or from the top of the apple to the furthermost point on the side of the earth away from the apple, or the average of the two, i. e., the distance between their centers. Newton was able to prove, by applying the integral calculus, that two uniform spheres would attract each other gravitationally just as if the total mass of each were concentrated at its respective center. This magnificent theorem [6] meant that for most considerations of gravitation, and the explanation of the mechanism of the heavens and the earth, we can forget about any property of a body save the position of its center and its mass. The sun may be hot and have light of its own, the moon may be innately cold and dark and shine by reflected sunlight, but in discussing their gravitational pull on the seas to produce the tides we need only consider where the sun and moon happen to be and what their respective masses are. When Newton discussed the " falling " of the moon to the earth, he had no need to consider any other properties of these two bodies save their respective masses and positions. They could be treated as mere " mass points " and the moon might very well be made of " green cheese " so far as gravitation was concerned. In the same way, if an apple and a glass sphere were let fall from the same tree, the gravitational pull of the earth would be just the same for both, provided only that they had the same mass and position—again, simply because all bodies can be treated as " mass points " in discussions of gravitation.

But from any other point of view the behavior of an apple and a glass sphere are markedly different. In optics we would note that one is transparent and the other opaque—and because they are made of different materials; they differ in hardness, brittleness, electrical conductivity, color, density, and a host of other physical properties. But even if we omit such gross distinctions between bodies, and restrict our attention to transparent bodies—say cubes of glass, quartz, diamond, calcite, and ice—we find that the optical behavior varies from one material to the next; as shown by the index of refraction or critical angle for the several colors, the degree of dispersion, and possible birefringence. Optical studies, therefore, reveal characteristics produced by the material of which a body is made, and also by the internal construction. In Newton's day, as in ours, it was therefore recognized that optical investigations are a primary key to knowledge of the nature and state of different substances under various conditions (as temperature, internal stress, etc.) .†

Hence we are led at once to a major difference between Newton's *Principia* and his *Opticks*. The problems investigated in the *Opticks* in almost every case arise from properties of composition and state that serve to distinguish bodies from one another, even if they might have the same mass or weight. But in the *Principia*, largely, problems are investigated which depend wholly on the masses, motions, and positions of bodies and the medium in which they move: problems which lend themselves to treatment in independence of the state (save for motion or rest) of a body, its internal constitution, and the kind of material or materials of which it may be made. The *Principia*, in other words, presents a kind of physics of mass abstracted from real bodies, while the *Opticks* explores the actual varieties of mass as encountered in real bodies in the laboratory and in the world at large.

Eighteenth-Century Reactions to the Principia *and the* Opticks

We can readily see the relative roles of the *Opticks* and the *Principia* in the advancing science of the eighteenth century by making a list of those properties of bodies that would be of major concern to an experimental natural philosopher in the century following Newton. What properties of bodies would he study? How, in other words, would such an eighteenth-century investigator characterize a body?

(I) By its *size*: i. e., its three dimensions, length, breadth, and thickness.

(II) By its *mass*: measured in practice by its weight, and in theory by its inertia.

(III) By its state of *motion or of rest*.

---

† Newton recognized that among the major optical properties related to the composition of bodies were the colors of light they reflected or absorbed, but he did not pay too much attention to the colors they emitted under suitable experimental conditions. Newton's total lack of interest in the kind of light emitted by different bodies when heated seems curious, especially since he pioneered in the subject of light analysis. Agricola, whom Newton had read at about the time of his optical experiments, had already suggested that the emission of light could be used in mineral analysis.

(IV) By its *electrical* properties: whether a conductor or an insulator ("non-electrick" or "electrick *per se*"), and—later in the century—whether exhibiting resinous or vitreous electrification when rubbed with silk or fur.

(V) By its *thermal* properties: whether a conductor of heat or not, and how good a conductor; boiling point and melting point.

(VI) By its *thermo-chemical* properties: combustible or non-combustible, combustion temperature.

(VII) By its general chemical properties and behavior: kind of substance (metal, acid, base, calx, salt, etc.; elemental or complex, and chemical composition) ; types of reaction with other substances; whether hygroscopic, etc.; odor.

(VIII) By its *optical* properties: color, transparency, dispersion, index of refraction, birefringence, etc.

(IX) By its *mechanical* properties: hardness, elasticity, etc.; density.‡

The first three properties do not result from the nature of the matter in any given body, but rather from its particular history. The size of a piece of tin (and, hence, its mass) depends only on how you cut it; but however you may cut a piece of tin, tin it remains. So, too,

‡ A popular book on the Newtonian philosophy contained a dialogue on this subject:
" A. How is matter, or body, commonly considered? *B.* As having three dimensions, viz. *length, breadth*, and *thickness.*
" *A*. Is this consideration of matter the most philosophical? *B.* No; it is too vulgar and defective.
" *A*. What is a more accurate method to acquire the best knowledge and ideas of matter, or bodies, that we are capable of? *B.* By considering those properties and affections thereof, which are obvious to us, and best known to us.
" *A*. How are the properties of bodies distinguished? *B.* Into those which are common to all alike, and those which are peculiar to each in particular: the rest are called common and essential, the latter specific and accidental.
" *A*. Which are the properties of the first sort? *B.* They are generally reckoned these which follow: I. *Extension*, for all bodies are extended. II. *Divisibility*, for all bodies may be divided. III. *Solidity*, for the particles of all bodies are hard. IV. *Figurability*, for all bodies have some form or figure. V. *Mobility*, for all bodies are capable of being moved.
" *A*. Is this enumeration of the common properties of bodies every way just, and equal in all things? *B.* No, I do not think it is; for, first, they may all be asserted of the whole body, except *solidity*, which agrees only to the particles of bodies: again, other properties may as universally be asserted of bodies as some of these, as *durability*; for a body is no less infinitely durable, from its nature, than it is divisible.
" *A*. Which are those . . . properties of bodies, which you call *specific* or *accidental?* B. They are generally reckoned the following: I, *Light*; II, *Colours*; III, *Sound*; IV, *Gravity* and *Levity*; V, *Attraction* and *Electricity*; VI, *Transparency* and *Opacity*; VII, *Density* and *Rarity*; VIII, *Hardness* and *Softness*; IX, *Rigidity* and *Flexibility*; X, *Consistence* and *Fluidity*; XI, *Heat* and *Cold*; XII, *Humidity and Siccity*; XIII, *Elasticity*; XIV, *Odours* and *Sapours.*" ⁷

whether that piece of tin happens to be resting on the table or falling
to the floor is independent of its being tin. But properties IV to IX
are quite different and characterize the material (or condition of
the material, esp. IX) of which the body is made. These are the
very properties that Newton had studied in his *Opticks*; they comprise the major topics of physical investigation during the eighteenth
century. Not primarily in the *Principia*, then, but in the *Opticks*
could the eighteenth-century experimentalists find Newton's methods
for studying the properties or behavior of bodies that are due to
their special composition. Hence, we need not be surprised to find
that in the age of Newton—which the eighteenth century certainly
was!—the experimental natural philosophers should be drawn to
the *Opticks* rather than to the *Principia*. Furthermore, the *Opticks*
was more than an account of mere optical phenomena, but contained
an atomic theory of matter, ideas about electricity and magnetism,
heat, fluidity, volatility, sensation, chemistry, and so on, and a theory
(or hypothesis) of the actual cause of gravitation.

The achievements of the eighteenth century in the physical sciences were both conceptual and experimental.§ Many new types of
phenomena were uncovered, including such diverse ones as pyro-
electricity and the electricity of the " upper " air, the existence of
a variety of new " airs " or gases, the aberration of light, and latent
heats. There were produced a number of theories or " conceptual
schemes " to integrate or coordinate diverse phenomena and to permit accurate prediction of the issue of experimental manipulation.
We may note a kinetic theory of gases, the theories of heat invoking
concepts of " phlogiston " and of " caloric," theories of electrical
action invoking one or two electrical " fluids," Lavoisier's theory of
combustion and calcination as oxygenation and the French reform of
chemistry, and at the century's end the beginning of electrochemistry
based on experiments with Volta's " pile " and " crown of cups."
Much of the research in physics during the century was done in
fields other than dynamics or celestial mechanics until, later on in
the century, the important work of the French school—notably
Clairaut, d'Alembert, Lagrange, and Laplace—produced significant
alterations of the Newtonian scheme displayed in the *Principia*, while
the Bernoullis and Euler placed rational fluid mechanics on a surer
foundation.

§ In many ways, such achievements are more striking than the advances in mathematical physics like the development of the theory of perturbations or rational fluid
mechanics. An inspection of the *Philosophical Transactions* of the Royal Society of
London or the *Mémoires* of the Académie Royale des Sciences (Paris) at about the
middle of the century indicates a far greater concentration of interest in the experimental aspects of physical science and the concepts invented to explain the new phenomena than in the mathematical theories of physical science.

In an age of science characterized to some degree by experimental advances and the production of new concepts and theories based on experimental manipulation and observed data rather than mathematical deduction from axioms or " first principles," the *Opticks* was widely read as a classic of the experimenter's art—or, if you will, as a gadgeteer's delight. Many of the ingenious experiments of Newton had been performed only with a prism, a lens, a slit, and a straight edge: apparatus so simple that almost everyone who had the inclination could repeat the experiments, and many men did. Newton invited his readers to try his experiments, and in his descriptions he " set down such circumstances, by which either the phænomenon might be rendered more conspicuous, or a novice might more easily try them." [8] Not that the *Principia* was devoid of experiment (or the results of observation)—this is far from true.[9] Newton continually displayed experimental data to control the validity of his mathematically derived results.[10] But the main purpose of the *Principia* was to set forth the " mathematical principles of natural philosophy," just as the *Opticks* was an endeavour to " propose and prove " " the properties of light . . . by reason and experiments." [11]

The *Opticks* provided a mechanical basis for understanding the phenomena of matter in the great tradition of Bacon and Boyle and it was appreciated as such by those who upheld the latter tradition. Diderot, for example, whose ardent Baconianism is well known,[12] admired Newton's *Opticks*, just as he greatly admired Franklin's book on electricity and the writings of the chemists.* When he drew up plans for a national university of Russia for Empress Catherine the Great, he stressed the need for including in any such university programme the study of " science expérimentale." In the eighteenth century, such a point of view did not lead to the erection of laboratories so that all students could perform experiments on their own; that was a revolutionary innovation of the nineteenth century. Diderot's notion implied only the conviction that the most fruitful way of understanding nature is through direct questioning of nature by experiment, rather than mathematical or logical deduction from *a priori* principles. To this end he recommended that students study the great writings of experiment—the books of such heroic figures as Boyle, Pascal, and the Abbé Nollet, and Newton's *Opticks*. By contrast, under the rubric " Le système du monde," Diderot did not recommend that the students read the *Principia*, but noted: " Pour les élèves, cent bons abrégés de la Philosophie de Newton." [13]

Diderot's indifference to the *Principia* † and approval of the *Op-*

* This subject is discussed at greater length on pages 124-125.
† To the book, not necessarily to the doctrine.

ticks was not a unique phenomenon in the eighteenth century. In part, this attitude was a result of the stern and forbidding geometric visage of the *Principia* and the fact that Newton deliberately chose to write in the difficult geometrical language of Apollonius.‡ Within a short time, as Newton's methods of fluxions, or the calculus, also invented (independently) by Leibniz, came into use, Newton's great work became even more difficult to read than at the time of its composition, because the old mathematical language had become archaic. Book Three, "The system of the world," was the most intelligible of all, but even it made severe mathematical demands upon the reader. It is clear that Benjamin Franklin could never have read the *Principia*, although we know that he read the *Opticks* more than once—and with pleasure and profit.§ A brief glance at the austere array of definitions, theorems, scholia, and demonstrations would frighten away all but the hardiest student. Richard Bentley, in part responsible for the second edition of the *Principia*, wrote to the Scottish mathematician, John Craige, and to Newton himself for a list of works to be studied preparatory to understanding the *Principia*; both lists are formidable,[15] even for the limited goal described by Newton to Bentley: "It's enough if you understand the propositions with some of the demonstrations which are easier than the rest." [16]

Bentley's primary concern with the Newtonian doctrines was to

‡ Although dynamics is a science whose obvious language seems to us to be the infinitesimal calculus, it was presented by Newton in the old Greek way—the proofs being geometric or synthetic rather than algebraic or analytic; there are no fluxions to greet the eye. For this reason, Newton's *Principia* cannot be "read" as a "classic" by the modern mathematician or physical scientist in the sense that Laplace's *Mécanique céleste* can be "read." The difference in readability between these two classics is somewhat like that which exists between Shakespeare and Cynwulf. Many who have written about Newton have seen him through the pages of Laplace.

According to Pemberton, Newton purposely made the *Principia* difficult, so that his discoveries would "lie very much concealed from all who have not made the mathematics particularly their study." Pemberton, who knew Newton intimately and who prepared the third edition of the *Principia*, explained that Newton chose "to explain himself only to mathematical readers" because he believed his discoveries could be proved only on "geometrical principles." In the beginning of Book III of the *Principia*, Newton advised his readers to study the definitions, the laws of motion, and the first three sections of Book I, and then to skip all the rest up to Book III (that is, to omit the remainder of Book I and all of Book II), because the study of every proposition in Book I and Book II "might cost too much time, even to readers of good mathematical learning."

Riguad has presented an argument that in 1687 fluxions would have added to the difficulties of the *Principia*. Men of science of that time knew the Greek methods; "If the *Principia* had rested upon analytical demonstrations, Newton must not only have previously published an elementary treatise of fluxions, but must have allowed time for this new branch of science to become familiar to his readers; otherwise the conclusions to be established in this manner could not to any purpose have been laid before them." [14]

§ See, below, Chapter Seven.

discover a " confutation of atheism " in the physical principles of the universe. John Locke, as a philosopher, also felt the need of comprehending the new system. He recognized that the mathematics of the *Principia* would be forever beyond him and he wisely satisfied himself with the "physical discoveries," taking the mathematical propositions for granted; he " carefully examined the reasonings and the corollaries drawn from them, became master of all the physics, and was fully convinced of the great discoveries contained in that book." In this way Locke was " the first who became a *Newtonian Philosopher* without the help of geometry." By contrast, Locke "read the *Opticks* with pleasure, acquainting himself with every thing in them than was not merely * mathematical." [18]

The great influence of the *Principia* was produced in the eighteenth century by a series of splendid vulgarizations made by men of genius—including Pemberton, Maclaurin, and Voltaire.† Even today, few people read the *Principia* through; most students consider its doctrine, not in terms of the synthetic geometric expression of its author, but rather in the simpler analytic formulation (using analytic geometry and the calculus) given by Laplace in his *Mécanique Céleste* and *Système du Monde*. It may not be entirely correct to say that the *Opticks* was easier to read in the eighteenth century because it was written in English, while the *Principia* was written in Latin, since university students and educated men at that time read Latin. Yet there can be no question but that reading was easier in the vernacular, and the rich, gentle, personal English style of the *Opticks* was far more conducive to pleasure than the severe and formal Latin phrases of the *Principia*. Of course, Newton's "greatest work" is the *Principia*, as his most recent biographer observes; yet a reading of the *Opticks* gives the impression "that Newton wrote it with more creative joy, that the beautiful presentation represents him at the height of his pleasure in shaping." [19]

Furthermore, the *Principia* was in many ways a tantalizing book. It showed how Kepler's laws imply the action of a central force which Newton identified with the gravity of ordinary bodies on the earth. But the great question of why bodies gravitationally attract each other was merely set but never answered. The vexing matter of repulsion—introduced by Newton as a property of gas particles so that he could explain Boyle's law mathematically [20] in terms of the

---

* The *Opticks* originally contained an appendix of " Mathematical tracts," which Newton withdrew from the second edition, " as not belonging to the subject " of optics.[17]

† This statement does not, of course, include that small company of able mathematicians who needed no intermediary between themselves and Newton.

"corpuscular philosophy"—was totally incomprehensible, even to Newton himself, just as the repulsion between two negatively charged bodies was later to prove incomprehensible to Franklin. And although Newton's subtle elastic fluid (æther) might account for gravitation, what merit was there in substituting for the attraction of gross bodies a repulsion between tiny corpuscles in such a fluid? Only that the "action" was reduced from great distances (of the order of the radii of planetary orbits, or the radius of the earth, at the minimum) to small distances between æther particles. For a long-range attraction between gross bodies there was substituted an equally incomprehensible short-range repulsion between subtle particles.

The combination of abstruse mathematics and guarded hints infuriated Diderot. In his "Thoughts on the interpretation of nature," dedicated to "young people who are disposed to study natural philosophy," he indicated that it is not enough to make a discovery (*révélation*), but the revelation must be complete and clear (*entière et claire*). There is a kind of obscurity, he noted, that is "the affectation" of the great masters. It is a veil which they like to put between mankind (*le peuple*) and nature." Such was the obscurity Diderot found "in certain works of Stahl and in the *Principia mathematica* of Newton." It would have taken Newton merely one month to make everything plain, said Diderot, and this month would have saved three years of work and exhaustion to a thousand "bons esprits." Nature, after all, has enough of a veil; we should not double the veil with that of mystery. "Open the work of Franklin; leaf through the books of the chemists," wrote Diderot, "and you will see how the experimental art calls for insight, imagination, sagacity and resource: read them attentively, because if it be possible for you to learn in how many ways an experiment turns on itself, it is there you will learn it." [21]

We shall, in succeeding chapters, document the degree to which the experimental scientists of the eighteenth century esteemed the *Opticks* at the expense of the *Principia*, but a single example may be cited here. One of the founding treatises in plant physiology was the *Vegetable Staticks* of Stephen Hales, a work also of importance in the history of chemistry and one that strongly influenced Benjamin Franklin's scientific thought. This book may be described as an essay in quantitative biology and pneumatic chemistry; on the verso of the title page, it bears Newton's imprimatur as President of the Royal Society: "Feb. 16, 1726/7. *Imprimatur* Isaac Newton. *Pr. Reg. Soc.*" A thoroughly "Newtonian" book, it refers to "attraction: that universal principle which is so operative in all the very different works of nature." Including the preface, there are by actual count eighteen references to Newton (often with a quotation) in this experimental classic. Of these, sixteen are either quotations from the *Opticks* or references to the *Opticks*, and neither of the remaining two have anything to do with the *Principia*.‡

The special appeal of the *Opticks*—in contrast to, or perhaps even to the exclusion of, the *Principia*—was not confined to experimenters. More than half of Voltaire's book on Newtonian philosophy (the first part, at that) was devoted to the ideas of the *Opticks*, and practically the whole of Algarotti's popular and oft translated and reprinted "Newtonianism for the Ladies" presented the *Opticks* for popular consumption.[23] Curiously enough, while my research on the electricians and other experimenters was indicating the unique seminal role of the *Opticks* for science, Miss Marjorie Nicolson had been studying the influence of science on the eighteenth-century imagination and had found that poets and other literary men in England had been influenced in a unique way by the *Opticks* and not the *Principia*. An understanding of the scientific background of the eighteenth century thus seems to demand a clarification of the roles of these two great books and an estimate of the degree to which they stimulated (or, perhaps, were symbolic of) two separate Newtonian traditions in scientific thought.

Speculations in the Opticks *and not in the* Principia

The *Opticks* differs from the *Principia, inter alia,* in that Newton freely indulged in hypotheses and speculations. In this quality, it had a special appeal to those physical scientists who were attempting to construct physical rather than mathematical theories that might explain (coordinate and predict) experimental phenomena in such fields as electricity, heat, chemistry, animal physiology. Yet we cannot conclude that the tradition in science engendered by the *Opticks* was simply an opposition to the main Newtonian tradition of framing no hypotheses, although in a particular sense it was. Before making positive judgments about the two books, their respective doctrines must be carefully appraised.

Newton has so often been characterized by the phrase *Hypotheses non fingo*—I frame no hypothesis §—that it is difficult for us to ap-

‡ One of these is a discussion of Newton's mode of calibrating thermometers as published in the *Philosophical Transactions* and the other is a quotation containing Newton's theory about the dissolution of metals arising from the attractive force exerted by the "particles of acids," which comes from Newton's *De natura acidorum* (published in the introduction to volume 1 of John Harris's *Lexicon technicum*), and is also discussed in Query 31 of the third edition of the *Opticks*.[22]

§ The rendition of *Hypotheses non fingo* as *I frame no hypotheses* has the sanction of time because it was used by Andrew Motte in his translation of the *Principia* (1729),

preciate that these words appeared for the first time in the second edition of the *Principia* (issued only in 1713), in the General Scholium to Book Three, as a kind of epilogue to the whole work. In the first edition, the word " hypothesis " was used freely in a number of different senses, as it was also in the second and later edition. Indeed, in that first edition, Book Three began with a whole section plainly labelled " HYPOTHESES," and there were other plain " hypotheses " scattered throughout the treatise.

In presenting Newton's doctrine and the character of his hypotheses, I shall try to do so, in so far as possible, without prejudice or interpretation. In other words, I shall attempt to make clear the various senses in which Newton employed the word " hypothesis " in the *Principia*, and then compare his usage with that of some of his contemporaries. It is very difficult to write about " hypotheses " in science without overtones of the many philosophical quarrels over the nature of hypothesis in logic and in science, and the validity of using hypotheses at all. From Comte to Mach and the " Vienna Circle," the continued attack on hypotheses has given the word a pejorative sense, save for a limited use as in " working hypothesis." Some of our foremost philosophers of science—e. g., Whewell, Mill, Bernard, Poincaré, Duhem—have wrestled with the problem of hypotheses, and their views have necessarily colored our thoughts to some degree. I hope the reader will do his best to keep as close as possible to Newton's own definitions and usages in the following pages, even though the temptation may be strong to view a Newtonian statement as a philosophical proposition for our day. If we conclude that Newton did use " hypotheses " in science, it must not be taken to prove that his method was similar to that of Descartes. The latter employed a type of " hypothesis " that was wholly repugnant to Newton. In this sense Newton certainly did not use hypotheses. Nor should we ever find ourselves thinking that because Newton used " hypotheses " in his arguments, his science was " hypothetical " in some modern or general sense. Such a position would ignore the fact that Newton's use of " hypotheses " was limited to a set of restricted meanings of the word, generally recognized in his day.

An examination of Newton's usage is necessary to an understand-

which has often been reprinted and which served as the basis for the modernized twentieth-century version of Florian Cajori. Henry Pemberton, who knew Newton well and who prepared the third edition of the *Principia* for Newton, also used this translation of the phrase in describing Newton's attitude. Yet when Newton wrote in English, in the *Opticks*, he said (Query 28) that " the main business of natural philosophy is to argue from phænomena without feigning hypotheses "; he also (Query 31) wrote of " feigning the particles of air to be springy and ramous." [24] Although both " feign " and " frame " are legitimate renderings of " fingere," it would seem that the best Newtonian translation of *Hypotheses non fingo* would be *I feign no hypotheses.*

ing of eighteenth-century science as a whole, and thus important to a comprehension of what Franklin did in science, because, as we have already observed, hypotheses can be challenged, altered, or discarded, whereas good experiments and exact mathematical demonstrations cannot. To be sure, experiments can be extended, and important new variations introduced, but Newton's prismatic resolution of white light into non-resolvable components has remained to our day an unchallenged primary fact of experience. We have altered it only by the production of spectra through diffraction gratings, the extension to the complete range of electromagnetic radiation by introducing suitable detecting devices; with better resolution, we can show—for example—that the visible solar spectrum is not continuous but contains dark absorption (Fraunhofer) lines. But Newton's " hypotheses " invoked the possibility of extension to new domains of experience not envisaged by their " framer," and the production of relevant experimental data to render them more meaningful or more probable, or perhaps less so. The job for the men of the eighteenth century was only in part to provide simpler or more ingenious mathematical proofs than Newton's, and to translate his synthetic proofs into the language of analysis. They also found a need to improve certain sections of the *Principia*, notably Book Two. Above all, it was plain to them that it would be profitable to explore that shadowy region of Newton's thought in which the statements were neither mathematical, nor a recapitulation of phenomena, nor even what Newton called " deductions " from phenomena. Every hypothesis or speculation of Newton's constituted a challenge to the men of the eighteenth century as a key to a possible new theory of nature. The scientists in the " age of Newton " could seek progress in realms in which Newton was not sure of himself or in which new experimental data were needed, and in those areas which Newton himself had not studied at all or which he had not been able to investigate fully. Speculative hypotheses particularly abound in the *Opticks*. In order to see that their presence in Newton's writings is not contrary to some Newtonian doctrine of *Hypotheses non fingo*, we must examine Newton's use of hypotheses in the *Principia* while analyzing certain aspects of that book in terms of the main concerns of eighteenth-century natural philosophers.

" *Hypotheses* " *in the* Principia

The burden of the first two books of the *Principia* was, as Newton indicated, to lay down " the principles of philosophy; principles not philosophical but mathematical." [25] The mathematical principles—

" the laws and conditions of certain motions, and powers or forces "
—would by themselves appear " barren and dry." Since they " chiefly
have respect to philosophy," even though they are mathematical,
Newton illustrated these principles by " philosophical scholiums,
giving an account of . . . the density and resistance of bodies, spaces
void of all bodies, and the motion of light and sounds." In the third
book, his aim was to apply the same principles to " demonstrate the
frame of the System of the World." [26]

Like any good mathematical work, e. g., Euclid's " elements " as
known to Newton in the lovely edition of his teacher and benefactor,
Isaac Barrow, the *Principia* begins with a series of definitions:
" quantity of matter " (mass) as the product of density and volume,
" quantity of motion " (momentum) as the product of velocity and
quantity of matter, and so on. Next come the " axioms, or laws of
motion," the famous three laws studied in every course in elementary physics, together with a few corollaries, including the principle
of the parallelogram of forces. Then there are the lemmas, theorems,
problems, and corollaries of Book One in mathematical array, with
their figures, their geometrical proofs, and constructions: abstract
and mathematical to the highest degree. Thus Newton refers to
" centripetal forces of bodies," with occasional allusions, as in the
scholium to Proposition IV (Theor. IV), that these abstract centripetal forces have a discoverable ratio to " other known forces, such
as that of gravity." Much of Book One is devoted to the geometry
of conic sections as such. More than half way through, Newton
admitted that the subject had been developed in a wholly mathematical way without considerations for physical reality. Section XI
begins: " I have hitherto been treating of the attraction of bodies
towards an immovable centre; though very probably there is no such
thing in nature." Yet, since his intention was to make himself
" easily understood by a mathematical reader," he would now lay
" aside all physical considerations " and make use of " a familiar
way of speaking " [27]—a process justified by the fact that the " propositions are to be considered as purely mathematical." The method
is explained further in the scholium preceding Section XII, " The
attractive force of spherical bodies." In mathematics, wrote Newton,
the job is to investigate " the quantities of forces with their proportions consequent upon any conditions supposed." Later, " when we
enter upon physics, we may compare those proportions with the
phenomena of Nature, that we may know what conditions of those
forces answer to the several kinds of attractive bodies." [28]

Not all of the scholia are physical. One physical scholium reveals
Newton's standpoint in the *Principia* in a striking way. He had been

considering the motion of bodies going from one medium to another, where the two media are separated by a plane. The whole problem seemed to Newton to suggest a parallel to the phenomena of optics, notably the " sine law " discovered by Snel (and Descartes) and the " bending " or " inflection " (diffraction) of light discovered by Grimaldi. Because of the analogy between " the propagation of the rays of light and the motion of bodies," Newton added a few propositions " for optical uses," just as the whole set of preceding propositions was destined for eventual use in the dynamics of celestial bodies and terrestrial objects. Yet, Newton insisted, this procedure implied no considerations whatever concerning " the nature of the rays of light . . . whether they are bodies or not." He had merely determined " the curves of bodies which are extremely like the curves of the rays." [29]

Book Two of the *Principia* is devoted to the " motion of bodies in resisting mediums." First there is a treatment of motions of bodies that are resisted by the medium in proportion to their velocity,[30] concluding with Newton's admission that this supposed resistance " is more a mathematical hypothesis * than a physical one." [32] Succeeding sections discuss motions in media in which resistance is assumed to be proportional to the square of the velocity,[33] or in part proportional to the velocity and in part proportional to its square,[34] and so on. In this way Newton proceeded to the motion and resistance of pendulums, which led him to a General Scholium devoted entirely to some physical experiments. First he showed how experiments with pendulums in any medium (e. g., air, water, quicksilver, etc.) might be used to find the actual resistance of that medium; then how he had actually tested " the opinion of some that there is a certain ætherial medium extremely rare and subtile, which freely pervades all bodies." [35]

In Proposition XL, Problem IX, we encounter a departure from practically every other " proposition " in that it is not a statement to be proved by mathematics, but rather a genuine " problem " of experiment: " To find by experiment [*invenire per phænomena*] the resistance of a globe moving through a perfectly fluid compressed medium." Having shown how the job may be done, Newton next presented a long scholium containing the details of how he had actually proceeded " to investigate the resistances of fluids from experiments [*per experimenta*]." [36] Newton then introduced his studies of motions propagated through fluids, especially pulses and

---

* The original Latin, as in the first edition of the *Principia*, reads: " Cæterum corpora resisti in ratione velocitatis hypothesis est magis mathematica quam naturalis." [31]

waves, and a general scholium illustrated the application of his results to phenomena of light and sound.

The concluding section (IX) of Book Two was devoted by New-ton to an attack on the Cartesian vortices, under the general title of " The circular motion of fluids." The section begins with an " HYPOTHESIS," plainly marked as such: " The resistance arising from the want of lubricity in the parts of a fluid, is, other things being equal, proportional to the velocity with which the parts of the fluid are separated from one another." In the proof of the first proposition (LI, Theor. XXXIX) based upon it, there occurs the expression " per hypothesin " which is rendered into English as " by the hypothesis." Yet, when these same words appear in the proof of the next proposition, they are no longer rendered as " by the hy-pothesis," but rather as " by the supposition," in both the eighteenth-century version of Motte and the twentieth-century one revised by Cajori.[37] The use of the word " hypothesis " here and elsewhere is of some interest to us because it appears in all three Latin editions of the *Principia* that were published in Newton's lifetime, thus plainly belying statements such as Whewell's about Newton's sup-posed " horror of the term *hypothesis*." [38] Newton's use of " hypothe-sis " here is equivalent to " assumption " in an argument. Newton assumed the proposition (hypothesis) quoted above as a part of his development of fluid mechanics. This proposition is plainly not a description of phenomena or an induction from the data of experi-ments. It is not a theorem which could be deduced by mathematics or logic within the framework of the *Principia*, nor could it be sup-ported by empirical data. Hence, in accordance with Newton's definition, this statement is an hypothesis. With simple candor, Newton wrote above it its proper designation—" HYPOTHESIS." In this way, we may observe, Newton made no commitment as to whether it is a true description of real fluids or merely a supposition introduced as a necessary element in the argument.

We may learn of Newton's intentions by seeing how he used the pre-ceding hypothesis. His endeavour had been " to investigate the prop-erties of vortices, that I might find whether the celestial phenomena can be explained by them." [39] In point of fact, he proved the har-monic law of Kepler (obtaining for the satellites of Jupiter as well as the sun-planet system " with the greatest accuracy, as far as has yet been discovered by astronomical observation ") was inconsistent with the conclusions to be drawn from vortex theory. Newton said that he had adopted for the sake of simplicity, i. e., " for the sake of demonstration," an " hypothesis "—the word is Newton's—about the resistance being proportional to the velocity, although the actual

HYPOTHESES.

Hypoth. I. *Caufas rerum naturalium non plures admitti debere, quàm quæ & vera fint & earum Phænomenis explicandis fufficiunt.*

Natura enim fimplex eft & rerum caufis fuperfluis non luxuriat.

Hypoth. II. *Ideoque effettuum naturalium ejufdem generis eædem funt caufæ.*

Uti refpirationis in Homine & in Beftia; defcenfûs lapidum in *Europa* & in *America*; Lucis in Igne culinari & in Sole; reflexionis lucis in Terra & in Planetis.

Hypoth. III. *Corpus omne in alterius cujufcunque generis corpus transformari poffe, & qualitatum gradus omnes intermedios fucceffivè induere.*

Hypoth. IV. *Centrum Syftematis Mundani quiefcere.*

Hoc ab omnibus conceffum eft, dum aliqui Terram alii Solem in centro quiefcere contendant.

Hypoth. V. *Planetas circumjoviales, radiis ad centrum Jovis ductis, areas defcribere temporibus proportionales, eorumque tempora periodica effe in ratione fefquialtera diftantiarum ab ipfius centro.*

Conftat ex obfervationibus Aftronomicis. Orbes horum Planetarum non differunt fenfibiliter à circulis Jovi concentricis, & motus eorum in his circulis uniformes deprehenduntur. Tempora verò periodica effe in ratione fefquialtera femidiametrorum orbium confentiunt Aftronomici : & *Flamftedius*, qui omnia Micrometro & per Eclipfes Satellitum accuratius definivit, literis ad me datis, quinetiam numeris fuis mecum communicatis, fignificavit rationem illam fefquialteram tam accuratè obtinere, quàm fit poffibile fenfu deprehendere. Id quod ex Tabula fequente manifeftum eft.

Satellitum

FIG. 3 on this and the following page.

Two pages from the first edition of Newton's *Principia* (1687), showing Hypotheses I to VII.

Satellitum tempora periodica.

1d. 18h. 28'$\frac{3}{5}$. 3d. 13h. 17'$\frac{9}{10}$. 7d. 3h. 59'$\frac{3}{5}$. 16d. 18h. 5'$\frac{7}{5}$.

Distantiæ Satellitum à centro Jovis.

Ex Observationibus	1.	2	3	4	
Cassini	5.	8.	13.	23.	Semidiam. Jovis.
Borelli	5$\frac{2}{3}$.	8$\frac{2}{3}$.	14.	24$\frac{2}{3}$.	
Tounlei *per Micromet-*	5,51.	8,78.	13,47.	24,72.	
Flamstedii *per Microm.*	5,31.	8,85.	13,98.	24,23.	
Flamst. *per Eclips. Satel.*	5,578.	8,876.	14,159.	24,903.	
Ex temporibus periodicis.	5,578.	8,878.	14,168.	24,968.	

Hypoth. VI. *Planetas quinque primarios Mercurium, Venerem, Martem, Jovem & Saturnum Orbibus suis Solem cingere.*

Mercurium & Venerem circa Solem revolvi ex eorum phasibus lunaribus demonstratur. Plenâ facie lucentes ultra Solem siti sunt, dimidiatâ è regione Solis, falcatâ cis Solem; per discum ejus ad modum macularum nonnunquam transeuntes. Ex Martis quoque plena facie prope Solis conjunctionem, & gibbosa in quadraturis, certum est quod is Solem ambit. De Jove etiam & Saturno idem ex eorum phasibus semper plenis demonstratur.

Hypoth. VII. *Planetarum quinque primariorum, & (vel Solis circa Terram vel) Terræ circa Solem tempora periodica esse in ratione sesquialtera mediocrium distantiarum à Sole.*

Hæc à *Keplero* inventa ratio in confesso est apud omnes. Eadem utique sunt tempora periodica, eædemq; orbium dimensiones, sive Planetæ circa Terram, sive iidem circa Solem revolvantur. Ac de mensura quidem temporum periodicorum convenit inter Astronomos universos. Magnitudines autem Orbium *Keplerus* & *Bullialdus* omnium diligentissimè ex Observationibus determinaverunt: & distantiæ mediocres, quæ temporibus periodicis respondent, non

 diffe-

resistance is in all probability smaller. But he noted with pride that the more probable assumption made the vortex theory even more inconsistent with Kepler's third law.

In the final scholium to Book Two, appearing a few pages later, Newton concluded that " the hypothesis of vortices is utterly irreconcilable with astronomical phenomena." And here we must note that Newton's rejection of the Cartesian hypothesis of vortices was not based on its being an " hypothesis " as such; it was an hypothesis which led to the wrong results. It could readily be rejected because it was in contradiction with the data of exact experience.

For those who would understand the complexity of analyzing Newton's use of the word " hypothesis," it should be pointed out that in this final scholium to Book Two, Newton began the discussion with the statement that ". . . according to the Copernican hypothesis [*secundum Hypothesin* Copernicæam], the planets going round the sun revolve in ellipses, having the sun in their common focus, . . . ," and that the phrase " Copernican hypothesis " has appeared in all Latin and English editions from Newton's days to ours! †

I have mentioned the lack of a critical or even a variorum edition of Newton's *Principia*; a result is that few writers on Newton have been easily able to compare the changes that occurred in the editions published during Newton's lifetime. Curiously enough, there is in print a good account of the changes that occurred from the second to the third edition,[40] but not of the more significant changes, namely, those introduced into the second edition. Many authors have quoted with great approbation Newton's " Rules of Reasoning in Philosophy," with which Book Three of the *Principia* begins. Thus, Ernst Mach, who stated that the phrase *Hypotheses non fingo* entitles Newton to be considered a philosopher of the highest rank, quoted these " rules " *verbatim*.[41] Yet, in the first edition of the *Principia*, these so-called rules were called " hypotheses," and they were part of an introductory section set apart and marked clearly in capital letters " HYPOTHESES." This is a fact for which one may search in vain throughout practically the whole corpus of secondary literature on Newton and Newtonianism. Furthermore, in the first edition of the *Principia*, the section of " Hypotheses " contained not only the later " rules " but also the statements that were later called " Phænomena." How a statement could at one time be called by Newton an " hypothesis " and at a later time a " phænomenon " is all the more baffling when we recall that this transition

† This particular use of the word " hypothesis " is discussed at greater length on page 134.

occurred in that very second edition for which Newton wrote the famous concluding General Scholium containing the words *Hypotheses non fingo*. In this scholium, Newton stated that " whatever is not deduced from the phenomena is to be called an hypothesis." Evidently, Newton had changed his mind in the interval between the two editions. But in what sense could Newton possibly have designated " phænomena " as " hypotheses " ?

Newton's Irreducible " Hypotheses "

We have seen above that in Book Two of the *Principia*, Newton did not disdain the use of the word " hypothesis," which occurred in several different usages; the same situation is found in Book Three. For example, the proof of Proposition IV (Theor. IV) in Book Three, " That the moon gravitates towards the earth, and by the force of gravity is continually drawn off from a rectilinear motion, and retained in its orbit," is demonstrated by a calculation " founded on the hypothesis of the earth's standing still." [42] Now of course Newton believed that the earth is in motion, but in computing the " falling " of the moon, it was simpler to consider the earth at rest. Today we would be more prone to write " assumption " instead of " hypothesis," but it is significant that Newton chose the latter term. The same type of argument was adopted in " Newton's System of the World," where we find, " The circumterrestrial force decreases inversely as the square of the distances from the earth. This is shown on the hypothesis that the earth is at rest." Immediately following the proof is another, " The same proved on the hypothesis that the earth moves." [43] Since these mutually exclusive hypotheses exhaust the possibilities, the proof is general.

A somewhat different use of the word " hypothesis " is encountered in Book Three of the *Principia*, in the second and third editions, where we find (immediately following Prop. X, Theor. X) :

HYPOTHESIS I
That the centre of the system of the World is immovable.

This is acknowledged by all, while some contend that the earth, others that the sun, is fixed in that centre. Let us see what may from hence follow.

Plainly, this proposition cannot be " deduced from phenomena " and so, according to Newton's definition, it must be an hypothesis. Newton proved by this hypothesis that the common center of gravity of the solar system (earth, sun, and all the other planets) is itself immovable, and concluded that this center of gravity " is to be esteemed [*habendum est*] the centre of the world." This particular hypothesis is related to Newton's general concept of space, which was in part the result of his theological convictions. It is an example, according to Hermann Weyl, of a resort " to a hypothesis unfounded in experience and a dialectical dodge " which strikes

a discordant note in the midst of the magnificent and cogent inductive development of his system of the world in the *Principia*. The hypothesis states that the universe has a center and that this center is at rest. The common center of gravity of the solar system, like that of any system of bodies not subjected to external forces, moves uniformly along a straight line; thus he concludes correctly from the mechanical laws. And now we read, " but if that center moved, the center of the world would move also, against the hypothesis," no attempt whatever being made to give a reason for this identification of the center of gravity of the planetary system with the hypothetical stationary center of the world. . . .[44]

All the instances of hypotheses we have found in the *Principia* so far seem trivial in comparison to this one, which remained prominent in Newton's final version of the *Principia*. Newton's statement that this hypothesis " is acknowledged by all " may seem to beg the question, because it indicates that the statement is in no ordinary sense to be taken as an " hypothetical " statement or possibly as " not true "; rather it is true, and so " acknowledged by all," but it cannot be proved from " phenomena."

The hypothesis about the immovability of the center of the world system is followed by another one in the second and third editions of the *Principia*. Immediately preceding Prop. XXXIX, Prob. XX, we find:

HYPOTHESIS II

If the other parts of the earth were taken away, and the remaining ring was carried alone about the sun in the orbit of the earth by the annual motion, while by the diurnal motion it was in the meantime revolved about its own axis inclined to the plane of the ecliptic by an angle of $23\frac{1}{2}$ degrees, the motion of the equinoctial points would be the same, whether the ring were fluid, or whether it consisted of a hard and rigid matter.

This Hypothesis II is quite different from Hypothesis I. Newton gave no reason to support it. It could not be " deduced from phenomena," nor could it be derived from previous theorems. As a theorem, it was necessary for the proof of Proposition XXXIX (Prob. XX), " To find the precession of the equinoxes," but Newton was incapable of proving it. Thus Newton boldly called it an hypothesis, rather than a theorem, and left the problem for some other mathematician. Laplace found a proof [45] which, had it been available to Newton, would have enabled him to change the name of " Hypothesis II " to " Proposition. . . ." We may observe, then, that in Newton's usage an hypothesis might represent both a provable and an unprovable proposition, although Newton himself did not ever make a distinction between the two.

Thus we have encountered two " hypotheses," called so by Newton, which are present in the revised (second and third) editions of the *Principia*. Each represents a proposition necessary to the structure of Book Three, but one which Newton was unable to prove mathematically or to establish from phenomena. That this procedure considerably weakens the alleged principle of *Hypotheses non fingo* must be admitted, but there are even grosser departures and these, in fact, lead us to understand how the " Rules " and " Phænomena " may have been originally considered to have been " hypotheses."

The scholium which appears at the very end of Book Two of the *Principia* contains an argument intended to deliver the final death blow to the Cartesian doctrine by showing that " it is manifest that the planets are not carried round in corporeal vortices; for, according to the Copernican hypothesis [*secundum hypothesin Copernicæam*], the planets going round the sun revolve in ellipses, having the sun in their common focus; and by radii drawn to the sun describe areas proportional to the times." Newton concluded that " the hypothesis of vortices [*hypothesis vorticum*] " leads to conclusions that cannot be reconciled with " astronomical phenomena," and so this hypothesis " rather serves to perplex than explain the heavenly motions." [46] Newton accepted the Copernican " hypothesis " in the form given it by Kepler, but hypothesis the latter apparently remained, even for Newton, to judge by his own words. We may recall that when the *Principia* was received in manuscript by the Royal Society for approbation and printing, it was described as " a mathematical demonstration of the Copernican hypothesis as proposed by Kepler." [47] In this same sense, Coke referred, in 1660, to " a perpetuall motion of the earth from west to east according to the new hypotheses in astronomy, or of the sun from east to west, after the former hypotheses." [48] In Newton's day and well into the eighteenth century, the three major systems of the world, the Ptolemaic, Tychonian, and Copernican, were almost always referred to as hypotheses.

The famous General Scholium at the end of the *Principia* (added in the second edition) begins with the statement that " The hypothesis of vortices is pressed with many difficulties," following which the

" difficulties " are listed so that the hypothesis might be rejected. In " Newton's System of the World," we find a reference to the " hypothesis of solid orbits " in the old geocentric system, which had " the unavoidable consequence . . . that the comets should be thrust into spaces below the moon." But this hypothesis, too, had its " difficulties "; later astronomers found by observation that comets were not sub-lunary but actually moved through the whole solar system, and thus there was a rejection of the hypothesis of solid spheres around the earth to which planets were affixed.[49]

The penultimate paragraph of the General Scholium to Book Three, following the discussion of God, begins:

Hitherto we have explained the phenomena of the heavens and of our sea by the power of gravity, but have not yet assigned the cause of this power. This is certain, that it must proceed from a cause that penetrates to the very centres of the sun and planets, without suffering the least diminution of its force; that operates not according to the quantity of the surfaces of the particles upon which it acts (as mechanical causes used to do), but according to the quantity of the solid matter which they contain, and propagates its virtue on all sides to immense distances, decreasing always as the inverse square of the distances.

What is gravity? Its properties or effects were made manifest by Newton, but what was the cause?

. . . hitherto I have not been able to discover the cause of those properties of gravity from phenomena, and I frame no hypotheses; for whatever is not deduced from the phenomena is to be called an hypothesis; and hypotheses, whether metaphysical or physical, whether of occult qualities or mechanical, have no place in experimental philosophy. In this philosophy particular propositions are inferred from the phenomena, and afterwards rendered general by induction. Thus it was that the impenetrability, the mobility, and the impulsive force of bodies, and the laws of motion and of gravitation, were discovered.

Newton insisted that, even though the cause might be unknown, the major problems of celestial mechanics had been solved:

And to us it is enough that gravity does really exist, and act according to the laws which we have explained, and abundantly serves to account for all the motions of the celestial bodies, and of our sea.[50]

The original version of this paragraph apparently ended with the statement, " and I frame no hypotheses," *Hypotheses non fingo.* The remainder did not at first appear as finally printed, or as quoted above. Newton wrote to Cotes on 28 March 1713, three and a half weeks after sending him the scholium,

And for preventing exceptions against the use of the word hypothesis I desire you to conclude the next paragraph in this manner: Quicquid enim ex phænomenis non deducitur Hypothesis vocanda est, et ejusmodi Hypotheses seu Metaphysicæ seu Physicæ seu Qualitatum occultarum seu Mechanicæ in Philosophia experimentali locum non habent. In hac Philosophia Propositiones deducuntur ex phænomenis & redduntur generales per Inductionem. Sic impenetrabilitas mobilitas & impetus corporum & leges motuum & gravitatis innotuere. Et satis est quod Gravitas corporū revera existat & agat secundum leges a nobis expositas & ad corporum cœlestium et maris nostri motus omnes sufficiat.[51]

This new statement seems to have rendered the phrase *Hypotheses non fingo* more general than at first. Even so, we must keep in mind that it never characterized Newton's scientific thought as a whole, or even his thought on gravitation. The repeated use of hypotheses in the second and third editions of the *Principia* and in "Newton's System of the World" (which was published after the second edition of the *Principia* and of which the manuscript is partly in Cotes's hand) indicates that Newton did not completely reject hypotheses of any sort. He merely refused to advance an hypothesis on the nature of the gravitational force in the *Principia*.

The additional statement added by Newton to the final General Scholium was occasioned by Cotes's objection to the words *Et cum attractio omnis mutua sit,* and his stricture that " till this objection be cleared I would not undertake to answer any one who should assert that you do *hypothesim fingere.* I think you seem tacitly to make this supposition that the attractive force resides in the central body." [52] Furthermore, Cotes was particularly annoyed by the recent publication of the letter by Leibniz to Hartsoeker, to which we have already referred. Leibniz's letter, Cotes told Newton, exhibits some " prejudices which have been industriously laid against it [The *Principia*]. As that it deserts mechanical causes, is built upon miracles, & recurrs to occult qualitys." Newton's statement about occult qualities and " mechanical hypotheses " was provoked by Cotes's reference to Leibniz. Newton also made clear to Cotes the sense in which he understood the word " hypothesis ":

. . . the difficulty you mention which lies in these words [*Et cum Attractio omnis mutua sit*] is removed by considering that as in geometry the word hypothesis is not taken in so large a sense as to include the axiomes & postulates, so in experimental philosophy it is not to be taken in so large a sense as to include the first principles or axiomes which I call the laws of motion. These principles are deduced from phænomena & made general by induction: which is the highest evidence that a proposition can have in this philosophy. And the word hypothesis is here used by me to signify only such a proposition as is not a phænomenon nor deduced from any phænomena but assumed or supposed without any experimental proof.[53]

Newton's comparison of experimental philosophy to geometry is enlightening. If we consider the three laws of motion (and later, perhaps, the law of universal gravitation) to be a part of the " axiomes & postulates," we may prove a number of theorems by mathematics and test them by phenomena, as Newton did in the first two books of the *Principia*. Then, as in geometry, additional propositions or sets of propositions may be derived from further assumptions—other than the primary axioms—and in this sense the further assumptions may be called hypotheses. If we examine a standard dictionary of the early eighteenth century, however, such as John Harris's *Lexicon Technicum, s. v.* hypothesis, we find that the general usage is merely a proposition or principle supposed or taken for granted " in order to draw conclusions from it, in order to the proof of a point in question." But in natural philosophy, astronomy, etc., it is a " supposition " or a set of principles that are " supposed as granted, that from thence an intelligible and plausible account of the causes may be given." Furthermore, although an hypothesis is " a supposition of that which is not, for that which may be," so that it does not matter whether " what is supposed be true or not," Harris insisted that an hypothesis must always " be possible " and " should always be probable." Hence, no hypothesis should ever be considered which is manifestly absurd, a position taken firmly by Newton's teacher, Isaac Barrow. Harris noted, furthermore, than an " elaborately contrived " hypothesis of the universe, " in relation to the dispositions of the heavens, and the motion of the stars " is called a system as well as an hypothesis, as the Ptolemaic, Copernican, or Tychonian. An hypothesis is thus a " sort of system laid down from one's own imagination, by which to account for some phænomenon or appearance in nature."

Newton was justified in believing that the three laws of motion were, therefore, not hypotheses. Although they were the axioms of the system of dynamics he presented, they were proved by experiment, i. e., deduced from phenomena, or, at any rate, consistent with observations as far as they go. As Newton explained to Cotes, the laws of motion and the law of gravitation are originally " deduced from phænomena."

We may illustrate Newton's point of view by a simple example. Galilean experiments on a body rolling down an inclined plane can yield a set of data (the phenomena), from which it can be deduced that the acceleration was proportional to the sine of the angle of inclination of the plane. Applying Galileo's principle of the composition of vectors, it can further be deduced that the component of the weight-force producing the acceleration was in every case also proportional to the sine of the angle of inclination. Hence the principle of the proportionality of force and acceleration (as in the second law of motion) was in the first place " deduced from [the] phenomena " of the inclined plane and " made general by induction." From this point of view, the laws of motion (the " axiomes " or " postulates " of the *Principia*) are not hypotheses, in the sense in which Newton used the word. We need not quarrel with Newton's view. Taking him at his word, we may understand why " Hypothesis I " and " Hypothesis II " were labeled as such in the second and third editions of the *Principia*. They are propositions which are neither phenomena nor are they deduced from phenomena, but are assumed or supposed without any experimental proof. This is also the sense in which reference is made in " Newton's System of the World " to " that hypothesis which places the fixed stars at different distances."

Varieties of Newtonian Hypotheses

Since Newton used hypotheses of many sorts in the *Principia*, as well as in the *Opticks* and other writings, we must distinguish carefully amongst the types of Newtonian hypotheses. The major senses in which Newton used the word hypothesis are listed below.‡

1. *A system of the world.* As in " the Copernican hypothesis."

2. *The " premise " of a particular mathematical proposition.* Lemma VII at the beginning of Book One of the *Principia* reads: " The same things being supposed, I say that the ultimate ratio of the arc, chord, and tangent, any one to any other, is the ratio of equality." The phrase, " the same things being supposed," is the hypothesis of the lemma.

3. *A general proposition in mathematics that is not proved.* These general propositions are presented and their consequences deduced by mathematics. Thus Newton hypothesized various mathematical conditions of forces: attractions between bodies inversely proportional to the distance between them, inversely proportional to the square of the distance between them, etc.; resistances in fluid media proportional to the speed of a body moving in the fluid, proportional to the square of the speed, and so on. Such statements have obvious physical connotations, but Newton presented them as mathematical conditions, and as such he did not have to test their possible appli-

‡ A more complete discussion of Newtonian hypotheses, and the change of Newton's views relating to " hypotheses " and " phænomena " will be found in Appendix One.

cations in nature. Because such statements are possible mathematical conditions, they are hypotheses and need not be proved.

4. *The premise in a philosophical (or physical) proposition.* A major example is the hypothesis of gases being composed of small bodies with a mutually repulsive force. The mathematical hypothesis of a law of repulsion inversely proportional to the distance between the small bodies was shown by Newton to lead to Boyle's law of gases, while the converse was also mathematically true. Newton tried to evade the question of the validity of this hypothesis as a statement about nature. Thus he recognized that the hypothesis of gases being composed of mutually repellent particles could be a physical or philosophical hypothesis as well as a mathematical hypothesis.

5. *Propositions which Newton was unable to prove.* The two theorems, quoted on pages 132 and 133, " Hypothesis I " and " Hypothesis II " in the second and third editions of the *Principia*, are examples of this type. Newton was not clever enough to prove " Hypothesis II," as Laplace did; " Hypothesis I " is, by its nature, unprovable.

6. *Counter-to-fact conditions.* Newton might assume (make the hypothesis) that first the earth is at rest and then that the earth is in motion. If the theorem could be proved in both cases, the proof would be general. One of the two mutually exclusive conditions must be contrary to what exists in nature.

7. *Mechanisms supposed in order to explain laws or phenomena.* In order to explain diffraction or interference phenomena, Newton suggested (and advocated) in the *Opticks* the hypothesis of waves in the æther being caused by the motions of particles of light. For instance, the phenomenon we call " Newton's rings " was said to be caused by the waves " overtaking " the particles and putting them into successive " fits " of " easy " reflection or refraction. In the *Principia*, when Newton discussed waves, he indicated that his results might apply to such an hypothesis of æther waves but that he would not commit himself to this hypothesis at that time. Presumably this is the kind of hypothesis that Newton refused to frame or feign in the *Principia* with respect to gravitation.

8. *" Philosophical romance."* This is an hypothesis that produces an arbitrary theory in the absence of experience. The followers of Descartes could be held to have adhered to a " philosophical romance " because their system was contrary to empirically derived results, and actually inhibited the obtaining of new results.

The expression " philosophical romance " became common among

Newtonians, particularly in criticizing the system of Descartes. Maclaurin wrote that Descartes himself, " amongst his familiar friends, used to call his system his philosophical romance."

9. *Axioms or postulates.* Newton used the term hypothesis and axiom interchangeably. In optics he referred to Snel's law in both ways: as axiom and as hypothesis. In an early draft of the *Principia*, the laws of motion were called hypotheses, even though Newton considered them to be generalizations from experiment or experience.

*   *   *

The classification of some of the major senses in which Newton used the word " hypothesis " indicates the danger of basing interpretations of Newton's philosophy of science on a single phrase *Hypotheses non fingo*. From the point of view of the scientists of the eighteenth century, the major type of hypothesis to be avoided was the " philosophical romance," of which a typical instance was the kind of wild speculation about the history of the earth in the absence of any sort of empirical evidence. But the invention of mechanisms in order to explain phenomena or to account for theories could be fruitful, even though depending on hypotheses. For example, a theory—conceived as a set of empirically derived laws, or laws that are generalizations of experience—could by means of such an hypothesis be related to a second theory. Thus the hypothesis of a subtle elastic fluid of heat might suggest the usefulness of a similar hypothesis for electricity. The similarity between the two hypotheses might indicate experiments: are good conductors of heat also good conductors of electricity?

Newton's hypothesis about gases being composed of mutually repelling particles was widely applied during the eighteenth and even the nineteenth century.§ By the 1740's it was generally assumed by Newtonian scientists that Newton had " demonstrated " that the particles of gases (or elastic fluids) repel one another with a force inversely proportional to the distance between them. John Dalton, for instance, never questioned the fact that this result had been proved.

By Franklin's day, the nice distinction made by Newton, between the laws which compose a theory and the physical hypotheses which explain or correlate those laws, had been lost. Thus we find references to Franklin's " one-fluid theory of electricity " or the " theory of positive and negative electricity " and the rival " theory of the two electric fluids." The scientific work in heat, electricity, chemis-

§ For Newton's views on this subject, see the concluding section of Chapter Six; the later interpretations of Newton's views have been studied by Professor Partington.[54]

try, meteorology, and even certain aspects of biology was characterized in the eighteenth century by the development of theories that
included hypotheses of mechanisms of subtle fluids—all in the name
of Newton! This type of hypothesis had been developed by Newton
at large in the *Opticks* and in other writings, notably the *De Natura
Acidorum*, but not in the *Principia*. Hence the scientists who wished
to make advances in the experimental sciences comparable to Newton's work on light and on the varieties of matter, were led to study
the *Opticks*. There they learned the Newtonian method of posing
hypotheses of the sort that might lead to new experiments, to the
discovery of new laws that would accurately predict the observed
phenomena, and to the creation of new theories that would embrace
ever wider ranges of empirical knowledge.

Is God an Hypothesis in Newton's Experimental Philosophy?

The final General Scholium of the later editions of the *Principia*
contains a discussion of the "being and attributes" of God. Newton—having disposed of the hypothesis of vortices—pointed out that
the constitution of the solar system (six planets revolving about the
sun in the same sense and in the same plane, together with their
moons) precludes our conceiving "that mere mechanical causes
could give birth to so many regular motions." "This most beautiful
system of the sun, planets, and comets, could only proceed from
the counsel and dominion of an intelligent and powerful being."
Is not the existence of a deity an hypothesis in the sense of this
scholium, as not deduced from phenomena? In this connection, we
are apt to read Newton from the point of view of the famous anecdote about Laplace who, when asked why God did not appear in
the pages of his treatise, is said to have replied that he did not need
that hypothesis. But Newton held no such view. In his letters to
Bentley, he indicated his opinion that the observed properties of
the universe required the hand of God, and in the *Opticks* he declared that it appears "from phænomena that there is a Being,
incorporeal, living, intelligent, omnipresent, . . ." [55] In the very
discussion of God in the General Scholium to Book Three, Newton
had shown to his own satisfaction that the solar system could not
proceed from mechanical causes alone; hence, the existence of God
was derived from phenomena. Newton sent the General Scholium
to the editor, Cotes, on 2 March 1712/3; after Cotes had raised some
objections, Newton suggested the addition of these words to justify
his discussion: "Et hæc de Deo: de quo utiq: ex phænomenis
dissere, ad philosophiam experimentalem pertinet." [56] Curiously

enough, this has always been rendered as: "And thus much concerning God; to discourse of from the appearance of things, does certainly belong to Natural Philosophy." The sense would be more in keeping with the remainder of the scholium and the Latin words themselves if it read: "And thus much concerning God; to discourse of from *phenomena*, belongs to *experimental philosophy*."

The Hypotheses of the Æther and Corpuscularity of Light

Although Newton wrote in the General Scholium that he framed no hypotheses, it should now be plain that we must interpret this statement to mean that he did not propose to place any hypothesis about the nature or cause of gravitation into the framework of the *Principia*. Gravity, he noted, "must proceed from a cause . . . ," but he had not been able to discover the cause of the properties of gravity from phenomena; hence any discussion of it must remain on the level of discourse of hypothesis. There certainly is no warrant in Newton's words for assuming that he would not, and did not, speculate about such hypotheses elsewhere. Newton concluded the scholium, and the great book, with that curious paragraph about " a certain most subtle spirit which pervades and lies hid in all gross bodies," i. e., an æther. By its force and action, the particles composing bodies attract one another at close range, and cohere on contact; * electrified bodies act at greater distances, attracting and repelling nearby corpuscles; and light is " emitted, reflected, inflected and heats bodies." The " vibrations of this spirit, mutually propagated along the solid filaments of the nerves " convey sensation from the sensory organs to the brain, and the commands of the will are similarly communicated from the brain to the muscles. Newton commented that he could not explain these matters " in a few words," and that there was not a " sufficiency of experiments " for " an accurate determination and demonstration of the laws by which this electric and elastic spirit operates "—*FINIS*.

This concluding paragraph to the ultimate approved version of the book introduced a variety of topics which had not been discussed in the *Principia* at all, but they had been the subject of Newton's speculation for about half a century. The reader whose appetite had been whetted by this paragraph would, therefore, naturally turn to Newton's amplified speculations, which, during Newton's lifetime, were to be found in the Queries at the end of the *Opticks* and,

---

* When Newton first sent the General Scholium to Cotes, he indicated an earlier intention to say "much more about the attraction of the small particles of bodies, but," he added, "upon second thoughts I have chose rather to add but one short paragraph about that part of philosophy." [57]

later on in the century, in a famous letter to Boyle and a long communication published in Birch's *History of the Royal Society*. In those sources, the reader would find that this subtle and elastic æther was supposed to account for at least one other major set of phenomena not included in the above list: gravitation. Newton's omission of falling bodies and the action of the sun and moon from his list is understandable, since the existence of the æther is an hypothesis and he had stated that he would frame no hypothesis about the cause of gravitation in the *Principia*, but the mystery is why he mentioned the æther at all.†

The *Opticks* is the only one of Newton's two major books on physical science to have been read by every Newtonian scientist. The reason is that readers of the *Principia* in the eighteenth century, to whom the first edition was unavailable and who would encounter the second and later editions, would be led logically to the *Opticks* after studying the final General Scholium. In this sense the *Opticks* is the more important of the pair for our understanding of Newtonian natural philosophy in the eighteenth century.

From the point of view of the eighteenth-century scientists, who read Newton's writings, there was no need to take Newton's famous three words—*Hypotheses non fingo*—seriously. They were aware that Newton did not restrict himself to descriptive statements about experiments and observations and that he framed or feigned hypotheses

† My guess is that Newton's artistry reflected his unique personality. He wanted to avoid any discussion of large hypotheses in the *Principia*, to avoid any semblance of having written a " philosophical romance." The " mathematical theory " of dynamics and the " philosophical " theory of the solar system depended on a series of axioms, but not on any particular hypothesis about the cause of the forces that act in or on terrestrial and celestial bodies. Thus, as Newton wrote to Cotes, ". . . he that in experimental philosophy would except against any of these [propositions] must draw his objection from some experiment or phænomenon & not from a mere hypothesis. . . ." [58]

Yet Newton was always ambivalent. He wanted to avoid speculative hypotheses and yet he could not resist telling his readers about his thoughts concerning the cause of phenomena. Every time he wrote out the hypothesis of the æther, he began with an apology, and a deprecation of all such hypotheses. Such apologies are often taken at their face value, but I do not believe they should be interpreted as a sign of Newtonian modesty. After all, he might have kept his speculations in his notebooks if he had been a different sort of person.

I have often wondered whether Dean More was serious when he wrote that in the General Scholium Newton showed " the will to refrain from conflating speculation with true knowledge," that Newton " proves that his humility does not result from a lack of imagination equal to those who, then and now, confidently discuss the causes and nature of the universe. For, he concludes, if we prefer an occult substance to an occult cause, he might add something about a subtle spirit which pervades all bodies and whose actions are the cause of gravitation, electrical energy, light, heat, sensation, and nervous stimuli." [59] But the fact remains that Newton did " add something about a subtle spirit . . ." and a true humility or modesty would have made him suppress the whole paragraph rather than publish it.

of the several sorts which have just been classified. Modern philosophers have attempted to make of Newton an operationalist or a positivist and have said that his rejection of hypotheses was characteristic of his empirical point of view. But just as the positivism of Mach does not " place in the correct light the essentially constructive and speculative nature of thought and more especially of scientific thought " (the words are Einstein's) , so the positivist interpretation of Newton robs his work of those qualities of imagination which caused his contemporaries to admire him and led successors to be inspired to explore new areas of scientific thought. Having read Newton, his friends and disciples could use hypotheses to aid in the correlation, prediction, and explanation of scientific events—without compromise to their Newtonianism. And because the men of Franklin's generation saw that hypotheses and speculations guide the scientific mind, they reaped the full fruits of the Newtonian philosophy and established new branches of experimental science.

Today we are apt to consider hypotheses and all sorts of axioms as arbitrary assumptions, but in Newton's day both were always based to some degree on experience. From a philosophical point of view, we may disagree with Newton and insist that the second law of motion presupposes the idea of force, that forces do not " exist " in nature, that they are hypothetical mental constructs which are actually unnecessary.‡ But when Newton wrote about force, as in his discussion of the third law of motion, he used physical examples to show that his concept was drawn from experience: the sensation in a finger pressing down on a stone; or the muscular effort of a horse pulling a stone and the visible tension in the rope. These forces were not hypothetical in Newton's sense, but they were contact forces. Some of Newton's contemporaries disliked gravitational forces because these were forces acting at a distance, and experience showed no analogue to muscular strain on a tension in a rope in the space between attracting bodies.§ And so Newton introduced an hypothesis—but not in the *Principia* itself—to reduce the action of long-range forces like gravitation to something more nearly analogous to contact.

Now every theory, according to the modern point of view, must rest on unverifiable assumptions, as Newton's did. But we must not on that account introduce the concept of arbitrary hypotheses into Newton's " theories," because this would cause an anachron-

‡ Thus Mach attempted to reduce mechanics to a system in which " force " was replaced by a mutual acceleration which one body may give to another; and Hertz eliminated the concept altogether.[60]

§ A century later, Faraday introduced the concepts of " strains " in the æther and lines of force under " tension " in order to account for electro-magnetic phenomena.

istic perversion of what he said and of what the scientists of the eighteenth century did. There were no observations of the æther or of particles of light that could be considered in any respect similar to the observations of muscular forces, and so the particles of light and the medium of the æther were hypotheses in the Newtonian sense (category 7). Nor did Newton ever hope to be able to " see " a " particle of light " or to be able to " feel " the " æther "; they were both beyond the range of sensation. But the particles of which bodies are made were not in this category, and Newton expressed the hope that improvements in microscopes would bring such particles within the limits of the sensation of sight.[61] It is possible, of course, to say that in Newton's day the proposition that all matter has a granular structure was an hypothesis, but this would be to introduce a further sense to the word that goes a little beyond Newton's intent. For Newton, as for his contemporaries, the " corpuscular philosophy " was an accepted general condition of scientific thought, almost as basic to science as the principle of cause and effect. It would not be correct, therefore, to refer without qualification to a " corpuscular hypothesis " held by Newton. We should rather note a basic " corpuscular postulate " that underlay all scientific thought in that age and that did not therefore need experimental justification, in the sense that the laws of motion did, even as axioms. The " new science " or the " new philosophy " which Newton called " experimental philosophy " was simply a " corpuscular philosophy."

I have assumed in the preceding pages that the corpuscularity of light is an hypothesis in a Newtonian sense. In this particular case, the followers of Newton would not have agreed, although Newton himself had been accused of arguing the hypothesis of the corpuscularity of light and had denied that he had done so, making this hypothesis—so he said—but a plausible consequence of his doctrine (empirically based theory) of color.

The Eighteenth-Century View of Newton's Hypotheses

The scientists of the eighteenth century often took a curious position with respect to hypotheses in the Newtonian philosophy. For instance, they would attack Cartesian philosophy as resting on hypotheses and quote Newton's phrase about *Hypotheses non fingo*. Then, without further ado, they would present Newton's own hypotheses as if they derived from phenomena and were accepted principles of natural philosophy.

The eighteenth-century view of Newton's hypotheses may be seen in a typical Newtonian book, B. Martin's *Philosophia Britannica*.

Martin attacked hypotheses in the orthodox fashion, saying " I do not know that I have advanced any thing here, which I have not one way or another proved to be true," since "nothing but what is demonstrated may be accounted to deserve the title of *Newtonian Philosophy*." Newton "seemed quite averse to *hypotheses*; and . . . did himself never make use of this *fallacious way of reasoning. . . .*" Yet, Martin admitted, Newton "indulged them to others under proper restrictions" and, to be sure, "he once condescended to form an *hypothesis* to shew that it [*attraction*] might be done by *impulsion* . . . of a very subtle elastic spirit or æther. But as he was not able to prove the existence of any such thing, he seemed not at all delighted with the thought, nor ever laid any stress upon it; and accordingly we have not admitted it as a principle of the *Newtonian* philosophy." A few sarcastic words then follow about "how very fond people seem of this *subtle æther*; one accounts for the *cause of gravity* thereby, another for *muscular motion*, a third for *electricity*, a fourth. . . ." Whether or not Newton himself ever gave sanction for such a procedure, Martin did so proceed, as is clear from the following discussion:

The power of attraction or cause of gravity, we presume not to define, or say what it is, but only that it is, or does exist; and the laws of its action we shall endeavour to assign by what may be discovered by reason and experiment. To this end we must consider, that *any kind of power or virtue, proceeding or propagated from a body in right lines every way as from a centre, must decrease in its energy or strength as the squares of the distances from the body increase*; for 'tis evident, the force will be every where as the number of particles issuing from the central body on a given space, which number of particles will decrease as the squares of the distances increase. Thus the number of particles which at any one *distance A B*, from a point in the body at *A*, falls on a square inch *B E F G*, will be *four times* as great as the number which falls on a square inch *C H I K* at *twice* that distance *A C*; and *nine times* as great as the number which falls on the said square inch *D L M N* at *three times* that distance *A D*; and so on. . . .

Hence, since we have no reason to doubt but that all kinds of attraction consist in fine imperceptible particles or invisible effluvia, which proceed from every point in the surface of the attracting body, in all right-lined directions every way, which in the progress lighting on other bodies urge and sollicit them towards the superior attracting body; therefore the force or intensity of the attracting power in general must always decrease as the squares of the distances increase.[62]

Martin said that light is "a real body, or distinct species of matter" and "consists of inconceivably small particles of matter of different magnitudes, which are emitted or reflected from every point in the surface of a luminous body in right lines, and in all directions, with an unparalled velocity, and whose power or intensity decreases as the squares of the distances increase." This was presumably "manifest" from experiment, which shows amply that "light is a material substance." First of all light "has motion, or is propagated in time." It acts upon bodies, and it produces "great alterations and changes in their natures and forms." Light, furthermore, is something that bodies act upon," because bodies reflect, inflect, and refract light "on their surfaces, and in their pores." As a body, light should have weight, as well as other "sensible qualities" of ordinary matter. And so it does, but the "smallness of its quantity" makes the weight of the particles of light and other "sensible qualities" entirely imperceptible to us.[63]

Martin's attempts to present the corpuscularity of light "from phenomena" were no more successful than Newton's. Franklin was able to dispose of this particular hypothesis by raising against it Newton's own arguments.

Martin, in another work, asked: "What kind of hypotheses, and how qualified, do you allow may be used in philosophy?" The The reply consisted of eight "qualifications"; a legitimate hypothesis must have "most or all" of them:

1. They must be agreeable to just reasoning.
2. They must be necessary for want of experience.
3. They must be consentaneous to experience.
4. They must be sufficient to satisfy the phænomena.
5. They must be naturally adapted to the case.
6. They must be possible on every account.
7. They must be probable in their own nature.
8. They must be free from all suspicion of prejudice, affection, or prepossession, in their author.[64]

In the next chapter, it will be seen that Newton's hypotheses met these eight qualifications. Next, it will be shown how Franklin learned about them. And then it will be possible to see how Franklin's own hypotheses grew out of the Newtonian framework of ideas which he had encountered just prior to undertaking research in electricity.

SOURCES

The discussion of Newton's physical principles as developed in the *Principia* is based chiefly on an analysis and comparison of the three editions published under his supervision. I shall not list here the many authors who have assumed that the phrase *Hypotheses non fingo* characterizes the whole of the *Principia*, or those who have stated Newton's supposed abhorrence of the very word *hypothesis*, much less the books in which the famous phrase is used to describe Newton's concept of science, presumably from the very beginning and in all his works. Of the greatest value in studying the *Principia* are the many commentaries, too numerous to list here, of which a number are listed in the general bibliography. But for the special point of view developed in this chapter, Edleston's splendid edition of Newton's correspondence with Cotes, Edleston (1850), is of the utmost value, as are Rigaud (1838) and Ball (1893). Bloch (1908), Metzger (1938), Rosenberger (1895) and Brunschvicg (1949) contain valuable insights, as does Burtt (1932). Many important documents relating to this topic are printed in Brewster (1855) and Rigaud (1841). The series of articles published by Jourdain, although somewhat derivative from secondary sources, contain a mine of useful details and provide perspective on the use of hypotheses by Newton.

The development of celestial mechanics and fluid mechanics after Newton has been described in Todhunter (1873 and 1886); for the latter subject, however, I am particularly indebted to the more recent penetrating research of Truesdell, especially Truesdell (1954).

The books of Whewell contain much of value on Newton's use of hypotheses. The subject of the proper use of hypotheses in science has been discussed by many scientists and philosophers and the pejorative sense of the word has been developed by the "positivists": Comte's philosophy is summarized in Martineau (1855), and the reader may also consult Frank (1949), Mach (1911 and 1919), and Mises (1951). In the development of my own thinking on the philosophical aspect of the topic, I have found the following works particularly helpful: Einstein's autobiography in Schilpp (1949), Duhem (1954), Hobson (1923), Meyerson (1931), Nunn (1907), Poincaré (1929), Weyl (1949).

Many of the ideas presented in this chapter derive from conversations with M. A. Koyré and from lectures given by him; see the discussion of the first edition of the *Principia* in Koyré (1955). I have also profited from a discussion of these topics with the late Albert Einstein; see Cohen (1955c). The publications on Newton by Andrade have been most illuminating. Dr. George Sarton kindly allowed me to read his doctoral dissertation on Newton's mechanics, Sarton (1911). For Newton's mathematics there is an admirable account in Turnbull (1945).

References to the *Principia* have been made, in general, by "book," "theorem," "problem," and "scholium," save where the text of a particular edition has been cited. The English translations have been taken from Florian Cajori's version of Andrew Motte's translation, Newton (1934) except for quotations from the first edition.

REFERENCES

1. See Newton, 1952: intro., p. xii.
2. Thomson, 1930: 13.
3. Newton, 1952.
4. Crew, 1935: 127.
5. *Principia*, bk. II, corollaries to prop. xxiv; Newton, 1934: 304. Also bk. III, prop. vi; Newton, 1934: 411.
6. *Ibid.*, bk. I, sect. xii, props. lxx sqq.
7. Martin, 1738: 1: 33-35.
8. *Opticks*, bk. I, scholium to prop. i; *Newton*, 1952: 25.
9. See Newton, 1952: intro., p. liv, n. 28.
10. See *Principia*, bk. III.
11. *Opticks*, bk. I; Newton, 1952: 1.
12. See Dieckmann, 1943.
13. Diderot, 1875*b*: 460-463.
14. Rigaud, 1838: 24.
15. They are printed in Brewster, 1855: 1: 464-465.
16. *Ibid.*, 465.
17. "Advertisement" (16 July 1717) to the second edition of the *Opticks*; Newton, 1952: cxv.
18. Desaguliers, 1734-1744: 1: preface.
19. Andrade, 1947: 12
20. *Principia*, bk. II, prop. xxiii & scholium; Newton, 1934: 300-302.
21. Diderot, 1875*a*: 38-39 §§XL-XLI; see Dieckmann and Cohen, 1955.
22. Hales, 1738; see Newton, 1952: preface, pp. xviii-xix.
23. See Gray, 1907: 22-35, 41-45; Babson Collection, 1950: 21-65, 73-83.
24. Newton, 1952: 369, 396.
25. Opening sentence of *Principia*, bk. III; Newton, 1934: 397.
26. *Idem.*
27. Newton, 1934: 164.
28. *Ibid.*, 192.
29. *Ibid.*, 231; scholium following prop. xcvi, bk. I.
30. *Principia*, bk. II, sect. i; Newton, 1934: 235.
31. Newton, 1687: 245.
32. Newton, 1934: 244.
33. *Principia*, bk. II, sect. ii.
34. *Ibid.*, bk. II, sect. iii.
35. *Ibid.*, General Scholium at conclusion of bk. II, sect. vi; Newton, 1934: 316-326.
36. Newton, 1934: 353.
37. Newton, 1729*b*: 1: 184, 187; 1934: 385. In the 1729 version, prop. LI is incorrectly numbered as th. XXXVIII.
38. Whewell, 1860: 182.
39. *Principia*, bk. II, scholium to prop. LII; Newton, 1934: 393.
40. Prepared by J. C. Adams, it is printed in Brewster, 1855: 2: 549-556.
41. Mach 1919: 193.
42. Newton, 1934: 409.
43. *Ibid.*, 559-561.
44. Weyl, 1949: 100-101.
45. See Ball, 1893: 110.
46. Newton, 1934: 395-396.
47. Birch, 1756-1757: 4: 479, see More, 1934: 304.
48. A number of such references may be found in the *O. E. D.*, *s. v.* "hypothesis."
49. Newton, 1934: 550.
50. *Ibid.*, 546-547.
51. Edleston, 1850: 155.

52. *Ibid.*, 153.
53. *Ibid.*, 154.
54. Partington, 1949: 1: 731.
55. Bk. III, qu. 28; Newton, 1952: 370.
56. Edleston, 1850: 147, 155.
57. *Ibid.*, 147.
58. *Ibid.*, 156.
59. More, 1934: 554.
60. See Mach, 1919; Hertz, 1899.
61. *Opticks*, bk. II, pt. III, prop. VII; Newton, 1952: 261.
62. Martin, 1747: 1: preface; 12.
63. *Ibid.* 2: 129.
64. Martin, 1738: 20.

CHAPTER SIX

EXPERIMENTAL NEWTONIANISM AND THE ROLE OF HYPOTHESES: THE "EXACT" CORPUSCULAR PHILOSOPHY OF THE *OPTICKS*

> The investigation of the mode in which the minute particles of bodies act on each other is rendered more difficult from the fact that both the bodies we consider and their distances are so small that we cannot perceive or measure them, and we are therefore unable to observe their motions as we do those of planets. . . . Hence the investigations of molecular science have proceeded for the most part by the method of hypothesis, and comparison of the results of the hypothesis with the observed facts. The success of this method depends on the generality of the hypothesis we begin with. If our hypothesis is the extremely general one that the phenomena to be investigated depend on the configuration and motion of a material system, then if we are able to deduce any available results from such an hypothesis, we may safely apply them to the phenomena before us.
>
> If, on the other hand, we frame the hypothesis that the configuration, motion, or action of the material system is of a certain definite kind, and if the results of this hypothesis agree with the phenomena, then, unless we can prove that no other hypothesis would account for the phenomena, we must still admit the possibility of our hypothesis being a wrong one.
>
> —J. Clerk Maxwell (1876)

In A BRILLIANT ARTICLE of a few years past, Alexandre Koyré—one of the outstanding historians of scientific thought in our day—has reminded us that a complete analysis of the *Principia* indicates the dependence of Newton's system of the world on a corpuscular view of nature.[1] We cannot, in other words, understand the creation of Newton's dynamics of the universe unless we are cognizant of the continuous background of Newton's atomism, even though the geometric presentation in the *Principia* may tend to mask the major preconceptions. The dependence of Newton's dynamical ideas on his atomism was probably more obvious to his contemporaries * than to us. The scientists of the eighteenth century gener-

---

* In his *Sermons preached at Boyle's lecture*, Bentley (Sermon VII, preached 7 Nov. 1692) showed that according to the Newtonian doctrine, "all bodies weigh

ally recognized that Newton was the major exponent of the corpuscular philosophy, in a new and exact form. What Newton had accomplished was to give some means of estimating (perhaps only guessing) from experimental data the physical properties of the corpuscles, if not the atoms, of which bodies are made: their size and shape, and the kinds of short-range forces that might be acting between them. Thus Newton had gone beyond Bacon and Boyle and had transformed their atomic or corpuscular view of nature into a semi-quantitative or a kind of " exact " science. This magnificent achievement was to be found described chiefly in the *Opticks*.

The first edition of the *Opticks* was published in English in 1704, and it did not contain the Queries (17-23) about the nature of the æther; nor were they among the new Queries in the Latin edition of 1706, prepared at Newton's suggestion by S. Clarke. But when Newton reprinted the concluding General Scholium in edition three of the *Principia* (1726), his speculations on the æther had already been in print for nine years and they included a discussion of the æther as a possible cause of gravity—a topic which was deliberately omitted from the concluding sentences of the new edition of the *Principia*. In point of fact, when the second English edition of the *Opticks* appeared (1717), Newton drew the reader's attention to his speculations on the nature of gravity, by adding an " advertisement " stating in part: " And to shew that I do not take gravity for an essential property of bodies, I have added one question concerning its cause. . . ." In this matter, Newton seems to have indicated for us the fundamentally differing character of his two books: the *Principia* as a rigorous, closely-knit mathematico-deductive system, with an avoidance of speculation, and the *Opticks* as a more loosely joined work, based on experiment rather than on mathematical deduction, and characterized by a generous speculative attitude, enabling the reader to share with the author his most cherished hypotheses on the nature of matter and force and the cause of major phenomena of the external world.

In the end of the preceding chapter, a brief outline of the *Principia* was presented, with an emphasis on the role of hypotheses in that book. This analysis was necessary in order to allow a discussion of Newton's hypotheses; if Newton did not wholly eschew hypotheses in the book in which he stated *Hypotheses non fingo*, we need not be afraid to seek out his hypotheses in the *Opticks*. It was the latter book, as I have indicated, which was the major inspiration

according to their matter," and " since gravity is found proportional to the quantity of matter, there is a manifest necessity of admitting a *vacuum*, another principal doctrine of the atomical philosophy." [2]

for the Newtonian experimental scientists of the eighteenth century and it was the *Opticks*, not the *Principia*, which Franklin could, and did read. In this chapter, I shall present the *Opticks* in terms of certain aspects of it that influenced the eighteenth-century speculative and experimental movement in the physical sciences, to which Franklin belonged and of which he proved to be a most notable example. Since the aim is to understand Franklin's contribution to scientific thought in relation to the Newtonian tradition, and to clarify the various aspects of that tradition by placing Franklin in the character that his own age ascribed to him, I have made no attempt to describe the *Opticks* from the rather strict point of view of the history of our knowledge of optical phenomena. Furthermore, since by Franklin's time, the *Opticks* was being read extensively, I have not devoted much space to Newton's earlier optical publications in the *Philosophical Transactions*.†Finally, consistent with the aim of presenting Newton as the eighteenth century knew him, I have not attempted to show " what Newton thought "—in terms of letters and other documents which were not printed until after about 1750, save for an occasional document which may clarify an issue in an important way. But I have made extensive use of letters and notes of Newton's which were available and in print prior to 1750: mainly his famous letter to Boyle, the hypothesis he submitted to the Royal Society during the first controversy on light and color and which was not printed during his lifetime, his letters to Bentley, and *De Natura Acidorum*.[3] I have, in other words, chiefly presented the Newtonian documents which were available to Franklin, which he either certainly or probably read, and which could therefore have influenced the growth of his own thinking and that of the other men of his age.

The Opticks: *" Proof by Experiments "*

The *Opticks* is composed of three " books." The first opens with the statement that in this particular book Newton's design " is not to explain the properties of light by hypotheses, but to propose and prove them by reason and experiments." ‡ It begins with a series of

---

† Newton's " optical lectures " which he gave as Lucasian Professor were published posthumously in English (1728) and in Latin (1729). The physical doctrine they contain had already been published in the early papers in the *Philosophical Transactions* and the *Opticks*, although certain aspects of geometric optics are to be found only in these lectures.

‡ It may be observed that both the *Principia* and the *Opticks* were divided into three " books." In the " advertisement " to the first edition of the *Opticks* (1 April 1704), Newton called the whole work a " discourse about light "; the title was *Opticks: or, a treatise of the reflections, refractions, inflections and colours of light.*

definitions of primary concepts, such as the angle of incidence, the angle of reflection or refraction. There follows a series of " axioms," which are the results of experiment, such as that the angle of reflection equals the angle of incidence, or that the sine of the angle of incidence is in a constant ratio to the sine of the angle of refraction for any two media.§ Reading through the introductory discussion, one cannot help being struck by the difference in intrinsic interest for the average reader between even the most technical parts of this book and the *Principia*. Almost immediately the reader of the *Opticks* learns why some people need eyeglasses, the difference between shortsightedness and farsightedness and the general phenomena of presbyopia,[5] how to find out just where the image of an object will be behind a mirror, and so on. In the axioms, and the pages devoted to their " explication," Newton gave what he described as " the sum of what has hitherto been treated of in opticks." [6]

Then come the propositions, of which the first is the famous one, stating: " Lights which differ in colour, differ also in degrees of refrangibility." Immediately, contrast with the *Principia* becomes apparent in " The PROOF by Experiments "—not by geometry or logical deductions from first principles. At the end of the experiments, Newton observed that he had set down all the circumstances so that " a novice might more easily try them." [7] Next comes Proposition II, Theorem II, " The light of the sun consists of rays differently refrangible." Here again we find " The PROOF by Experiments." The contrast to the *Principia* continues and is marked throughout the whole of the *Opticks*, as proposition after proposition is demonstrated by experiment rather than geometry or logic. Newton's discussion of Proposition VII contains mathematical computa-

In that original " advertisement " Newton referred twice to " the third book." In the " advertisement " to " this second edition of these *Opticks* " (16 July 1717) he referred again to the " third book." The " preface " to the first edition of the *Principia* (8 May 1686) described the work as a " treatise " (". . . in hoc tractatu . . .") and the parts as " books " (" Et huc spectant propositiones generales quas libro primo & secundo pertractavimus. In libro autem tertio . . ."), as he did also in the preface to the second edition (28 March 1713).

It is usually assumed that the " design " stated in Part I of " The First Book of Opticks " was intended to apply to all three " books," but a critical examination indicates that in both the second and third " books " the " properties of light " are discussed in terms of " hypotheses," as well as " by reason and experiments." Furthermore, since Newton usually meant by " book " one of the three parts of his two major treatises, I believe we must follow his custom and assume that the statement of " design " in Book One referred specifically to Book One in which it appeared.

§ Whereas Newton had stated expressly that the *Principia* had been designed for the reader previously initiated into mathematics, the axioms in the *Opticks* were explained in such simple terms and in so complete a fashion as to " suffice for an introduction to readers of quick wit and good understanding not yet versed in opticks. . . ." [4]

tions, such as also appear elsewhere in the book, but the non-mathematical reader may skip them.

At one point in the *Opticks*, Newton noted in the course of a verbal discussion that is really of a mathematical character, " The demonstration mathematicians will easily find out, and therefore I shall not trouble the reader with it." [8] Plainly, the *Opticks* had no mathematical prerequisites as the *Principia* had. In certain propositions, Newton's proof might invoke deductions based upon earlier experiments, but the argument always went back to experiments, and to reasoning about experiments from the first principles.

One of the major propositions in Book One states: " The sine of [the angle of] incidence of every ray considered apart, is to its sine of refraction in a given ratio." Newton was proud to note that the demonstration of it was " general," in that it took into account neither what light is nor by what kind of force its refraction may be produced; no assumption whatever was made save " that the refracting body acts upon the rays in lines perpendicular to its surface "—a " very convincing argument of the full truth of this proposition." [9] Evidently Newton wished to avoid any disparagement or even rejection of this proposition on the possible ground of the assumption, however tacit or unintended, of an hypothesis, such as that light is a " body," a " substance," or a stream of corpuscles. Even in 1704 Newton could remember all too well the controversies engendered by his first publication in physics, the discussion of the nature of white light and color, which he had called a " new theory of light and colours," and his annoyance at having his own " theory " or " doctrine " referred to as an " hypothesis." When Pardies had called the new " doctrine an hypothesis," Newton had replied, " I believe it only proceeded from his using the word which first occurred to him, as a practice has arisen of calling by the name hypothesis whatever is explained by philosophy: and the reason of my making exception to the word, was to prevent the prevalence of a term, which might be prejudicial to true philosophy." [10] Newton's avowed aim had been to prove certain properties of light by experiment and if he " had not considered them as true," he wrote, " I would rather have rejected them as vain and empty speculation than acknowledged even, as an hypothesis." [11] Even so, the contradictory quality of Newton's mind is indicated by the fact that immediately before chiding Pardies for using the term hypothesis, he indicated that hypotheses have their uses:

For the best and safest method of philosophizing seems to be, first diligently to investigate the properties of things, and establish them by experiment, and then to seek hypotheses to explain them. For hypotheses ought to be fitted merely to explain the properties of things, and not attempt to predetermine them except in so far as they can be an aid to experiments.[12]

This admirable advice certainly characterized Newton's thought in physics and may be taken as a kind of epitome of eighteenth-century experimental procedure in physical science. Furthermore, it must be pointed out that from the days of his original paper on light and color, Newton had maintained an obvious preference for the hypotheses of the corpuscularity of light—although, in a disclaimer, Newton wrote that ". . . from my theory I argue the corporeity of light, but I do it without any absolute positiveness . . . ," [13] the degree of positiveness is not as relevant as Newton's admission.

When Newton first allowed the *Opticks* to be printed, all those who had objected to his first optical publication were dead. Book One had certainly been written long before publication, when some of the objectors were still alive, which may well account for the guarded tone, in contrast to the rest of the treatise, and the bold introductory statement against hypotheses. Be that as it may, the readers of Book One would reap a wonderful harvest of delight since the conclusion would explain fully to them the formation of the primary and secondary rainbow and the reason why colored objects present to our eyes the particular colors they do.

Light as the Key to the Constitution of Bodies

The first book of the *Opticks*, comprising about one half of the whole work, may be described as an account of the properties of light and color. Newton said at the beginning of the second book that he had not yet treated of the colors formed by thin plates, " because they seemed of a more difficult consideration, and were not necessary for establishing the properties of light there discoursed of." [14] But now he could no longer avoid that difficult subject, because such colors are related to some important discoveries for " compleating the theory of light," and " especially as to the constitution of the parts of natural bodies." [15] So that the reader might not be put off by complex explanations, Newton began with observations or experiments, without drawing very many conclusions from them. He described how he had pressed two prisms close together and had noted the formation of colored rings which are now known by Newton's name. He also produced " Newton's rings " by pressing together two object glasses from telescopes, one plano-convex and the other bi-convex. The observations of these rings comprise the first part of Book Two. The second part contains " remarks upon the

foregoing observations ": [16] an attempt to show, amongst other
things, " that there is a constant relation between colours and refrangibility; the most refrangible rays being violet, the least refrangible red, and those of the intermediate colours having proportion-
ably intermediate degrees of refrangibility." [17] He showed " that the
colorifick dispositions of rays are also connate with them, and immutable; and by consequence, that all the productions and appearances of colours in the world are derived, not from any physical
change caused in light by refraction or reflexion, but only from the
various mixtures or separations of rays, by virtue of their different
refrangibility or reflexibility." [18] Then, Newton introduced a famous
statement, which is often quoted, " And in this respect the science of
colours becomes a speculation as truly mathematical as any other
part of opticks. I mean, so far as they [colours] depend on the nature
of light, and are not produced or altered by the power of imagination, or by striking or pressing the eye." The sense of a " speculation " becoming " mathematical " is not immediately perceived.
Perhaps what Newton intended was that color theory might become
as certain as dioptrics and catoptrics, the geometric part of the
subject.*

In Part II of the second book, Newton was not yet ready to use
his observations of the colors of thin plates " to unfold the causes
of the colours of natural bodies." [20] First he had to use " the simplest " of his observations to " explain the more compounded." In
the course of this " explanation " he introduced some tables of quan-

---

* A report by Hooke on Newton's paper on light and colors was read at the Royal
Society on 15 Feb. 1671/2: Hooke said, in part, " I cannot think it be the only
hypothesis, nor so certain as mathematical demonstrations." In reply, Newton wrote:
". . . In the last place, I should take notice of a casual expression, which intimates
a greater certainty in these things, than I ever promised, *viz. the certainty of Mathematical demonstrations.* I said, indeed, that the science of colours was mathematical,
and as certain as any other part of Optics; but who knows not that Optics, and many
other mathematical sciences, depend as well on physical sciences, as on mathematical
demonstrations? And the absolute certainty of a science cannot exceed the certainty of
its principles. Now the evidence, by which I asserted the propositions of colours, is in
the next words expressed to be from experiments, and so but physical: whence the
Propositions themselves can be esteemed no more than physical principles of a science.
And if those principles be such, that on them a mathematician may determine all
the phænomena of colours, that can be caused by refractions, and that by disputing or
demonstrating after what manner, and how much, those refractions do separate or
mingle the rays, in which several colours are originally inherent; I suppose the
science of colours will be granted mathematical, and as certain as any part of Optics.
And that this may be done, I have good reason to believe, because ever since I became
first acquainted with these principles, I have, with constant success in the events,
made use of them for this purpose.

" Thus much I have thought fit to return to Mr. *Hooke's* considerations, which, that
it may bring satisfaction in this part of Optics to the honourable members of the
Royal Society, hath been the rule of my intensions. Yours, &c." [19]

titative data and a little geometry, but concluded that " as all these things follow from the properties of light by a mathematical way of reasoning, so the truth of them may be manifested by experiments." [21] An account of such experiments is then given. Generally free of speculations, this Part II has only two references to anything hypothetical. One invokes the æther: a statement that " the unequal refractions of difform rays proceed not from any contingent irregularities; such as are veins, an uneven polish, or fortuitous position of the pores of the glass; unequal and casual motions in the air or æther, . . ." [22]

The " pores " in glass were a necessary consequence of atomism, but the " æther " was—in Newton's words—an hypothesis. Of far greater interest is the subtle introduction of light waves of a sort, but with no reference whatever to a medium in which such waves might exist; there is no expressed " subject " of the verb " to undulate." By " what hath been said," Newton wrote, " the like phænomena of water and thin plates of glass may be understood. But in small fragments of those plates there is this farther observable, that where they lie flat upon the table, and are turned about their centers whilst they are viewed with a prism, they will in some postures exhibit waves of various colours. . . ." Newton may have intended " waves " to mean merely a " succession " of colored regions and not " light waves " corresponding to the several colors. Yet such expressions, as the " very small and narrower parts of the glass [prism], by which these waves for the most part are caused," [23] are confusing to the critical reader—and all the more so in that some pages later Newton compared the waves in the hypothesized æther to water waves.

The third part of the second book deals with the permanent colors of natural bodies and " the analogy between them " and the colors produced by thin transparent plates. [24] Newton had concluded that the reason why bodies appear to have their various colors is their disposition to reflect most " copiously " the " rays originally imbued with those colours ": as we would say today, they tend to reflect selectively certain wave lengths or frequencies. But now, said Newton, the " constitutions " of bodies, which must produce the property of reflecting " some rays more copiously than others," is still to be discovered; and " these I shall endeavour to manifest in the following propositions." [25] Here we encounter propositions that are truly speculative, such as Proposition V, which states that according to their several sizes, the " transparent parts " of bodies will reflect rays of one color and transmit those of another—which Newton takes " to be the ground of all their colours." [26] And so Newton is led to his

Proposition VII, which states that by the colors of natural bodies we may "conjecture" the "bigness" of their component parts.[27] The first order is whiteness, followed by the order of scarlets and other reds, oranges and yellows, then greens, and perhaps blues and purples, while "for the production of black, the corpuscles must be less than any of those which exhibit colours." Hence, we may see how the development of subjects in the *Opticks* led Newton to the fundamental investigation of the nature of matter itself. Bodies turn out to be "much more rare and porous than is commonly believed." [28] Even the metal gold is so rare as to "transmit the magnetick effluvia" without the least opposition, and the magnet may act upon iron "through all dense bodies not magnetick nor red hot, without any diminution of its virtue; as for instance, through gold, silver, lead, glass, water."

In this portion of Book Two of the *Opticks*, we may see Newton developing the "exact" form of the "corpuscular philosophy" which was considered in the eighteenth century to be one of his greatest achievements. "Most probably," [29] said Newton, the "parts of natural bodies" exhibit the same colors as a "plate of equal thickness, provided they have the same refractive density." The "diameter of a corpuscle" of "equal density with glass" that "shall reflect green of the third order" is 0.001625 inch. In his discussion of the size of corpuscles producing the several colors of bodies, Newton was "the more particular, because it is not impossible but that miscroscopes may at length be improved to the discovery of the particles of bodies on which their colours depend, if they are not already in some measure arrived to that degree of perfection." [30] A simple computation indicated that an instrument that would represent objects "five or six hundred times bigger than at a foot distance they appear to our naked eyes" would enable us to see the biggest corpuscles, and one with a magnification of $3000\times$ or $4000\times$ would show us all but the very smallest, those that produce blackness. And yet, despite these remarkable conclusions, there was nothing "material" that Newton could see "that may rationally be doubted of" save for one "position": "that transparent corpuscles of the same thickness and density with a plate, do exhibit the same colour." This assumption comes under the category of an "hypothesis" in a physical argument. But this factor is of less interest to us than Newton's view of the nature of the corpuscles themselves, and the structure of bodies.

Newton argued that the one "position" that might be doubted should be "understood not without some latitude," because the corpuscles might have irregular shapes ("and many rays must be obliquely incident on them, and so have a shorter way through them than the length of their diameters ") and " because the straitness of the medium put in on all sides within such corpuscles may a little alter its motion [i. e., the motion of the light] or other qualities on which the reflexion [of the light] depends." This latter possibility was doubtful. Newton had observed that plates of Muscovy glass of even thickness showed the same color everywhere, even at the edges and corners when examined through a microscope, the very edges and corners " where the included medium was terminated." [31]

What medium, we must ask, is supposed to be " terminated " at the edges and corners of bodies? A kind of æther? And if so, is it the same æther that exists outside of bodies? ' Newton advanced the idea elsewhere that the only difference between the æther inside and outside of bodies is its density. Yet this property does not explain the sense of the previous statement, because the density was not assumed to change sharply at the boundaries of bodies but rather gradually, by imperceptible degrees. Some hidden thought is contained in Newton's statement, perhaps too radical an hypothesis for public display. But, immediately, as if to allay rising doubts, Newton said that " it will add much to our satisfaction if those corpuscles can be discovered with microscopes." [32] " For it seems impossible to see the more secret and noble works of nature within the corpuscles by reason of their transparency." Apparently, the corpuscles producing color might not necessarily be the ultimate atomic particles of which bodies are made. Are we to conclude that solid transparent bodies contain corpuscles in a medium which terminates at the boundary of the body, and that there is within each such corpuscle a second medium in which there are atoms or even sub-corpuscular structures built of atoms? Newton simply did not tell us at this point, although he returned to it a little later.†

Next Newton indicated that " the parts of bodies do act upon light at a distance." Reflection of light does not arise from an " immediate contact " of the ray from the body. If it did, we would not obtain regular reflection from a polished body, since the latter is never absolutely smooth but only has its " protuberances " broken, its " roughness " brought to a " very fine grain, so that the scratches and frettings of the surface become too small to be visible." [33]

Some rays are not reflected but are " stifled and lost " within the body. Hence we are led to the conclusion that bodies, though appearing solid, must be rare and porous. Water is nineteen times " lighter " than gold and thus " nineteen times rarer than gold." [34]

---

† Franklin, as we shall see in Chapter Eight, also wrote about media subsidiary to other media in terms very much like Newton's.

Gold, in fact, has " more pores than solid parts " and water has more than " forty times more pores than parts." These " parts " or " corpuscles " or " particles " may be composed " of other particles much smaller," and these in turn may be composed " of others much smaller " and " so on perpetually till you come to solid particles, such as have no pores or empty space within them." Newton's scheme is ingenious and is reduced to numbers, but he was forced to admit that " there are other ways of conceiving how bodies may be exceeding porous. But what is really their inward frame is not yet known to us." [35] However reasonable his arguments might be, they are speculative and they impress us chiefly as manifestations of the force of Newton's scientific imagination.

In Proposition X, Newton attempted to apply the previous considerations about the structure of bodies by attempting a study of the " refractive power " of different bodies considered in mathematical proportion to their density.[36] The refractive power he computed geometrically from the index of refraction for yellow light. The numbers he obtained in this manner for " the refractive power of the body in respect of its density " [37] vary from 3,979 to 14,556. Several substances which differ greatly in density—including a " pseudo-topaz," a " selenitis," rock crystal, calcite, vulgar glass (" that is, sand melted together ") and antimony glass, and air (" which probably arises from such substances by fermentation ") —were found to exhibit ratios between their densities and their refractive powers which are not very different. These ratios vary only from 3,979 to 6,536, although air is 3,500 times rarer than the " pseudo-topaz," 4,400 times rarer than antimony glass, and 2,000 times rarer than the " selenitis," the vulgar glass, or the rock crystal. Why should rare substances have approximately the same ratio of refractive power to density as those very much denser substances? Very likely, Newton thought, the answer lies in the observation that the difference between the members of the group depends only on the degree to which the respective bodies " partake more or less of sulphureous oily particles, and thereby have their refractive power made greater or less." So, from an attempt to relate properties of light to densities, Newton concluded that " it seems rational to attribute the refractive power of all bodies chiefly, if not wholly, to the sulphureous parts with which they abound. For it's probable that all bodies abound more or less with sulphurs." [38]

At this point we must pause for a moment to emphasize several aspects of the preceding discussion which assumed a great importance in the development of physical theory during the eighteenth century. First of all, there is Newton's firm conclusion about the porosity of solid, even incompressible matter. This was an essential postulate of any " fluid " theory of heat or electricity, since the particles of the fluid have to be lodged in the interstices between the particles of matter. We have seen that Newton indicated that " a medium " might exist between the corpuscles; if this medium were an elastic æther, then sanction of the Master was available for the supposition of a kind of " elastic fluid " existing inside solid bodies, lodged as it were in the pores. Since Newton held the view that light (a " body " or " substance ") entered bodies and was trapped within them, a Newtonian scientist—in the tradition of the *Opticks*—could well assume that the electric fluid or the caloric fluid of heat might also enter into bodies under proper conditions. Furthermore, the property of catching or trapping light varies, according to Newton, from one body to another because of structure and composition—the size and distribution of the corpuscles. So too, depending on the kind of body, there would be a more or less ready absorption of the electric fluid or caloric. Finally, the density of bodies was generally shown to be related to their optical properties and we shall see the attempt made to relate electrical and thermal properties of bodies to their density. An exception was noted by Newton in bodies containing sulphureous or unctuous matter, and this too was relevant to theories of electricity and heat. Thus we may see at once how Newton's *Opticks* became a great stimulus to the growth of the speculative experimental physical sciences of heat and electricity.

It is plain that Newton's optical studies led directly to a correlation of various properties of bodies. By studying refraction and reflection in relation to color, Newton indicated that density is a fundamental characteristic in relation to optical phenomena. Since density is a measure of the closeness of the packing of corpuscles, optics thus leads directly to the analysis of matter. Hence we may see that light is a key to the classification of the different kinds of matter and thus may be a fundamental tool of the chemist. Since thermal and electrical properties also serve to classify matter, the chemist must use optics, heat, and electricity to supplement his investigations of the changes in matter produced by chemical reactions. The abounding in " sulphureous parts " affects the " refractive power of all bodies " and is related to their possibility of combustion. Newton, therefore, was led at once to studies of light and chemistry. In the later eighteenth century it was generally agreed that chemistry alone would not suffice for the proper study of matter, but had to be pursued together with electricity and light. This point of view is stated plainly by Joseph Priestley, who said that the " study of chymistry seems to have led Mr. Boyle to attend

to electricity, as well as to other occult qualities of particular bodies."
Of all the branches of natural philosophy, Priestley added, none is
more useful to " the electrician " than chemistry—" for chymistry and
electricity are both conversant about the latent and less obvious
properties of bodies." An almost equally close link exists between
electricity and " the doctrine of light and colours," according to
Priestley, the latter branch of natural philosophy having been what
" Newton thought would be the key to other, at present, occult
properties of bodies." [39]

Hypotheses in the Opticks

In the foregoing account, we have seen the introduction by Newton of many explicit assumptions, or hypotheses. The nature of
hypothesis in the *Opticks* becomes even clearer in the famous discussion of conditions (" transient " constitutions or states) of " easy
reflection " and " easy refraction." Newton used the term " fits "
of easy refraction and " fits " of easy transmission to describe the
disposition of the ray to be reflected or transmitted. He stated that
he would not inquire (in Book Two) as to whether this action or
disposition consists " in a circulating or a vibrating motion of the
ray, or of the medium, or of something else." He noted, however,
that those who are

. . . averse from assenting to any new discoveries, but such as they can
explain by an hypothesis, may for the present suppose, that as stones
falling upon water put the water into an undulating motion, and all
bodies by percussion excite vibrations in the air; so the rays of light, by
impinging on any refracting or reflecting surface, excite vibrations in the
refracting or reflecting medium or substance, and by exciting them agitate the solid parts of the refracting or reflecting body, and by agitating them cause the body to grow . . . hot; that the vibrations thus excited
are propagated in the refracting or reflecting medium or substance, much
after the manner that vibrations are propagated in the air for causing
sound, and move faster than the rays so as to overtake them; and that
when any ray is in that part of the vibration which conspires with its
motion, it easily breaks through a refracting surface, but when it is in
the contrary part of the vibration which impedes its motion, it is easily
reflected; and, by consequence, that every ray is successively disposed to
be easily reflected, or easily transmitted, by every vibration which over-
takes it.[40]

Newton, however, did not at this point wish to consider whether any
such hypothesis were " true or false " but merely contented himself
with the bare discovery " that the rays of light are by some cause or
other alternately disposed to be reflected or refracted for many vicis-

situdes." It is important to note that Newton himself indicated that the explanation he offered without considerations of its truth or falsity *is* an "hypothesis." Later on in the *Opticks* he adopted it as his own view of the situation, thus plainly advocating an hypothesis.

Speculative Newtonian Experimental Science: The "Queries"

Book Three of the *Opticks* is composed only of a "Part I," of which the first portion contains Newton's experiments on "inflexion" or what we would call today the diffraction of light. He then proposed "some queries, in order to a farther search to be made by others." This section of Queries is beyond all doubt the most stimulating part of the book. The form of queries, we may note, allowed Newton to state his views on a great many subjects, without fear of argument or contradiction, and without any anxiety that an unkind adversary might accuse him of having held a particular hypothesis. Yet it is perfectly obvious to any reader today, as it was to many in the eighteenth century, that the questions are all phrased in the negative and are thus purely rhetorical questions rather than genuine interrogations. Newton did not ask, for example: "Do bodies perhaps act upon light at a distance?" Rather he stated: "Do not bodies act upon light at a distance?" [41] The answer, in any case, was plain to a reader of the *Opticks*, since he would have encountered earlier in the book a statement to this effect: "For that the parts of bodies do act upon light at a distance shall be shewn hereafter." [42] When Newton wrote: "Are not all hypotheses erroneous, in which light is supposed to consist in pression or motion, propagated through a fluid medium?" [43]—there was no doubt as to Newton's answer, especially since the discussion of this particular topic occupied about nine pages of argument and evidence to prove the point. Newton's rejection of this hypothesis arose from the proven fact that it led to results wholly inconsistent with the observed phenomena.

Newton, by his own testimony, placed in the Queries a discussion of topics for which there was not sufficient experiential data to give a positive answer. Even if we take the question form seriously (as Newton may possibly have expected his readers to do), then we have a set of hypotheses about which Newton asks: are they not true?—or, perhaps, are they not very probable? Some ‡ of Newton's disciples

---

‡ In view of Newton's personality, it is highly doubtful that he would have allowed to appear in print any statement, even a rhetorical query, which might show him in error. Good Newtonians like Desaguliers and Hales (both read by Franklin) saw that the query form was only a means for making a milder assertion than a proposition. Gregory was convinced that Newton believed in the answers to his queries which he indicated plainly. Whiston once said of Newton: "And when he did but propose conjectures in natural philosophy, he almost always knew them to be true at the same time." [44]

were convinced that Newton had expressed a positive opinion in each proposition stated as a query; thus we find Newton's action described as making an explanation by way of query.

The rather loose form of the *Opticks* permitted Newton to let himself go, so to speak, and to unburden himself of all the physical speculations that had been absorbing his mind for decades. The closely knit mathematical structure of the *Principia* would not permit him such a luxury, and his recognition that the *Opticks* was a repository for his untested (or untestable) ideas is demonstrated by the addition of further queries in each successive edition.§ And what a vast range was encompassed in these queries! They begin simply with (Qu. 1) the action of bodies on light "at a distance" to bend the rays to produce reflection, refractions, and "inflection" by "one and the same principle, acting variously in various circumstances." We may note here, in contrast to the *Principia*, that action-at-a-distance is admitted freely. Then there is (Qu. 5) a mutual action of bodies and light upon one another; bodies reflect, refract, and inflect light, and light heats bodies putting their parts into "a vibrating motion wherein heat consists." Black bodies (Qu. 6) most easily conceive heat from light because the light is not reflected outwards, but entering such bodies is reflected and refracted within them until "stifled and lost." Thus (Qu. 7), we may understand why sulphureous bodies are so easily ignited.* All bodies (Qu. 8) when heated to more than a certain temperature, will emit light and shine; this emission is "performed by the vibrating motion of their parts." Bodies which "abound with terrestrial parts . . . especially with sulphureous ones" emit light whenever those parts are "sufficiently agitated," whether by heat, friction, percussion, putrefaction, or any "vital" motion or any other cause. In Query 8, we find references to electrical phenomena: the light produced by a globe of glass, mounted on an axle in a frame, which will shine where it rubs against the palms of hands which may be applied to it. If, at the same time, the end of one's finger or a piece of white paper or cloth be held about a quarter of an inch to a half inch from the part of the glass most in motion

the electrick vapour which is excited by the friction of the glass against the hand, will by dashing against the white paper, cloth or finger, be put into such an agitation as to emit light, and make the white paper, cloth or finger, appear lucid like a glow-worm; and in rushing out of the

§ The best account of the alterations and additions to the queries in successive editions of the *Opticks* is to be found in the papers of Philip E. B. Jourdain; [45] there has never been a critical or variorum edition of the *Opticks*.

* This observation became particularly important in the eighteenth century, as we shall see in the next chapter.

glass will sometimes push against the fingers so as to be felt. And the same things have been found by rubbing a long and large cylinder of glass or amber with a paper held in one hand, and continuing the friction till the glass grew warm.†

Although heat, in Query 5, was said to consist of the vibrating motion of parts of bodies, in Query 9 the question is raised as to whether "fire" is not merely a body "heated so hot as to emit light copiously?" A "red hot iron" is nothing else than "fire," and a "burning coal" is nothing else than "red hot wood." In Query 10, we are told that flame is a vapor, fume or exhalation which is heated red hot, "that is, so hot as to shine." This is followed by a two-page chemical discussion of the heat evolved in chemical reactions, fumes, smoke, light and heat. Query 11 contains an amplification of the previous discussion, with reference to boiling water or heating a mixture of tin and lead in air and in vacuo, with application to the general problem of the origin and continuation of heat in the sun and fixed stars. Query 12 introduces, as the cause of seeing, vibrations which are propagated along the solid fibres of the optic nerve into the brain, such vibrations being excited by the rays of light which fall upon "the bottom of the eye" and excite vibrations in the *tunica retina*.

The several sorts of rays make (Qu. 13) "vibrations of several bignesses, which according to their bignesses excite sensations of several colours, much after the manner that the vibrations of the air, according to their several bignesses excite sensations of several sounds." The harmony and discord of colors (Qu. 14) may arise from the proportions of the vibrations "propagated through the fibres of the optick nerves into the brain," just as the harmony and discord of sound arise "from the proportions of the vibrations of the air." Query 15 contains an explanation of binocular vision, and Query 16 introduces and accounts for persistence of vision and the visual sensations produced by pressing the eye with a finger.

Newton's Grand Hypothesis on the Æther

Query 17 (and Qu. 18-23) appeared for the first time in the second English edition of 1717, reprinted 1718. In them we find Newton's hypothesis about waves being "excited in the refracting or reflecting medium by the rays of light." The "fits" of easy reflection and easy transmission, which Newton introduced into Book Two, were hypothetical properties at best, although the term "fits" does seem to describe the alternate bands of brightness and darkness.

---

† These observations of Newton's derive from the experiments of Hauksbee.[46]

In Book Two, however, Newton had stated explicitly that the " hypothesis " (his own term) of waves producing the " fits " had been introduced only because some readers would not accept any discovery unless an " hypothesis " were advanced to supply a cause, and that he had presented this particular " hypothesis " without any regard whatever for its truth or falsity. But in Query 17, he gave very convincing arguments to support the hypothesis that the waves " overtake the rays of light, and by overtaking them successively, . . . put them into the fits of easy reflexion and easy transmission described above."

Throughout the Queries in Book Three of the *Opticks*, Newton indicated at least two degrees of probability for his speculations and hypotheses. I pointed out earlier that most of the Queries demand " Is not . . . ? " or " Are not . . . ? " or " Do not . . . ? " Yet some few use an expression which indicates plainly a lesser certainty. In Query 14, for example, Newton did not write: Do not the harmony and discord of colours arise from the proportions of the vibrations propagated through the fibres of the optick nerves into the brain . . . ? as in Query 13 he had written, " Do not several sorts of rays make vibrations of several bignesses, which according to their bignesses excite sensations of several colours . . . ? " Rather, when he came to Query 14, he carefully said: " May [!] not the harmony and discord of colours arise . . .? " In Query 17, he stated as a phenomenon that when a stone is thrown into water, waves are produced in the medium (water) and continue to spread to great distances after the stone has passed by, a phenomenon supposedly similar to the air waves produced by percussion. In a like manner, " may [!] not " waves be excited in the reflecting or refracting medium at the point of incidence whenever a ray of light " falls on the surface of any pellucid body, and is there refracted or reflected? " Such waves continue and spread to great distances and are similar to the waves excited in the eye by the pressure of a finger. And " do [!] they not overtake the rays of light, and by overtaking them successively, do they not put them into the fits of easy reflexion and easy transmission described above? " Note the curious variations with respect to certainty. First: water waves *are* produced by the motion of a stone. Then: *may not* rays of light cause waves in a medium in a like manner. But next, as Newton warmed up to his subject: *do not* the waves overtake the rays, and *do they not* put the rays into the stated fits? Presumably, the use of the words " may not " was intended to convey doubt only about such waves being produced in a manner similar to the water waves, and not so great an uncertainty about the possible existence of light waves.

Query 18 begins with an account of an experiment in which two jars (one evacuated and one full of air) containing thermometers were carried from a cold place to a warm one; the thermometer in vacuo "will grow warm as much, and almost as soon as the thermometer which is not in vacuo." The two thermometers cooled off with apparently the same speeds when they were carried back to the cold place. Thus Newton was led to argue that "the heat of the warm room [is] conveyed through the vacuum by the vibrations of a subtiler medium than air, which after the air was drawn out remained in the vacuum." This medium is the same as that by means of which light is refracted and reflected, put into fits of easy reflection and easy transmission, "and by whose vibrations light communicates heat to bodies." This medium is much more subtle or rare than air, and much more "elastick and active"; it readily pervades all bodies and, by "its elastick force," it is expanded through all the heavens. In Query 19 Newton developed the properties of this "ætherial medium." The cause of the refraction of light is simply "the different density of this æthereal medium in different places, the light receding always from the denser parts of the medium." The density is greater in "free and open spaces void of air and other grosser bodies" than it is inside the pores of "compact bodies" such as water, glass, crystal, and gems; were this not so, there could be no internal reflection in such transparent substances.‡ We are told in Query 20: in passing out of water, or glass or crystal or any other body, into the empty spaces beyond such bodies, the æthereal medium grows denser in a continuous variation; thus light is refracted only by gradual degrees. The æther reaches its full density only at some distance from the edges of bodies; the density gradient near bodies is the cause of inflexion or the bending of light.

Query 21 relates the æther to the heavens at large. We are told that this medium is rarer within the "dense bodies of the sun, stars, planets and comets, than in the empty celestial spaces between them." From these bodies to great distances, the æther grows denser and denser "perpetually," and thereby causes "the gravity [attraction] of those great bodies towards one another, and of their parts towards the bodies; every body endeavouring to go from the denser parts of the medium towards the rarer." Within the body of the sun the æther is much rarer than at the surface, and at the surface it is rarer than at one-hundredth of an inch from the surface, and rarer still at the distance of Saturn from the sun. Newton "saw no reason

‡ This is Newton's hypothesis of the æther, varying in density continuously from the interior of bodies to outer space. This hypothesis was presented by Newton on numerous occasions. We shall, in the next chapter, see its application by eighteenth-century physical scientists to problems of heat, electricity, light, and chemistry.

why the increase of density should stop any where, and not rather be continued through all distances from the Sun to Saturn, and beyond." The rate by which the æther density increases may diminish greatly at great distances, but if the elastic force be large enough, " it may suffice to impel bodies from the denser parts of the medium towards the rarer, with all that power which we call gravity." Newton computed that the elastic force of the æther was to its density more than 490,000,000,000 greater than the ratio of the elastic force of the air to its density, which was probably sufficient to account for gravitation.[47]

In proportion to their bulk, Newton observed, attraction is stronger in small magnets than in large ones: just as gravity is relatively greater in the surfaces of small planets than in large ones, and the force of " electric attraction " agitates small bodies more than large ones, and " the smallness [of the particles?] of the rays of light may contribute very much to the power of the agent by which they are refracted." Now, said Newton, " I do not know what this æther is." Yet " if any one should suppose that *æther* (like our air) may contain particles which endeavour to recede from one another, . . . and that its particles are exceedingly smaller than those of air, or even than those of light," then the smallness of these æther particles may contribute to their elastic force (" the force by which those particles may recede from one another ") and thus make the æther so elastic and rare that it will not resist the motion of projectiles and yet be able to " press upon gross bodies, by endeavouring to expand it self." Having shown in the *Principia* that the Cartesian æther must be banished from natural philosophy, Newton then introduced an æther of his own, at once more " elastick " and more " subtle " than Descartes'.

How (Qu. 22) can a medium, " this æther (for so I will call it) ," be so rare? For it does not produce enough resistance to make any " sensible alteration " in the motions of planets in 10,000 years. If any one should ask this question, (i. e., object to the hypothesis of the rarity of æther) said Newton, let him tell me " how an electrick body can by friction emit an exhalation so rare and subtile, and yet so potent, as by its emission to cause no sensible diminution of the weight of the electrick body, and to be expanded through a sphere, whose diameter is above two feet, and yet be able to agitate and carry up leaf copper, or leaf gold, at the distance of above a foot from the electrick body." Or, let such a doubter tell " how the effluvia of a magnet can be so rare and subtile, as to pass through a plate of glass without any resistance or diminution of their force, and yet [be] so potent as to turn a magnetick needle beyond the glass."

Here then is Newton's grand hypothesis on gravitation. Wholly apart from the general considerations which have indicated the validity of our calling the Queries a set of hypotheses, we have sufficient collateral evidence that this was Newton's " hypothesis " about the cause of gravity (which he would not " frame " in the *Principia*). We know that he was proud of it. At the height of the controversy raised by Newton's first physical publication, on light and colors, and in which the whole question of hypotheses had been raised by his commentators, Newton wrote out and sent to the Royal Society a long paper read serially at many meetings, which was entitled: " A theory of light and colours, containing partly an hypothesis to explain the properties of light discoursed of by him in his former papers, . . ." [48] After sending the paper in December 1675, Newton wrote to Oldenburg in a letter dated 25 January 1675/76 of the hope that " such an hypothesis would much illustrate the papers I promised to send you." [49] Although in this letter, Newton stated that he did not concern himself " whether it shall be thought probable or improbable," who can believe that Newton would have bothered to write out a long paper to be read at the Royal Society unless he believed the hypothesis it contained to be more than just barely probable? Furthermore, since Newton rewrote this hypothesis into several Queries for publication in the Latin edition of the *Opticks* (1706) and reprinted them in the second English edition of the *Opticks* (1717) and later editions, he apparently stuck to his notions about it for more than half a century.

This hypothesis contains Newton's " suggestion " about colors corresponding to wave-lengths of æther waves just as sounds correspond to wave-lengths of air waves. Assuming the " rays of light to be small bodies," Newton said they must excite " vibrations in the æther as stones do in water when thrown into it." Thus Newton offered an explanation of how, by exciting vibrations, reflection and refraction can be " explicated." He also applied the hypothesis to account for the production of heat by the sun's light, the emission of light from burning and putrefying substances, the phenomena of " thin transparent plates and bubbles," etc., and all the topics discussed in Queries 12 through 17 of the *Opticks*. Were Newton to assume an hypothesis, he wrote to the Royal Society, " it should be this, if propounded more generally so as not to determine what light is, further than that it is something or other capable of exciting vibrations in the æther." The chief supposition of the hypothesis is the existence of such an æther, not uniform, but composed of the " main phlegmatic body of æther " mixed with various other " vapours and exhalations." Such variety is indicated by " the electric and magnetic effluvia, and the gravitating principle."

I shall not attempt to summarize the many examples presented by Newton, in which this subtle, elastic, vibratory medium was invoked to explain the properties of light, most of which (with some new ones added) were repeated in the Queries of the *Opticks*, even the notion that " Ætherial vibrations are . . . the best means by which such a subtle agent as light can shake the gross particles of solid bodies to heat them." Here, as in Query 21, the æther is supposed to be rarer within solid bodies than in " the free ætherial spaces," and also to be operative in chemical reactions and in muscular motion. The latter topic, discussed again by Newton in Query 24, was introduced by Newton in 1675 in terms of a power in man to condense and dilate the æther in his muscles by the action of his will and hence produce a contraction or relaxation of his muscles. In the second English edition of the *Opticks* in 1717, Newton supposed that the " power of the will " excites vibrations of the æther in the brain and that these vibrations are transmitted along " the solid, pellucid and uniform capillamenta of the nerves into the muscles, for contracting and dilating them." [50]

The most interesting part of the hypothesis, from the point of view of eighteenth-century electrical theory, is Newton's account of electrical experiments and his indication that " electrical effluvia seem to instruct us that there is something of an ætherial nature condensed in bodies." But our interest in Newton's statement as a whole is that so large a part of the Queries added to the second edition of the *Opticks* deals with topics originally found in it. By one and the same concept, Newton sought to explain gravitation as well as the phenomena of light and colors and other topics.

These ideas were again written out by Newton in a letter to Boyle dated 28 February 1678/9.[51] The hypothesis sent to the Royal Society was first made available to eighteenth-century readers in Birch's *History of the Royal Society* in 1757, at which time the major aspects of it had been already made known through the presentation in the many editions of the *Opticks* and the letter to Boyle. The latter was first printed in Boyle's works, edited by Birch, in 1744,[52] and was reprinted in the mid-century by Bryan Robinson.[53] Here Newton apologized for his speculations (as was his wont), but he wrote them out just the same (as he always did). A considerable portion of this letter to Boyle is devoted to chemical subjects, an interest which Newton shared with Boyle. There is a corpuscular explanation of the action of " menstruums " on bodies; and the now familiar explanation of the bending (inflexion), reflection, and refraction of light is also present. We may note, too, that Newton included his explanation of the colors of bodies resulting from the size of their particles.

This letter contains a fine statement of the way in which Newton supposed the æther to produce gravitation. This discussion is more detailed than that of the " hypothesis " of 1675/6 and Query 21 of the *Opticks*. The æther is said, as always, to be non-uniform and consisting of "parts differing from one another in subtilty by indefinite degrees." Thus the æther within bodies is rare and outside bodies is dense. From the center of the earth to the upper atmosphere, the æther changes continuously in density. Suppose a body lies on the surface of the earth or is suspended in the air above the earth. Then " the æther being by the hypothesis grosser in the pores, which are in the upper parts of the body, than in those which are in its lower parts, and that grosser æther being less apt to be lodged in those pores than the finer æther below, it will endeavour to get out and give way to the finer æther below, which cannot be, without the body's descending to make room above for it to go out into."

When the first edition of the *Principia* was being published, Newton corresponded with Halley about (amongst other matters) Hooke's claim to the discovery of the inverse-square law of gravitation. On 20 June 1686 Newton wrote to Halley, in defense of his own claim to discovery, that some ten or eleven years earlier there was registered in the books of the Royal Society " an hypothesis of mine " wherein " I hinted a cause of gravity towards the earth, sun, and planets, with the dependence of the celestial motions thereon; in which the proportion of the decrease of gravity from the superficies of the planet . . . can be no other than reciprocally duplicate of the distance from the centre. And I hope I shall not be urged to declare, in print, that I understood not the obvious mathematical conditions of my own hypothesis." [54] Without venturing into the dispute as to Newton's independence and priority, we may note that Newton claimed his hypothesis as such and without any apology for it. And in a postscript as long as the letter itself, he begged the " favour you would consult your books for a paper of mine entitled, An Hypothesis explaining properties of light. . . ." After quoting from it, Newton stated unequivocally, " In these and the foregoing words you have the common cause of gravity towards the earth, sun, and all the planets, and that by this cause [the ætherial spirit that " the sun ⟨may⟩ imbibe . . . copiously to conserve his shining, and keep the planets from receding further from him "] the planets are kept in their orbs about the sun." These words " contain the cause of the phænomena of gravity," wrote Newton. " This was but an hypothesis, and so to be looked upon only as one of my guesses. . . ."

Newton's Hypothesis on the Æther in the Eighteenth Century

By the middle of the eighteenth century, a reader of the *Opticks* could encounter in Book Two and in the Queries at the end of Book Three, an hypothesis about the æther which contained a mechanism proposed to explain gravitation, optical phenomena, muscular action, and so on. He could read in Birch's *History of the Royal Society* the early statement of Newton's views in 1675/6, while in Boyle's *Works* he could find an amplification written in 1678/9. Knowing that Newton had produced such an hypothesis in the 1670's and had published this hypothesis in the second edition of the *Opticks* in 1717, four years after the second edition of the *Principia*, such a reader would be puzzled by the General Scholium to Book Three. If he made a careful study, he would find that by the time of publication of the third edition of the *Principia* in 1726, Query 21 about the æther and gravity was then available in the second English edition of the *Opticks* of 1717, its reissue in 1718, the third edition of 1721, and the second Latin edition of 1719. We can only wonder, therefore, who was misled by those three words *Hypotheses non fingo*. Looking at the record, the first answer that comes to mind is: those scholars and philosophers who have not bothered to read Newton's works during 150 years.

The scientists of the mid-eighteenth century who read the *Principia* carefully would note that in the final paragraph of the last General Scholium the various actions attributed to the "subtle spirit" did not include gravity, although gravity was mentioned along with light and muscular motion in the paper sent to the Royal Society, the letter to Boyle, and the Queries in the *Opticks*. Presumably Newton was acting as we have seen Galileo and Boyle act when they said "this" is not the place to discuss "why" or the "cause." Guesses were to be excluded from the *Principia*, at least in relation to gravitation. Newton's system of the world was to be valid independently of any particular concept of a gravity-causing medium. The theories of electricity and chemistry developed by the speculative Newtonian experimental scientists of the eighteenth century were similarly intended to correlate known phenomena and to predict accurately the outcome of experiments whether the particular hypotheses underlying those theories were later accepted or rejected. Franklin's principle of conservation of charge and his analysis of the condenser have remained the cornerstones of electrostatics even though his hypothesis of a single elastic fluid of electricity has been subjected to major alterations and to some degree discarded. And Lavoisier's theory of combustion is as valid today as it was 150 years ago, even though we have abandoned the hypothesis of a caloric fluid of heat which he advocated and used. Newton hoped that his theory of light and colors was independent of any particular hypothesis on the nature of light, so that "all allowable hypotheses in their genuine constitution should be conformable to my theories" which were deduced from phenomena and therefore as valid as the phenomena themselves.

The Final Queries

In the *Opticks*, after Newton's discussion of the æther and its presumed action in light, heat, vision, muscular action, and gravitation, a series of Queries appears (first printed in Latin in 1706 as the new Queries 17-23), discussing light itself. Their burden is to indicate (Qu. 26) that the rays of light have "several sides, endued with several original properties." Thus (Qu. 28) all hypotheses are erroneous "in which light is supposed to consist [merely] in pression or motion, propagated through a fluid medium." And so Newton was led to reject a "dense medium" but not "an exceedingly rare ætherial medium as we described above," for which rejection there was the authority of "the oldest and most celebrated philosophers of Greece and Phœnicia." These philosophers took as their "first principles" atoms, the vacuum, and the gravity of atoms, but they attributed gravity (tacitly) to a cause other than dense matter. Later philosophers, wrote Newton,

. . . banish the consideration of such a cause out of natural philosophy, feigning hypotheses for explaining all things mechanically, and referring other causes to metaphysicks: whereas the main business of natural philosophy is to argue from phænomena without feigning hypotheses, and to deduce causes from effects, till we come to the very first cause, which certainly is not mechanical; and not only to unfold the mechanism of the world, but chiefly to resolve these and such like questions.[55]

We must note the dig at hypotheses; but Newton meant only that they should not get in the way when arguing from phenomena. The counsel given by Newton to Pardies makes it clear that Newton was concerned to use hypotheses with care, only after the phenomena had been carefully observed and the laws deduced, except in the matter of suggesting new experiments. Perhaps Newton re-introduced a warning against the substitution of the imagination for genuine experimental investigation (phenomena and theories or laws deduced from them: causes deduced from effects) because of the continual conflict in his own mind. We have seen both his strictures against hypotheses and his continual indulgence in their use. It may have been the case that the speculations in the previous Queries had been so extravagant that he felt he must warn his readers against them.

Be that as it may, the " such like " questions that Newton thought would be resolved by proper enquiry into phenomena were listed in beautiful poetic terms, reminiscent of the Book of Job, that could not fail to stimulate any reader:

What is there in places almost empty of matter, and whence is it that the sun and planets gravitate towards one another, without dense matter between them? Whence is it that nature doth nothing in vain; and whence arises all that order and beauty which we see in the world? To what end are comets, and whence is it that planets move all one and the same way in orbs concentrick, while comets move all manner of ways in orbs very excentrick; and what hinders the fixed stars from falling upon one another? How came the bodies of animals to be contrived with so much art, and for what ends were their several parts? Was the eye contrived without skill in opticks, and the ear without knowledge of sounds? How do the motions of the body follow from the will, and whence is the instinct in animals? [56]

And thus Newton was led to his observation—the argument from design—that "these things being rightly dispatched, does it not appear from phænomena that there is a Being incorporeal, living, intelligent, omnipresent . . . ? " And " though every true step made in this philosophy brings us not immediately to the knowledge of the first cause, yet it brings us nearer to it, and on that account is to be highly valued."

Query 29 presents Newton's views about the rays of light being " very small bodies emitted from shining substances," a concept that has appeared *en passant* throughout the earlier queries. Newton showed that considering light to be a body conforms to the observed facts; that it is a physical " hypothesis " may be seen in every statement ever made by Newton about a possible discussion of " what light is." Newton restated what had appeared in the earlier queries to show the reasonableness of the belief that light is corpuscular. On this basis, Query 30 was presented, dealing with the convertibility of light and gross bodies into one another and the probability that " bodies receive much of their activity from the particles of light which enter their composition."

The final query (31) poses the problem of whether the small particles of bodies have " powers, virtues, or forces, by which they act at a distance, not only upon the rays of light for reflecting, refracting, and inflecting them, but also upon one another for producing a great part of the phænomena of nature." The attractions of gravity, magnetism, and electricity provide well-known examples of bodies acting

upon one another and show the " tenor and course of nature." Are there other such forces? Very likely, and perhaps they may reach only to such small distances as " hitherto escape observation "—perhaps there may even be short-range electrical attraction, so short-ranged as to escape " vulgar eyes," and existing without being " excited by friction." In this final query, Newton did " not here consider " how " these attractions may be performed," since the object was to " learn from the phenomena of nature what bodies attract one another, and what are the properties of the attraction, before we enquire the cause by which the attraction is performed." §
There follows a discussion of chemical reactions. The evolution of heat and light, the dissolution of metals by acids, the action of spirit of vitriol on common salt, and kindred topics are explained in terms of a theory of attraction applied to the atomic theory or corpuscular philosophy. Analogy was one of the chief tools used by Newton in his arguments, on the ground that " Nature is very consonant and conformable to her self." Thus, since gravity causes the sea to flow " round the denser and weightier parts of the globe of the earth, so the attraction may make the watry acid flow round the denser and compacter particles of earth for composing the particles of salt."

What shall we say to explain how the parts of all " homogeneal hard bodies which fully touch one another, stick together . . . strongly " ? Those who " invent " hooked atoms beg the question altogether, Newton wrote, while others merely say they are " glued together by rest, that is, an occult quality, or rather by nothing." From their cohesion, Newton inferred, rather, that the particles exert a strong attractive force on one another (extremely strong " in immediate contact " but not reaching far from the particles " with any sensible effect ") and that at " small distances " this force " performs the chymical operations above mentioned."

All bodies " seem " to be made of " hard particles " since, among other properties, fluids would not otherwise congeal. " Even the rays of light seem to be hard bodies," since otherwise they would not " retain different properties in their different sides." The smallest particles may have, paradoxically, the strongest attractions and thus combine to form larger particles " of weaker virtue," and these may combine . . . until the " progression end in the biggest particles on which the operations in chymistry, and the colours of natural bodies depend." When metals are dissolved in acids, they attract

§ It should be observed that Newton did not deny the validity of inquiry into the " cause " but merely indicated that the proper mode of investigation in natural philosophy is to leave the subject of " cause " until the last, rather than beginning with the assumption of some hypothesis of " cause " in independence of the " phenomena of nature " and their generalization by deduction and induction.

but a small part of the acid, since their attractive force reaches " but to a small distance from them." And at the extreme range of these attractive forces, we should expect a " repulsive virtue " to begin— just as in algebra, " where affirmative quantities vanish and cease, there negative ones begin." That in nature there is such a " repulsive virtue " is shown in the reflection of light (assuming Newton's explanation of this phenomenon) and also in its inflection, and it " seems " also to follow from the speed with which emitted light leaves shining bodies. Repulsion in air and vapors causes the particles to spread out in all directions. Referring to Boyle's discussion of the cause of the elasticity or spring of the air, Newton noted that the vast contraction and expansion of air " seems unintelligible, by feigning the particles of air to be springy and ramous, or rolled up like hoops, or by any other means than a repulsive power." Thus Newton showed that Nature is " conformable to her self and very simple," since the motions of the heavenly bodies are produced by the attraction of gravity between them and " almost all the small ones of their particles " by some other " attractive and repelling powers " between them.

We are then led to a theological natural philosophy: the " origin of the world " and the nature of the " Creation by the counsel of an intelligent agent." The evidence of the physical world and animate nature is presented to exhibit " the wisdom and skill of a powerful ever-living agent." The " bounds of moral philosophy " are said to be enlarged by " natural philosophy," since " what is the first cause, what power he has over us, and what benefits we receive from him, so far our duty towards him, as well as that towards one another, will appear to us by the Light of Nature."

The Influence of the Opticks

No one can read the closing pages of the final version of the *Opticks* without being moved by the intensity of Newton's religious beliefs, confirmed for him in natural philosophy, and expressed in a poetic language of sensory color which makes the final General Scholium to the *Principia* seem stilted and halting by comparison. To the eighteenth-century reader, as to us, these queries reveal the mind of Newton in its innermost thoughts just as the reading of the book of Nature revealed to Newton the mind of the creating God. In the *Opticks*, as Albert Einstein has remarked, we are afforded " the enjoyment of a look at the personal activity of this unique man." [57] Here is the Newton respected in the eighteenth century: a speculative genius for whom all natural philosophy was his province, whose ideas were not limited to natural philosophy and the data of experience, but were extended to theology and morality. The *Principia* presented the results with little clue to the thoughts of their inventor, but the *Opticks* showed the mind of Newton as it leapt from one problem to another. Virtually every stage of research and thinking, save only the peculiar quality of his genius, is made manifest to the reader. Hence, anyone who was at all interested in the scientific process, who wished to see the mind of the Prince of Natural Philosophers at work, was drawn to the *Opticks* as a piece of iron to the magnet: a quality wholly absent from the *Principia*. In the twentieth century, as in the eighteenth, great experimenters like J. J. Thomson and Lord Rayleigh have found in the *Opticks* a masterpiece of their art and have recommended it to their students.* We have seen that even the purely optical portions of this treatise (Books One and Two) were presented in terms of experimental observation and physical conjecture rather than rigid mathematical analysis, and so had a wholly different ring from the dynamics of the *Principia*. The approach of the *Principia* would not do for optics because, in Newton's day, this subject was in a crude, immature, and empirical state; there had not yet been either a Copernicus or a Galileo in this field: the closest was Newton himself. The Newton of the *Opticks* was working with raw, experimental data in just the same way that Franklin was to do in electricity a half century or so later, and as Lavoisier was to do in chemistry later still. Newton in his *Opticks*, Franklin in electricity, and Lavoisier in chemistry, exemplify that process in which explanations are formulated in the creative region of thought in which theory and experiment meet and are mutually operative; there the scientist lets his creative imagination go—limited only, as Faraday used to say, by the experiments.

The *Opticks* had a special appeal for those first-rate men in the eighteenth century who believed that the progress of our knowledge of nature lay in the new experimental sciences—electricity, heat, magnetism, optics, natural history, plant and animal physiology, chemistry. They were convinced that their science would be inductive or Baconian, based on the discovery and explanation of new major experiential data, and would not necessarily proceed along the immediate lines of mathematical deduction. Such men universally admired Newton's *Opticks* as they came also to admire Franklin's *Experiments and Observations on Electricity*. Hence, we can see why

* In the article on Newton, in which he " re-echoed " the advice of Lord Rayleigh that every student of physics should read the *Opticks*, J. J. Thomson made this sage comment: " At the end of the Opticks come the Queries. In these Newton abandons the severe, almost Euclidean, style of the earlier part of the book; he flings away his policy of ' hypotheses non fingo '; he makes up for lost time." [58]

there was, in eighteenth-century science, a kind of cleavage (although not always absolutely sharp) between the Newtonian science of the *Principia* and the Newtonian science of the *Opticks*. Two almost separate and warring traditions divided not only the scientists and philosophers, but also the scientifically minded poets.

Varieties of Newtonian Philosophy

This situation may seem a little bewildering; how can the writings of Newton present so different an aspect, depending upon which one we study? Indeed, it is one of the astonishing aspects of Newton's genius that he could have made significant contributions of such diverse sorts. Usually in science we encounter two rather distinct kinds of creation, one the mathematical or purely theoretical and the other the experimental or speculative-experimental—by which is meant not only the design of new apparatus and the discovery of new data, but also the creation of working hypotheses as data accumulate, and even their eventual fruition in a conceptual scheme. These types of scientific creativity may be symbolized for us in the twentieth century by two giants in physics—J. J. Thomson and Albert Einstein. Although the parallel is somewhat inexact, they are the end-products of the ancient warring traditions of the Aristotelians and the Platonists. The greatness of Isaac Newton lay in his representing within one person the best of both traditions, of having been—if you wish—both the Einstein and the Thomson of his day. How much this unique position is a reflection of his extraordinary genius (and unique scientific personality) and how much an indication of the nature of the times in which he lived is an interesting question, but one which is not relevant to our present study. But we must note that this aspect of Newton's scientific character was often baffling to the men of science of the eighteenth century, just as it is baffling to historians today.

Although we have had, perforce, to investigate Newton's scientific character and the intention of his words, it has been the constant aim of this study to concentrate on the eighteenth-century views of Newton, rather than to make an analysis of Newton. That there were in the eighteenth century two quite different traditions of Newtonianism—the hypothetico-experimental or speculative-experimental tradition associated with the *Opticks* and the mathematico-deductive (although not wholly unempirical) tradition associated with the *Principia*—is plain from studying the respective sources of the experimentalists and the mathematical physicists in the age of Newton. One of the best ways of sampling the eighteenth-century views of Newtonianism is to look at the many scientific dictionaries of that time, in which a universal agreement may be found on the several senses of Newtonianism.

The prototype seems to have been John Harris's *Lexicon Technicum* (I have used the fifth edition, 1736).† Here, *s. v.* " NEWTONIAN *Philosophy*," we find that although this is " the doctrine of the universe, and particularly of the heavenly bodies; their laws, affections, etc., as delivered by Sir Isaac Newton," the term Newtonian Philosophy is " applied very differently," and that this is a source of confusion. There follows a list of five meanings then current.

The very first of these is " the corpuscular philosophy considered as it now stands corrected and reformed by the discoveries and improvements made in several parts thereof, by Sir I. Newton." This is, according to Harris, the sense in which 'sGravesande calls his " Elements of Physics " an " Introduction to Newtonian Philosophy " and it is the sense in which the " Newtonian Philosophy " is the same as the " New Philosophy " in distinction " to the Cartesian, the Peripatetic, and the antient corpuscular." Attention may be called to Harris's use of Boyle's phrase, " the corpuscular philosophy," and also to the fact that in this usage, the Newtonian Philosophy may be said to be embodied in the third book of the *Opticks* (chiefly in the Queries) and sundry papers such as the *De Natura Acidorum*, which was actually printed for the first time in 1710 in Harris's preface to his dictionary.

The second usage was " the method or order which Sir I. Newton observes in philosophizing." This method of " reasoning " implies the " drawing of conclusions directly from phænomena, exclusive of all previous hypotheses; the beginning from simple principles; deducing the first powers and laws of nature from a few select phænomena, and then applying those laws, etc., to account for other things." This description seems to fit in part the first two books of the *Opticks* and most of the *Principia*, and it is said to be " the same with the experimental philosophy."

The third meaning of Newtonian Philosophy is equivalent to " the Mechanical and Mathematical Philosophy," and is somewhat similar to the preceding one, except that it would exclude any part of the *Opticks*. It implies that " Physical bodies are considered mathematically; and . . . geometry and mechanics are applied to the solution of phænomena."

† Harris's *Lexicon* appeared in a single volume in 1704; a supplemental volume, with its own alphabetical arrangement, appeared in 1710. In the third edition, 1726, as in all later editions, the contents of both volumes were combined into a single alphabetical arrangement.

The fourth sense in which "Newtonian Philosophy" was used was merely to indicate "that part of physical knowledge, which Sir I. Newton has handled, improved, and demonstrated, in his *Principia*." Hence, this fourth sense is in contrast to the first, in which the Newtonian Philosophy is conceived to be the extension by Newton of the mechanical corpuscular philosophy of Galileo, Bacon, and Boyle, and found chiefly in the Queries at the end of the *Opticks*.

Finally, there was the fifth sense of "the new principles which Sir I. Newton has brought into philosophy; the new system founded thereon; and the new solution of phænomena thence deduced: or that which characterizes, and distinguishes his philosophy from all others." This philosophy, we are told, is found chiefly in Book Three of the *Principia*. The first two books prepare the way, laying down the principles of mathematics having the "most relation to philosophy." Since such "laws and conditions of powers" are "dry and geometrical," according to Harris, Newton illustrated them by "scholia in philosophy" concerning such physical problems as the density and resistance of bodies, the motion of light and sound, the vacuum, etc. But not until the third book did Newton proceed "to the philosophy itself." There, "from the same principles" he deduced the structure of the universe, the "powers of gravity, whereby bodies tend towards the sun and planets," and then from these powers he deduced the motions of planets and comets and the true theory of the moon and the tides.

We may see the continued presence of the foregoing discussion in seven editions of Ephraim Chambers's *Cyclopædia* (beginning with the first edition of 1728), which will be remembered by students of Franklin as the source of many articles reprinted by him in the *Pennsylvania Gazette*. In the famous *Encyclopédie* of Diderot and d'Alembert, *s. v.* "NEWTONIANISME, s. m. *ou* PHILOSOPHIE NEWTONIENNE, Physiq.," we find (I have used the Lausanne edition of 1780) a word for word translation of the discussion given by Harris and repeated by Chambers. Nor is there any change in the *Dictionnaire Encyclopédique des Mathématiques* par MM. d'Alembert, l'Abbé Bossut, de la Lande, le Marquis de Condorcet, &c. (1789, *s. v.* "Neutonianisme, . . ."), nor in Charles Hutton's *Mathematical and Philosophical Dictionary* (1795, *s. v.* "Newtonian Philosophy"). In other words, the definitions to be found in the scientific dictionaries of the age of Newton draw a continued sharp distinction between Newtonianism as a corpuscular philosophy and Newtonianism as a mathematico-deductive system of celestial dynamics; and it is significant that the former sense is always found at the head of the list.

If we look at the discussion of " CORPUSCULAR *Philosophy* "
in Harris's dictionary we find a summing up under four particulars
" of the mechanical hypothesis or corpuscular hypothesis " according
to " Mr. Boyle," who " very properly " called the corpuscular philosophy " that way of philosophizing which endeavours to explain
things, and to give an account of the phænomena of nature by the
motion, figure, rest, position, etc., of corpuscles or minute particles
of matter," i. e., the " physical atoms of a body." But as to " COR-
PUSCLES," we are told that Sir Isaac Newton was the first person
who showed the " way of guessing with great accuracy, at the sizes
of the component corpuscles or particles of which bodies are constituted," and that he did so in the *Opticks*. Under " COLOR," it
is shown how Newton's method yields the result that a corpuscle
having the density of glass that " shall reflect green of the third
order " will be $\frac{16\frac{1}{4}}{100000}$ part of an inch." That the *Opticks* contained
the doctrine of the nature of matter may be seen, *s. v.* " PARTI-
CLES," where we also find the statement that the general problem
of " how to make any conjecture at the several sizes of these component particles of bodies " is " what philosophers have hardly yet
had data or discoveries enough to determine." Hence we may truly
appreciate the importance of the great work of " the wonderful Sir
Isaac Newton, [who] in his excellent book of *Opticks*, hath opened
a door into this new world." Again, in the discussion of " FLU-
IDITY," a property that seems to depend on the " parts of any
bodies being very fine and small, . . . so disposed by motion and
figure, as that they can easily slide over one another's surfaces all
manner of ways," the explanation is given in terms of Boyle's corpuscular philosophy, with an addendum containing an observation
by Hooke; and then, " Besides what hath been said of this quality,
I must add here, that the Corpuscular Philosophy, before Sir Is.
Newton's wonderful improvement of it, did not go to the bottom of
this matter; for it gave no account of the cause of the chief condition
requisite to constitute a fluid body, *viz.* the various motions and
agitations of its particles "—a topic then presented by Harris in a
lengthy paraphrase of some of the Queries. Can there be any further
doubt that the *Opticks* contained a major revision of the Bacon-
Boyle corpuscular philosophy and was esteemed as such in the eighteenth century? And can it be doubted that this achievement rivalled
the dynamics of the *Principia*?

Newton's Experimental Method

At the end of the *Opticks,* Newton addressed himself to some general questions of procedure in science, which provided a thesis for discussion by many experimental scientists throughout the eighteenth century. The "synthetic" and "analytic" methods,‡ described by Newton in the final "Query," were given particular attention by Franklin's disciple, Joseph Priestley, in his *History and Present State . . . of Electricity.* Newton said:

As in mathematicks so in natural philosophy, the investigation of difficult things by the method of analysis, ought ever to precede the method of composition. This analysis consists in making experiments and observations, and in drawing general conclusions from them by induction, and admitting of no objections against the conclusions, but such as are taken from experiments, or other certain truths. For hypotheses are not to be regarded in experimental philosophy. And although the arguing from experiments and observations by induction be no demonstration of general conclusions; yet it is the best way of arguing which the nature of things admits of, and may be looked upon as so much the stronger, by how much the induction is more general. And if no exception occur from phænomena, the conclusion may be pronounced generally. But if at any time afterwards any exception shall occur from experiments, it may then begin to be pronounced with such exceptions as occur. By this way of analysis we may proceed from compounds to ingredients, and from motions to the forces producing them; and in general, from effects to their causes, and from particular causes to more general ones, till the argument end in the most general. This is the method of analysis.

This method was contrasted with that of "synthesis":

And the synthesis consists in assuming the causes discovered and established as principles, and by them explaining the phænomena proceeding from them, and proving the explanation.

Newton freely admitted that almost all of the first two books of the *Opticks* proceeded by "analysis," but that with respect to the "method of composition" or "synthesis," he had provided an "instance" in "the end of the first Book." [59] §

‡ The history of the use of the words "synthetic" and "analytic" in philosophy and in science covers a wide range. In projective geometry, for example, a distinction is made between synthetic and analytic proofs; an analytic proof uses algebra or the calculus and a synthetic proof does not. In this sense, the geometrical proofs in the *Principia* are synthetic while the methods used by Laplace are analytic. Recent philosophical discussion (e. g., by Morton White and W. V. Quine) has cast doubts upon the distinction between analytic and synthetic propositions in general. But in discussing the method of Newton and the speculative Newtonian experimental scientists of the eighteenth century, we must maintain the definitions of "analysis" and "synthesis" that they employed.

§ Newton was evidently referring to the final proposition of Book One: "By mixing

As to the third book, in which the " Queries " were to be found, Newton wrote, " I have only begun the analysis of what remains to be discovered about light and its effects upon the frame of nature, hinting several things about it [in the " Queries "], and leaving the hints to be examined and improved by the farther experiments and observations of such as are inquisitive." [60] This procedure may be contrasted with the aims of the *Principia*; there Newton described Book Three, " The System of the World," as follows:

. . . by the propositions mathematically demonstrated in the former books, in the third I derive from the celestial phenomena the forces of gravity with which bodies tend to the sun and the several planets. Then from these forces, by other propositions which are also mathematical, I deduce the motions of the planets, the comets, the moon, and the sea. I wish we could derive the rest of the phenomena of Nature by the same kind of reasoning from mechanical principles, for I am induced by many reasons to suspect that they may all depend upon certain forces by which the particles of bodies, by some causes hitherto unknown, are either mutually impelled towards one another, and cohere in regular figures, or are repelled and recede from one another.[61]

Once again we encounter Newton's admission of the difference between his two books. This " wish " that the constitution of bodies might be reduced to a *Principia*-like system was natural enough, but we may note today—about two centuries and a half later—that it has never been realized. In Newton's day as in ours, the experimental data were insufficient and perhaps too complex or too changing for the realization of this ideal.

Analytic and Synthetic Methods in Science

The pre-Newtonian history of analytic and synthetic methods in physical science has been explored carefully by A. C. Crombie, who has defended the claim that " the natural philosophers of Latin Christendom in the thirteenth and fourteenth centuries created the experimental science characteristic of modern times." [62] In studying the cause of the rainbow these natural philosophers distinguished between " bare empirical knowledge (*scientia quia*) of the facts " and the goal of " ' demonstrated knowledge ' (*scientia propter quid*)." Such " demonstrated knowledge of a fact " consisted only of being able to deduce that fact from a theory " which related it to other

coloured lights to compound a beam of light of the same colour and nature with a beam of the sun's direct light, and therein to experience the truth of the foregoing propositions." Having shown that the sun's light is a mixture of light of many colors and degrees of refrangibility, Newton now showed that a mixture of light of these colors and degrees of refrangibility is like sunlight.

facts and showed its cause." Beginning with Aristotle's double procedure of induction and deduction, as found in the *Posterior Ana-
lytics,* Robert Grosseteste and his followers (in the thirteenth century) related the philosophical method to empirical enquiry.[63]
Recognizing that the truth of a theory could never be strictly inferred
from generalizations of empirical results, they saw that theories
could nevertheless be proved false by simple empirical tests. Experiment, they believed, might never show more than that a given
theory is not true or that another is only "sufficient to save the
appearances." Furthermore, these natural philosophers recognized
that experiment can never prove that a particular theory is the only
possible theory to fit the known facts.

A late sixteenth-century writer, Jacopo Zabarella, summed up the
two methods which had been developed: "resolution" is the discovery of causal relations by inductive analysis of the phenomena,
the experiential data; "composition" is the demonstration of the
effect by deduction from the assumed cause.[64] Newton used the expression "composition" as well as "synthesis." He wrote: "As in
mathematicks, so in natural philosophy, the investigation of difficult
things by the method of analysis, ought ever to precede the method
of composition." [65]

Newton's method differed from that of the pre-Galilean natural
philosophers primarily in regard to the role of mathematics in physical theory. In this respect he was the heir of Galileo, who had added
to the late mediaeval and Renaissance methods of logic and experiment the concept of science as a mathematical description of
physical relations observed between bodies. For Galileo as for Newton, the main problem was how to relate mathematics to experience.
In applying the methods of resolution and composition, Galileo saw
the importance of introducing concepts which were divorced from
experience—frictionless planes, isolated bodies, and so on—just as
Newton in the *Principia* considered all sorts of centrifugal and centripetal forces. Accelerated motion, Galileo noted, might proceed
according to a law in which the speed is proportional to the space
traversed or one in which the speed is proportional to the elapsed
time. The first of these two possibilities could be rejected because
it leads to a logical inconsistency, but the second leads to a result
that agrees with the results of experiment. Galileo's genius thus
seems to lie in his recognition that descriptions of empirical relations
do not constitute science and his ability to consider the "ideal"
case and then introduce the relevant factors one by one. Hence we
may understand what has been called Galileo's "freedom from naive
empiricism," [66] and the full sense of such statements of his as: "I

cannot find any bounds for my admiration how reason was able in Aristarchus and Copernicus to commit such a rape upon their senses as in despite thereof to make herself mistress of their belief." [67]

In applying his *metodo resolutivo,* or "analysis," Galileo would disregard a great many factors, so as to find a simple mathematical law, as for the "ideal" pendulum: the period is proportional to the square-root of the length and independent of the amplitude of the swing—ignoring "the opposition of the air, and line, or other such accidents." [68] Mathematical principles of natural philosophy must apply to the real world and so Galileo introduced step by step the factors that distinguish an "ideal" pendulum from an "experiential" pendulum: resistance of the air, the effect of the motion of each part of a non-weightless thread, and so on. Galileo called his procedure "*argomento ex suppositione.*" This procedure is described by Crombie as follows:

After a "resolution" of the mathematical relations involved in a given effect, he set up a "hypothetical assumption" from which he deduced the consequences that must follow. This second stage he called the *metodo compositivo.* The third stage, to which he also applied the term "resolution," was to analyse by experiment examples of the effect, in order to discover whether the deduced consequences did in fact occur. For, as he said, "I know very well that one sole experiment or concludent demonstration, produced on the contrary part, sufficeth to batter to the ground these and a thousand other probable arguments. . . . ." A good example of his whole method is his establishment of the law of the acceleration of freely falling bodies, in which the verification consisted in the series of measurements of concomitant variations between space travelled and time passed with the ball rolling down the inclined plane. Firmly putting aside any suggestion that he was going "to investigate the cause of the acceleration of natural motion, concerning which various opinions have been expressed by various philosophers," he insisted that he intended simply "to investigate and demonstrate some of the properties of accelerated motion, whatever the cause of this acceleration may be." [69]

The double method of induction and deduction, called resolution and composition by the mediaeval commentators on Aristotle, appears also in Descartes who, like Newton, preferred the Greek terms "analysis" and "synthesis." In the matter of synthesis Descartes allowed himself to follow the consequences of deductions from first principles without constant regard to their relation to "phenomena," thus producing an ideal construction of the world in the manner of a geometer constructing any type of space which logic would permit. It was to avoid such results that Newton took pains to produce a science that originated in experience, transcended experience on the level of mathematics or logical theory, but that returned to experience in the correlation of derived results with actual observations or experiments.

The experimental Newtonian scientists of the eighteenth century, establishing new levels of science in physics, chemistry, and biology, proceeded according to Newton's version of the traditional methodology. They recognized the dangers of adopting an arbitrary hypothesis and believing its consequences in independence of the facts of experience, but they saw that the imagination was required at every stage in analysis. This situation may be illustrated in the eighteenth-century science of electricity. We never observe " charge " but only " electrification," the power a body has to attract or repel other bodies. Analysis leads to classification and generalization, the conclusion that there are two sorts of electrification, vitreous and resinous. Further experiment yields the empirical relation that if two bodies have opposite electrifications, contact between them may destroy both electrifications, whence the idea of " equal electrification " arises; similarly, " greater " or " less." From a variety of such results, based on experience, general laws arise, which are statements of the effects that follow from particular causes or conditions. According to Newton's precepts, the experimenter must always be on guard to note exceptions. Up until the middle of the eighteenth century, it would have been considered a general law based on experience that electrification proceeds only from friction or attrition; then it was found that certain crystals show signs of electrification on being heated.

During the kind of analysis that has been presented, the experimenter must advance hypotheses, chiefly premises in physical arguments. These are checked by putting their consequences to experimental test. Thus when it is observed that lightning resembles the spark discharge produced in the laboratory, the hypothesis may arise that lightning is a motion of electric fluid from clouds. This hypothesis cannot be tested directly, just as no test has ever been devised to check directly Galileo's hypothesis that the speed of a freely falling body varies as the time of descent. Like us, Galileo could only test the deductions of his hypothesis, that then the distance fallen would be proportional to the square of the time of descent.* Franklin could test the deductions of the hypothesis that lightning is an electrical discharge: it must then be attracted by

* Galileo did not make his test for bodies falling freely with the acceleration of gravity, but in the case of " diluted " gravity on an inclined plane. With modern electrical devices, we can perform the test for a falling body, but the quantities we compare are still *distance* and *time*, not *speed* and *time* (because we cannot measure speed directly and must deduce it from other measured quantities).

pointed conductors, and produce the other effects noted for electrical discharges in the laboratory. Thus, as analysis proceeds, the method of synthesis is applied to yield statements to be tested—a combination of deduction and induction controlled by recourse to experience.

In addition to this type of hypothesis—a working hypothesis suggesting experiments—men of the eighteenth century used hypotheses in the axioms of theories invented to correlate observed phenomena and empirically derived laws, according to Newton's view of proceeding from particular causes to more general ones. On this level we would note the hypothesis of an electric fluid, made up of mutually repellent particles which are attracted by the particles of ordinary matter. The value of this hypothesis lies wholly in its degree of correlation and prediction of observed phenomena, and suggestion of new phenomena which can be observed. On the basis of this hypothesis, various ancillary hypotheses enable the experimenter to construct more than one theory and the choice amongst the possible theories is determined by further experiments, and also by analogy to other theories.

In this procedure, the eighteenth-century experimenters introduced speculation, just as Newton had done in the Queries of the *Opticks* and elsewhere. The danger was that physical argument be wholly evaded by hypothesis. To this end, the more cautious scientists often tried to keep distinct their opinions or conjectures and the accepted generalizations from experience. But they were not always successful. The concept of " charge " was a consequence of the hypothesis of an electric fluid, but almost all of the Franklinians couched their empirical statements in terms of charge rather than the empirical concept of electrification and confused the two.† Newton's hypothesis that gases are composed of particles repelling one another according to the reciprocal of the distances between them also lost its hypothetical character and became accepted as an almost empirical statement, one supposedly proved by Newton.

It is, therefore, easy for us to criticize the men of the eighteenth century for having, in the end, perverted the Newtonian method of analysis, for having debauched themselves in all sorts of extravagant hypotheses of electric fluids, magnetic fluids, caloric and phlogistic fluids of heat, an æther, and so on. Yet to note such extravagances without the full measure of achievement of the eighteenth-century sciences would be absurd. Even if the hypothesis of a subtle fluid of *negative* weight—phlogiston—seems to contravene the first

---

† This situation prevails today. Physicists speak of a " current in a wire " as if there were a way of knowing what goes on *inside* a conductor connecting the positive and negative terminals of a battery.

principles of matter, we must keep in mind that the deductions from such hypotheses agree with the general principles established empirico-inductively. In old age Priestley could reject Lavoisier's ideas on oxidation because the deductions from the theory based on the concept of phlogiston could be verified in the laboratory and encompassed so many of the known facts.

The value of the eighteenth-century theories and the hypotheses on which they were based was thus only partially testable by the method of synthesis, assuming causes as discovered or established as principles, and then deducing the phenomena from them. There was apt to be a choice, perhaps on purely metaphysical grounds, between the various hypotheses of causes assumed as discovered. But so far as the progress of science is concerned, those theories and their underlying hypotheses that led to results of importance (like Franklin's one-fluid theory of electricity, or its later rival, the two-fluid theory) can readily be distinguished from those that did not (like the electrical theory based on " effluences " and " affluences ").

Newtonian " Analysis " and " Synthesis " in the Eighteenth Century

The scientific work of the Newtonian scientists in the eighteenth century exemplifies the methods of analysis and synthesis. These methods were the subject of discussion even in the nineteenth century,‡ especially in relation to the role of mathematics in physical theory. They appear in the twentieth century, although under new names, and seem to need classification still as part of the philosophy of science.

In the eighteenth century Joseph Priestley criticized the " synthetic " method when used in teaching, because it " is a great discouragement to young and enterprising geniuses." The synthetic method, deducing the observed phenomena from general principles, " means to see philosophers proposing that first, which they themselves attained the last; first laying down the propositions which were the result of all their experiments, and then relating the facts, as if everything had been done to verify a true preconceived theory." Priestley added, " This *synthetic* method is, certainly, the most ex-

---

‡ Thus Sir William Thomson [Lord Kelvin] wrote in 1848, " The varied problems which occur in the mathematical theory of electricity in equilibrium may be divided into the two great classes of Synthetical and Analytical investigations. In problems of the former class, the object is in each case the determination either of a resultant force or of an aggregate electrical mass, according to special data regarding distributions of electricity: in the latter class, inverse problems, such as the determination of the electrical density at each point of the surface of a conductor in any circumstances, according to the laws stated above, are the objects proposed." [70]

peditious way of making a person understand a branch of science; but the *analytic* method, in which discoveries were actually made, is most favourable to the progress of knowledge." [71]

In *The Aims of Education*, Whitehead referred to these two approaches to natural science as the "logic of discovery" and the "logic of the discovered." The logic of discovery "consists in the weighing of probabilities, in discarding details that seem irrelevant, in divining the general rules according to which events occur, and in testing hypotheses by devising suitable experiments." The logic of the discovered is "the deduction of the special events which, under certain circumstances, would happen in obedience to the assumed laws of nature." [72] Thus the logical thought evoked by science is of two kinds: inductive logic and deductive logic. The *Principia* exemplifies the latter, and the reason for its mathematical character becomes clear once we appreciate that "mathematics is nothing else than the more complicated parts of the art of deductive reasoning, especially where it concerns number, quantity, and space." [73]

Priestley presented the two Newtonian methods and observed the contrast between Newton as we see him in "his astronomical discoveries" and Newton as "we see him most in the character of an experimental philosopher, as in his optical inquiries (though the method of his treatise on that subject is by no means purely analytical) . . . ." [74] Priestley, himself a gifted experimenter, rather liked the idea that he was a part of the Newtonian tradition stemming from the *Opticks* and referred to the latter on several occasions. In his book on the history and present state of electricity, like Newton he introduced a set of queries. In another work, *Experiments and Observations on Different Kinds of Air*, Section VIII was entitled: "Queries, Speculations, and Hints." Here Priestley disclosed his apprehensions of being considered "a dry *experimenter*"; but even worse was the possibility that readers might give him "the opposite character of a *visionary theorist*." Some theory had of course been scattered throughout the earlier part of the book. Most of the "conjectures," however, had been collected together so that readers of little "imagination," who did not care to go beyond "the regions of plain fact," could omit all conjectural material and thus prevent their delicacy from being offended. Yet, said Priestley, it is a mistake to believe that theory and experiment can be separated, because they necessarily go "hand in hand, every process being intended to ascertain some particular *hypothesis*, which, in fact, is only a conjecture concerning the circumstances or the cause of some natural operation."

Priestley was undoubtedly thinking of himself, and perhaps of his friend, Benjamin Franklin, when he said that " the boldest and most original experimenters are those who, giving free scope to their imaginations, admit the combination of the most distant ideas; and that though many of these associations of ideas will be wild and chimerical, yet that others will have the chance of giving rise to the greatest and most capital discoveries; such as very cautious, timid, sober, and slow-thinking people would never have come at." Now Priestley was certainly aware that many of his critical contemporaries had begun to conceive the whole Newtonian natural philosophy in terms of those three words, *Hypotheses non fingo*, so he added his own views on Newton: " Sir Isaac Newton himself, notwithstanding the great advantage which he derived from a habit of *patient thinking*, indulged bold and eccentric thoughts, of which his Queries at the end of his book of optics are a sufficient evidence." [75] It is to this tradition of " analytical " Newtonianism, to use Newton's own terms and Priestley's, as presented in the *Opticks*, rather than the tradition of " synthetic " Newtonianism, as presented in the *Principia*, that Franklin belongs.

The two strands of Newtonianism are also to be found presented in Colin Maclaurin's *Account of Sir Isaac Newton's Philosophical Discoveries*: in Chapter II, " A general view of Sir Isaac Newton's method . . . ," the introductory portion of Book I, " On the method of proceeding in natural philosophy. . . ." After describing Newton's conceptions of " analysis " and " synthesis," Maclaurin contrasted the *Principia* and the *Opticks*. In the former, Newton established his " system of the world " by relying upon " the best astronomical observations "; in the latter, he himself performed, " with the greatest address, the experiments by which he was enabled to pry into the more secret operations of nature, amongst the minute particles of matter," searching " into the motions that are amongst the minute particles of matter, the most abstruse of all natural phænomena."

In the first [of these two works], he had the observations of astronomers for many ages to build on, with valuable consequences that had been derived from them, by the laborious calculations of diligent and ingenious men. The constancy and regularity of the celestial motions had contributed, with the observations of some thousands of years, to render astronomy the most exact part of the history of nature; the doctrine of comets only excepted. The vast distances of the great bodies which compose the system, from each other, rather favoured a just analysis of the powers by which they act on one another; since by the greatness of the distance, these must be reduced to a few simple principles, and be the more easily discovered.

In the second treatise, he enquires into more hidden parts of nature, and had most of the phænomena themselves to trace, as well as their causes. The subject is rather more nice and difficult, because of the inconceivable minuteness of the agents, and the subtilty and quickness of the motions; and the principles combined in producing the phæ-nomena being more various, it could not be expected that they should be so easily subjected to an analysis. Hence it is that what he has delivered in the first (tho' still capable of improvement) is more complete and finished in several respects; while his discoveries of the second sort are more astonishing.[76]

Mid-eighteenth-century electrical science was in much the same state that optics had been in the seventeenth. What Maclaurin wrote about Newton's *Opticks* might easily have been rewritten to apply to the work of Franklin in electricity.

Newton's distinction between " analytic " and " synthetic " methods explains at once why the revisions of the *Principia* are markedly different from the changes in the *Opticks*. In the *Principia*, the " causes " had been " discovered, and established as principles " in the very first edition. Revisions, therefore, could be confined to the level of " explaining the phænomena proceeding from them, and proving the explanation," i. e., making better explanations, improving the proofs, and tightening up the ancillary assumptions. But in the *Opticks* Newton had followed the method of analysis, " making experiments and observations, and . . . drawing general conclusions from them by induction. . . ." New aspects of the various problems in relation to the composition and structure of matter, treated from the point of view of reasoning about experiments and not making deductions from causes assumed to be known, could thus be legitimately added to the third book of the *Opticks*, even though they introduced problems that had not appeared in the main part of the treatise. The long sections on chemistry in the later Queries were related only distantly to optics, through the common problem of the behavior of the corpuscles of different varieties of matter. But almost all the topics in the Queries are aspects of one major theme: the study of matter or " body " by the method of analysis described by Newton. The method was stated by Newton as a series of procedural steps without explicit reference to the major ingredient of the controlled scientific imagination, but the Queries themselves showed the role of speculation.

Hence the Queries at the end of the *Opticks* were examples of incomplete " analysis " and not questions to be asked of Nature: at best, questions that had been answered, but whose answers would not as yet fully satisfy the Newtonian standards. This was the sense in which the *Opticks* was read during the eighteenth century and it was also the sense in which Newton wrote the later Queries. When the very first additions to the *Opticks* were being written (the new

Queries added to the Latin version of 1706), Newton visited David Gregory and told him about the " 7 pages of addenda." Gregory wrote out a memorandum, dated 21 December 1705, which is especially interesting because of the phrases he used to describe the firmness of Newton's beliefs; it is plain that Newton did not indicate to Gregory any great uncertainty about the subjects he explained by query. " Sir Isaac Newton was with me," Gregory wrote, "and told me that he . . . has by way of quære explained the explosion of gun powder, all the chief operations of chymistry. He has shewed that light is neither a communication of motion nor of a pressure. He inclines to believe it to be projected minute bodys. He has explained in those quærys the double refraction in Iseland christall." § The propositions in the third book of the *Opticks* might have been

§ The remainder of Gregory's memorandum is so important a document, as the first recorded statement of what Newton intended, that it is reprinted in full:
" His doubt was whether he should put the last Quaere thus. *What the space that is empty of body is filled with.* The plain truth is, that he believes God to be omnipresent in the literal sense; and that as we are sensible of objects when their images are brought home within the brain, so God must be sensible of every thing, being intimately present with every thing: for he supposes that as God is present in space where there is no body, he is present in space where a body is also present. But if this way of proposing this his notion be too bold, he thinks of doing it thus. *What cause did the ancients assign of gravity.* He believes that they reckoned God the cause of it, nothing els, that is no body being the cause; since every body is heavy.
" One of the great scruples that men commonly have about matter's being proportional to weight, is that water that is more than 12 times lighter than gold, & gold scarce half full, as appears by many experiments; that water is not one part of twenty full matter, & yet by the strongest machine incomprehensible [incompressible]. Sir Isaac Newton proposes this as one theory of making bodys in any degree porous & yet solid. The smallest parts, or of the first row, are so cast together (and kept by their mutual attraction) as to leave half void: Then those masses thus formed, by their mutual attraction are kept together in one mass, so that the void of this last composition is one half, reckoning the masses of the first row intirely solid, so that in such a mass as this (which we shall call of the 2d composition or row) there is but a fourth part matter, and $\frac{3}{4}$ void. If now these masses be cast together so as to touch one another, and leave $\frac{1}{2}$ void, and make up a mass of the 3d row, the matter in such a body is but $\frac{1}{8}$ of full matter. And in this progression, the affair stands thus:

Row	1.	2.	3.	4.	5.
Matter	$\frac{1}{2}$	$\frac{1}{4}$	$\frac{1}{8}$	$\frac{1}{16}$	$\frac{1}{32}$
Void	$\frac{1}{2}$	$\frac{3}{4}$	$\frac{7}{8}$	$\frac{15}{16}$	$\frac{31}{32}$

and generally if the row (or order, or composition) be a; the void left in the interstices of the parts of every row $1/b$; then the quantity of matter in every row will be $1/b^a$ and the void in that row will be $(b^a-1)/b^a$.
" Sir Isaac Newton believes that the rays of light enter into the composition of most natural bodys, that is the small particles that are projected from a lucid body in the form of rays. Its plain this may be the case with most combustible, inflammable bodys.
" Gun-powder fired in vacuo produces common air. The first explosion seems to produce more; but after two, or more days there is about $\frac{1}{5}$ or $\frac{1}{6}$ of the powders weight of air, that is permanent." [77]

incapable of proof, but there was no doubt in the eighteenth century that they were a vital part of the Newtonian philosophy, hypotheses and all.

Newton's Experimental Philosophy

Since to a considerable degree the *Principia* embodied a "synthetic" approach to nature, as Newton expressed it, there was little place for physical speculation. Apart from a "General Scholium" here and there, and occasional obscure hints, Newton was content to set forth mathematical implications of fundamental axioms without being particularly disturbed by their physical consequences. A comparison of Newton's treatment of repulsion in the *Principia* and in the *Opticks* will show, in a particular example of some importance, just how these two books were related to the rise of such physical theories as electricity in the eighteenth century. In the *Principia* Newton treated repulsion in purely mathematical terms. Thus his treatment of Boyle's law consisted in proving a pair of theorems which may be stated: (*i*) If a gas be composed of mutually repellent particles and if the density of a given quantity of that gas be proportional to the pressure, then the force of repulsion between particles will be inversely proportional to the distance between the centers of the particles; (*ii*) A collection of gas particles, repelling one another with a force inversely proportional to the distance between their centers, will have a density proportional to the pressure.* These he generalized: [78] If D be the distance between particles, and E the density of the compressed gas, then if the repulsive power between particles be inversely proportional to D^n, the "compressing forces" will be as $\sqrt[3]{E^{n+2}}$.

What steps underlie the above reasoning? First the application of the method of "analysis"—"making experiments and observations, and . . . drawing general conclusions from them by induction" —the Baconian method, applied by Boyle to show that at constant temperature the density of a confined gas (or a constant mass of gas) is proportional to the pressure. Finally, the fruit of "analysis" —"from motions to the forces producing them," a repulsive force between the particles. "Synthesis" then consisted in "assuming the causes discovered . . . and by them explaining the phænomena proceeding from them." Newton not only did so, but generalized the mathematical relation. Yet, after proceeding so far, Newton stated only: "But whether elastic fluids do really consist of particles so repelling each other, is a physical question. We have here demonstrated mathematically the property of fluids consisting of particles

---

* This topic is presented from a different point of view in Appendix One.

of this kind, that hence philosophers may take occasion to discuss that question." †

But if the mathematical connexity between propositions might suffice in the *Principia*, it did not in the *Opticks*. In " Quest. 31 " of the latter, Newton asked: " Have not the small particles of bodies certain powers, virtues, or forces, by which they act at a distance, not only upon the rays of light for reflecting, refracting, and inflecting them, but also upon one another for producing a great part of the phænomena of nature? " The " parts of all homogeneal hard bodies which fully touch one another, stick together very strongly. . . . I had rather infer from their cohesion, that their particles attract one another by some force, which in immediate contact is exceeding strong, at small distances performs the chymical operations above-mentioned, and reaches not far from the particles with any sensible effect." [79] Furthermore, Newton provided evidence to show that there " are therefore agents in nature able to make the particles of bodies stick together by very strong attractions. And it is the business of experimental philosophy to find them out." [80]

How " experimental philosophy " proceeds is shown as follows. First Newton pointed out that

. . . the smallest particles of matter may cohere by the strongest attractions, and compose bigger particles of weaker virtue; and many of these may cohere and compose bigger particles whose virtue is still weaker, and so on for divers successions, until the progression end in the biggest particles on which the operations in chymistry, and the colours of natural bodies depend, and which by cohering compose bodies of a sensible magnitude.[81]

After a discussion of the internal forces of attraction in bodies as related to their hardness, elasticity, malleability, fluidity, and so on, Newton shifted from a discussion of attraction to a discussion of repulsion. Just " as in algebra, where affirmative [i. e., positive] quantities vanish and cease, there negative ones begin; so in mechanicks, where attraction ceases, there a repulsive virtue ought to succeed." That such repulsion does actually exist was made reasonable by a number of examples. The last example was that of a gas, an

† Newton indicated that his argument was based on a presupposition " of particles whose centrifugal forces terminate in those particles that are next them, or are diffused not much farther. We have an example of this in magnetic bodies. Their attractive force is terminated nearly in bodies of their own kind that are next them. The force of the magnet is reduced by the interposition of an iron plate, and is almost terminated at it: for bodies farther off are not attracted by the magnet so much as by the iron plate. If in this manner particles repel others of their own kind that lie next them, but do not exert their force on the more remote, particles of this kind will compose such fluids as are treated of in this Proposition. If the force of any particle diffuse itself every way *in infinitum*, there will be required a greater force to produce an equal condensation of a greater quantity of the fluid."

" elastick fluid," which, according to Newton, was unintelligible " by feigning the particles of air to be springy and ramous, or rolled up like hoops, or by any other means than a repulsive power." The state of a body being liquid or being a " true permanent air " was accounted for in terms of the extent of the repulsion between the particles of which it is composed.

Newton proceeded to the conclusion that " thus Nature will be very conformable to her self," producing " all the great motions " of the various heavenly bodies in their respective orbits " by the attraction of gravity which intercedes those bodies," and producing all the " small " motions of the particles within those bodies " by some other attractive and repelling powers which intercede the particles." [82]

Where does motion come from?—Newton asked next. Not from the *Vis inertiæ*, since that is a " passive principle "; by its action alone " there could never have been any motion in the world." Hence some other principle was initially " necessary for putting bodies into motion." And, once in motion, yet another principle was " necessary for conserving the motion." The necessity of the latter principle was rendered evident by a few examples showing that motion tends to decrease, e. g., the loss of motion when two swinging pendulums, whose bobs are made of a soft, inelastic material, collide. Whence, concluded, Newton,

Seeing therefore the variety of motion which we find in the world is always decreasing, there is a necessity of conserving and recruiting it by active principles, such as the cause of gravity, by which planets and comets keep their motions in their orbs, and bodies acquire great motion in falling; and the cause of fermentation, by which the heart and blood of animals are kept in perpetual motion and heat; the inward parts of the earth are constantly warmed, and in some places grow very hot; bodies burn and shine, mountains take fire, the caverns of the earth are blown up, and the Sun continues violently hot and lucid, and warms all things by his light. For we meet with very little motion in the world, besides what is owing to these active principles.[83]

Having proved to his own satisfaction that the continuance of the universe, of the earth and the life upon it, depended on the principles activating matter and putting the particles of matter into motion, Newton was led to the conclusion so often to be quoted in the following two centuries:

All these things being considered, it seems probable to me, that God in the beginning formed matter in solid, massy, hard, impenetrable, moveable particles, of such sizes and figures, and with such other properties, and in such proportion to space, as most conduced to the end for which he formed them; and that these primitive particles being solids, are incomparably harder than any porous bodies compounded of them; even so very hard, as never to wear or break in pieces; no ordinary power being able to divide what God himself made one in the first Creation. . . .

And therefore, that Nature may be lasting, the changes of corporeal things are to be placed only in the various separations and new associations and motions of these permanent particles; compound bodies being apt to break, not in the midst of solid particles, but where those particles are laid together, and only touch in a few points.[84]

Furthermore, it seemed to Newton that these particles not only have a *Vis inertiæ*, " but also that they are moved by certain active principles, such as is that of gravity, and that which causes fermentation, and the cohesion of bodies." [85]

Now these principles were not to be confused with " occult qualities, supposed to result from the specifick forms of things," in the manner in which " the *Aristotelians* gave the name of occult qualities . . . to such qualities as they supposed to lie hid in bodies, and to be the unknown causes of manifest effects." Rather, Newton considered these principles " as general laws of nature, by which the things themselves are formed; their truth appearing to us by phænomena, though their causes be not yet discovered." In other words, though the cause might remain hidden, the effects were " manifest qualities." Newton insisted that the " forces or actions " of " gravity, and of magnetick and electrick attractions, and of fermentations " could not arise from " qualities unknown to us, and incapable of being discovered or made manifest." The introduction of the theory of " occult qualities " has been deleterious to the advancement of learning and actually " put a stop to the improvement of natural philosophy." (So Newton ranged himself beside Bacon and Boyle and applauded their labor to replace the doctrine of " forms " and " qualities " by the " mechanical " or " corpuscular philosophy.") Therefore, " occult qualities . . . of late years have been rejected. To tell us that every species of thing is endowed with an occult specifick quality by which it acts and produces manifest effects, is to tell us nothing."

Newton endorsed the ideal of experimental natural philosophy: ". . . to derive two or three general principles of motion from phænomena, and afterwards to tell us how the properties and actions of all corporeal things follow from those manifest principles, would be a very great step in philosophy, though the causes of those principles were not yet discovered." Thus the development of one problem, repulsion, in relation to attraction, brought to light the whole method of experiment and " analysis," and discovered a complete philosophy. A single query in the *Opticks* could set forth a programme of research and study, based on experiment, observation, and the formulation of general principles.

The statement of Newton quoted in the preceding paragraph offers a proximate description of the attack on the subject of electricity by the early eighteenth-century investigators, which reached its first successful stage in Benjamin Franklin's theory of electrical action. The penetrating character of Franklin's analysis rendered his principles general, applying to some extent to all corpuscular phenomena and therefore having a useful transfer value to non-electrical phenomena, e. g., heat, magnetism, optics, pneumatics, and chemistry. It is in this sense, I believe, that we must view Franklin's work in science. Newton's contributions, in the *Opticks*, placed the corpuscular philosophy on a new level of profundity and application that was highly esteemed by his contemporaries and that made his book the guide for speculative experimenters of the next generations. Franklin provided an instance of the next stage in the growth of the corpuscular philosophy by showing how ingenious experiment and brilliant "analysis" could extend the Newtonian achievement into new areas and in wholly unexpected ways. Viewed in this light, of speculative-experimental Newtoniansm, the role of Benjamin Franklin in the development of the physical thought of the eighteenth century becomes clearer and the contemporary references to him as a "Newton" lose their former ambiguity. In other words, by looking at Franklin as his contemporaries saw him, and appreciating Newtonianism as having two parts, of which one—that of the experimental "analytic" Newton of the *Opticks*—has been obscured by the more obvious glamor of the other, we gain a picture of Franklin in the age of Newton that at once explains the nature of the tributes paid to him by his own age and the degree to which these laudatory sentiments may have been appropriate.

SOURCES

In presenting aspects of Newton's *Opticks* in this chapter, I have followed the leads given by the eighteenth-century commentators on Newton and a variety of eighteenth-century experimental scientists. The most popular vulgarizations of Newton include Maclaurin (1748), Voltaire (1737), and Pemberton (1728). Some of the major Newtonian textbooks will be discussed in Chapter Seven. The writings of Priestley have been most helpful, as have been the scientific dictionaries of the eighteenth century.

The best secondary accounts of Newton's work in optics are Mach (1926), Priestley (1772), Roberts and Thomas (1934), Ronchi (1939), Rosenberger (1895), and Wilde (1843). Jourdain's articles are also of value.

The influence of Newton's *Opticks* on the experimental science of the eighteenth century has been studied thus far chiefly in relation to chemistry, notably in Metzger (1930), although a valuable hint in this regard was given in Duhem (1902) and in Meldrum (1910). The influence of the *Opticks* on Hales is made clear in Guerlac (1951). Much useful information may be found in McKie (1942*b*).

I have had considerable help in understanding the structure of Newton's *Opticks* from the labors of a former student and colleague, Professor Duane H. D. Roller of the University of Oklahoma, who has made the valuable analytical table of contents to the 1950 edition, in which I have discussed the history of the reputation of Newton's views on light and the æther. Another former student and colleague, Professor Robert E. Schofield of the University of Kansas, was my guide through the writings of Priestley.

References to the *Opticks* are made by " book," " proposition," and " query," so that they may be found in any edition. In general, I have used the final corrected version made by Newton. The pages of Newton's text in the 1931 edition of the *Opticks* (published by G. Bell & Sons in London) are identical to those in Newton (1952), but only the latter has an analytical table of contents.

The section dealing with the pre-Newtonian history of " analytic " and " synthetic " methods in physical science derives chiefly from Crombie (1953*b*), and from suggestions made by Professor Marshall Clagett of the University of Wisconsin.

REFERENCES

1. Koyré, 1950.
2. Bentley, 1838: 3: 150.
3. See Babson Catalogue, 1950; Gray, 1907.
4. Newton, 1952: 20.
5. *Ibid.*, 15-16.
6. *Ibid.*, 19.

7. *Opticks*, bk. I, pt. I, prop. I, theor. I, scholium; Newton, 1952: 25.

8. *Opticks*, bk. I, pt. I, prop. VI, theor. V, expt. 15: Newton, 1952: 80.

9. *Opticks*, bk. I, pt. I, prop. VI, theor. V, expt. 15; Newton, 1952: 82.

10. More, 1934: 88.

11. More, 1934: 87.

12. Newton to Oldenburg, 2 June 1672, More, 1934: 87; see the comment by F. Cajori in Newton, 1934: 673.

13. Newton to Oldenburg, 11 July 1672, Newton, 1779-1785: 4: 324.

14. *Opticks*, bk. II. pt. I, intro.; Newton, 1952: 193.

15. *Idem.*

16. *Opticks*, bk. II, pt. II, intro.; Newton, 1952: 225.

17. *Opticks*, bk. II, pt. II, conclusion; Newton, 1952: 243-244.

18. *Idem.*

19. Newton to Oldenburg, 11 July 1672, Newton, 1779-1785: 4: 342.

20. *Opticks*, bk. II, pt. II, intro.; Newton, 1952: 225.

21. *Opticks*, bk. II, pt. II; Newton, 1952: 240.

22. *Opticks*, bk. II, pt. II; Newton, 1952: 240-242.

23. *Idem.*

24. *Opticks*, bk. II, pt. III, intro.; Newton, 1952: 245.

25. *Idem.*

26. Newton, 1952: 251.

27. *Ibid.*, 255.

28. *Opticks*, bk. II, pt. III, prop. VIII; Newton, 1952: 267.

29. *Opticks*, bk. II, pt. III, prop. VII; Newton, 1952: 255.

30. *Opticks*, bk. II, pt. III, prop. VII; Newton, 1952: 261.

31. *Opticks*, bk. II, pt. III, prop. VII; Newton, 1952: 262.

32. *Idem.*

33. *Opticks*, bk. II, pt. III, prop. VIII; Newton, 1952: 266.

34. *Opticks*, bk. II, pt. III, prop. VIII; Newton, 1952: 267.

35. *Opticks*, bk. II, pt. III, prop. VIII; Newton, 1952: 269.

36. *Opticks*, bk. II, pt. III, prop. X; Newton, 1952: 270; see also prop. IX.

37. *Opticks*, bk. II, pt. III, prop. X, table; Newton, 1952: 272.

38. *Opticks*, bk. II, pt. III, prop. X; Newton, 1952: 275.

39. Priestley, 1775: 2: 79-81.

40. *Opticks*, bk. II, pt. III, prop. XII; Newton, 1952: 280.

41. *Opticks*, bk. III, qu. 1; Newton, 1952: 339.

42. *Opticks*, bk. II, pt. III, prop. VIII; Newton, 1952: 266.

43. *Opticks*, bk. III, qu. 28; Newton, 1952: 362.

44. See Andrade, 1954: ch. 8.

45. Jourdain, 1915*a*; 1915*b*; 1915*c*.

46. See Roller and Roller, 1953; 1954.

47. *Opticks*, bk. III, qu. 21; Newton, 1952: 351.

48. Birch, 1756-1757: 3: 248-260, 261-269, etc.; Brewster, 1855: 1: 390-409.

49. Birch, 1756-1757: 3: 247-248; Brewster, 1855: 1: 132-134. Jourdain, 1915*a*: 89, says that the date "seems to be a mistaken one."

50. *Opticks*, bk. III, qu. 24; Newton, 1952: 353.

51. Newton, 1779-1785: 4: 385-394; Brewster, 1855: 1: 409-419.

52. See Fulton, 1932*b*: 131-135; the first printing was in Boyle, 1744: 1: 70-74.

53. Robinson, 1743.

54. Ball, 1893: 158.

55. *Opticks*, bk. III, qu. 28; Newton, 1952: 369.

56. *Idem.*

57. Newton, 1952: lx.

58. Thomson, 1927.

59. *Opticks*, bk. III, qu. 31; Newton, 1952: 405.

60. *Idem.*

61. *Principia*, preface to first edition; Newton, 1934: xviii.

62. Crombie, 1953*b*: 290.
63. *Ibid.*, 25.
64. *Ibid.*, 299.
65. *Opticks*, Qu. 31; Newton, 1952: 404.
66. Crombie, 1953*b*: 306.
67. Galileo, 1953*a*: 341; 1953*b*: 328.
68. Galileo, 1953*a*: 28; 1953*b*: 23.
69. Crombie, 1953*b*: 307-308.
70. Thomson, 1872: 50.
71. Priestley, 1775: 2: 166.
72. Whitehead, 1929: 80.
73. *Idem.*
74. Priestley, 1775: 2: 168.
75. Priestley, 1781: 1: 258.
76. Maclaurin, 1748, 21.
77. Gregory, 1937: 29-31.
78. *Principia*, bk. II, prop. XXIII, th. XVIII, & scholium; Newton, 1934: 300-302.
79. *Opticks*, bk. III, qu. 31; Newton, 1952: 389.
80. *Opticks*, bk. III, qu. 31; Newton, 1952: 394.
81. *Idem.*
82. *Opticks*, bk. III, qu. 31; Newton, 1952: 397.
83. *Opticks*, bk. III, qu. 31; Newton, 1952: 399.
84. *Opticks*, bk. III, qu. 31; Newton, 1952: 400.
85. *Opticks*, bk. III, qu. 31; Newton, 1952: 401.

PART THREE

Newton and Franklin:
The New Corpuscular Philosophy

CHAPTER SEVEN

EXPERIMENTAL NEWTONIANISM IN EXAMPLES— FRANKLIN'S INTRODUCTION TO SCIENCE

> . . . The truth, however, will never be discovered if we rest contented with discoveries already made. Besides, he who follows another not only discovers nothing, but is not even investigating. What then? Shall I not follow in the footsteps of my predecessors? I shall indeed use the old road, but if I find one that makes a shorter cut and is smoother to travel, I shall open the new road. Men who have made these discoveries before us are not our masters, but our guides. Truth lies open for all; it has not been monopolized.
>
> —SENECA (first century)

How, most economically, can we explore the development of the Newtonian speculations that nourished Benjamin Franklin's scientific genius? The literature of Newtonian science that had been written by 1750, the period of the zenith of Franklin's scientific creativity, is enormous. After examining a great many of the books and articles produced during the first fifty years of the eighteenth century, I believe that the works read by Franklin in the 1740's are representative of a great tradition in Newtonian philosophy. They provide convincing evidence to support the conclusion that, despite his ignorance in mathematics, Franklin was well grounded in the Newtonian natural philosophy. At least, the books he read acquainted him with the speculative experimental Newtonian philosophy, which derived in large measure from the consideration of the third book of the *Opticks* and which was in a line of descent from Bacon and Boyle: the speculative exact corpuscular philosophy of which Franklin became an acknowledged master.

In the course of this chapter it will be shown that Franklin read and admired the works of Boyle and Newton's *Opticks*; and that the scientific books he read before he began his research in electricity conveyed to him the atomistic concepts of Newton, and the Newtonian speculations and hypotheses about the æther and the nature and construction of matter. We shall be prepared, then, to see Franklin applying Newtonian principles to the explanation of electrical phenomena and to problems of heat and light. The significant alterations of generally received notions which were implied by Franklin's work show us his original creative power.

205

Franklin's Scientific Preparation

It is usually assumed that Franklin became seriously interested in the study of science on one of two occasions: his encounter with Dr. Adam Spencer in Boston in 1744 or the receipt by the Library Company of a gift of electrical apparatus from Peter Collinson in either 1746 or '47.[1] A moment's reflection on the rapid progress Franklin then made in clarifying the whole subject of electricity should indicate that he must have already had some grounding in scientific principles. He not only devised clever experiments to uncover new facts or phenomena, but also was able to construct a Newtonian theory of electrical action which exhibits a thorough familiarity with the basic principles of speculative experimental Newtonian philosophy.

In 1744, the year when Franklin first met Dr. Spencer, he published a pamphlet describing the new stove he had invented and referred in it to certain great masters of experimental science.[2] From yet other sources we learn of the authors of scientific treatises he had read: among them were Boerhaave, Desaguliers, 'sGravesande, and Hales. Clare's book on fluids, written in the spirit of Robert Boyle with overtones of the Newtonian philosophy, was well known to him, and was an important source of many of his later meteorological observations and conjectures, notably on winds and cloud formation. We do not know exactly when Franklin first studied Newton's *Opticks*, but in 1752 he wrote to Cadwallader Colden that he had "resolved to read and consider more carefully Sir Isaac Newton's *Opticks*, which I have not looked at these many years."[3] We may presume from the use of the word "many" that Franklin may well have read Newton's *Opticks* prior to 1746 or '47 when he began his work in electricity. We know of Franklin's study of the writings of the Hon. Robert Boyle, for whom he had great admiration, since in 1744 he wrote to William Strahan that the Library Company already had both "Bolton's and Shaw's abridgments of Boyle's works,"[4] printed respectively in 1699 and 1738, but that he would "mention to the directors the edition of his works at large." The Library agreed to Franklin's suggestion of purchasing the complete edition of 1744 and still possesses it. Franklin had evidently read Shaw's "abridgment," because he quoted from it (with reference to page and number) in his pamphlet on the "Pennsylvanian fire-places."[5]

Franklin had been interested in science from the days of his youth, although the period of his most intensive reading of scientific books seems to have occurred in the mid-1740's, just before he began his research in electricity. One can see, therefore, that Franklin received the electrical apparatus from Collinson at just the right time; absorbed as he was in studying science from books, he quickly used the apparatus to perform the experiments he had been reading about. His scientific interests were profitably diverted from the study of books to the study of nature. Yet earlier than the 1740's, Franklin had been studying scientific questions with his fellow Junto members, and they had all been doing simple experiments even before Franklin undertook the systematic exploration of electrical phenomena.

We have no idea of just when Franklin began to hear about science, but we may be certain that one of the important early sources of Franklin's scientific knowledge was Cotton Mather, F.R.S.* As a boy, Franklin often listened to Mather's sermons,[7] many of which were Newtonian discourses with " religious improvements." Mather referred to Newton, in a sermon delivered in 1712, as our " perpetual Dictator," [8] a phrase he also used later on in recommending the new experimental science to candidates for the ministry.[9] Before Franklin left Boston for Philadelphia, Cotton Mather had published in 1720 his *Christian Philosopher*, an account of the " best discoveries " in science (of course with " religious improvements ") [10] which may be described as the first general or popular book on science to be written by an American; it is larded with glowing encomiums of the Newtonian natural philosophy. One of the authors quoted by Mather was Sir Richard Blackmore, whose poem *The Creation* was warmly recommended by Franklin to be read as part of a private religious ceremony he devised in 1728.[11] Incidentally, we may observe that Blackmore, in a passage reprinted by Mather, suggested an explanation of the phenomena of light by undulations of an æther: an hypothesis which Franklin later advanced with considerable firmness. One of the members of James Franklin's circle, while Franklin was an apprentice, was Dr. William Douglass, who received the *Philosophical Transactions* of the Royal Society. It will be recalled that one of Cotton Mather's incentives to recommend the practice of inoculation against smallpox was an article in the *Philosophical Transactions* which he had borrowed from Douglass. Franklin, an omniverous reader, may also have borrowed some issues of the *Transactions* from Douglass.

Yet another source of scientific ideas was the Boyle Lectures,

---

* In later life Franklin acknowledged a debt to Mather as one who had influenced his career as a " doer of good." Evidently Franklin soon forgot the animosity to Mather he had felt as a boy of sixteen, when he had joined his brother James's anti-Mather crusade and had written a series of burlesques under the pen-name of " Silence Dogood," a double-thrust at Cotton Mather.[6]

which had been established by the will of the Hon. Robert Boyle. These lectures or sermons were intended to present a confutation of atheism. In his autobiography, Franklin recalled how, at the age of fifteen, he had been reading some books " said to be the substance of sermons preached at Boyle's Lectures " which had altered his religious beliefs in a way not intended by the founder of the lectures.† By the time Franklin was fifteen, in 1721, some thirty years had elapsed since the establishment of the lectures. The first series, delivered by Richard Bentley, concluded with two lectures or sermons that may be considered the first printed popular exposition of Newton's *Principia* and they were many times reprinted.[12] Samuel Clarke's *Demonstration of the Being and Attributes of God* (read in 1704 and 1705, printed in 1706) was also popular. Clarke was a master exponent of the Newtonian philosophy and later prepared the Latin version of Newton's *Opticks* at Newton's suggestion; he was the editor of the famous edition of Rohault's book on Cartesian physics which contained anti-Cartesian Newtonian notes.‡ Franklin would not have had to read very far in Clarke's *Demonstration* before he began to find Newton's *Principia* being cited as the supreme reference; he would also have encountered laudatory citations of Boyle. William Derham's *Physico-Theology* (read in 1711-1712, printed 1713) was widely reprinted and translated and was also grounded solidly on the Newtonian philosophy. It is no exaggeration to say that the Boyle Lectures as a whole constituted a major source for the propagation of the Newtonian natural philosophy during the first decades of the eighteenth century. One cannot imagine an intelligent lad like Franklin reading them and remaining ignorant of Newton and the significance of his work.

When Franklin went to London for the first time in 1724, at the age of 18, he had already developed a serious interest in science and was undoubtedly an admirer of Newton. In London he made the acquaintance of a number of London scientists, among them Sir Hans Sloane, to whom he sold a purse made of asbestos, which is still one of the treasures in the British Museum (natural history) which Sloane founded.[13] Among Franklin's intimates was Dr. Henry Pemberton, who was then preparing—under Newton's direction—the third edition of the *Principia*. One can easily imagine Franklin's elation when Pemberton promised to introduce him to the great man and the bitter disappointment when the proposed meeting did not come off. The sense of frustration at his failure to meet Newton

† ". . . the arguments of the Deists, which were quoted to be refuted, appeared to me much stronger than the refutations; in short, I soon became a thorough Deist."
‡ The Clarke edition of Rohault has been discussed earlier in Chapter Four.

lingered on with Franklin for the rest of his life, as such things do. Fifty years later, when writing his autobiographical memoirs, Franklin could not help referring with regret to the ill-fated attempt to come into the presence of Newton. He had sat at table with royal persons, but had never met the prince of science.

One possible effect of Franklin's many conversations with Pemberton was suggested by the first important biographer of Franklin, James Parton, about a hundred years ago. Soon after Franklin returned to Philadelphia from London, he wrote out a religious creed in which he intimated the possibility of many Gods, each of which had created a sun and a system of planets.[14] Franklin's statement has provoked a considerable discussion of " Pythagoreanism " and the like, but Parton showed that Newton had been expressing a similar belief at the very time when Franklin was in London,[15] and that Pemberton might well have been expected to have relayed the " old man's " extravagant ideas to his coffee-house companions.[16]

Franklin's reading in Pemberton, Boerhaave, 'sGravesande, Desaguliers, and Hales, prepared him for his research in electricity by making him a Newtonian scientist. The kind of Newtonian science Franklin encountered in these writings, one which we shall explore, was related to the tradition of Boyle (whose works Franklin had studied and admired in the mid-1740's), and Newton's *Opticks* (which Franklin had also read in the 1740's). I shall present the work of each of these authors separately, treating it in relation to speculative Newtonian experimental science and to the growth of Franklin's scientific thought.

1. Pemberton's *View of Sir Isaac Newton's Philosophy*

In 1728, two years after the appearance of the third edition of the *Principia* which he had edited, Pemberton published a non-technical *View of Sir Isaac Newton's Philosophy*. At this time Franklin was back in America, and had just begun his own printing business in partnership with Meredith. Could Franklin have failed to be interested in a book by his London companion on a subject which had so excited his curiosity and attention? Soon after the establishment of the Library Company of Philadelphia, Peter Collinson, F.R.S., agreed to become their London agent for the purchase of books. To encourage the Philadelphia group, Collinson sent them a personal gift in 1732 which included a copy of Pemberton's book.

The *View of Sir Isaac Newton's Philosophy* is one of the three outstanding popular introductions to Newtonian science of the eighteenth century, the other two being Colin Maclaurin's *Account of Sir Isaac Newton's Philosophical Discoveries* and Voltaire's *Elements of ... Newton's Philosophy.* Voltaire's *Elements,* printed in French in 1738, was published in the same year in an English translation, and in 1742 in Italian. Maclaurin's *Account* appeared in 1748, a posthumous publication for the financial benefit of his children, and further editions were published in 1750 and 1775.[17] Maclaurin was acquainted with Newton, who had recommended him for the Professorship of Mathematics in the University of Edinburgh, but he was not in direct contact with Newton at the time of writing his *Account,* so that like Voltaire's *Elements* it is a free interpretation.§ Pemberton was practically in the situation of writing with Newton peering over his shoulder. His book is, therefore, a statement more nearly in accordance with what Newton said about science, and less in accordance with what Newton did, than either Maclaurin's book or Voltaire's.

Although Pemberton's *View* was published in 1728 after Newton's death (in March, 1727), he had written it while Newton was still alive. Pemberton recorded that as a result of his collaboration with Newton in editing the third edition of the *Principia,* " [I was obliged] to be very frequently with him, and as he lived at some distance from me, a great number of letters passed between us. . . ." [18] The *View of Sir Isaac Newton's Philosophy* * was drawn up not just for those " whose turn of mind had led them into a course of mathematical studies," but was intended " to give a general notion of our great philosopher's inventions to such as are not prepared to read his own works, and yet might desire to be informed of the progress he has made in natural knowledge." [19] Newton had at one time intended to present " that part of his inventions which relates to the system of the world " in a more familiar way than the *Principia,* Pemberton observed, but " upon farther consideration he altered his design." [20] Apparently, Newton was willing to consider Pemberton's book a reasonable substitute for that purpose, and we may take Pemberton's word for it that his presentation of the Newtonian natural philosophy was authorized by the master; Pemberton was proud that Newton " approved of the following treatise, a great part of which we read together." [21]

Some three hundred pages were devoted by Pemberton to the

§ Some aspects of Maclaurin's *Account* have been presented at the end of Chapter Six.
  * The preface begins: " I drew up the following papers many years ago at the desire of some friends, who, upon my taking care of the late edition of Sir Isaac Newton's *Principia,* perswaded me to make them publick. I laid hold of that opportunity, when my thoughts were afresh employed on this subject, to revise what I had formerly written." One purpose in writing the book " was to encourage such young gentlemen as have a turn for the mathematical sciences, to pursue those studies the more chearfully, in order to understand in our author himself the demonstrations of the things I here declare."

Principia, but less than a hundred to the *Opticks.* Pemberton admitted that Newton had not made " so full a discovery " of the principle by which the " mutual action between light and bodies is caused " as he had " in relation to the power by which the planets are kept in their courses." Even so, Newton had led us to " the very entrance upon " this principle and had " pointed out the path so plainly which must be followed to reach it, that . . . whenever mankind shall be blessed with this improvement of their knowledge, it will be derived so directly from the principles laid down by our author in this book [the *Opticks*] that the greatest share of the praise due to the discovery will belong to him." Pemberton said that the *Opticks* discloses Newton's genius no less than the *Principia,* and perhaps even more, since it " gives as many instances of . . . unbounded invention, though unassisted in great measure by those rules and general precepts which facilitate the invention of mathematical theorems." [22]

Pemberton defended Newton against those who seek " to cover the defects in our knowledge with the vain ostentation of rash and groundless conjectures," but he did point out that proofs in natural philosophy can never be " so absolutely conclusive " as in mathematics, and that in " natural knowledge " any method of arguing must " fall a little short of absolute perfection." What is required is " to steer a just course between the conjectural method of proceeding " and " demanding so rigorous a proof as will reduce all philosophy to mere scepticism and exclude all prospect of making any progress in the knowledge of nature." † Hence, in the science of nature

† Of particular interest in the light of the eighteenth-century opinion of Bacon, and his relation to the whole tradition of Newtonian science, is the general Introduction to Pemberton's book, with its continual insistence that Bacon was the best guide to principles of scientific investigation. Pemberton also referred wherever possible to the " usefulness " of Newton's discoveries. Contrasting Newton's *Opticks* to the *Principia,* at the beginning of Book Three of his *View,* Pemberton observed that the *Opticks* was not " inferior to the other in usefulness; for as that has made known to us one great principle in nature, by which the celestial motions are continued, and by which the frame of each globe is preserved; so does this point out to us another principle no less universal, upon which depends all those operations in the smaller parts of matter, for whose sake the greater frame of the universe is erected; all those immense globes, with which the whole heavens are filled, being without doubt only designed as to many convenient apartments for carrying on the more noble operations of nature in vegetation and animal life."

Pemberton particularly insisted that a sound knowledge of natural phenomena was " useful " even if " the original cause " were not fully disclosed. Not only was this true in gravitation, and in physiology, but even in that practical subject, optics. Pemberton pointed out that for a long time philosophers had busied themselves " to no purpose in endeavouring to perfect telescopes, by forming the glasses into some new figure." Then " Sir Isaac Newton demonstrated that the effects of telescopes were limited from another cause than was supposed; which no alteration in the figure of the glasses could remedy." We need not insist that a half century later Pemberton would

as opposed to mathematics, certain "concessions" must be made, and these were stated very strictly by Newton "under a very few simple precepts," by which Pemberton meant the "Rules of Philosophizing." [23] Although Pemberton referred to certain "hints," as those in Query 21 of the *Opticks,* he stated expressly that Newton made no "pompous pretense of explaining the cause of gravity." For Pemberton the one very important step toward such an explanation had been made by Newton in showing that "this power in the great bodies of the universe is derived from the same power being lodged in every particle of the matter which composes them." [24]

Pemberton described in detail Newton's experiments on dispersion, the composition of white light, and the origin of the colors observed in bodies in their ability to reflect "rays of one colour in the greatest plenty." Then he showed that Newton had indicated that the selective absorption and reflection of different colors were due to "nothing more than the different magnitude of the particles which compose each body: this, I question not, will appear no small paradox." [25] Pemberton agreed that the discussion of this subject contains assertions that are "almost incredible, though the arguments for them are so strong and convincing, that they force our assent." Whether it was the effect of Newton's presence, or the result of having been too steeped in Newton's own words, Pemberton said there was no true conjectural quality to Newton's conclusions, that Newton had "proved" that "bodies are rendered transparent by the minuteness of their pores, and become opake by having them large." [26] Yet a little later on, Pemberton observed "that the colours of bodies give a very probable ground for making conjecture concerning the magnitude of their constituent particles." Pemberton insisted that his use of the word "conjecture" does not imply that the principle is in any doubt, but only that there is some question as to the "order," and hence "the magnitude," to be assigned to any given color: "my reason for calling it a conjecture is, its being difficult to fix certainly the order of any colour." [27] This is in line with the orthodoxy to be expected of an "authorized" book, approved by Newton, and we may observe that Pemberton usually referred to Newton as "our author."

Surely, Pemberton had sufficient intelligence to recognize the hypothetical, speculative, or conjectural character of the conclusions he described: as "our author's" observations "that the action be-

have been forced to admit that on the practical side Newton had here been mistaken, at least in so far as the possibility of achromatic doublets was concerned. But we may take note of the doctrine of "usefulness" expounded in a book whose author indicated his admiration for Bacon was not limited to practical gadgets, but included the usefulness in correlating or explaining observed natural phenomena.

tween light and bodies is mutual, since sulphureous bodies, which are most readily set on fire by the sun's light, when collected upon them with a burning glass, act more upon light in refracting it, than other bodies of the same density do." [28] Furthermore, " the densest bodies, which have been now shewn to act most upon light, contract the greatest heat by being exposed to the summer sun." ‡

After presenting Newton's views on fits of easy reflection and fits of easy transmission, Pemberton admitted that what the power in nature is which causes the action between light and bodies,

our author has not discovered. But the effects which he has discovered of this power are very surprising, and altogether wide from any conjectures that had ever been framed concerning it. . . . Sir Isaac Newton has in general hinted at his opinion concerning it; that probably it is owing to some very subtle and elastic substance diffused through the universe, in which such vibrations may be excited by the rays of light, as they pass through it, that shall occasion it to operate so differently upon the light in different places as to give rise to these alternate fits of reflection and transmission, of which we have now been speaking. He is of opinion that such a substance may produce this, and other effects also in nature, though it be so rare as not to give any sensible resistance to bodies in motion; and therefore not inconsistent with what has been said above, that the planets move in spaces free from resistance. [29]

Pemberton concluded by observing that at the end of the *Opticks* Newton had proposed " some thoughts concerning other parts of nature which he had not distinctly searched into." Then Pemberton mentioned once more the " very subtle spirit of a great elastic force diffused thro' the universe," which Newton thinks might be the cause of gravity. Pemberton next said a word or two about Newton's chemical experiments and stated that from numerous observations Newton " makes no doubt, that the smallest parts of matter, when near contact, act strongly on each other, sometimes mutually attracted, at other times repelled." The attractive power is more manifest than the power of repulsion, since it is the principle by which " the parts of all bodies adhere." The " name of attraction," which Newton gave to it, " has been very freely made use of by many writers, and as much objected to by others. He has often complained to me of having been misunderstood in this matter. What he says upon this head was not intended by him as a philosophical explanation of any appearances, but only to point out a power in nature not hitherto distinctly observed, the cause of which, and the manner of its acting, he thought was worthy of diligent inquiry. To acquiesce

‡ The relative ability to absorb heat in materials of different color is discussed at greater length, below, on pages 216-222.

in the explanation of any appearance by asserting it to be a general power of attraction, is not to improve our knowledge in philosophy, but rather to put a stop to our farther search." [30] Restrained though Pemberton was, he did allude to Newton's hypothesis on a grand scale of a universal all-pervading æther, admitting that Newton " thinks it not impossible, that the power of gravity itself should be owing to it." [31]

Pemberton's presentation offered a splendid introduction to what Newton had done, but it would not have stimulated a reader to go out and perform experiments. As such, its major influence was in the dissemination of scientific knowledge; unlike the books of Boerhaave, Desaguliers, and Hales, it was not a book that produced doubt and encouraged wonder. It was rather a sort of self-congratulatory message on what had been accomplished to date. Although indications were offered that further progress might be made here and there, Pemberton made it perfectly clear that the credit for all future work would have to go to Newton since he had undoubtedly laid the foundations for any progress that would ever be made in the physical sciences.

2. Boerhaave's *Chemistry*

The rise of experimental science in early and mid-eighteenth-century Holland has been marked by many students and was the subject of an important monograph by the late Pierre Brunet. Three of the leading Dutch exponents of " experimental philosophy " were Boerhaave, 'sGravesande, and Musschenbroek. The large number of students from different countries who came to Holland to study with these three men provides some measure of their prominence and influence, as do the many editions and translations of their works.

Hermann Boerhaave is a fascinating figure to the historian of science because he was so widely admired in his own day and is virtually unknown (save to historians) today. If we read history of science backwards—that is, looking through the records for great discoveries that contain the germs of what we believe today—Boerhaave does not appear. His name is not associated with any effects, principles or fundamental laws of nature. Yet it would be extremely difficult to find any important scientist of the early and mid-eighteenth century who was not affected by his teaching, and more difficult still to find any scientific teacher more widely known or more influential than he was.

When Boerhaave died in 1738, " Western medicine lost its undisputed master." Henry E. Sigerist adduces evidence for this statement as follows: " Never before had a medical teacher exerted such a far-reaching influence. Never before had a physician been so universally admired and beloved." In some measure, the cause of this universal admiration was, according to Sigerist, Boerhaave's " fascinating personality "; the fame of his books was not due only to their excellence, but to the personal reputation of their author.[32]

Born in 1668, Boerhaave became in 1701 lecturer on the institutes of medicine at Leiden; in 1709, professor of botany and medicine; in 1714, professor of practical medicine as well; and in 1718, he added to these posts the professorship of chemistry. This remarkable man, who occupied not one academic chair " but a whole settee," began as a philosopher or theologian, but turned to biology and medicine as a partial consequence of having studied Spinoza. His teaching not only emphasized the fundamental sciences—anatomy, physiology, botany, physics, chemistry, and mathematics—as a basis for medicine, but also embraced clinical or bedside teaching. A class list of 1737 shows 97 members, including 37 Dutchmen, 23 Englishmen, 5 Scotsmen, 3 Irishmen, 10 Germans, 3 Swedes, 2 Russians, 2 Swiss, 1 Dane, I Frenchman, and a Greek from Constantinople.[33]

Boerhaave's influence on eighteenth-century American medicine was as great as it was on European medicine, and his works were widely read in colonial America. Franklin, in 1744, mentioned his name twice. In a letter to his parents, written from Philadelphia on 6 September 1744, in which he indulged " in prescribing and meddling in the doctor's sphere," Franklin observed that " salt " was the principal ingredient of " Mrs. Stevens's medicine for the stone and gravel, the secret of which was lately purchased at a great price by the Parliament," and he noted that Boerhaave had called salt " the most universal remedy." [34] In his *Account of the New-invented Pennsylvanian Fire-places*, published in 1744, Franklin cited " the great Dr. Boerhaave, whose authority alone might be sufficient, [who] in his *Aphorisms* [:*concerning the knowledge and cure of diseases*] mentions, as one antecedent cause of pleurisies, ' a cold air driven violently through some narrow passage upon the body, overheated by labour or fire.' " [35]

Of all Boerhaave's books, the one that had the greatest influence on eighteenth-century physical thought was his treatise on chemistry. This work had a curious history in that the earliest form of it was issued without the author's knowledge or consent. Entitled *Institutiones et Experimenta Chemiæ*, it appeared in 1724 in two octavo volumes bearing a Paris imprint (but no publisher), although it seems likely that the place of publication was actually Leiden.[36] A production of his pupils, based on their lecture notes, this " spurious " edition was reprinted in Venice in 1726 and was translated into English by Peter Shaw and E. Chambers under the title, *A New Method of Chemistry; including the theory and practice of that art: laid down on mechanical principles, and accommodated to the uses of life. The whole making a clear and rational system of chemical philosophy* (1727).

Boerhaave became angry at the deception of the public in the presentation of his lectures from notes as if they were a finished product of his pen, and he undertook to prepare a genuine edition, which appeared in Latin in 1732 in two quarto volumes, under the title *Elementa Chemiæ*. The genuine work was translated for the English-reading public by Peter Shaw in 1741. Shaw entitled this 1741 translation in a somewhat misleading fashion, presenting it as a " second edition " of the 1727 translation made by him and Chambers. The popularity of this textbook was sufficient to warrant a " third " English edition in 1753. A rival translation of the genuine edition had been made by a former student of Boerhaave—Timothy Dallowe—and had appeared in 1735, but it never became as widely used as the Shaw translation.

Franklin certainly had read Boerhaave's *Chemistry*. In 1744 he issued *A Catalogue of Choice and Valuable books . . . to be sold for ready money only by Benj. Franklin*,[37] in which the " second edition " (by Shaw alone, 1741) appeared under " Books in quarto " as No. 74, " Boerhaave's Chemistry, with a curious appendix by Dr. Shaw, 2 vols." To be sure, the mere presence of this work in a catalogue of books does not prove that Franklin had read it, but we must remember that 1744 was the year in which Franklin published his account of the Pennsylvanian fireplaces (in which Boerhaave's *Aphorisms* were quoted with great approval) and in this pamphlet Franklin was very much concerned with heat and " fire "—subjects for which Boerhaave's *Chemistry* was particularly noteworthy. Furthermore the English version by Shaw and Chambers (1727) was bought by the Library Company in 1732 and the " second edition " (1741) was ordered in 1743, and received in 1744. We know from other sources that by 1744 Franklin had already studied either Boerhaave's genuine Latin edition of 1732 or Timothy Dallowe's English version of 1735.

The Origin of Franklin's Experiments on Heat Absorption

Franklin's eventual knowledge of Boerhaave's *Chemistry* (Shaw's second edition, Dallowe's translation, or the Latin version on which they were based) is made manifest by a letter he wrote some years later to Miss Mary Stevenson, describing an experiment to test the absorption of solar heat by materials of different colors.[38] In this letter, Franklin recommended that Mary try the experiment of walking for fifteen minutes in her garden, on a bright sunny day, wearing a dress partly black and partly white. If she would then apply her hand, first to one part of the dress, and then the other, she would find " a very great difference in their warmth. The black will be quite hot to the touch, the white still cool." Another simple experiment that Franklin suggested was to try igniting paper by focussing the sun's rays with a " burning glass." If the rays were brought to a focus on a white spot, the paper would not burn as readily as if they were brought to focus on a black spot, " or upon letters, written or printed." This effect, Franklin noted, was well known to fullers and dryers, who found that " black cloths, of equal thickness with white ones, and hung out equally wet, dry in the sun much sooner than the white, being more readily heated by the sun's rays." Incidentally, he pointed out that the same phenomenon would be observed by a man wearing black stockings who sat before a fire, since his shins would get hotter than if he had been wearing white stockings. Similarly, beer set before a fire would become warmer much sooner in a black mug than in a white one or in a bright " silver tankard." Franklin then recalled from memory an experiment he had made some time previously:

My experiment was this. I took a number of little square pieces of broad cloth from a taylor's pattern-card, of various colours. There were black, deep blue, lighter blue, green, purple, red, yellow, white, and other colours, or shades of colours. I laid them all out upon the snow in a bright sun-shiny morning. In a few hours (I cannot now be exact as to the time), the black, being warmed most by the sun, was sunk so low as to be below the stroke of the sun's rays; the dark blue almost as low, the lighter blue not quite so much as the dark, the other colours less as they were lighter; and the quite white remained on the surface of the snow, not having entered it at all.

This was the occasion of Franklin's remark, so often quoted, " What signifies philosophy that does not apply to some use? " What man can learn from this experiment is that black clothes should not be worn in a " hot sunny climate or season " because " in such cloaths the body is more heated by the sun when you walk abroad," and that white clothes should be worn in hot weather. In the East or West Indies, soldiers and seamen " who must march and labour in the sun " should have white uniforms; the summer hats for men and women should be white " as repelling that heat which gives head-achs to many, and to some that fatal stroke that the French call the *coup de soleil* "; and so on.

The particulars in the above letter to Miss Stevenson very closely resemble the discussion of this subject in Boerhaave's book on chemistry. The details do not appear in the " spurious " Latin edition of 1724, but only in the genuine edition of 1732 and its later versions and reprintings, hence not in the Chambers and Shaw translation of 1727, but in the Shaw translation of 1741 and the Dallowe translation of 1735. While Franklin's letter to Miss Stevenson, dated 1761, might have been drawn from Boerhaave's Latin edition or from the translations of either Dallowe or Shaw, a record of experiment dated 1737 contains evidence that Franklin had already been reading Boerhaave. We may conclude that as early as 1737 Franklin had read Boerhaave's chemistry in either the genuine Latin original (1732) or Dallowe's translation (1735), and that later on he may very well have looked at Shaw's second version, which was particularly distinguished for the translator's extensive annotations.

Boerhaave had described the observable difference between two parts of a piece of cloth hung out in the sun, one part dyed black and the other white, and also had indicated the differential effect to be observed in pieces of cloth dyed scarlet and " others of different colours." Boerhaave had also noted, as Franklin did, that a wet black cloth will dry more quickly in the sun than a white one. Like Franklin, Boerhaave had observed that black bodies are set on fire more easily than those of any other color, and had even used the same example of igniting a piece of paper by the sun's rays focussed by a " burning glass," finding that the paper will ignite very quickly if black, slowly if white. Boerhaave, furthermore, gave the very same application of these observations as Franklin, recommending white outer garments as being " best to preserve the body from the scorching sun," while " black ones, on the contrary . . . increase the heat." From such evidence there can be no doubt that Franklin had read Boerhaave's *Chemistry*.

Though the experiment had been suggested by reading Boerhaave's chemistry, the form it took in Philadelphia was somewhat different from that described by Franklin's Dutch master. Boerhaave indicated a scale of absorption of solar heat from black to white in terms of how much a given color may " reflect the rays [of the sun] more strongly to the eye." § But the experiment as performed in Philadelphia, in which the pieces of colored cloth were placed on the snow, provided a typically Franklinian means of ascertaining the order of the colors exactly—by merely observing the depth of the melted snow under each. Furthermore, Franklin's choice of ma-

§ This is the phrase as translated by Shaw in the 1741 version; Dallowe's rendition reads: ". . . whose colours are most vivid, and affect the eyes most strongly."

terials, pieces of broadcloth from a tailor's pattern card, was ideal. That he made a greater number of applications of the phenomenon in question is apparent by comparing the two texts. The particular experiment of placing pieces of cloth of different colors on the snow, which Franklin described to Miss Stevenson as "my experiment," was original with Franklin, even if the principle illustrated by the experiment was derived from Boerhaave's book. Incidentally, although many secondary sources attribute to Franklin both the principle and the experiment, Franklin himself laid claim only to the experiment.

It has been stated above that long before the appearance of Shaw's English version of the authentic text of Boerhaave's chemistry in 1741, Franklin had read Boerhaave's book and the experiment on colors had been performed. A memorandum, dated 3 August 1737, written by Joseph Breintnal, a fellow-member of the Junto, begins as follows:

That the heat of the sun penetrates such things as are coloured more than such as are white, will appear by the following experiments, which I was induced to make about seven years ago, and lately to repeat, from some hints given me by Benjamin Franklin, and from observing that people who come among us from the warm islands do most of them wear whitish cloths, in which I suppose they find themselves cooler than in others tho' few of them may know the reason of it; from observing also that a small glass will not burn white paper, tho' it easily does if the paper be stained, and from taking notice of a young woman's complaining that her black gloves had burnt her hands.[39]

Breintnal's account of his experiments, which follows the paragraph just quoted, is dated 25 January 1736 (O. S., 1737 N. S.). He used bits of linen, silk, leather, paper, woolen cloth, feathers, and other materials, of various colors: white, light red, light yellow, light azure, lively blood-red, reddish-brown, bright cinnamon, deep grass-green, yellow-brown or dirty yellow, deep blue, gloomy red, dark olive or dark brown, and black. These objects were placed on the snow and it was soon observed that the snow underneath them had been melted to six observable degrees. Breintnal also compared the effects of the sun on the feather-end of a black quill and the like part of a white one, and on the parts of a slip of white paper of which one end had been blackened. Breintnal apparently made a copy of his account of the experiment, bearing the same date, 25 January 1736 (1737 N. S.), which is still extant among Franklin's papers in the Library of the American Philosophical Society.[40]

The memorandum, written by Breintnal under the date of 3 August 1737 and which preceded his own copy of the account of the experiment, does not afford any light on the nature of the hints given him by Franklin which had induced him to make the original experiments " about seven " years earlier, nor does it tell us about the occasion on which Franklin had given him the hints. But the similarity between the examples cited by Breintnal and by Boerhaave leaves little doubt that Franklin gave his hints to Breintnal after having read Boerhaave. In 1737, Shaw's second English edition had not yet appeared, although the Shaw and Chambers edition of the " surreptitious " or " spurious " version had been in print since 1727, prior even to Breintnal's date of " about seven years " earlier than 1736. This first version dealt more briefly with this subject than did the second; it included a discussion only of white, red, and black, but not of the different colors; nor did it mention the preference for white clothes in the summer, or the ignition of paper by focussing the sun's rays.*

Franklin's first thoughts on this subject, which he communicated to Breintnal, must therefore have been aroused by reading Boerhaave's genuine version of the *Elementa Chemiæ* in the original Latin edition of 1732, reprinted in that same year in London, or the English translation published by Dallowe in 1735. Hence when Breintnal wrote of the experiments as those " which I was induced to make about seven years ago, and lately to repeat, from some hints given me by Benjamin Franklin " and from some observations of his own, the " seven years ago " (i. e., seven years before 1737) very likely was an error for five years ago, 1732, the date of the first edition of Boerhaave's genuine work and the London reprint. A Leipzig reprint of 1732 was in James Logan's library. And we may guess that the occasion of Franklin's hints to Breintnal which induced him to repeat the experiments may have been Franklin's obtaining a copy of Dallowe's translation some time in 1736, a year after publication.

The question of the differential heat absorption of black and white objects arose originally in the *Opticks*. Proposition VII of Book Two, Part III, of the *Opticks* was intended to show that " the bigness of the component parts of natural bodies may be conjectured by their colours." This proposition is a mixture of observation and speculative hypothesis, in which Newton discussed the size of par-

---

* It reads, *in extenso*, as follows: " Thus if you hang up several different coloured clothes, in a dark place; some white, others red, and others black; and place your self at a little distance: you will perceive nothing at all where the black are; where the white are, there will something appear; so also where the red are, tho' less than where the white. Not that there is more fire in one than another; but one reflects more or fewer rays than another; so that the circumstances of light do not depend on fire, so much as on the surface of the body that reflects it." [41]

ticles and their " order " in terms of their chemical action, and such physical characteristics as density. Thus Newton essayed a discussion of the " bigness of metallick particles," and in general the " thickness " of the particles of matter. Towards the end of this proposition, Newton indicated:

. . . for the production of black, the corpuscles must be less than any of those which exhibit colours. For in all greater sizes there is too much light reflected to constitute this colour. But if they be supposed a little less than is requisite to reflect the white and very faint blue of the first order, they will . . . reflect so very little light as to appear intensely black. . . .

In this way we may understand why " fire, and the more subtile dissolver putrefaction, by dividing the particles of substance, turn them to black, why small quantities of black substances impart their colour very freely and intensely to other substances to which they are applied. . . ." Most important of all, Newton suggested that consideration of particle size affords an explanation as to " why black substances do soonest of all others become hot in the sun's light and burn, (which effect may proceed partly from the multitude of refractions in a little room, and partly from the easy commotion of so very small corpuscles;) . . . ."

It should, therefore, be noted that the part of the discussion of the problem relating to the difference in absorption of solar heat between black and white substances, and the example of the ease with which the sun's light may ignite black material as compared to white, had been posed by Newton. These questions entered Newton's discussion of the fundamental nature of matter, as related to the size of the ultimate particles or corpuscles of which bodies are composed. Since white and black were the extremes, and since the other colors ranged in order between these two extremes, the absorption of solar heat might well be expected to vary more or less continuously through the visible spectrum but Newton did not say so. Boerhaave's extension of Newton's observations was ingenious, if not particularly astonishing, although it must be noted that Newton did not take up the question of the heating of bodies, but only the upper limit of heating—that is, actual ignition and burning.

Newton returned to this question in the " Queries " at the end of Book Three of the *Opticks*. In Query 5, he discussed bodies and light acting mutually upon one another in the sense that bodies emit, reflect, refract, and " inflect " (diffract) light and that light heats bodies and puts " their parts into a vibrating motion wherein heat consists." Newton asked, " Do not black bodies conceive heat more easily from light than those of other colours do, by reason that the light falling on them is not reflected outwards, but enters the bodies, and is often reflected and refracted within them, until it be stifled and lost? " The " strength and vigor of the action between light and sulphureous bodies observed above " is probably, according to Newton's next query, one reason why " sulphureous bodies take fire more readily, and burn more vehemently than other bodies do."

Finally, it may be noted that the relative absorption of heat by dark and light bodies had been studied by Boyle.[42] Thus the experiments of Franklin and Breintnal derived directly from Boerhaave, from Boyle, and from Newton's *Opticks*.

Boerhaave and the Newtonian Tradition

The work of Boerhaave in relation to the Newtonian tradition was the subject of a most revealing investigation by the late Hélène Metzger, whose penetrating studies on eighteenth-century thought cause us to say of her as Newton did of Cotes: Had Mme Metzger lived, we would have known something! (Alas, Mme Metzger was brutally murdered by the Nazis during the occupation of France!)

A statement attributed by Mme Metzger to Peter van Musschenbroek is of great importance: Musschenbroek, a great Dutch experimental physicist of the eighteenth century, was one of the inventors of the condenser. He wrote that " one should have continually before one's eyes these two perfect models that the two great men of the century have left us, that is to say, the *Opticks* of Newton and the *Chemistry* of Boerhaave" [43]

The most casual reading of Boerhaave's *Elements of Chemistry* reveals his admiration for the British school of natural philosophy; there are references to the work of Hooke and Halley; Bacon is cited with veneration; Boyle is quoted again and again, always in terms of the highest admiration; respect is paid to Newton's *Opticks*; and mention is made of Stephen Hales, whose work had been published after the " spurious " student edition of Boerhaave's book and before his own genuine version. Shaw's edition is of particular interest because of the many notes and comments he inserted. Some are brief, while others run to several pages of fine print; it is not uncommon for a printed page to contain two lines of Boerhaave's text and fifty-five lines of commentary—the latter often being reprinted from the earlier English version by Shaw and Chambers of the " spurious " edition. These commentaries or annotations are apt to consist of quotations from Boyle and Newton, and in some instances Bacon, or summaries of their respective views; this is especially true of the section of the book dealing with heat. Most of Shaw's Newtonian quotations or summaries are based on the *Opticks*, and chiefly the Queries at the end of Book Three. Thus, in one note we find that " Sir I. Newton shews that the primitive, or component particles of all bodies, are hard: that they are only laid together; and that the cause of their cohesion is some attractive force superadded to 'em . . . ," etc.† Similar notes, throughout the work, indicated that Newton's experiments and speculations about the nature and transformations of matter, in the Queries of the *Opticks*, were considered to be of paramount importance to chemical theory. Peter Shaw,[45] as Henry Guerlac [46] has indicated, shared with John Friend ‡ and Stephen Hales § the hope that " chemistry could be made an exact science modelled upon physics "—in which Newton served as the inspiration. Shaw's point of view is made plain in a footnote to this effect: " It is by means of chemistry that Sir Isaac Newton has made a great part of his surprizing discoveries in natural philosophy "; as a matter of fact, " that curious sett of queries which we find at the end of his Optics are almost wholly chemical." * The reader need not be surprised, since " chemistry, in its extent, is scarce less than the whole of natural philosophy. . . ." [48]

Again we see evidence of the importance of the *Opticks* in the work of eighteenth-century experimental scientists. To be sure, the general concepts of the *Principia* were to be kept in mind and applied whenever possible, but there was no attempt on the part of

---

† The critical reader will observe that conjectures of Newton are taken to be convincing demonstrations. The above quotation comes from the Shaw and Chambers version of 1727; in Shaw's 1741 version, this note begins, " Sir Isaac Newton suspects. . . ." The notes to Boerhaave's *Chemistry* provide many examples of conjectures of Newton's presented dogmatically, e. g., " These alternate fits of easy reflection, and easy transmission, Sir Isaac accounts for, from the vibrations of a fine, subtile, æthereal, elastic medium; vastly finer and more elastic than air, which penetrates through all bodies, and is diffused through all space. The rays of light, by their attractive powers, or some other force, excite vibrations in this medium; which vibrations being swifter than the rays, overtake them successively, and agitate them so as by turns to increase and decrease their velocities, and thereby put them into those fits." [44] These notes reinforce the view that the Newtonian scientists of the eighteenth century were convinced that Newton's positive views were to be read in the Queries of the *Opticks*.

‡ John Friend, professor of chemistry at Oxford, wrote a famous textbook of chemistry based on Newtonian mechanics. By " his excellent genius," Friend wrote, the " prince of mathematicians and philosophers," [Newton,] " has taught us a sure way for the improvement of physics and has fixed natural knowledge on such weighty reasons that he has done more to illustrate and to explain it than all philosophers of all nations." [47]

§ For the work of Hales, see pages 266 ff.

* This sense of the Queries being chemical derives from the fact that chemistry is concerned with the composition of bodies and the combinations or separations of their parts, and the forces holding their particles together: the very problems attacked by Newton in Book Three of the *Opticks*.

eighteenth-century experimentalists to build a geometrical *Principia*-like structure. Boerhaave, for example, argued that the changes produced in bodies by chemistry must be mechanical, that all the operations of chemistry produce "alterations in bodies which are owing intirely to motion." [49] Chemistry can be distinguished from ordinary mechanics because the latter deals with the motion of translation of a body from one place to another, whereas the former deals with the motions of the "different kinds of corpuscles" that make up bodies. By motion of the parts of bodies, chemistry is employed "either in uniting, or in separating; there being no third [chemical] operation in nature." [50] Boerhaave's reduction of chemistry to a kind of corpuscular mechanics was illustrated by Shaw in terms of Newton's *Opticks*. One note referred to Newton's "fine inquiry into the nature, laws, and constitution of matter," with a quotation from Query 31 of the *Opticks* about how "God, in the beginning, created matter in solid, massive, hard, impenetrable, moveable particles." [51]

An important note of Shaw indicated that the science of mechanics or "the doctrine of motion" is the "key" whereby the operations of chemistry "are to be accounted for," since motion is "the means whereby chemistry operates." In other words: "So far, then, as we know of the nature, and laws of motion; so much we may conceive of the means whereby a chemical effect is produced." The whole doctrine is then stated as follows:

But our knowledge here, is in reality very scanty, and confined to narrow bounds: many of the laws of motion, percussion, etc., in sensible bodies, under various circumstances, as falling, projected, etc., are well ascertained by the later philosophers; but these will not reach to those more remote, intestine motions of the component particles of those same bodies, whereon the changes of texture, colour, properties, etc., induced by chemistry, depend. Beside the common laws of sensible masses, the minute parts they are composed of, seem subject to some others, which have been but lately taken notice of, and are yet little more than guessed at. Sir I. Newton, to whose happy penetration we owe the hint, contents himself to establish that there are such motions in the *minima naturæ*, and that they flow from certain powers, or forces not reducible to any of those in the great world. In virtue of these powers, he shews that the small particles of bodies act on one another even at a distance; and that many of the phænomena of nature are the result hereof. Even sensible bodies, we know, act on one another divers ways; as by gravity, magnetism, and electricity, which are directed by different laws: and as we thus perceive the tenor and course of nature, it will appear highly probable there may be other powers. These just mentioned reach to sensible distances, and so have been observed by vulgar eyes: but there may be others, which reach to such small distances, as have hitherto escaped observation; and 'tis probable electricity may reach to such distances, even without being excited by friction.†

The great author just mentioned, proceeds to confirm the reality of these suspicions from a great number of phænomena, and experiments which plainly argue such powers and actions between the particles, *e. gr.* of salts and water, oil of vitriol and water, *aqua fortis* and iron, spirit of vitriol and salt-petre. He also shews that these powers, etc. are unequally strong between different bodies. . . .

These actions, in virtue whereof the particles of the bodies above-mentioned tend toward each other, the author calls by a general, indefinite name, *attraction*; which is equally applicable to all actions whereby bodies tend towards one another, whether in virtue of their weight, magnetism, electricity, impulse, or any other more latent power: for 'tis not the cause determining the bodies to approach, that he expresses by this name; but the effect, *i. e.* the approach: the cause he has no regard to, till such time as the effect is well ascertained. In his philosophy, the research into causes is the last thing; and never comes in turn, till the laws and phænomena of the effect be settled: it being to these phænomena that the cause is to be accommodated. But the cause even of any, the grossest, and most sensible of these actions, is not adequately known: how impulse itself works its effect, would confound the deepest philosopher; yet is impulse received into mathematics, and the laws and phænomena of its effect make the greatest part of the *common mechanics.* The other species of attractions, therefore, when their phænomena are sufficiently ascertained, have the same title to be promoted from physical to mathematical consideration; and this without any previous inquiry into their causes, which our conceptions may not be proportionate to: let their *causes* be *occult,* as all causes ever will be; so as their effects, which alone immediately concern us, be but apparent. Our noble countryman, then, far from adulterating philosophy with any thing foreign or metaphysical, as some have reproached him; has the glory of opening a new source of sublimer mechanics, which, duly cultivated, might be of infinitely more extent that all the mechanics yet known. 'Tis hence alone we must expect to learn the manner of the *changes, productions, generations, corruptions,* etc. of natural things; which are the great object of that part of philosophy called *chemistry.*[52]

Thus in Shaw's translation of Boerhaave, Franklin and other eighteenth-century experimental scientists would—first of all—encounter the tradition of Bacon and Boyle in the repeated encomiums of these two philosophers by Boerhaave, and then the " exact " corpuscular philosophy of the *Opticks* in the translator's extensive footnotes.

---

† This discussion follows Newton's presentation in the first paragraph of Qu. 31 of the *Opticks* almost word for word.

Boerhaave's Doctrine of Fire

The section of Boerhaave's book that is most relevant to the background of Franklin's electrical theory is: " Of Fire," in the middle of the first volume. At the outset Boerhaave observed that one of the most wonderful aspects of fire is that " while it is the chief cause and principle of almost all the effects cognizable by our senses, yet itself is imperceptible by any sense; being so incomprehensible, by reason of its extreme minuteness, that it eludes our nicest research; so that with many it passes for a spirit rather than a body." [53] At this point Shaw opened a running debate with the author that continued in extensive footnotes throughout many pages. The conflict is significant in that Newton's writings were sufficiently obscure to permit two rival interpretations to be made of his views on heat. Shaw's first note begins as follows:

> The doctrine of fire here laid down by our author, will appear new and extraordinary; at least among us, who have been used to consider fire in the light it is set by Lord Bacon, Mr. Boyle, and Sir I. Newton.
> The great and fundamental difference in respect of the nature of fire is whether it be originally such, formed thus by the Creator himself at the beginning of things; or whether it be mechanically producible from other bodies, by inducing some alteration in the particles thereof. Among the modern writers, Homberg, Boerhaave, the younger Lemery and 'sGravesande maintain the former: the latter is chiefly supported by the English authors. [54]

This statement of Shaw's evidently made a great impression; it was repeated almost *verbatim* by William Watson in an important tract on electricity.‡

Immediately after stating that fire is " a body " and not " a spirit," Boerhaave addressed himself to the problems of method in scientific inquiry so that there would be no danger of any readers falling into error when " inquiring into the nature of a thing so deeply hid." We must abstain, he wrote, from every speculation that is " framed only in the mind " and give no credit to any " hypothesis or precarious opinion "—" however plausible "—" unless we have a mind to be bewildered and lost." A mistake made " in supposing fire of a certain nature " will " spread itself thro' all physics." We should, therefore, " conduct ourselves as if utterly ignorant of it [fire]; intirely rejecting all preconceived opinions relating to it." [55] After this gentle nod in the direction of Newton's famous statement *Hypotheses non fingo*, Boerhaave explained why the study of fire required more caution than any other physical subject. Since " the

‡ This will be presented in Chapter Nine.

elements of fire are found every where," in a solid like gold and " the most empty vacuum of an air-pump," it is difficult " perfectly to distinguish the very action of fire from that of other concurring causes." Shaw's postil to this paragraph is, appropriately, " Not by hypothesis," but the next paragraph contradicts it: " Another difficulty in the way of philosophers who study the nature of fire is that excessive minuteness of its constituent parts [!] which not only surpasses all other known bodies, but even penetrates to its solid, and even least particles that we can any way find."

No better evidence can be found of the confusion between what men say and what men do than Boerhaave's attack on hypotheses and his unequivocal statement of an hypothesis that fire is a granular or atomic fluid; it is worthy of the great Newton. Presumably what Boerhaave had in mind was that this " hypothesis " was agreeable to a very large body of phenomena, and was therefore based on a considerable data of experiment; it was not " hypothetical " in the sense of being an armchair speculation totally divorced from the solid evidence of the senses.§ Commonly, the " signs " of fire are (1) heat,

§ Boerhaave observed that natural philosophy is " the knowledge of all bodies, and of all the modifications which may be observed in them," and that " chemistry has it immediately in view to promote this science." " The business of a natural philosopher is to communicate a solid and accurate knowledge of all the bodies in being, and all the affections thereof. Nor can this science be acquired otherwise than by observing, by means of our senses, all the objects which the author of nature has made cognizable thereto: hence, the first and principal part of this science is to collect all the manifest and sensible appearances of things, and reduce them into a body of natural history."

" Now it is evident, that of all the sciences chemistry is best adapted for discovering these latent peculiar powers of bodies: whence we may safely conclude, that the chemical art is the best and fittest means of improving natural knowledge. They who are possessed hereof will be able, by a truly active knowledge, to produce physical effects, without resting in subtilties of words, or idle speculations of theory: it being the character of a chemist, that his speculations pass on to effects. Thus, when he explains glass, he will at the same time shew the manner wherein it may certainly be made; and in accounting for fermentation, he will at the same time produce it; his sayings will be effects; and being free from the enquiry of ultimate causes, he will give the present ones. He does not invoke dæmons, goblins, or spirits, but applies body to body, and thus works his end. He does not regard the names of substantial forms, but sticks to the consideration of the sensible powers peculiarly found in each body; which he exhibits by effects, and shews how they may be applied to the production of the noblest works. He pays no homage to occult qualities, but discovers by his art the effects ignorantly ascribed thereto; and teaches how, when discovered, they may be brought into action. He readily confesses his ignorance as to the creation of seeds, and the peculiar structure given to each body at its first origin; but carefully attends to the appearances arising therefrom, and after noting them faithfully down, applies them directly to the working changes in things. Such are the noble fruits which chemistry, duly cultivated, holds forth to natural philosophers; and from this will arise such a system of physical knowledge as the great Lord Bacon wished for, and begun; and which, in pursuance of his design, the immortal Mr. Boyle considerably promoted." [56]

(2) light, (3) color, (4) expansion [or rarefaction] of fluid or solid bodies, and (5) burning or fusion.[57] In discussing heat as a sign of fire, Boerhaave showed himself as the former student of philosophy by demonstrating that the sensation of heat in a man is not an objective sign of fire; for instance, the sensations of a man long exposed to the cold and suddenly brought into an ordinary room are quite different from those of a man who had been a long time in that room.[58] Two experiments showed that light is not " an infallible proof of the presence of fire "; [59] a red hot iron may give out no light in a dark room but will burn wood or animal tissue, and a convex glass will focus the moon's rays to an extreme brightness even though a thermometer brought to the same focal point will give no indication of heat or fire. If light itself is no " true characteristic of fire, no body will imagine that colours can be so." [60] There is only one effect of fire " which obtains always, and every where the same, being also utterly inseparable from fire, and not variable by objects." All " bodies to which fire is . . . applied, without one exception, are hereby rendered bigger, swell, and rarify, yet without any observable difference in their weight." [61] Such rarefaction or dilation is most pronounced in fluids, so that the most accurate observations by experiment of even " the smallest increments or decrements of the degree of fire " are to be had by using instruments in which fluids may expand [62] (gas or liquid thermometers), and in a way that does not depend upon any individual sensation of heat.

Some beautiful experiments then show that fire expands bodies; " thus [!] " we learn " that the particles of fire distributed through the mass, act every where with the same force upon the *moleculæ* which they possess." [63] Heat expands all bodies, according to Boerhaave, and cold contracts them, the degree of contraction increasing as the degree of cold increases, and apparently in a direct proportion. Boerhaave concluded that just as fire produces a motion that expands bodies, so " the mere absence of fire " (i. e., cold) produces a motion in all solid bodies that is " still more wonderful." * By virtue of this motion " all the atoms of the body tend towards its centre, and by that means also draw nearer, and cohere faster together." Hence, " the end of cold is a state of absolute rest between coherent particles; and the end of fire a perpetual agitation of dissolved particles." [64] In this way, Boerhaave showed that although " fire " is particulate (and a body), " heat " could be correlated with the motion of matter.

These investigations led Boerhaave to a general conclusion:

---

* For the later development of electrical theories, in which it was assumed that an electric fluid exists in all bodies, these ideas of fire entering bodies were of great importance: especially the concept of all bodies containing some fire, which quantity may be augmented or diminished.

. . . I shall call that unknown thing which has this property of penetrating all solid and fluid bodies, and dilating them so as to take up more
space, by the name of fire. In effect, I do not remember any body
hitherto known, which has all these conditions except fire alone. On the
contrary, fire is never known to be present in any body, but it immediately produces these two effects. Add, that in proportion as it is
increased, the expansion of bodies is also increased. Now such a criterion
suffices, in physical matters, to denote and distinguish particular bodies
by: nor are there any other marks but of this kind for that purpose;
whatever some fanciful philosophers may imagine. It therefore imports
us carefully to denote those properties, which we are able to discover in
fire; the first of which seems to be, that it exists always, and every where,
as will be clearly shewn by . . . experiment.[65]

Boerhaave indicated that hard materials, when rubbed, generate
more heat than soft ones, because their parts " cohere much closer
together." Shaw offered in rebuttal " a different principle," advanced
by " Sir Isaac Newton and the English philosophers," the former in
quotations from the *Opticks* and the latter in quotations from Boyle's
Mechanical Production of Heat and *Effects of Languid Motion* and
a general reference to Bacon.[66] We may see, therefore, that Shaw's
edition of Boerhaave's *Elements of Chemistry* bears a certain similarity to Clarke's edition of Rohault's *Elements of Physics*,† since
both present the Newtonian view of their respective subjects in
footnotes as a rebuttal to the author they have translated. But it must
be observed that the similarity between the two books is imperfect,
since Boerhaave expressed the greatest admiration for Newton. ⸜
  In Shaw's version, the notes are almost entirely devoted to presenting in greater detail the views of Bacon, Boyle, and Newton—
at least in the section on " fire." Yet it would be plain to any reader
that Boerhaave particularly esteemed Newton for his contributions
to the " corpuscular philosophy," his discoveries concerning light and
color, and his speculations on the æther. Thus Boerhaave said, " May
we not, therefore, after Sir Isaac Newton, lay down the vibration of
the particles which compose a body, for the sole entire cause to
which the continuance of fire is owing in a heated body? "[67] He
referred to " that observation of the great Newton, that water itself,
if ever it could be converted into earth, might be so impregnated
with fire as to shine."[68] He mentioned " the doctrine of the great
Newton " about bodies " diverging and deflecting coloured rays,"
and raised the question of matter being everywhere the same and
reflecting light equally; " for by Sir Isaac Newton's doctrine it appears that there may be a great diversity in bodies in this respect."[69]

† See Chapter Four.

Fire and the Structure of Matter

We need not follow Boerhaave throughout his examination of "vulgar fire," i. e., fire of burning. Having discussed "elementary fire" in terms of its properties—"considering it as it is created, and exists in nature, separate from all other created bodies," and "as it remains pure in bodies themselves, without taking any pabulum from them, but remaining pure and only driven into parallel or converging rays: and again having considered it as collected in bodies by motion and attrition alone"—Boerhaave naturally turned his attention to combustion.[70] Many philosophers had confused fire "as supported by combustible matter" with pure elementary fire. But the latter, according to Boerhaave, was quite different; for example, it might be collected in certain bodies (such as the metals) without in any way causing a destruction of them, whereas in the former "the bodies themselves are consumed and dissipated by the action thereof, so as almost to disappear from our notice." [71] Burning was presented under the general head of "Fewel, or the Pabulum of Fire," followed by "Fewels from animal bodies," "Fewels from fossil bodies," "Producing heat by the mixture of vegetable bodies," "Producing heat by the mixture of animal and vegetable substances," "Producing heat by the mixture of fossils," "Producing true fire in a cold body, by the sole access of the air," [72] and so on. We are more concerned with Boerhaave's observations on the *nature* of fire, since these are related to the later electrical theories.

Boerhaave's principles of fire embraced its non-destructibility, its dilation of bodies by causing the constituent parts to separate, its ability to enter and leave bodies without altering their shape, its tendency to spread out uniformly in all directions, and its lack of weight. Save for the dilation of bodies, or a decrease in the density of bodies, these principles could easily be translated into electrical principles. Furthermore, Franklin's doctrine that the excess "electric fluid" forms an "atmosphere" around charged bodies is reminiscent of Boerhaave's statement: "Fire . . . adhering to an ignited body, expands itself all around after the manner of an atmosphere; since from every point thereof we find its virtue diffused to a considerable distance, so as to produce all the effects belonging to fire. . . ." [73]

Since the principles laid down by Boerhaave for fire are similar to Franklin's principles of the electric fluid,‡ it is worth while to explore Boerhaave's general conclusions "concerning the nature of

‡ Franklin and his contemporaries wrote of "electrical fire" as well as "electrical fluid."

fire." First of all, " true elementary fire is corporeal." [74] Further-more, it must be " truly corporeal " ; " consequently every particle of it must consist of other lesser parts united together, but so strongly united, as that we have no reason to think there is any power in nature capable of dividing them.§ And hence again it appears prob-able, that the figures of those particles are not changeable by any natural power; so that the element of fire appears immutable in itself, and the great instrument or means of changing all other things." [75] Does fire have " also that further property, which some of the greatest men of the present age hold inseparable from all bodies, *viz.* weight or gravity, in proportion to its solidity . . ." ? Well, said Boerhaave, this does not " so certainly appear from the consideration of the whole history of fire." He rather believed that fire has no more " tendency to the centre of the earth than to any other point; that it has no natural or spontaneous determination at all; that it may be determined any way; that it is present every where, unless hindered by some foreign cause, through the whole universe. . . ." In this way Boerhaave tried to square his ideas on the matter of heat with the Newtonian properties of ponderable matter (mass) .

The " particles of fire " seemed to Boerhaave to be the smallest of all the bodies yet known. If they are corporeal—and they " have already been shewn to be corporeal "—they must be " exceedingly subtile," since they readily penetrate all bodies, even the densest, and are capable of pervading even the thickest parts of dense bodies. If a large globe of solid gold were placed on a fire, the fire would penetrate so deeply that if the gold sphere were divided into two hemispheres, we would find at every point along the inside plane of division " both light and heat, and the other properties and powers of fire." Boerhaave thus introduced the subject of the penetration of heat into solid bodies, but he did not inquire into the relative rate of penetration. Franklin went a step further and applied electrical concepts to thermal phenomena, introducing a concept of heat conductivity.

All other bodies thus far discovered, said Boerhaave, can be ex-cluded from entering " the vacuities of others." Air, water, spirits, salts, and oils will not enter a glass phial that is hermetically sealed, and when they are in such a phial, they cannot escape. But fire appears to be an exception; it has free ingress and egress, even in a sealed glass bottle. To be sure, Boerhaave admitted, the " cause of gravity and power of magnetism " seem also to pass through every

§ This statement is reminiscent of Newton's idea (see Chapter Six) that the cor-puscles of which bodies are made consist of aggregates of smaller corpuscles which cannot be separated from one another.

kind of body while preserving " their native properties and effects,"
yet we are not at all certain that gravity and magnetism act by
particles which issue from bodies. One great difference is apparent
between gravity or magnetism and heat, for " the cause of gravity,
and [of] magnetism, [will] pervade bodies instantaneously, . . . while
fire requires some space of time before it can penetrate the densest
bodies "—" hence the corporeity appears more evidently in fire, and
less so in them." [76] Of course, no one can say that " there may not
have been created some corpuscles, which are less than those of fire,"
but it can easily be affirmed that no physical effects have been observed by the senses of man from which it is necessary to infer that
" there are bodies smaller than fire." Boerhaave was not willing to
declare himself on the point of whether " the matter of light and
colours is the same with that of fire," but if this were the case, we
might conclude that the matter of fire is at least a thousand times
more subtle than would otherwise be supposed.

The small particles, which " constitute the ultimate elements of
fire," are the " most solid of all bodies." Here the sense of the word
" solidity " is " an extended thing which resists infinitely." [77] Boerhaave agreed with Newton that the " ultimate elements " or " particles of all bodies " are perfectly solid, but that when such elements
are compounded together to form ordinary bodies, there must be
" vacuities " between the joined particles, since they do not everywhere touch each other. Fire is " the great changer of all things in
the universe, whilst itself remains wholly unchangeable." The " corporeal, solid, subtile particles " are perfectly " smooth, even, and
polished on their surfaces ": which means that there are " no emi-
nencies or sinkings in any point of their whole circumference." [78]
Since fire can penetrate easily in any direction through all the pores
of a solid body, there can be nothing on the surface which could
offer any impediment to such motion, so that they cannot have
" hooks or points, or any thing downy and woolly." This discussion
reminds us of Newton's description of the nature of ultimate particles
in Query 31 of the *Opticks*.

Boerhaave next asserted that from " the whole history of fire, we
may infer its absolute simplicity." [79] This property is intended to
convey a condition of a body " whereby each particle of it retains the
same nature which is observed in the whole; so that the simplicity of
fire denotes such a disposition, as that each of its single particles
should consist altogether of body without any pores; otherwise all
the component particles would scarce be alike; and further, that they
probably are solid spherules, the whole congeries of which may thus
be the same." One of the reasons adduced by Boerhaave is that since

there are no corpuscles in nature known to be smaller than those
of fire, the latter cannot be compounded of other " lesser heterogeneous parts." Unfortunately, Newton's optical discoveries would
not permit the simplest view:

. . . Yet it must be owned the doctrine of the great Sir Isaac Newton
overthrows the absolute simplicity of fire; a philosopher whose subtile
and penetrating genius seems to have surpassed the limits prescribed to
human understanding; and who by a most artful anatomy, from a single
ray of light procures seven several ones, very different not only in their
primitive colours, but in their reflection and refraction: and yet how
fine and simple must that single ray have been? If then, after the nature
of fire and light had been with so much labour examined, for so many
ages, in so many countries, and after so many different manners, a single
person could arise in our age, and make such discoveries, who shall
assign any limits to the discoveries of future ages in natural things? Who
knows what additions may hereafter be made to the discoveries of Newton? 'Tis but half an age since all philosophers considered a single ray
of light, as so exceedingly slender, that in respect of thickness, they
unanimously pronounced it indivisible; yet this prince of geometricians
has, by invincible experiments and arguments, shewn, that such a single
ray is a fasciculus made of seven very different rays, which may be joined
to each other lengthwise, and again be parted from each other, so as to
form seven fine threads of different colours, which before made but one
apparent thread; and who knows but when dioptrical glasses come to
be further improved, and other means and instruments brought to a
greater degree of perfection, something like composition may be found
even in these simplest rays discovered by Newton? We are struck with
admiration, when, from these instances, we see what powers the Creator
has given to the human mind; whereby, when duly cultivated, we can
discover the laws he established in framing the world. Certainly we owe
the greatest veneration and thanksgiving to that Being, which impress-
ing his own image on our minds, gave us a disposition to understand,
study, and love the truth. Yet is not this all the diversity found in a
simple particle of fire; the same Newton having, in the different sides of
one of these simplest rays, discovered a further diversity.

By the refraction of Island crystal, it appears, that there is a different
power found on one side of a ray from that found on the other: and as
in one magnet with respect to another, the same pole is either attracting
or repelling; so in the same ray we find a like power, with respect to the
transparent medium it falls on. From the whole it appears, that fire,
however simple, contains the following diversities already discovered.
(1) With respect to colour, it contains seven different primitive ones.
(2) With respect to reflecting and refracting bodies, the rays act differently according to the colours they are of. And (3) that this diversity in
the sides of the rays appears in a more extraordinary manner in their
passing thro' Island crystal; such a manifold diversity is concealed in

the simplest of all bodies! What then may we suppose in the more compound kinds? The smaller every where hold forth an image or resemblance of the larger. And were it not for the discovery made by Sir Is. Newton, we should have believed that the particles of fire are the minutest possible, and perfectly simple: but now though we allow fire the simplest of all known bodies, we cannot deny but that a great diversity obtains in it.[80]

It is plain here that Boerhaave was referring to the great discoveries which Newton recorded in his *Opticks,* and the discussion of polarity (or " sides ") in light, discussed by Newton in Query 26 in Book Three of the *Opticks.* Shaw, in a very long note, spelled out Newton's discoveries and views at greater length.[81]

The reader will observe that in the foregoing account of Boerhaave's *Elements of Chemistry* I have not said much about his chemical theories as such, or the applications he made to chemical theory of the Newtonian doctrine of attraction (so ably presented by Mme Metzger). The reason is that my purpose has been to show the relation of Boerhaave's book to the Newtonian ideas about atoms and subtle, particulate æther-like fluids. It may be observed, however, that Boerhaave is the first author to be mentioned by name in Lavoisier's *Treatise on Chemistry* (in the opening sentence of the first chapter) and that Lavoisier stated that his concept of the fluid of heat, " caloric," was derived primarily from Boerhaave and—we may note—Franklin, and some of the older philosophers.

Franklin found in Boerhaave a source of a concept of fire that was suggestive of his own concept of electric fluid and an example of experimentally based theory and conjecture. Above all, Boerhaave's book was a veritable invitation to experiment, because it described every detail necessary—the equipment, the materials, and the way to use them. Reading the section on fire, Franklin was stimulated to the performance of the earliest experiment associated with his name: the relative absorption of solar heat as a function of the color of the absorbing material. We shall see, in Chapter Nine, that color was explored in relation to electrical effects at this same period, and that the question was resolved only by having recourse to Newton's original prism experiment on the dispersion of white light.

3. 'sGravesande's *Natural Philosophy*

In the preceding discussion of Boerhaave, mention was made of the close association of the Dutch experimental philosophy of the early eighteenth century and the British tradition of experimental science. Boerhaave did not conceal his admiration for Bacon, Boyle, Hooke, Newton, Halley, and Hales. In general physics, the most able Hollander—W. J. 'sGravesande—likewise had close ties with the British tradition. His fame, though it was of course not equal to Boerhaave's, was considerable, and his influence was spread through his widely reprinted textbooks and his personal association with students who came to Holland. He became the acknowledged leader in the field of " Newtonian philosophy " and to him Voltaire went to obtain approval of his exposition of Newtonianism.

'sGravesande obtained direct contact with the English school when, in 1715, he was chosen secretary of the embassy sent by the Dutch government to congratulate George I on his ascension to the British throne.[82] While in London, he made the acquaintance of many scientists, including Newton. Although a member of a diplomatic mission, he found time to perform experiments, especially with Newton's friend and disciple, J. T. Desaguliers (of whom we shall have more to say presently). Soon after his return to Holland, 'sGravesande was appointed (16 June 1717) professor of mathematics and astronomy at Leiden. He taught Newtonian philosophy— both as found in the *Principia* and in the *Opticks*—and developed his widely read *Mathematical Elements of Natural Philosophy, confirmed by experiments: or, An introduction to Sir Isaac Newton's Philosophy*. First appearing in Latin in 1720-1721, it was reprinted in revised form in 1725 and 1742 (the year of the author's death). A translation into French by Roland de Virloys was published in Paris in 1747. Two English translations were made, an " unauthorized " one appearing under the name of John Keill, and an authorized one by Keill's pupil, Desaguliers (first published in 1720-1721).

Franklin owned a copy of the sixth edition of Desaguliers's English translation, published in 1747, brought out after the translator's death with revisions by his son. This copy, at present in the library of the American Philosophical Society, was obtained by the Society in the " Dufief sale." We may note, incidentally, that an earlier edition appeared in the catalogue of books offered for sale by Franklin in 1744 as " 214 Dr. S. Gravesande's Elements of Natural Philosophy, demonstrated by Experiments, illustrated with Cuts. 2 Vols." Presumably, the copy Franklin had for sale was the fourth (1731) or fifth English edition.

A copy of the 1731 edition of Desaguliers's translation of this book was available in the Library Company of Philadelphia after 1732. Franklin read carefully Desaguliers's own book on natural philosophy and would unquestionably have examined another major work on Newtonian science presented in English by an author he admired.

The Newtonian Philosophy according to 'sGravesande

Desaguliers dedicated his translation of 'sGravesande's book to Isaac Newton. In the dedication he remarked that " there are more admirers of your wonderful discoveries, than there are mathematicians able to understand the first two books of your *Principia*." He observed that both he and 'sGravesande had substituted experiments for geometry, even though some of the experimental demonstrations " may not always prove, but sometimes only illustrate a proposition." Even so, 'sGravesande did use mathematics, but always as a supplement to his demonstrations by experiment. There was a short introductory section devoted to mathematical proofs " which have quantities infinitely small for their foundation ": the theory of limits, or fluxions. While making an appeal to the non-mathematical reader, 'sGravesande obviously hoped to teach enough mathematics for an appreciation of the Newtonian natural philosophy on a high level.

In the preface of the first edition, 'sGravesande noted that " philosophers do not equally agree upon what is to pass for a law of nature, and what method is to be followed in quest of those laws." He, therefore, " thought fit in this preface to make good the Newtonian method, which I have followed in this work." [83] This " Newtonian method " is described in full in the first chapter of the book proper, where we find three " rules " of Sir Isaac Newton which are founded upon a primary axiom. These rules are the familiar ones which had appeared in Newton's *Principia*. The first is that no more causes of natural things should be admitted than such " as are true, and sufficient to explain their phænomena "; the second, that " there are the same causes of natural effects of the same kind "; and the third, that only those " qualities of bodies, whose virtue cannot be increased and diminished, and which belong to all bodies, upon which experiments can be made, are to be looked upon as qualities of all bodies." The fundamental axiom upon which these rules are founded is: " That the Creator of the universe governs all things, by laws determined by His wisdom, or spontaneously flowing from the nature of the things." [84]

In the preface (to the first edition 'sGravesande indicated that we cannot " immediately judge of all physical matters by our senses," and that therefore we have " recourse to another just way of reasoning, tho' not mathematical." This other way of reasoning is Newtonian and follows the " three Newtonian laws " or " rules " which are printed in the preface as well as in Chapter I. But now the reader is told that the second and third " laws " (or " rules ") depend on the following axiom: " We must look upon as true, whatever being deny'd would destroy civil society, and deprive us of the means of living." From this axiom " the second and third rules of the Newtonian method most evidently follow." Since the second two " rules " imply the upholding of civil society and the first cannot be called in question by " any [one] that owns the wisdom of the Creator," 'sGravesande neatly removed any possible grounds for objection save subversion or atheism.[85]

These sentiments of 'sGravesande remind us forcibly of what is often denoted as Franklin's pragmatism and they indicate to us how superficial the judgment is that Franklin limited himself in scientific matters to the material aspects of life. Franklin would certainly have agreed with 'sGravesande that anything which would " destroy civil society " must be false and that no truth value could be implied in anything that would lead to a deprivation " of the means of living." As an empiricist, Franklin was convinced that the primary test of the value of all ideas is experience. He was, therefore, always willing to try out his ideas. Having concluded that lightning must be an electrical phenomenon, he at once devised a test and wrote, " Let the experiment be made." When he reached the conclusion that negroes are not innately inferior to whites, and that their environment and education must be responsible for their condition even when freed, he sought to establish schools for free negroes to prove whether with suitable training they could become as skilled artisans as white Americans. Yet from 'sGravesande Franklin could learn of the impossibility of judging every matter by the senses, that even in physics a kind of reasoning was required which might seem in contradiction to a rude empiricism. The controlled imagination, inspiration to produce ideas, reason to explore the consequences of ideas, experience as the final test of the validity of the whole process —this was the method of speculative Newtonian experimental science. 'sGravesande hinted that this method confuted atheism and anarchy, a comforting conclusion, even if it could not be proved. In the eighteenth century, the Newtonian scientists were sure that the methods of experimental science were applicable to a science of society, and that the truths of inanimate and animate nature must hold for man and all his organizations. Such views often led to extravagances of thought and action. We may note the curious poem by Desaguliers, translator of 'sGravesande, on the Newtonian system as the only basis of government and the attempts to envisage the American constitution as an exemplification of Newtonian laws. 'sGravesande said only that a denial of certain basic principles related to experience would upset society; later men stated that such principles would, in application, alter or improve society. Franklin, having introduced notable innovations in science and in the forms of organized society, expressed the wish that moral improvement might progress as much as science.

'sGravesande on Heat and Electricity

'sGravesande was among the early Newtonians to express the view of a possible connection between science and society. But he did not dwell long on this matter. His purpose was mainly to establish a sound non-mathematical way of reasoning in science that would go beyond the simplest or rudest empiricism.

In the preface to the first edition of his book, he did not devote much space to a discussion of the doctrine or nature of hypotheses,* although in the second he pointed out that only a man " who in physics reasons from phænomena, rejecting all framed hypotheses, and pursues this method inviolably to the best of his power, endeavours to follow the steps of Sir Isaac Newton, and very justly declares that he is the Newtonian philosopher; and not he who implicitly follows the opinion of any particular person." Hence, he believed, it was proper to keep in the second edition the original title of " Introduction to the Newtonian philosophy," even though in a number of things he had found his opinion to differ from Newton's; he had, after all, followed the methods of Newton. But in the third edition, he felt it necessary to discuss hypotheses at length. A new preface was written, restating the author's intention of giving " the mathematical elements of natural philosophy," for which reason he had chosen to treat of things " in which what was certain might . . . be separated from what was doubtful." Thus he thought that he might omit what was " deduced from feigned hypotheses." He admitted that hypotheses " may open the way to truth." Yet when that which was only supposed is proved to be true, there is " no longer any room for hypotheses." Some people, 'sGravesande noted, defend hypotheses differently, by arguing " that all our knowledge of natural things is imperfect; that our first reasoning about them is built on hypotheses; and that analogy, without which we can discover nothing in physics, is to be referred to hypotheses." [87] This view he had continually refuted. He also observed that if anyone should make it appear he had actually made use of one or two hypotheses, it would not follow from thence that hypotheses may be admitted; " at least I would not allow this conclusion myself, but would reject them." Thus he spoke with the words of Newton. In physics, ac-

---

* At the very end of this preface there is a brief mention of the need of " dismissing all feigned hypotheses out of philosophy." [86]

cording to 'sGravesande, the laws of nature are to be discovered by the phenomena, and then proved by induction to be general laws; thereafter, the development of the subject may be handled mathematically. Whoever, he observed, will seriously examine " what foundation this method of treating physics is built upon, will easily discover this to be the only true one, and that all hypotheses are to be laid aside."

Plainly, 'sGravesande was warning his readers not to build any philosophical romances and never to allow any prior hypotheses to obscure the plain evidence of experience. Working hypotheses were to be tested and, if proved valid, were to become laws or principles. As we shall see in later chapters, this was always Franklin's method and he never argued about experiments, only about speculations. Nevertheless, Franklin and 'sGravesande, like Newton himself, were led to basic hypotheses like Newton's hypothesis of the æther and of the corpuscularity of light, or Franklin's hypothesis of a single matter or fluid of electricity. This concept of Franklin's was influenced by the writings of 'sGravesande as it was by Boerhaave's chemistry.

In the second edition, 'sGravesande began his discussion of " fire " by pointing out that although we know " several properties " of fire, we are ignorant of a " great many things " relating to this subject; his procedure is stated as follows, " not [to] invent hypotheses, but [to] reason from experiments, and leave untouched what is not fully known." Then a few propositions are stated in rapid order: however dense and hard a body may be, fire will easily penetrate it; fire moves very swiftly (" as appears from astronomical obervations ") ; fire may unite itself to bodies, and make them expand or swell; even at certain distances from bodies, fire is attracted: all bodies contain some fire in them,[88] since all bodies may be heated by " attrition " or friction.

The second chapter on fire deals with electricity, defined as " that property of bodies, by which (when they are heated by attrition) they attract, and repel lighter bodies at a sensible distance." If two pieces of rock crystal are rubbed together, they will appear luminous, even though not acquiring any sensible heat by the friction. " Light (as well as heat) is a proof that there is fire in a body." We are then told that a glass tube rubbed with linen or woolen cloth will " emit light in the dark," and that it will also, upon being so " heated by rubbing," have a very " sensible electricity; for if light bodies, such as pieces of leaf gold, and soot, be laid upon a plane, and the tube be brought near them, they will be put in motion, attracted, repelled, and driven several ways by the tube."

There follows a description of various experiments to be made
with a rubbed glass globe, whirled in a frame, which are similar to
the experiments of Hauksbee. These experiments lead to certain
conclusions which " seem to be naturally deduced from them, which
we do not give out as certain, but very probable; for we must always
distinguish certainty from probability." One of these is that glass
contains and has about its surface " a certain atmosphere, which is
excited by friction, and put into a vibratory motion; for it attracts
and repels light bodies. . . ." The fire which is contained in the glass
is " expelled by the action of this atmosphere; at least it is moved
with it. For when light bodies are put in motion at a distance from
the glass, the bodies also become lucid at a distance."

In Chapter Three, heat and light are related to the motion of
fire. The very swift motion of fire may, " in different circumstances,
produce different effects. Heat and light are to be attributed to the
different motions of fire. Heat, in a hot body, is the agitation of the
parts of the body and the fire contained in it, by which agitation, a
motion is produced in our bodies, which excites the idea of heat in
our mind." Similarly, when fire enters our eyes, " by the motion
that it communicates to the fibers in the bottom of the eye, it excites
the idea of light. . . ." Actually, the definition of a lucid body is
one that " emits light, that is . . . gives fire a motion in right lines."
Noting that there are many things in respect to light and heat which
are worth pointing out, even though many of them may be hard to
explain, 'sGravesande stated that in " natural philosophy, when we
are ignorant of the causes, we must only mention the effects." Metals,
for example, are observed to become lucid when their heat is increased: " They emit fire by the agitation of their parts, but if the
motion of the parts be encreased, part of the fire is moved in right
lines, and the body shines." An example is provided by smoke, which
can be made hotter by the application of a flame, and then is changed
into flame.

'sGravesande's view, therefore, is that " fire " produces motion or
agitation in bodies and hence causes heat or sensation. Heat, therefore, is related to a mode of motion of the parts of matter in apparent
agreement with the British school, represented by Bacon, Boyle,
Hooke, and (to some extent) Newton, although the motion itself is
said to be due to " fire." 'sGravesande was not very specific about
ignis or fire; he never asserted that it was particulate, as Boerhaave
had done, but apparently he did consider fire to be a " body." For
instance, he said that it was " attracted " by other bodies at a distance. He even wrote about fire having no weight, a consideration
meaningful only for a " body." Furthermore, although he wrote

that heat and light have similar properties (e. g., traveling in straight lines), he never equated them, resting content with the statement that wherever "we find heat and light, we say that there is what we call fire." Heat and light are thus "tokens of the presence of fire" and proceed from "the same cause" (called "fire"), which fact no one can doubt even though it cannot be proved.[89]

'sGravesande referred in Newtonian fashion to the attraction between light and the particles of which bodies are made, but no indication was given as to whether light itself is a body and particulate, or the undulations of a medium, although some arguments are raised in the Newtonian manner against the latter position. Since nothing is ever said of particles of light, or of particles of fire, to translate the word "fire" or *ignis* by "light corpuscles" (as has been done of late [90]) seems entirely contrary to the whole spirit of 'sGravesande's book. He made a deliberate attempt to avoid any kind of gross speculation, limiting himself merely to the idea that bodies are composed of particles, or a general atomism. He never even discussed with any specificity Newton's brilliant suggestions that optical investigations might disclose the relative sizes of these ultimate particles of matter. As a matter of fact, at one point in his treatise, 'sGravesande indicated that infinite divisibility of matter may be possible, which would indicate that for him the particles of matter took on the character of a mathematical rather than a physical concept. 'sGravesande tried to keep as much as possible to the disavowal of hypotheses of Isaac Newton, and to such an extent that he omitted from his discourse practically all of the speculative material from the queries of the *Opticks*, even Newton's suggestion about the possibility of an elastic æther being the cause of gravitation, or indeed of other phenomena.

In the sixth English edition, the one that Franklin had in his personal library, the discussions of every topic were amplified, but the general tone remained the same. The properties of fire were set forth as in earlier editions, but little more was said about fire itself. Yet a number of properties of fire as described by 'sGravesande are similar to properties of the electric fluid as later developed by Franklin, and so must be considered here. Furthermore, these properties of fire are wholly consistent with the hypothesis of fire being a subtle, elastic, imponderable fluid made up of mutually repellant particles, even though this hypothesis is not stated explicitly.

Like the later electric fluid conceived by Franklin, fire according to 'sGravesande is attracted by bodies, unites itself to bodies, is contained in all bodies, but does not enter into all bodies with equal facility. On the other hand, this fire is always manifested by heat, and heat dilates bodies; but Franklin's fluid does not alter the dimensions of bodies in any way. The action of fire gives the particles of bodies a mutually repellent force; Franklin's electric fluid gives bodies themselves a mutually repellent force. Like the electric fluid, fire tends to seek an equilibrium, going from a body with a large quantity of it to another body with a smaller quantity. Finally there is a suggestion of an " atmosphere " about a piece of glass, made to vibrate when excited by friction, which produces electrical attraction; in Franklin's theory, rubbed glass is surrounded by an active " atmosphere " of electric fluid. This conclusion, 'sGravesande observed, was not " certain " but only " very probable." Interestingly enough, 'sGravesande allowed himself a momentary luxury in contemplating the " probable," but immediately returned to the stern necessity " of laying aside conjectures," even " tho' they have a great many experiments for their foundation." The " conjectures " and the apology for them appear in every edition.

'sGravesande's book was plainly conceived in the spirit that he supposed Newton to have exhibited in his *Principia*. The very title, *Mathematical Elements of Natural Philosophy, confirmed by experiments*, is indicative of his attempts to enlarge upon, without departing from the framework of, Newton's *Principia*. This is certainly not a book in the spirit of Newton's *Opticks*, and it did not exert a particularly creative influence on Benjamin Franklin's scientific ideas, although it did advance his scientific education. Reading Boerhaave provided a great stimulation to Franklin in relation to the whole doctrine of subtle fluids, and led him to perform his experiments on the relation of color to the absorption of heat; we shall see immediately below that Franklin likewise had read thoroughly, and either referred to, or was inspired by, or quoted from, the books of Hales and Desaguliers. It is significant, in the light of the two strands of Newtonian philosophy, that the books of Boerhaave, Hales, and Desaguliers, each of whom appreciated the speculative parts of the *Opticks*, conditioned the ideas of Benjamin Franklin, while that of 'sGravesande did not. Even so, 'sGravesande's *Natural Philosophy* must have taught Franklin a great deal of science, as it did most of the men of science of his generation. Above all, Franklin learned from 'sGravesande, as he learned from Boerhaave and Desaguliers, that many of the truths of Newtonian science could be apprehended without formal mathematics if every principle be illustrated by experiments. 'sGravesande began with verbal descriptions of phenomena and experiments and the statement of principles, before he introduced any mathematical apparatus, such a fluxions, in the sections on statics and dynamics. The non-mathematical reader, like

Franklin, could easily skip the mathematics. Franklin also learned that many original experiments had been made since Newton's time, and that they were daily disclosing new aspects of phenomena that might help to illuminate some of the questions which neither the "prince of natural philosophers" nor his ablest disciples had been able to answer to any degree of satisfaction.

4. Desaguliers's *Experimental Philosophy*

Jean Théophile Desaguliers was a singularly important author for Franklin during the 1740's, when he was in the preparatory period for the decade of electrical research that was to follow. Desaguliers was the English translator of the treatise of 'sGravesande, and also of a French work on the mechanism of fire †—both of which were read by Franklin—and he was the author of a work on physics of his own which Franklin read and admired in the early forties.

Desaguliers came from a French Protestant family which fled from France in 1685, when Jean Théophile was two years of age, going first to Guernsey and then to England.[92] After graduating from Christ Church, Oxford, Desaguliers entered orders in 1710 and became professor of experimental physics at Hart Hall, Oxford, succeeding his former teacher, John Keill. He removed to London in 1713, was elected F.R.S. the following year, and became "curator" of experiments to the Society and chaplain to the Duke of Chandos. During this period he became intimate with Newton, who was godfather to his third daughter. The friendship of Newton for Desaguliers raises the question as to whether Franklin might possibly have met Desaguliers while he was in London in 1726, since he knew another member of Newton's circle—Henry Pemberton, editor of the third edition of the *Principia*—who had promised Franklin an introduction to Newton.

Desaguliers was famous for his public lectures, particularly for his demonstration experiments. His courses in Newtonian science for the general public won wide acclaim. Even if Franklin never

† Gauger's book on fire will be discussed below. We may observe that Franklin also knew Isaac Greenwood, the first Hollis Professor of Mathematics and Natural Philosophy at Harvard University, who had studied in London under Desaguliers, with whom he boarded following his graduation from Harvard in 1721. In 1740 Franklin and others arranged for Greenwood to give some "mathematical & philosophical lectures & experiments" in the room adjoining the Library, and agreed to lend him the air pump belonging to the Library Company.[91] Franklin acted as Greenwood's agent and collected fees for the lectures at the Post Office. Surely Franklin attended these lectures and conversed with the lecturer; undoubtedly Greenwood drew heavily on the lecture-demonstration technique of Desaguliers and acquainted Franklin with the latter's book, of which the first volume had appeared in 1734.

met Desaguliers, he may well have attended one or more of these sessions, which Desaguliers held twice weekly in his house.

Another link between Franklin and Desaguliers arises out of Freemasonry. While Desaguliers was the Deputy Grand-Master of the Grand Lodge of Freemasons in London, he issued *The Constitutions of the Free-Masons. Containing the history, charges, regulations, &c. of that most ancient and right worshipful fraternity.* This famous work, originally issued in London in 1723, was reprinted by Franklin in 1734 and is held to be the first Masonic book printed in America.

Finally, we may note that Desaguliers, like Stephen Hales,‡ was very much interested in the subject of ventilation. He invented a machine for breweries to dry " malt with hot air," which was exploited by a rival; a variant device designed by Desaguliers was introduced into the House of Commons in 1723 to clear it " of foul air "; and he later designed an " engine " to " clear a coal, lead, copper, or any other mine, from any kind of damp, be those damps specifically lighter, or specifically heavier than common air." [93] It is well known that Franklin gave considerable thought to the problem of adequate ventilation and wrote many times on this subject. Considering the esteem in which he held the writings of Desaguliers and Hales, there can be no doubt that his interest in this topic, if not arising from their inspiration, was at least greatly stimulated by their writings.

Despite his official post in the Royal Society and his friendship with Newton, and although he published some articles of interest, Desaguliers was known in his day chiefly for his popular lecturing style and for his originality in designing, and his skill in performing, demonstration-experiments—in a word, as master of the art of exposition of Newtonian philosophy: without mathematics. His position in the scientific world may, perhaps, best be illustrated by the reception accorded him in Holland, where he went to lecture following an invitation in 1731. Peter van Musschenbroek—one of the discoverers of the principle of the condenser, or Leyden jar, a pupil of Boerhaave who for nine years before Desaguliers's visit had occupied the chair of mathematics at Utrecht—has given us a vivid impression of the performances given by Desaguliers at Amsterdam, Rotterdam, and The Hague. Author of an introduction to natural philosophy [94] that was to become renowned in its own right, Musschenbroek was an able representative of the Dutch school of experimental Newtonian physics.

One gathers that Desaguliers appeared, in the terms used by Jean Torlais, as a semi-official kind of " ambassador of Newtonian

‡ Hales's work will be presented in a later section of this chapter.

thought." Musschenbroek described him as one of the most famous (natural) philosophers of the century with an "ability to make experiments joined to an incomparable eloquence." His method of teaching was remarkable. He showed his hearers through their eyes what "their reading had taught them only imperfectly" and "of which they had only a superficial notion." His experiments were "completely convincing," and without doubt nothing could have made a stronger impression upon the audience than the ocular proof of the Newtonian philosophy provided in his lectures.[95]

Desaguliers's Influence on Franklin

The evidence that Benjamin Franklin knew Desaguliers's *Course of Experimental Philosophy* in 1744 is provided by Franklin's *Account of the New-invented Pennsylvanian Fire-Places* which he wrote and published in that year. In it Franklin wrote of the "ingenious and learned Dr. Desaguliers, to whose instructive writings the contriver of this machine [i. e., Franklin] acknowledges himself much indebted." Although Franklin did not refer explicitly to Desaguliers's *Course of Experimental Philosophy* by title, he did describe at length one of Desaguliers's experiments to see "whether heated iron would yield unwholesome vapours": a question of obvious importance to the inventor of the "Pennsylvanian fire-place," since the latter was a kind of stove made of iron. In this experiment, a receiver was exhausted by an air-pump and the air, subsequently admitted, was first made to pass through a small hole in a hot iron cube. A bird placed in this receiver, according to Franklin, "breathed that air without any inconvenience, or suffering the least disorder." But when the same experiment was performed with a heated brass cube rather than an iron one, the bird died in a few minutes.[96]

These experiments had been described by Desaguliers in great detail in a "Postscript: air changed, purified, and conveyed from place to place . . . ," which was placed at the end of the second volume of his *Course of Experimental Philosophy*. Although Desaguliers had published the first volume in 1734, the second volume did not appear until a decade later, the year of publication of Franklin's pamphlet on the Pennsylvanian fire-place. A second edition of Desaguliers's *Experimental Philosophy* was published in London in 1745; Franklin owned a copy of this edition which is now in the Library of the American Philosophical Society. A third edition, "corrected," appeared posthumously in 1763.§

§ The Library Company of Philadelphia acquired a copy of volume one the first edition (1734) in 1744.

Franklin had read the 1734-44 edition by 1744 and thought so well of the book that he later obtained a copy of the 1745 edition for his own library. Desaguliers's *Experimental Philosophy* was a work that must have delighted Benjamin Franklin since the second half of the second volume was devoted almost entirely to a description of all sorts of practical machines, including steam engines, illustrated with beautiful plates; it is, in fact, said to have been the first book to contain a description of a railway, i. e., the wooden railway constructed by Ralph Allen of Prior Park, Bath, to bring stone from the quarries to the waterfront.

Desaguliers as a Newtonian Philosopher

Desaguliers, demonstrator of physics to George I and George II, friend of Newton and master expounder of experimental Newtonian philosophy, died in 1744 in extreme poverty. Cawthorn wrote the following lines on his death:

> *Here poor neglected Des Aguliers fell,*
> *He who taught two gracious Kings to view*
> *All Boyle ennobled and all Bacon knew,*
> *Died in a cell without a friend to save*
> *Without a guinea and without a grave.*[99]

The third line is of particular interest because it places this great experimental Newtonian in the heroic line of Bacon and of Boyle.

Desaguliers published his *Experimental Philosophy* at the desire of the auditors of his course. Since the " greatest part " of them " are but little versed in mathematical sciences," he wrote in his preface, " the lectures are free from difficult geometrical demonstrations and algebraical calculations; and the same thing is often proved by several experiments; that where one does not immediately strike with a clear conviction, another may." It must have sounded to Franklin almost as if Desaguliers had had him in mind when he wrote, " I only require attention and common sense, with a very little arithmetick, in my readers, to qualify them for understanding these lectures. . . ." In the preface he remarked that the very " thoughts of being obliged to understand mathematicks have frighted a great many from the Newtonian philosophy." The " truth " of the Newtonian philosophy " is supported by mathematics, yet its physical discoveries may be communicated without " mathematics. Even in cases where the principles of the true philosophy " have been deduced by a long train of mathematical consequences," Desaguliers had " contrived experiments, which step by step bring us to the same conclusions." As a matter of fact, Desaguliers said, he had heard from several Cartesians that if their conversion to the Newtonian philosophy depended on a " knowledge of geometry," they " had rather continue in their own way of philosophy than to be at so much trouble."

Desaguliers made it perfectly plain that he held Newton's *Opticks* in the highest esteem. This book of Newton's, he wrote, is not devoted merely to the properties of light, but also contains " a vast fund of philosophy," which Newton " has modestly delivered under the name of Queries, as if they were only conjectures." Conjectures indeed! ". . . daily experiments and observations confirm [them]; a notable instance of which may be seen in the Rev. Dr. Stephen Hales's excellent book of *Vegetable Staticks*, which, by putting several of Sir Isaac's Queries out of all doubt, shew how well they are founded." Desaguliers, as we shall see in a moment, provided ample evidence of this position later on in the book.

In the opening lecture, Desaguliers explained that in " the actual division of matter by separating the parts from each other, it is not possible beyond a certain degree; because there are *atomes*, or extremely small parts, which are called the constituent or component parts of natural bodies, which the Wise and Almighty Author of Nature did at first create as the original particles of matter. . . ." [98] These atoms were described as being " without pores, solid, firm, and impenetrable perfectly, passive, and moveable." By " the union of several of them together, there are made bigger lumps or parts . . . which have interstices between them . . . called the pores. . . ." Thus the very beginning of the book announced the atomic constitution of matter as discussed in Newton's *Opticks*.

Then came a discussion of gravity, a universal property of matter, " tho' not essential," since all " parcels of matter, however modified, (or all bodies) have a gravitation or attraction towards one another." Another force is called " attraction of cohesion "—the force by which the parts of bodies cohere. That this force is much stronger than gravity follows from the obvious fact that " it is easier to raise most bodies from the ground than to break them in pieces." It " decreases much faster than gravity " when parts of bodies, " that were before in contact, cease to touch; and when they come to be at a sensible distance, this attraction of cohesion becomes almost insensible." [99]

One of the points made by Desaguliers, as we would expect, was that he abhorred the use of hypotheses. If ever " we come to know the causes of the various operations of magnetism," he wrote, " it will sooner be owing to a comparison of the experiments and observations " of good inquirers (" who acknowledge themselves ignorant of the causes of those surprising effects ") than " to twenty hypotheses of men whose warm imaginations supply them with what may support their solutions, while daily observations and common laws of motion can easily confute them." [100] The end of this quotation makes it plain that Desaguliers was referring particularly to the Cartesians. But we cannot help being astonished at the relatively minor place given by Desaguliers to the expected Newtonian attack on hypotheses. And it is perfectly clear that Desaguliers insisted only that hypotheses should not be maintained when they were in conflict with the data of experience or established (" true ") principles of natural philosophy, that hypotheses should not hinder the prosecution of experiments to determine the laws of nature's action. Such a position is similar to Newton's; at least it may be taken as a fair description of Newton's scientific thought if not his words. And it is the position adopted by Hales, by Franklin, and by Lavoisier: it is, in fact, the position of every research scientist, for whom an hypothesis is a " supposition put forward in explanation of observed facts," whether as a working hypothesis or as an hypothesis on a grand scale.

Desaguliers's exposition is of exceptional interest because it indicates the experimenter's loose construction of Newton's statements about hypotheses. The book affords many instances of the ways in which Newton's own hypotheses were accepted by his friends and admirers. Desaguliers wrote of " particles of light " and " subtile effluvia " that could penetrate the glass walls of a bell jar and enter the vacuum within the jar. Furthermore, he said that, in our arguments about forces, " we can go no higher than gravity, whose cause we don't pretend to know." [101] This is the classical Newtonian position. Desaguliers explained that the true philosopher does not show " from an hypothesis " how the celestial motions " might " be performed, but gives a " proper account " of the world by demonstrating the real causes of those motions.[102] Gravity is the " cause " and its nature remains unknown or hidden. So Desaguliers rejected any hypotheses that led to a " philosophical romance " such as the Cartesian vortices, the Aristotelian doctrine of " forms " and " qualities," and the " universal harmony " of Leibniz. On the other hand, he took as true the Newtonian axioms and postulates and demonstrated them by experiments. He accepted such mechanisms as particle-repulsion to explain phenomena like elasticity, and—above all —he accepted the premises of Newton's mathematical and philosophical propositions as being true laws of nature rather than hypotheses in the Newtonian sense.* We have seen that Newton showed that if a certain law of repulsion held between the particles of an elastic fluid such as air, then Boyle's law would follow. If in

---

* See §§ 2, 4 in Chapter Five, pages 138, 139; also Appendix One.

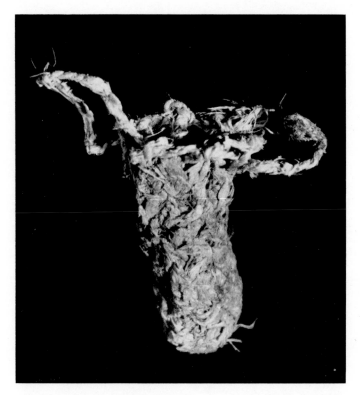

FIG. 4. Asbestos purse brought from America by Benjamin Franklin and sold by him to Sir Hans Sloane in 1725. *Courtesy of the British Museum (Natural History)*.

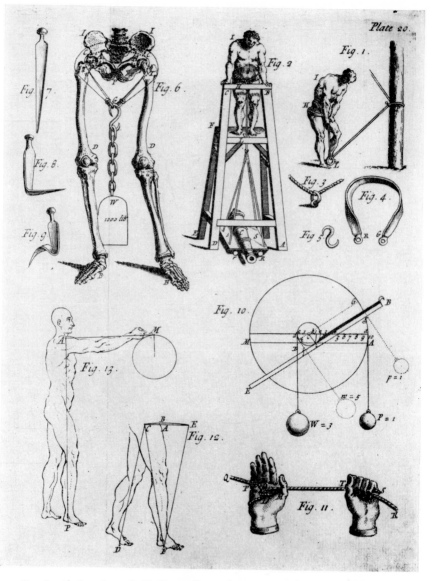

FIG. 5. A plate from J. T. Desaguliers: *Course of Experimental Philosophy*
(vol. 1, 1734).

the argument he made use of this law of repulsion, he did so only *per hypothesin* and did not assert thereby that such a law of repulsion actually existed in nature. I believe that in all probability Newton thought that this law of repulsion was not merely a mathematical hypothesis to be used in this particular lemma, but was a law of nature: all elastic fluids are elastic because of the mutual repulsion of the particles of which they are composed. In Query 21 of the *Opticks*, he introduced the supposition that " æther (like our air) may contain particles which endeavour to recede from one another (for I do not know what this æther is) . . ."—a statement which could be interpreted as saying that whatever may be true about the æther, " our air " does " contain particles which endeavour to recede from one another." The concept of such a mutual repulsion was basic to Desaguliers's thoughts on elasticity, Hales's on gases, Franklin's on the electric fluid, Lavoisier's on caloric, and Dalton's on atoms; and the ultimate source in each case was Newton. But Desaguliers went so far as to state that such repulsion had been " demonstrated " by Newton in the *Principia*, and referred as his authority—as we shall see in a moment—to that very lemma in which the mutual repulsion had been introduced by Newton as a " mathematical " assumption or hypothesis rather than a phenomenon or a law † deduced from phenomena, or even a physical hypothesis.

Electricity in the Newtonian Framework

No words of description can convey the charm of Desaguliers's *Experimental Philosophy*. Only an examination of the book itself can suggest the delight that Franklin must have found in leafing through its pages. For not only are the major principles of Newtonian physics explained in words, without any mathematics such as used by 'sGravesande, but the illustrations have an attractiveness of their own. One plate shows the way in which forces act on the human body in a variety of circumstances, which incidentally permits Desaguliers to explain many of the conjurer's tricks, such as the lifting of great weights. There is even an explanation of why it is that if a cord is wound around the hand in a certain way, it can be broken by having an end grasped by the other hand and yanked suddenly, even though the force of the two hands by themselves could never effect a breaking of the cord. We have seen that Desaguliers pointed out that the form of Newton's queries in the *Opticks* derived simply from the author's " modesty "; many of Newton's conjectures are interspersed throughout the book. For example,

† This was the identical procedure followed by Dalton.

when discussing the motion of the planets, Desaguliers pointed out that the medium through which the planets move is called a vacuum. Yet there must be some resistance offered by that " medium " to the motion of planets, since light is propagated through it and " some fine effluvia may be separated from the comets and planets." Even though the resistance may be many thousands of times less than that of ordinary air, " that resistance after a great number of years must so alter the motion of the planets, as to require the Author of Nature's mending hand." Accompanying this statement is a postil: " This is Sir Isaac Newton's opinion [!]. See the Queries at the end of his *Opticks*." [103]

In the very first chapter, when Desaguliers noted that in matter there are attractive and also repulsive forces, he pointed out that such words as gravity, gravitation, or attraction are used in the sense of having " a regard not to the cause, but to the effect; namely to that force, which bodies have when they are carried toward each other, . . . whether it be occasioned by the impulsion of any subtile fluid,‡ or by any unknown and unmechanical concomitant § to all matter." [104] Another attractive force is cohesion, which holds the parts of bodies together.

Magnetic attraction was introduced in order to compare it to gravitation, and repulsion was presented in a number of different examples, such as the dissolution of salts in water and the production of air and vapors. When salt water is evaporated, the parts of the salt attract one another and unite into hard lumps, that is, they come so near to each other as to be within the power of their attraction.

That they repel one another at farther distances, appears from the regular figures into which they coalesce, when by the evaporation of part of the fluid in which they float, they are brought within each other's sphere of attraction; these regular figures depending entirely upon the equality of their distances one from another before this evaporation, and this equality of distance being owing to an equality of repelling force.

In good Newtonian fashion, Desaguliers attempted a theory of chemistry based on the attractions and repulsions of particles.

Yet another attractive force exists in nature; it is " not so strong as the attraction of cohesion, but stronger than gravity." This force decreases not as the square of the distance, but " nearly as the cube and a quarter of the encreased distance." [105] This force is magnetism, which exhibits repulsion as well as attraction. There are other ex-

‡ Desaguliers made allowance for the possibility of a Newtonian æther.

§ He also made allowance for the Newtonian " first cause " which was not mechanical.

amples of repulsion in nature, and bodies which " attract one another at certain distances, and under certain circumstances, do repel one another at different distances, and under other circumstances." Thus, according to " Sir Isaac Newton's Optics, Book II, Part III, Prop. 8," [106] the reflection of light does not occur from the " particles of light " striking the surface and rebounding, but from their being " repelled from the surface at a small distance before they touch it "; so, too, the rays of light are " repelled by the edges of bodies as they pass near them," making the shadows larger than they would otherwise be; " and see Book III, Part I, where the same author . . . likewise proves this repulsive force from other phænomena."

An important example of the possibility of "attraction and repulsion in the same body at a considerable distance, is evident in several electrical experiments." Hence, Desaguliers felt the need of devoting the last five pages of the opening lecture to a discussion of electricity. When Franklin read Desaguliers's book in 1744, he must have encountered in it some simple basic facts of the new science of electricity.

Desaguliers observed that the name electricity has been given to " that attracting and repelling force which is excited in any other body by the same friction as is given to the amber." [107] Glass has such a power more than any other body, but it is also to be found in wax, resin, sulphur, silks, paper, ribbons, hair, and feathers. In the experiments he described, a glass tube was rubbed " with a dry hand pretty briskley," and it would then attract a feather or any other light body which would stick to the tube for a moment and then fly away and be repelled. Although the electricity is aroused in a glass tube by rubbing, Desaguliers observed that warming the tube at the fire without rubbing it would produce no effect. When the tube is rubbed in the dark, " the effluvia will appear lucid; and when it is made to snap there appears a light upon the finger ends. . . ." These electrical experiments are described in the first lecture, at the conclusion of which Desaguliers indicated that he would say no more on this subject at the moment because he would have occasion to " consider it more fully in another part of my course." Yet, in the annotations accompanying this first lecture, fuller descriptions were given of the experiments of Hauksbee, and there was included an admirable summary of the experiments of Stephen Gray. Gray's discoveries had been published in the *Philosophical Transactions* after Desaguliers had begun to write his book. For the sake of those who " may not have an opportunity of seeing the *Transactions*," Desaguliers described Gray's discoveries under eleven heads, as follows: [108]

1. Every substance that "cannot be made electrical by rubbing" can "receive an electrical virtue" either by contact with a rubbed glass cane, or though a "string" to the length of more than 800 feet. The "electrical virtue will run along" the string even if the tube is rubbed near the string without being in direct contact with it. But, to have "the virtue run" along a hempen string, the string must be supported by hair or silk lines, since "the propagation of the virtue to a distance" is stopped by supporting strings of hemp or flax "or even wire."

2. Large surfaces, such as maps or tablecloths may be "impregnated with electrical effluvia."

3. The "electrical virtue" can be received by a lodestone or a piece of iron hanging from it, so that apparently the "electrical virtue" is not "disturbed by magnetick effluvia."

4. "The electricity" can be "carried several ways at the same time." Thus, if balls of ivory are hung at the ends of a very long string, and a tube is rubbed near the middle of the string, the two balls will become electrified.

5. "The electrical attraction received" is not in proportion to the quantity of matter in bodies, since a solid and a hollow cube of wood attract "the one as much as the other."

6. "The effluvia" are also "carried round in a circle, and communicated from one circle to another."

7. "This virtue" can be communicated to the leaves of trees, and to fluids, including "bubbles of soaped water."

8. Animals may "receive this virtue." If a man is suspended horizontally by hair lines, and the tube is rubbed at his feet, his face will attract and repel pieces of gold leaf; if, in his hand, he holds a fishing rod with a ball at the end, then the ball too will attract and repel pieces of gold leaf. The "virtue is strongest at that part of the impregnated body, which is the farthest from the tube"; if the rubbed tube is held over the man's head, "not the head, but the face will then attract, and so vice versa." Of course, if the man touches the floor with a cane or wire, "the virtue runs to the floor, and the man is no longer electrical."

9. If two boys are suspended by hair lines, then even if they are at a considerable distance from one another, the "virtue may be communicated from the one to the other by a string, which both hold," and "the electricity" is stronger "in him who is at the greater distance from the tube."

10. (A later discovery of Gray.) If a man stands upon a cake of

resin, or glass, or any other substance which is of itself " electrical, or become so by rubbing," the effect will be just the same as if he were to be hung from a hair line. That is, a man may be as well insulated by standing on such a cake as by being suspended by hair lines from the ceiling.

11. It has also been found " that electricity will be communicated through dense and large bodies."

Desaguliers presented to readers like Franklin a succinct account of the experiments which mark the beginning of experimental electricity in the eighteenth century: the facts about conduction and non-conduction and what was later called " electrostatic induction." It must be observed, however, that between the time of Gray's experiments, reported chiefly in the mid-1730's and the time when Franklin began his research in the mid-1740's, many diverse new phenomena had been reported and the whole subject had become more challenging to the would-be theorist.

From our point of view, the introduction of electricity in Desaguliers's book is of the greatest interest. In Volume Two, he reprinted the whole of his *Dissertation concerning Electricity*, which he wrote in 1742 and which had been awarded the prize of the Academy of Bordeaux. The inclusion of this essay in Desaguliers's *Course of Experimental Philosophy* carried the implication that electricity in its own right was a major topic of investigation for the experimental natural philosopher; it was in fact the chief field of Desaguliers's own research. But in Volume One, he introduced electricity only as an example of " attractive virtue " and its cognate phenomenon, repulsion. He wrote of " effluvia " just as Boyle had done, and as his master, Newton, had done in the *Opticks*. In Query 22 Newton had raised the question of the great " rarity " and " elasticity " of the æther. In showing the plausibility of his conjectures, he referred to " an electrick body," which can " by friction emit an exhalation so rare and subtile, and yet so potent, as by its emission to cause no sensible diminution of the weight of the electrick body, and to be expanded through a sphere whose diameter is above two feet, and yet be able to agitate and carry up leaf copper . . . at the distance of above a foot from the electrick body." It should be observed that there was no question raised as to the emission of such a " rare and subtile, and yet so potent exhalation," just as there was no question about the existence of magnetic " effluvia." If there was any " question " in Query 22, it was only about the possible resistance of the æther to the motion of the planets and comets.

Desaguliers concluded the first lecture as follows:

I shall say no more on this subject [electricity] now; because I shall have occasion to consider it more fully in another part of my course: And the intent of this lecture is only to shew,—That those properties of bodies, such as gravity, attractions, and repulsions, by which we shall hereafter explain several phænomena, are not occult qualities or supposed virtues, but do really exist, and are by experiments and observations made the objects of our senses. These properties produce effects, according to settled laws, always acting in the same manner under the same circumstances: And, tho' the causes of those causes are not known, since we do not reason about these hidden causes; it is plain that we reject occult qualities, instead of admitting them in our philosophy, as the Cartesians always object to us.[109]

Desaguliers on the Queries in the Opticks

Desaguliers's *Course of Experimental Philosophy* is made up of twelve " lectures," each of which is followed by " annotations," in which supplementary material, occasionally of a simple mathematical character, is presented. Interspersed throughout the work are reprintings of articles written by Desaguliers and previously published in the *Philosophical Transactions*, and correspondence on controversial topics between Desaguliers and others. Following the introductory chapter or lecture on the nature of matter, there are discussions of the mechanics of bodies (statics and dynamics) , and then the mechanics of the parts of bodies (the second sense of Newtonianism; as found in the *Opticks*) introduced by way of hydrostatics and pneumatics (physics of gases) , with some account of heat and light.

The " Annotations upon the eleventh lecture " have a particular interest from the point of view I have presented in Chapter Six, on the role of Newton's *Opticks* in eighteenth-century physical thought. Here Desaguliers pointed out that the Queries (in the first two editions of the *Opticks*) contain an " excellent body of philosophy." These Queries " upon examination, appear to be true." [110] The form of question, Desaguliers asserted, arose from Newton's " modesty "; he had " observations enow " to satisfy himself that the things he had proposed " by way of queries " were " true." Newton, however, was not willing to assert anything that he " could not prove " by " mathematical demonstrations or experiments." The result of the question form may have been that readers thought of the Queries as mere " conjectures," but a few—including himself and Dr. Stephen Hales—" look upon them as we do on the rest of his works." *

---

* It should be observed that this sentiment about the character of the Queries in the *Opticks* appears twice in Desaguliers's book. See pages 249-250, above.

Desaguliers had personally made many experiments which confirmed his belief in Newton's " opinions," and Hales had " made a great many more " which " cleared up many of his hints, and shewed that Sir Isaac had made no rash assertions." At this point Desaguliers referred the reader to Hales's writing on " air " in his *Vegetable Staticks*, to his own " abstract " of that book in the *Philosophical Transactions*, and to Hales's " Treatise of *Hæmastaticks*." He then related " some thing observed by the Doctor [Hales], and a few things which I take to be natural consequences of his and my experiments concerning air." We may be sure that Franklin would have accepted willingly the testimony of Desaguliers and Hales, and that he too would have been sure that the Queries in the *Opticks* contain a " true " and " excellent body of philosophy "—hypotheses and all. Desaguliers concluded the " Annotations upon the eleventh lecture " as follows;

There seem to be but two powers, or general agents in nature, which, according to different circumstances, are concerned in all the phænomena and changes in nature; *viz.* attraction (meaning the attraction of gravity, as well as that of cohesion, etc.) and repulsion. It seems not reasonable to admit elasticity for a principle, since it may be generated and destroyed in solids, and likewise in fluids, as appears by many observations and experiments.

Then, in the style of the book he so greatly admired, Desaguliers appended a series of seventeen numbered " queries," one more than had appeared in the first edition of Newton's *Opticks*.

Desaguliers on Attraction and Repulsion in the Particles of Matter

In the beginning of the second volume of *A Course of Experimental Philosophy*, Desaguliers referred to the fact that in his first lecture " the mutual attraction of small particles of matter, and mutual repulsion of others, have already been shewn." He concluded that attraction and repulsion seem to be " settled by the great Creator as first principles in nature; that is, as the first or second causes; so that we are not solicitous about their causes, and think it enough to deduce other things from them." If elasticity were to be admitted as another first cause, we would then be guilty of too many " principal causes in nature," an idea plainly contrary to the " rules of good philosophy." Hence philosophers have endeavoured to deduce elasticity from attraction, from repulsion, or from both. That particles of one kind may repel one another strongly and yet attract other kinds of particles seems indicated by " chymical dissolutions, especially by the alternate dissolution and precipitation of metals in acid menstruums." This has been proved in many ways by Stephen Hales in his *Vegetable Staticks* and *Hæmastaticks*. " The elasticity of air seems to consist wholly in the repulsive power of its particles, which do not touch one another while the air is in its elastick state; and if those particles be brought nearer and nearer together, the effects of their repulsive force will increase, the air's elasticity being always proportionable to its density by compression." [111]

If air is compressed by the application of an external force, the elasticity of the air increases as its volume decreases. By contrast, " fermentation [may] diminish its bulk very much, without [its] gaining any more elasticity." Let another fluid " whose parts repel one another, but attract the parts of air, be mixed with air "; the repulsion between " any two particles of air will be diminished, in proportion as a particle of the other fluid insinuating itself between them, attracts them towards itself on either side." Meanwhile, of course, the repulsion between particles of the other fluid will be similarly diminished by the action of the air particles. If " we allow an attraction strong enough between the parts of two elastick fluids," Desaguliers concluded, " fermentation " can possibly produce a solid out of two elastic fluids. When brimstone matches burn, " the effluvia of the sulphur repel each other to great distances, as may be known by the sulphureous smell upon such an occasion." But " tho these particles repel each other, they attract the air very strongly," as may be shown by experiment.

The experiment consisted of burning some brimstone matches inside of a glass " receiver " (bell jar) holding about four quarts of air and inverted over water. The water level rises, even before the flame is extinguished, although one might have suspected that the heat of combustion would have expanded the air. This effect " plainly happens by some of the effluvia, or little parts of the sulphur, attracting some of the particles of the air, so as to make an unelastic compound that precipitates into the water." What conclusion may be drawn? " If the elasticity of the air is quite lost when the repulsion of its particles is taken off, or sufficiently counter-acted, it must follow that its elasticity depends upon repulsion ": a splendid paralogism, arguing from *petitio principii*. To prove his point from phenomena, Desaguliers cited some of Dr. Hales's chemical experiments.[112] Newton's ideas, developed by Desaguliers and Hales, and others, thus paved the way for Franklin's concept of particles of electric fluid which repelled one another and were attracted by other particles, as of matter.

Desaguliers returned to the subject of the air's elasticity in Lecture Ten. After repeating the statement that "*the air consists of particles which do not touch one another, and that repel each other*," [113] he indicated that the force by which the particles of air " fly from each other " increases in " the same ratio as the distance in which the centers of the particles are diminished," that is, " the force is inversely " proportional to the distance.† Some pages later, Desaguliers reprinted a letter of his from the *Philosophical Transactions* (no. 407) , " An Attempt to solve the Phænomenon of the Rise of Vapours, Formation of Clouds and Descent of Rain." In this letter, Desaguliers introduced a lemma proving that the particles of all fluids have a repellent force. Fluids, he observed, are either elastic or unelastic, and elastic fluids have their density proportional to the pressure (Boyle's law) . He then pointed out that Isaac Newton " has demonstrated, (*Princip. Lib. 2. sect. 5.*) that they consist of parts that repel each other from their respective centers." [114] So we see how even a friend and disciple would make positive statements out of Newton's conjectures, even those which were purely mathematical hypotheses. In the discussion of this lemma, Desaguliers explained how particles may attract only on contact, in which case the normal repulsion is so completely overcome as to render the fluid unelastic. By heat or fermentation the particles can be separated from such contact; the repulsion then grows stronger, so that the particles may exert a force of repulsion at even greater distances, expand into a very large space " by becoming fluid, and may sometimes take up more than a million of times more room than it did in the solid or incompressible fluid." The reader was then referred to " the Queries at the end of Sir Isaac Newton's *Opticks*," and the experiments made by Stephen Hales. [115]

Electricity and Heat

Desaguliers also included in the second volume a dissertation on the cause of the rise of vapors and exhalations in the air. At the outset he declared his philosophy: to explain natural phenomena, we are to admit no causes " but such as really exist, and which are sufficient to produce the effects ascribed to them: for without this, however ingenious an hypothesis may be; he that makes it, has only shewn how nature may have operated, but not how it has really acted." [116] Desaguliers then inveighed against those who have attacked " the Newtonian philosophers " as men who " wanted to readmit the occult qualities of the ancients, long exploded, by speaking of attractions and repulsions." Desaguliers argued that these

† Newton's " hypothesis," from which he had derived Boyle's law.

qualities are not really occult at all, but rather " visible and evident qualities "; only their causes may be occult.

The first principle stated to explain vapors is that " the particles of water have a repulsive quality of immense force." The proof lies in the many experiments which have shown the impossibility of compressing water. This repulsive force, " whose sphere of activity extends but a little way (perhaps not beyond the surface of the constituent particles of water) ," is succeeded by " an attractive force, which we shall call attraction of cohesion, which begins where the other ends, and confines its extent." So, once again, we have the supposed conjectures of the *Opticks* stated as fact: that where the one type of force leaves off, the other begins. The tenth principle relates to the attraction of air by moist vapors. When vapor " particles adhere to those of the air, it only loses its elasticity in part." Later, the air disengages itself from the watery particles which it then repels after having previously attracted them.‡ These particles then repel one another, " having, as it were, received their repellent virtue from the air. This property of air is what I call its *electricity*." Hence Desaguliers had to prove that the air " is electrical," and he introduced some electrical experiments made in France, England, Holland, etc.[117]

In dry weather, summer or winter, he said, a rubbed glass tube will attract a down feather " let loose in the air," which will stick to the tube for " a little while," and then be repelled with such great force that it will float in the air, " being driven about by the tube." If the feather is brought near some solid body which is " non-electrical," it is attracted by that body; after contact, the feather " returns again to the tube, that attracts it a-new, and presently repels it again." The feather may thus jump back and forth, alternately, from the tube to some other body and from that body to the tube.

The experiment of the feather, and the many variations of it which Desaguliers described, were introduced at this point to prove that " electrick bodies " will " repel one another all the time that they keep their electricity." Desaguliers observed that if the air is very dry, only a little friction is needed to excite " a glass tube to electricity, and the virtue lasts a great while." The reason is that the " electrical emanations " are " repelled by the air, return to the tube, and from the tube fly back into the air, making a great many vibrations. After the same manner also the down feather, when the tube has made it electrick, is repelled by the air, and keeps its electricity a great while." But if the air is moist, the feather after

‡ The attraction between particles of air and particles of water vapor was an important ingredient in Franklin's conjectures about cloud formation and rain.

having " become electrical " by the action of the tube, will attract
the particles of vapor floating in the air, and in a little time will lose
" its electricity." This " is the reason that the tube attracts it a-new,
as if it had touched some other visible body." [118]

In a " P. S." [119] Desaguliers wrote that he had forgotten " to take
notice here that the late Mons. Du Faye has observed . . . two sorts
of electricity," and " that bodies which are endowed with one sort
of electricity attract those which are endowed with the other sort
of electricity, whilst they repel those which have the same electricity." One of these Du Fay has called resinous and the other
vitreous. Du Fay's discovery helps to explain many phenomena
relating to vapors and exhalations. Thus " sulphureous and fuligi-
nous exhalations are of a resinous electricity; and the nitrous and
tartarous exhalations, as also the particles of air, have the vitreous
electricity. Hence it comes that sulphureous exhalations attracting
the nitrous, come together with great force, and produce so great a
fermentation that they enflame with lightnings and explosions." By
this means, concluded Desaguliers, " several pernicious exhalations
precipitate, or destroy one another." Franklin encountered an hypothesis about the cause of lightning in many of the authors he read
in the 1740's, Desaguliers, Hales, Clare, and others. He must, therefore, have found a special delight in going so far ahead of his teachers
in finding a better cause of the lightning discharge.

Desaguliers approached the subject of fire and heat during a discussion of thermometers. He observed that the " consideration of fire
and heat is very difficult: we know yet but very little of their nature; and think that philosophers, who assert the being of an elementary fire (or that fire is contained in all bodies) assume a little
too much. Whoever reads with attention Dr. Hales's *Vegetable
Staticks*, will soon be of a different opinion." [120] He then pointed
out that the late Brook Taylor and he had made some experiments
from which it appeared " that *actual heat* was to *sensible heat*, as
motion is to *velocity*." To explain this curious statement, he said
that if a certain quantity of heat which might warm, let us say, a
quart of water, and " which shewed a certain degree of heat on the
thermometer, was applied to warm twice the quantity of water (for
example) two quarts, the thermometer put into this last quantity of
water would shew but half the heat." This difficult point required an
" annotation " and it informed the reader that " in Dr. Hales's *Vegetable Staticks*, Vol. I. Page 28, *& seq.* you'll find Sir Isaac Newton's
opinion and his about the nature of fire in the following words." A
series of quotations from the *Opticks* began: " Is not fire a body
heated so hot as to emit light copiously? For what else is a red-hot

iron than fire? And what else is a burning coal than red-hot wood?
Qu. 10. Is not flame a vapour, fume or exhalation heated red-hot;
that is, so hot as to flame? For bodies do not flame without emitting
a copious fume, and this fume burns in the flame. . . ." There followed a discussion of chemical reactions. Then Desaguliers discussed
how "sulphur and air are supposed to be acted upon by that ethereal
medium by which (the great Sir Isaac Newton supposes) light is
refracted and reflected, and by whose vibrations light communicates
heat to bodies, and is put into fits of easy reflection and easy transmission. . . ." [121] Quotations follow from Queries 18 and 21 of the
Opticks. Although Desaguliers attacked the ideas of Homberg and
Lemery that "fire" is "a particular distinct kind of body inherent in
sulphur," and supposed "that the heat of fire consists principally in
the brisk vibrating action and re-action between the elastick repelling
air and the strongly attracting sulphur," he also appeared to have
supported the notion of "fire particles." From the "manifest attraction, action, and re-action that there is between the acid, sulphureous, and elastic aërial particles," he wrote, "we may not unreason-
ably conclude that what we call the fire-particles in lime, and several
other bodies, . . . are the sulphureous and elastick particles of the
fire fixed in the lime. . . ." But it is clear that Desaguliers's "fire-
particles" were not the "matter of heat" of Boerhaave. The latter
were weightless. But, as Desaguliers pointed out, "that the sulphureous and aërial particles of the fire are lodged in many of those
bodies which it acts upon," "is evident in minium or red lead,
which is observed to increase in weight about $\frac{1}{20}$ part in undergoing
the action of the fire. . . ." [122] In other words, the problem to which
he had addressed himself was the vexing one of what happens during
calcination, a problem to which Boyle had particularly addressed
himself, and which in Franklin's day achieved a solution in terms of
the phlogiston theory, finally overthrown by Franklin's friend
Lavoisier.

No one could have read Desaguliers's book without delight. The
speculations of Newton and the Newtonian Hales, and those of Desaguliers himself, opened the way for further speculations in an inquiring mind like Franklin's. This book was informative about
many different aspects of physical science and it must have had a
special appeal for a man like Franklin because the presentation was
made wholly without mathematics and because there were so many
practical applications of each principle. Above all, it stressed the
repulsion and attraction of different kinds of particles, the possibility
of an ætherial fluid made up of mutually repellent particles, and the
interactions between the various sorts of particles. The many refer-

ences to new developments in science, such as electricity,§ indicated the possibility of experiment opening up new areas of scientific knowledge that had not been fully explored by Newton. And, since the book was written by a friend and disciple of Newton, it gave a kind of official sanction to the belief that the Queries in the *Opticks* were not questions, but statements of belief, and that the interpretation of experiments in the Newtonian natural philosophy could legitimately include speculations and physical hypotheses—so long as the latter did not produce a travesty of science, i. e., a " philosophical romance " rather than a series of explanations based on the inductive laws which are derived from phenomena.

5. Gauger's *La Mécanique du Feu* and Clare's *Motion of Fluids*

Of interest because they contain information about heat and elastic fluids—although of obviously less importance in Franklin's education than Boerhaave, 'sGravesande, Desaguliers, or Hales—are two books to which Franklin referred in his 1744 pamphlet on the Pennsylvanian fireplace: Gauger's *La Mécanique du Feu* and Clare's *Motion of Fluids*. In Desaguliers's *Course of Experimental Philosophy* (in the very " post-script " which Franklin cited in 1744), there was a notice of a translation he had made in 1715 " from the French [of] a book called *La Mecanique du Feu*, which I knew to be written by Monsieur Gauger, a very ingenius gentleman of Paris, tho' he concealed his name." Franklin referred to Gauger's book twice in his account of the new fireplaces. Although he obviously had read the book, he did not make it plain whether he had used the French version or the English translation by Desaguliers; his reference was merely to " Gauger's'*La Mechanique de Feu.*"

Since Franklin used the French title of Gauger's book, one might believe that he had known it in the original edition. More likely, he knew the English version by Desaguliers, in the second edition of 1736, where Desaguliers referred to the book by its French title; he had not done so in the first edition of 1715.* The translator's preface

§ In addition to the references to discoveries in electricity scattered through the book, there was a reprint of Desaguliers's essay on electricity,[123] which had been written in 1742 and had won a prize of the Academy of Bordeaux. Franklin, then, found in Desaguliers's *Course of experimental philosophy* a copious introduction to the subject in which he was soon to make his mark.

Desaguliers's own contribution to electricity, summarized in the prize essay he reprinted in his *Course*, will be described and evaluated in Chapter Nine.

* From the French edition, Franklin would not have learned the name of the author, which was disclosed by Desaguliers. The first of Franklin's two references to Gauger's book mentioned " Fire-places with hollow backs, hearths and jams of iron, (described by Mons. Gauger) . . . ," with a footnote reading " In his tract entitled ' La méchanique

(in the second edition) stated that the "usefulness of this little book" which is "Intitled LA MECHANIQUE DE FEU" had induced him "to give it to the world in English." In the spirit of the times Desaguliers pointed out, "the matter contained in it will be entertaining to every gentleman; and the manner of reducing it to practice, easily comprehended by the meanest workman." In reading this book, Franklin would have found testimony to the reputation of Boerhaave's *Chemistry,* since Desaguliers had included an appendix entitled, "A description of a fire-place, and the chimney without smoke, the smoke being burnt, as described by Dr. Boerhaave in his Chemical Lectures."

Gauger's book contained not only practical instructions on the construction of fireplaces, stoves, and chimneys, but also an epitome of the basic physics of heat. Thus, on the first page, Franklin would have found the theorem, that "fire" sends out rays of heat in all directions just as luminous bodies throw out rays; proof: no matter from what direction we approach a fire, we are sensible of the "impulse" of the rays which gives us a sensation of pain. By "rays of heat" Gauger meant "the particles of the fuel which are darted from the fire"; they are reflected and obey the "optical laws," having the angle of incidence equal to the angle of reflection. Those rays moving upwards follow a right line, but all others follow a curve compounded of the original direction imparted by the fire and an upward component; "Experience shews us, that all little bodies heated, endeavour to go upwards: thus in water or air, the warmest particles go towards the upper parts, and still rise as they are heated." A room, and the people in it, may receive heat from a fire according to three chief modes: (1) by direct rays, (2) by reflected rays, (3) by a "kind of transpiration, that is, when its heat is transmitted thro' a solid body, as in the case of stoves."

Gauger indicated that by "heat of the fire" he meant "that motion of its parts, which causes in us that sensation which is called heat; and sometimes pain, when it is too violent." [125] A property of air which was of great importance in stove design was illustrated by many experiments: they all proved "that the warmest air always gets above the cold." He noted that "several experiments shew warm air

de feu.'" The spelling "méchanique" and the word "de" were used by Desaguliers, but the original French version used the spelling "mécanique" and the word "du."

Franklin's second reference indicated how "the Sieur Gauger gives us, in his book entitled *La méchanique de feu,* published 1709, seven different constructions. . . ." [124] But there appears to be no 1709 edition; the first French printing is dated "MDCCXVIII" and carries an "approbation" signed by Varignon, dated 13 June 1713, while the "privilège du roy," signed by Fouquet, carried a registration date of "1 Septembre 713," an obvious misprint for 1713 which appears immediately below, "De l'imprimerie de Jacques Quillau, 1713."

to be lighter than that which is cold; and therefore there is no doubt, but that air rarefied by heat, is specifically lighter than cold air." [126] A quantitative discussion illuminated the question as to whether light, warm air exists at a lower pressure than heavy, cold air and the relation of this condition to the entrance of smoke into a room.

Gauger noted that if " the rays of heat were of the same nature as smoke, then indeed the air would hinder them from coming into the room." However, Gauger mistakenly assumed that " the smoke is hardly any thing else but the moisture of the wood, reduced into a vapour by the heat; the rays of fire are made up of the solid parts of the fuel darted with a great force from the fire, which easily pass thro' the air; and the more so, the more it is rarified: Nay, we know that they will pass thro' silver, iron, or brass. Thus sounds are hindered by contrary winds, whilst the particles of light are darted to us with the same force, which way soever the wind blows." [127]

Of particular interest are Gauger's discussions of the sensation of heat, since this topic was one to which Franklin later devoted much attention.[†] Gauger observed that the air in cellars appears to be warm in winter and cold in summer, but " it is only comparatively so," since the thermometer readings prove that the summer temperature of the cellar air is actually much higher than the winter temperature. He devised a nice demonstration in which the experimenter cooled one hand and warmed the other (as by walking in winter with a glove on one hand; or by dipping one hand in cold water and the other in hot water). Then he plunged the two hands into the same bowl of lukewarm water, which would appear warm to the cold hand and cool to the hot one. Why is it, Gauger asked, that warm air seems cold to us when blown (as in the wind) on our bodies? He did not say anything about the phenomenon of cooling by evaporation (latent heat), but argued that warm air, " by its violent motion, . . . beats away those warm particles about the surface of the parts (of the body), which causes the heat of our bodies by their motion, or rather stops their motion by its pressure, as we may see such an effect produced when we cool hot coffee by blowing upon it." [128]

Gauger's book is plainly not a great classic in the tradition of eighteenth-century empirical science. Probably its only value to Franklin was to give him specific information on various practices used in building chimneys and constructing fireplaces. Yet we may observe that the English version he appears to have used provided an additional link between Franklin and Desaguliers and thus rein-

---

[†] Boerhaave, too, as we have just seen, was careful to introduce a distinction between temperature and the sensation of heat.

forces the conclusion of the importance of the latter's *Course of Experimental Philosophy* during Franklin's formative years. Furthermore, in Desaguliers's version, Franklin would have found warm approbation of Boerhaave, another author of significance to Franklin. Franklin made use of Gauger's discussion of temperature and sensation in framing his own views on the nature of heat.‡

Although Martin Clare was a Fellow of the Royal Society, and author of a book of sufficient importance to be at least twice reprinted, he does not appear in the *Dictionary of National Biography*. Franklin held his work in esteem and the long quotation from him (in the pamphlet on the new fireplaces) is introduced by the statement, " As the writer [B. Franklin] is neither physician nor philosopher [i. e., natural philosopher, or scientist], the reader may expect he should justify these his opinions by the authority of some that are so." [129] Franklin's declaration that he was not a " philosopher " is especially interesting to note, since he later became the leading " philosopher " of the age and referred to himself as a " natural philosopher," and also because the title of Clare's book indicated that it was intended for the non-" philosopher " rather than the specialist. The title of the second edition § reads in full: *The motion of fluids, natural and artificial; in particular that of the air and water: in a familiar manner proposed and proved by evident and conclusive experiments, to which are added many useful remarks. Done with such plainness and perspicuity, as that they may be understood by the unlearned. For whose sake is annexed, a short explanation of such uncommon terms, which in treating on this subject could not, without affectation, be avoided. With plain draughts of such experiments and machines, which, by description only, might not readily be comprehended.*

The " advertisement " to Clare's book pointed out that the beginning " philosopher " would be greatly assisted in his " first searches after truth " and his mind prepared for " receiving lectures in *natural* and *experimental philosophy*." [130] By experiment, many things of advantage to the world have already been discovered, for the " interests, . . . necessities, or . . . convenience of mankind." Within the last hundred years the arts and sciences have advanced more than in " several ages before " because of the application of " experiments performed with accuracy and judgment." Clare was obviously presenting the empirical approach to nature, rather than

‡ See Chapter Eight.

§ That Franklin used the second edition may be seen in the fact that the quotation from Clare used by Franklin is described as being on page 246. It does so in the second edition (1737), but not in the first (1735); the third edition (1747) appeared three years after Franklin's pamphlet.

the mathematical, and he did so in Newtonian terms, deprecating
" the *hypotheses*, or rather *philosophical romances* of antiquity."
Conjectural schemes and the " productions of warm and pregnant
imaginations," he wrote, no longer bias inquiries into natural causes;
principles are founded only on a sure and rational basis: " That of
experiment and *fact*; which cannot but be always acceptable to those
who admire *demonstration*, and delight in *truth*."

Clare's book is largely devoted to a straightforward presentation
of hydrostatics and pneumatics. There is not much speculation in
it, although mention is made of Newton's statement about a repulsion between air particles leading to Boyle's law, an hypothesis accepted by Clare as a fact of nature. Reference is made to the work
of Bacon, Boyle, Newton, Halley, Descartes, Hales, and so on, and
there are digressions on smoky chimneys, the rise of sap in plants,
lightning, and the like. A few hypotheses are introduced and defended, e. g., " our hypothesis for the general formation of clouds
over islands, promontories, capes, and the sea-coasts." [131] Another
" hypothesis " about " particles of fire, separated from the sun-beams,
adhering to those of water, [so as to] make together little masses of
matter lighter than air " is objected to on the authority of Desaguliers, since " fire has never yet been proved to be a distinct element,
or a particular substance." [132]

We may conclude that the chief service of Clare's book in Franklin's scientific education was to provide information and to indicate
the fecundity of the experimental method of inquiry in the advance
of science. Franklin must certainly have been impressed by the lavish
praise bestowed on Hales and Desaguliers.

Franklin and his circle did use Clare's book. In the weekly meetings of the Junto, a society for mutual improvement organized by
Franklin in Philadelphia, and a kind of fore-runner of the American
Philosophical Society, part of the time was spent in discussing scientific problems. Of such problems discussed, the following survive: [133]

[1] Is sound an entity or body?
[2] How may the phenomena of vapors be explained?
[3] What is the reason that the tides rise higher in the Bay of Fundy
than the Bay of Delaware?
[4] How may smoky chimneys best be cured?
[5] Why does the flame of a candle tend upwards in a spire?

Each of these questions is answered by Clare. [1,] The section " On
sounds " begins with the statement, " Sound is itself not a body, but
a motion accidently impressed on the body of the air. . . ." [134] [2,]
As to the " phenomena of vapours," Clare devoted about twenty
pages to " the rise of vapours, their formation into a cloud, and their

resolution into a rain, etc." [135] [3,] The difference in the height of tides in various bodies of water was discussed by Clare in the concluding portion of the book, " On the tides," wherein Clare had devoted himself particularly to some major examples of " the phænomenon of the flux and reflux of the water in particular places." [136] [4,] The " cure " of smoky chimneys was the subject of " A digression concerning faulty chimneys, etc.," which was called, in the Table of Contents, " Smoky chimneys." [137] Finally, [5], the tending upwards of " flame " was discussed twice by Clare, in terms of specific gravity (". . . flame or smoke ascend not because they are really light; but because they are buoyed up by the air, which is denser . . .") .[138]

6. Hales's *Statical Essays*

The Rev. Stephen Hales, F.R.S., Vicar of Teddington, is best known to historians of science for his animal experiments in which he investigated the dynamics of the circulatory system, making the earliest recorded measurements of blood pressure, and for his pioneering studies of plant physiology. In an important recent article, Henry Guerlac has called attention to the Continental reputation of Hales, noting particularly the role of Hales's advocacy of the doctrine that " air could take part in chemical processes and was a constituent of many common substances," a doctrine " quite generally opposed in Hales' day on the Continent on the authority of such influential figures as Boerhaave and Stahl." Hales, as we saw in a previous chapter, was a great admirer of Newton's *Opticks*, especially the Queries, taking his departure from those passages described by Guerlac as Newton's speculations " about the fixation of air in bodies " and his attempts " to explain this phenomenon in terms of corpuscular attractions and repulsions." [139]

Hales's discussion of " air " * was not only of importance in the history of chemistry, but had some effect on the development of the theories of electrical action. Hales, furthermore, wrote of electricity in relation to animal fluids and advocated the theory that lightning might be associated with the cause of earthquakes. In Franklin's scientific education Hales was important in several ways. Certainly he provided to Franklin an example of the kind of progress that might be made in fields other than Newtonian mechanics—by the application of the experimental art to new areas of inquiry. Furthermore, in Hales, Franklin saw an exemplification of experimental

---

* Hales, of course, had no idea that our air is a mixture of different gases. His term " air " is a generic term for any mixtures of the " permanent gases," water vapor, and other aeroform matter.

Newtonianism inspired by the *Opticks* and he encountered a concept of chemical action in relation to the corpuscular philosophy that with several modifications may have served as one of the models for his own concept of electrical action.

Educated in the mathematical and physical sciences at Cambridge, Hales entered the life of science a confirmed Newtonian. His scientific work he did largely in solitude, as an avocation, and he published few scientific papers; his reputation being based chiefly on two books—*Vegetable Staticks* (first ed. 1727) and *Hæmastaticks* (first ed. 1733), both issued together as *Statical Essays* and translated into French by Buffon and de Saussure; there were also translations into Dutch and Italian.[140]

In addition to his foundational research on the circulatory system in animals, and on the chemistry of the air, the mechanism of plant growth, and general plant physiology, Hales devoted himself to " useful " projects, in a manner reminiscent of Franklin. He worked on such problems as obtaining fresh water from salt water by distillation, preserving foods, cleaning harbors, preventing fires, and the like. He devised a pressure gauge for determining the depth of the sea and is said to have " invented the use of the tea-cup to prevent the crusts of pies and tarts from collapsing." [141] He was active in combatting excessive alcoholism and pamphleteered (anonymously) for the gin acts. At his death in 1761, his library was bequeathed to the colony of Georgia.[142] All in all, he was a very Franklinesque character.

Hales's most important invention was a system of " artificial ventilators." He was successful in having them installed in English prisons and also in a French prison for British sailors. In 1741 he read before the Royal Society a paper on this subject which was printed as: *A description of ventilators: whereby great quantities of fresh air may with ease be conveyed into mines, gaols, hospitals, work-houses and ships, in exchange for their noxious air* . . . ; the title page bore a quotation from Milton, " *And God made The Firmament, Expanse of liquid*, Pure, *Transparent*, Elemental *Air*." The " dedication " is of interest in that Hales's sentiments concerning the delight and usefulness of scientific study are similar to those often expressed by Franklin:

We have here an instance, that the study of natural philosophy is not a meer trifling amusement, as some are apt to imagine: For it not only delights the mind, and gives it the most agreeable entertainment, in seeing in every thing the wisdom of the great Architect of Nature: But it is also the most likely means, to make the gift of kind Providence, this natural world, the more beneficial to us, by teaching us how, both to avoid what is hurtful, and to pursue what is most useful and beneficial to us.

In hospitals, Hales said, his ventilators would be of particular value since " fresh air is of great importance to the sick." An inlet and outlet at opposite ends of the room, as near the ceiling as possible, would serve to convey the " fresh " air in and the " rancid " air out " in an almost imperceptible " manner.[143] On ships, especially, and in jails, this invention would be of value, and also in greenhouses; the latter need ventilation, as Hales had shown in his *Vegetable Staticks*, since " fresh air is as necessary for the healthy state of vegetables, as of animals." [144] " It is well known," he wrote, " that infections are principally drawn in by the breath," and that the fumes of " fermenting wine, beer or vinegar " will kill animals by being drawn into the lungs. He cited an experiment by Dr. Langrish of Petersfield in Hampshire, who cut open the " wind-pipe " of a live dog, inserted a cork to stopper the upper part of the " windpipe " leading to the mouth, and then placed the dog's head into a box with a tight-fitting collar. The fumes of burning brimstone were admitted to the box and, although they were " so strong, and continued so long, as to put out his eyes," these fumes could not reach the dog's lungs and the " dog received no harm as to his life." [145]

Since Franklin knew the two major books of Hales and admired them, and may even have known him in person, there can—I believe —be little doubt that Franklin knew also of Hales's writings and sentiments on ventilation. He did not ever refer to Hales's invention for an improved circulation of fresh air, being more interested in the adaptation of his own inventions to this purpose. Yet Franklin's ideas on the need of fresh air, even if possibly conceived independently of Hales, certainly must have been re-enforced by Hales's writings.

In 1761 Franklin wrote to Mary Stevenson about the problems of obtaining drinking water by evaporating salt water. " It is true," he said, " that distilled sea water will not be salt, but there are other disagreeable qualities that rise with the water in distillation; which indeed several besides Dr. Hales have endeavoured by sundry means to prevent; but as yet their methods have not been brought much into use." Franklin owned Hales's " pieces on the subject which I will leave with your mother for your perusal." [146]

In electricity, Hales's name was brought to Franklin's attention in 1750 by Peter Collinson. Collinson wrote Franklin a letter from London, telling him that his suppositions on the electrical nature of the lightning discharge had been noticed favorably at the Royal

Society, especially by those who saw in electricity a *modus operandi* for the lightning-earthquake theory, among them Stephen Hales Franklin read the piece Hales had published describing an electrical effect accompanying the firing of the cannon in St. James's Park on "great days." Franklin had asked Collinson in a letter of 27 July 1750 "how it was observed that the firing a cannon in the park, electrified the glass of the windows of the Treasury, mentioned by Dr. Hales in his piece on earthquakes." [147] Franklin's name was certainly known to Hales. When Franklin's book on electricity was translated into French, the experiments described in it were performed before the French King and, soon afterwards, the experiment to test Franklin's hypothesis of the electrification of clouds was successfully carried out at Marly-la-ville and Paris. The letter from France announcing these events, published in the *Philosophical Transactions* of the Royal Society, was addressed by the Abbé G. Mazéas to Stephen Hales. This letter concluded with Mazéas's observation: "I do not know, Sir, whether Mr. Franklin's letters were before your considerations upon earthquakes: if they were, we are obliged to Mr. Collinson for his communication of Mr. Franklin's notions; if they were not, you deserve the honour of the discovery; and whosoever it be, it is still to the Royal Society we owe the communication of this ingenious thought. . . ." [148] Franklin's letters had been read at the Royal Society previous to Hales's communication. Hence, this paragraph of Mazéas's was silently suppressed when his letter was reprinted in the second supplement to Franklin's book, and in the later editions.

In addition to the above association of Hales's name and Franklin's, and Franklin's references to him, there is further evidence that Franklin had been reading Hales's *Statical Essays* in the 1740's. In a letter to Cadwallader Colden on 15 August 1745, Franklin wrote that he was pleased with Colden's "doctrine of the *absorbent vessels* intermixed with the perspiratory ducts both on the external and internal superficies of the body." After having read "Sanitorious," he had "imagined a constant stream of the perspirable matter issuing at *every* pore in the skin," but had been puzzled by certain unexplainable effects among them the passage of mercurial unctions into the body, since "whatever virtue or quality might be in a medicine laid upon the skin [must] if it would enter the body . . . go against wind and tide, (as one may say)." At this point, Franklin said, "Dr. Hales helped me a little, when he informed me, (in his *Vegetable Staticks*) that the body is not always in a perspirable but sometimes in an *imbibing* state, as he expresses it; and will at times actually grow heavier by being exposed to a moist air." [149] The remainder of the letter dealt with the mechanics of the circulation in a manner somewhat reminiscent of Hales's *Hæmastaticks* and, although Franklin did not mention the latter by name, we must remember that beginning with the second edition (1731-1733) these two books of Hales were issued as a two-volume set of *Statical Essays*.

Hales as a Newtonian Philosopher

The relation of Hales's *Vegetable Staticks* to the tradition of Newton's *Opticks* was discussed in the preceding chapter and we have just seen a statement by Desaguliers that Hales's studies on " air " were conceived as an exemplification, expansion, and establishment by experiment, of that complete body of philosophy contained in the Queries at the end of the *Opticks*. Without in any way disparaging the pioneering studies made by Hales on the subjects of transpiration, root pressure, leaf-growth and other aspects of plant physiology, we may concentrate most of our attention on that portion of the book which brought Hales his reputation in the eighteenth century, the sixth chapter (occupying almost half the book) entitled " A specimen of an attempt to analyse the air by chymio-statical experiments, which shew, in how great a proportion air is wrought into the composition of animal, vegetable, and mineral substances: and withal, how readily it resumes its elastick state, when in the dissolution of those substances it is disengaged from them." Hales described the burden of this chapter as follows:

Where it appears by many chymio-statical experiments, that there is diffused thro' all natural, mutually attracting bodies, a large proportion of particles, which, as the first great author of this important discovery, Sir Isaac Newton, observes, are capable of being thrown off from dense bodies by heat or fermentation into a vigorously elastick and permanently repelling state: And also of returning by fermentation, and sometimes without it, into dense bodies: It is by this amphibious property of the air, that the main and principal operations of Nature are carried on; for a mass of mutually attracting particles, without being blended with a due proportion of elastick repelling ones, would in many cases soon coalesce into a sluggish lump. It is by these properties of the particles of matter that he solves the principal phænomena of nature.[150]

Although trained in part as a mathematician, Hales did not (in his *Statical Essays*) use any higher mathematics; all that was required of his readers was a little ability in arithmetic. We may note that in the preface to the second edition of the *Vegetable Staticks* Hales found it necessary to take note of those who " complain that they do not understand the signification of those short signs or characters, which are here made use of in many of the calculations, and which are usual in algebra; this mark + signifies *more* or *to be added to*. Thus . . . *6 ounces + 240 grains*, is as much as to say *6 ounces more by*, or *to be added to 240 grains*. And . . . this mark × or cross signifies *multiplied by*; the two short parallel lines signify *equal to* . . . ." [151]

Hales observed that the area of knowledge remaining to be explored by the method of experiment was boundless and that there was " in so large a field, and among such an innumerable variety of subjects, abundant room for many heads and hands to be employed in the work."

For the wonderful and secret operations of Nature are so involved and intricate, so far out of the reach of our senses, as they present themselves to us in their natural order, that it is impossible for the most sagacious and penetrating genius to pry into them, unless he will be at the pains of analysing Nature by a numerous and regular series of Experiments, which are the only solid foundation whence we may reasonably expect to make any advance in the real knowledge of the nature of things.[152]

Hales insisted that he had " been careful in making, and faithful in relating the result of these experiments " but he appreciated the fact that the conclusions to be drawn were not absolutely certain. Earlier, we have seen statements (by such men as Pemberton, and 'sGravesande) that the conclusions of experimental physics could never have the conclusiveness of mathematics. Yet, while Hales wished that he " could be as happy in drawing the proper inferences from " experiments as in performing and reporting them, he believed " that considerable advances in the knowledge of their nature [i. e., of plants] may, in process of time, be made by researches of this kind."

In Hales, in other words, Franklin found a superb justification of the experimental method of inquiry. We must note, however, that Hales's insistence on quantitative experiments marks a great difference between Franklin's investigations and his. Franklin's research was based on comparisons of charges and not the assignment of numerical quantities to charges, which was a much later development. But Franklin certainly agreed with Hales's statement that " the all-wise Creator has observed the most exact proportions, *of number, weight and measure*, in the make of all things "; even if he could not follow Hales's precept that " the most likely way, therefore, to get any insight into the nature of those parts of the creation, which come within our observation, must in all reason be to number, weight and measure." [153] Franklin actually discussed this problem in

his " Opinions and Conjectures . . . , 1749," when he took up the
question of the " beneficial uses " of the electric fluid " in the creation," something " we are not yet well acquainted with." Franklin
showed that too much electric fluid on the globe of the earth would
be attended by " some pernicious consequences," and so we are
afforded " another occasion of adoring that wisdom which has made
all things by weight and measure! " [154]

Hales's Doctrine of Air

Chapter Six of Hales's *Vegetable Staticks*, on the analysis of the
air, opens with a statement that a multitude of experiments had
proved that air is " freely inspired by vegetables, not only at their
roots, but also thro' several parts of their trunks and branches."
Hales had thus been led to make " a more particular enquiry into
the nature of a fluid [air], which is so absolutely necessary for the
support of the life and growth of animals and vegetables." A reference was made to Boyle's many experiments on the air and his
discovery that when vegetables, fruits, or grains are put into " exhausted and unexhausted receivers, . . . they continued for several
days emitting great quantities of air." Hales had instituted a series
of researches " to find what proportion of this air I could obtain out
of the different substances in which it was lodged and incorporated."
His major research precept was that all advances that had been made
in the " knowledge of the nature of vegetables," had been " owing
to statical experiments." Nature, " in all her operations, acts con-
formably to those mechanick laws, which were established at her
first institution "; hence, it was reasonable to conclude that " the
likeliest way to enquire, by chymical operations, into the nature of
a fluid, too fine to be the object of our sight," must be to find some
means to estimate the " influence the usual methods of analysing
the animal, the vegetable, and mineral kingdoms, has on that subtle
fluid. . . ." [155] By " subtle " Hales's generation meant " exceeding
small, fine and delicate, such as the animal spirits, etc., the effluvia
of odorous bodies, etc., are supposed to be." [156]

Citing the authority of Newton's *Opticks* (Query 31), Hales told
his readers that " true permanent air " arises by fermentation or heat
from " those bodies which the chymists call fixed." As a result of
heat or fermentation the particles formerly in contact and in " contact most strongly united " are made to recede " from one another
with the greatest repulsive force." [157] Hales also cited Query 30,
about dense bodies rarefying by fermentation into several sorts of
air and this air, by fermentation, returning into dense bodies (and

sometimes even without fermentation). In the context of this monograph, Hales's discussion of air is notable chiefly for the development and application of the Newtonian concept of air as an elastic fluid in the sense of being composed of mutually repulsive particles.

Hales had been performing experiments on the " action of fermentation " to release the " air incorporated into the substance of vegetables." This air is " true permanent air " because it may be observed to continue in " the same expanded elastick state for many weeks and months; which expanding watry vapours will not do, but soon condense when cool." This " new generated air " is " elastical " and it dilates and contracts with heat and cold like common air; it is also " compressible, in proportion to the incumbent weight," or obeys Boyle's law. Experiments on the elasticity of this air " shew what the great force of these aerial particles is, at the instant they escape from the fermenting vegetables." [158]

According to Hales, the elasticity of this " new generated air " is " supposed to consist in the active aerial particles repelling each other with a force which is reciprocally proportional to their distances." Hales thus stated Newton's hypothesis with almost as much certainty as Desaguliers. But he did not refer to the *Principia* as Desaguliers had done, but rather to the *Opticks*. A quotation from Newton's Query 31 was offered to support by proper authority this view that the action of particles, " shaken off from bodies by heat or fermentation," and expanding to fill up vast volumes, is " unintelligible by any other means " than " a repulsive power." There is no help in " feigning the particles of air to be springy and ramous, or rolled up like hoops." Hales added: " The truth of which is further confirmed by these experiments, which shew the great quantity of air emitted from fermenting bodies; which not only proves the great force with which the parts of these bodies must be distended; but shews also how very much the particles of air must be coiled up in that state, if they are, as has been supposed, springy and ramous." [159] Hales, however, was careful to distinguish between the results of experiments and conjectural principles. The experiments had proved only that " this new generated air " has a great elasticity; and this elasticity was " supposed to consist " of the mutual repulsion of the particles in the inverse proportion of the distance between them.

Many of Hales's principles which are not purely chemical have been alluded to or described in our discussion of Desaguliers, who drew heavily on Hales. We may be certain, therefore, that the double authority of Hales and Desaguliers must have brought these principles to Franklin in the most forceful way possible. Most likely, he would have found Desaguliers's presentation more interesting, but perhaps Newton's *imprimatur* in Hales's book gave it the greater authority. Hales discussed the nature of heat, attacking the view that fire might be " a particular distinct kind of body inherent in sulphur," [160] as supposed by Homberg and Lemery. Among many quotations from the *Opticks* Hales used bits of Query 18 and Query 21 to show that both sulphur and air are acted upon by that ætherial medium " by which (the great Sir Isaac Newton supposes) light is refracted and reflected, and by whose vibrations light communicates heat to bodies, and is put into fits of easy reflection and easy transmission. . . ." [161] Hales did not say that Newton asked about the possible action of the æther, but stated unequivocally that this was what Newton " supposes "; we may recall that in Book Two of the *Opticks* Newton specifically cited this supposed action of the æther as an hypothesis.

One of the features of Hales's investigations of air that bears the greatest relevance to electrical theory is the study of the ways in which air loses its elasticity. Hales wrote that " an air greatly charged with vapours loses much of its elasticity, which is the reason why subterraneous damps suffocate animals, and extinguish the flame of candles." [162] We have seen a reference by Desaguliers to experiments in which the burning of sulphur matches in a closed vessel diminished the volume of contained air, a result which he interpreted as a lessening of the air's elasticity. Hales performed many experiments on this subject and supplied to Desaguliers the information reported in his *Course of Experimental Philosophy*. This topic had been a subject of study by the seventeenth-century chemist and physiologist, John Mayow.† Hales noted that Mayow " found the bulk of air lessened by $\frac{1}{30}$ part, but does not mention the size of the glass vessel under which he put the lighted candle. . . ." The capacity of the vessel in Hales's experiment " was equal to 2024 cubick inches; and the elasticity of the $\frac{1}{26}$ part of this air was destroyed." [164] We may observe that Hales mentioned the lessening of the " bulk " of air in Mayow's experiments, but in his own he referred to the destruction of the " elasticity " of a portion of the enclosed air. Fire, according to Hales, is " chiefly invigorated by the action and reaction of the sulphureous particles of the fuel and the elastick ones which arise and enter the fire, either from the fuel in which they abound or from the circumambient air." Since, as we have just seen, both sulphur and air are supposed to be acted on by

† The contributions of John Mayow have been of late the subject of acute controversy. The late T. S. Patterson provided a sharp criticism of accepted views, and the whole problem is currently being re-assessed by Henry Guerlac and J. R. Partington. [163]

the Newtonian æther, Hales's chemistry was closely tied to the speculative portion of Newton's *Opticks*. Furthermore, a reference by Hales to Queries 7, 9, and 10, with partial quotation, makes it plain that he ‡ found Newton's speculations on fire and flame to be of the greatest value.[165]

Hales on Attraction and Repulsion in Particles of Matter

Hales developed the Newtonian idea that by attraction and repulsion one could explain almost if not quite all of the operations of nature. The particles of air are mutually repellent when air is in its elastick state, but they may also be attracted by sulphureous particles which reduce the original elasticity. Furthermore, the elastic fluid of air can be " fixed " in bodies by various natural and artificial processes and can be released by similar processes. Ordinary matter, therefore, can be said to contain a special kind of matter that under proper circumstances may be released as an elastic fluid. The student of Franklin is especially struck by the similarity of this train of thought and Franklin's ideas about the electric fluid: the latter is also within bodies and can be released by suitable operations, notably friction which also produces heat. One of the features of Franklin's electrical theory is that the particles of the electric elastic fluid have a strong attraction for the particles of " common matter." It is, therefore, of special interest to observe that Hales had interpreted Newton's views in the *Opticks* to apply both to the general attraction of sulphureous particles for the particles of the elastic fluid air and electrical attraction. Sulphur, Hales wrote, " not only absorbs the air when burning in a homogeneal mass, but also in many fermenting mixtures. . . . Sir Isaac Newton observed § the attractive and refractive power of bodies to be greater or less as they partook more or less of sulphureous oily particles." Furthermore, Hales said " there is good reason from these experiments to attribute the fixing of the elastick particles of the air to the strong attraction of the sulphureous particles with which he [Newton] says it is probable that all bodies abound more or less." Hales argued, " Electrical

‡ It is to be observed that, in his many citations of Newton's *Opticks*, Hales never indicated that the Queries were in any sense questions to be answered. Here is a typical one: " And when a brimstone match, which was placed in an exhausted receiver, was heated by the focus of a burning glass so as to melt the brimstone, yet it did not kindle into fire, nor consume, notwithstanding the strength and vigour of the action and re-action that is observed between light and sulphureous bodies. Which is assigned by the illustrious Sir Isaac Newton, as ' one reason why sulphureous bodies take fire more readily, and burn more vehemently than other bodies do, *Q.* 7.' "

§ For a further discussion of Newton's views, see page 161 above.

bodies are also observed to attract more strongly in proportion to the greater quantity of sulphur which they contain." [166]

Although Hales did not refer at any length to electrical attraction and repulsion in his *Vegetable Staticks*, he did address himself to the cause of lightning and its effects. The air, he observed, may be "full of acid and sulphureous particles" to such an extent that noticeable effects arise from "the action and re-action between them and the elastic air." Great quantities of elastic air "are destroyed by sulphureous fumes." Thus it is likely that when animals are killed by lightning, without any wound being visible, the true cause of death is the sudden loss of elasticity in the air which makes the lungs "fall flat." To the same cause Hales attributed the "bursting . . . of glass windows outwards," since the elasticity of the air within the room must exert an unbalanced force on the glass whenever the outside air loses its normal elasticity. Fermented liquors are rendered "flat and vapid" by lightning, since the lightning destroys "the air's elasticity in fermented liquors." Referring to the "common practice of laying a bar of iron on a vessel" as a "preservative against the ill effects of lightning on liquors," Hales observed, " I should think that the covering a vessel with a large cloth dipped in a strong brine would be a better preservative; for salts are known to be strong attracters of sulphur." [167] I confess to ignorance about any "ill effects of lightning" on "fermented liquors," but perhaps they resemble the supposed "ill effects" of lightning in causing fresh milk to turn sour. In any event, the lightning rod invented by Franklin prevented the destruction of homes and other buildings, and I dare say preserved the fermented liquors within them, both in animate and inanimate vessels.

Hales also referred to lightning in the second volume of his *Statical Essays*, the *Hæmastaticks*, which Franklin had been reading in the 1740's. The discussion of lightning occurs in the Appendix, which contains "observations and experiments" relating to subjects in the first volume, *Vegetable Staticks*. Lightning came up for discussion under the general subject of the "brisk action and reaction there is between elastic air and sulphureous particles." [168] In the course of his presentation Hales explained why lightning cools the air, as is commonly observed, and how the "first kindling of lightning is effected"—there is a sudden mixture of the "pure serene air" above the clouds and the "sulphureous vapours" down below.*

---

* In discussing lightning, Hales referred to "the excellent and elaborate" treatise on chemistry of "the learned Dr. Boerhaave."

Animal Electricity

One of the most interesting aspects of Hales's *Hæmastaticks* from the point of view of electrical investigation is the discussion of the force of nerves in producing muscular action. Hales advanced the suggestion of a nervous elastic fluid and indicated the possibility that it might be electrical rather than merely Newton's æther. Whether this force or " active energy " be " confined in canals within the nerves," he wrote, " or acts along their surfaces like electrical powers, is not easy to determine." A " vibrating electrical virtue " can " be conveyed and freely act with considerable energy along the surface of animal fibres," and therefore also along the nerves. This effect may be seen in experiments [on electrical conduction] made by Stephen Gray, who, according to Hales, had proved " that electrical virtues from a glass heated by rubbing will not only be conveyed along the surface of lines to very great lengths, but will also be freely conveyed from the foot to the extended hand of a human body suspended by ropes in a horizontal posture in the air. . . ." [169]

Hales had been interested in the general problem of how the blood acquires its heat in the living animal, and had concluded that the principal source of warmth in the blood is " the brisk agitation " it " undergoes " as it " passes thro' the lungs." [170] How this line of thought led to electrical experiments is described by Hales in these words: " Now many solid bodies which, having acquired warmth by rubbing, being found to be electrical, it put me upon trying whether any much agitated fluids were so too." [171] He placed a small quantity of mercury in a glass flask and discovered rather quickly and easily that shaking the flask electrified the mercury " particles," even though " mercury heated by an effervescence with double *aqua fortis* had no electricity." Yet a variety of ingenious experiments on other liquids shaken in glass vessels produced no electrical effects; Hales was particularly disappointed that he found no electrification in blood. How could he explain that " blood thus agitated has no electricity, tho' shaken mercury has " ? Well, in blood there is a " watry part " which may " check electricity, tho' not the heat which is acquired by the mutual rubbing " of the " particles against each other." It is common knowledge, he added, that " electrical experiments . . . succeed best in dry air " and that the electricity of a rubbed glass tube will vanish instantly if the tube is moistened with water. Hence the " want of electricity in the blood " in such experiments may be readily explained. Hales, in any event, was not willing to abandon the possibility of heat being acquired by the blood through " brisk agitation and motion " in the blood vessels, even if there should be no " electricity in the blood." [172]

But in the " muscle shell-fish," Hales pointed out, there is a " remarkable instance of the electricity of its blood-globules." Cut off
a piece of one of the gills, put it in a concave glass with three or
four drops of its " liquor " and examine it under a compound
(" double ") microscope. At the cut edge of the piece of gill, it
will be seen that many " blood-globules " are " repelled from the
cut orifices of the blood-vessels, and attracted by other adjoining
vessels." Other globules will be seen to roll " round their centre "
and repel one another. It is, therefore, plain " that bodies, by brisk
rubbing and twirling about, may acquire, in a watry fluid, both
attractive and repulsive virtue or electricity." In general, it might
be doubtful whether the blood globules " acquire an electrical virtue
or no," as they pass rapidly (with " strong friction ") through the
capillaries. Yet, all " electrical bodies [like amber] acquire greater
degrees of electricity when rubbed in a cold than in a hot air," and
it is certainly reasonable to think of the blood globules acquiring
" considerable degrees of elastic vibrations in passing the lungs." [173]
The globules of blood, said Hales, are heated by friction and dilated
and are then refrigerated and contracted on contact with the fresh
air in the lungs. The insistence on electrification as a possibility
despite the negative evidence is curious and must be taken primarily
as a token of the great interest in electrical phenomena aroused by
the experiments of Stephen Gray. Whatever major books on science
Franklin had read in the 1740's, he could not escape notice of the
new subject, of which he would eventually become the acknowledged
master.

Hales's Influence on Franklin

Although in Hales, as in Desaguliers, Franklin found references
to electrical phenomena, I do not believe that Franklin was particularly indebted to Hales for specific electrical information. What
is significant perhaps is that in Desaguliers, 'sGravesande, and Hales,
the subject itself was mentioned, as also in Newton's *Opticks* and in
the General Scholium to Book Three of the *Principia*. In Franklin's
scientific education, Hales served primarily as a master of experimental inquiry: the design and performance of actual experiments
which produced a wholly new branch of knowledge. Franklin's great
Italian contemporary, Beccaria, the famous student of electricity who
became the first major supporter of Franklin's ideas in Italy, saw
Hales in precisely this role. His biographer said that, when Beccaria
first began to lecture on physics, he particularly devoted himself to
showing his pupils how much time had been wasted on pointless
questions which had robbed physical science " of its best ornament,
which is observation and experiment." Beccaria " undertook to give

back to that science what it had been deprived of, namely a multitude of useful and interesting data extracted from the works of Galileo, Newton, and Hales, always starting from facts before proceeding to conclusions." [174] Franklin learned from Hales what powerful applications might be made of the Newtonian doctrine of particulate attractions and repulsions, especially the possibility of kinds of elastic fluids of which the particles of one might repel one another and yet be attracted by the particles of another such fluid. Furthermore, in Hales's works, the Newtonian kind of exact corpuscular philosophy was presented in terms of the speculative portions of the *Opticks*, the Queries, which Hales accepted—even taking hypotheses as firm conclusions. Of particular importance was Hales's opinion that the particles of an elastic fluid might be " fixed " in solid bodies and, later on, released again by suitable operations, because, in Franklin's electrical theory, the particles of electric fluid behave in a similar manner.

On the subject of the " manifest attraction, action and re-action," between acid or sulphureous particles and elastic aerial particles, Hales had written that one could reasonably conclude that what are called " fire particles " in lime and other substances which have " undergone the fire " are merely " the sulphureous and elastick particles of the fire fixed in the lime." While the lime was hot, these particles were in an active state of attraction and repulsion. As the lime cooled, the particles were caught in the lime, " detained " in the solid matter. Depending on the distances between them, they must continue in their state of attraction or repulsion. [175] If the " solid substance " of the lime should be dissolved, these particles would be free once again to be influenced by their mutual attraction and repulsion. In a similar fashion Franklin explained how the mutually repulsive particles of the electric fluid could be lodged or fixed in solid glass. When glass is in a molten state and then cools, Franklin suggested, the fire particles leave it, and their place is taken by particles of electric fluid, which abounds everywhere. [176] As the glass cools and hardens, its " texture becomes closest in the middle," and the electric fluid can no more penetrate through that section of the glass than the particles could escape from Hales's cooled lime. Hales's thoughts and Franklin's are not exactly the same in every detail, but the two are parallel to each other. I have no doubt that Franklin's ideas about elastic fluids in solid matter were conditioned to a considerable degree by those of Hales.

Franklin and the Newtonian Tradition

The foregoing presentation of the major Newtonian authors whom Franklin was reading in the 1740's prepares us to view Franklin in the perspective of his day. His starting point in speculative Newtonian experimental science was the subject matter and point of view which those authors had derived largely from the set of hypotheses to be found in the Queries of the *Opticks* and *De Natura Acidorum*, printed in John Harris's *Lexicon*. Franklin surely recognized that one could learn some Newtonian natural philosophy without being an accomplished mathematician and that many of nature's secrets remained to be discovered by experiment. Newton's tripartite contributions to science—mathematics, dynamics, and the topics in the *Opticks*—were not all within Franklin's ken. But even if Franklin was limited to only the last of these three, that alone was sufficient for his work to be considered Newtonian. As he brought the subject of electricity to the first level of its becoming an exact science, Franklin could rejoice that his contribution was deemed by his contemporaries to have been worthy of his master, Isaac Newton, author of the *Opticks* and the speculations about the æther and the ultimate particles of matter. The history of physical science during the last one hundred and fifty years has shown that light and electricity, and the cognate phenomenon, magnetism (electrical in origin), are the major subjects that have revealed to us the composition of matter. In this sense, surely, Newton and Franklin may be considered as founding fathers of our modern physics of atomic and molecular structure.

SOURCES

The background of Newtonian thought in the eighteenth century has been discussed mainly in French monographs, notably Metzger (1930 and 1938), Brunet (1926 and 1931), and Mornet (1911). Franklin's reading in the 1740's has been reconstructed from internal evidence in his writings, but the list of books he owned—prepared by the late George Sherwood Eddy—has been helpful. Although Mr. Eddy published a note on this topic (Eddy, 1925), he never completed his list to his own satisfaction; the typescript of the list he compiled is in the Princeton University Library and a microfilm is available in the Library of the American Philosophical Society.

After discovering some of the sources of Franklin's reading from references in his own writings and from internal evidence, I was able to obtain information on the availability of these books in the 1740's in the Library Company of Philadelphia from the Curator, Edwin Wolf, 2nd, who has presented some of his findings in Wolf (1954).

No adequate study has ever been made of Pemberton. For Boerhaave, see Metzger (1930), the volume of essays, Boerhaave (1939), and the bibliography, Hertzberger (1927); the most recent publication on Boerhaave is Kerker (1955). The vicissitudes of Boerhaave's book on chemistry are described in Davis (1928); the career of the translator, Shaw, is described in Gibbs (1951). For Desaguliers, see Torlais (1937); for 'sGravesande, Brunet (1926). Hales's biography, Clark-Kennedy (1929), does not have much to say about the influence of his scientific work—a subject explored in Guerlac (1951).

Many of the eighteenth-century books on the Newtonian philosophy are listed in Babson Collection (1950) and Gray (1907). For a survey of eighteenth-century science see Wolf (1952), Hall (1954).

REFERENCES

1. See Cohen, 1943b, supplemented by Heathcote, 1955.
2. Franklin, 1907: 2: 246-276.
3. Franklin, 1907: 3: 97.
4. Franklin, 1907: 2: 279. For the editions of Boyle, see Fulton, 1932b.
5. Franklin, 1907: 2: 271n.
6. See Miller, 1953: 410; Franklin's indebtedness to Mather is discussed in Franklin, 1954: intro.
7. Franklin, 1907: 9: 209.
8. See Miller, 1953: 440.
9. Mather, 1938: 50.
10. See Holmes, 1940: 1: 129 ff., esp. p. 134.
11. Franklin, 1907: 2: 95.
12. A catalogue of the Boyle Lectures may be found in Fulton, 1932b. See Bentley, 1838: Clarke, 1732.
13. See Sweet, 1952.
14. Franklin, 1907: 2: 93.
15. Conduitt, 1806: 172.

16. Parton, 1864: **1**: 175.

17. For these and other accounts of the Newtonian philosophy, see Gray, 1907, and Babson Collection, 1950.

18. Pemberton, 1728: preface, second [unnumbered] page.

19. *Ibid.*, 2.

20. *Ibid.*, 1.

21. *Ibid.*, preface, penultimate [unnumbered] page.

22. *Ibid.*, 316-318.

23. *Ibid.*, 18, 23.

24. *Ibid.*, 259.

25. *Ibid.*, 338.

26. *Ibid.*, 338-339.

27. *Ibid.*, 350.

28. *Ibid.*, 369.

29. *Ibid.*, 376.

30. *Ibid.*, 407.

31. *Ibid.*, 406.

32. Boerhaave, 1939: 40.

33. *Ibid.*, 33.

34. Franklin, 1907: **2**: 281.

35. *Ibid.*, 253n.

36. See Davis, 1928; Hertzberger, 1927.

37. Franklin, 1744.

38. Letter dated 20 Sept. 1761, Franklin, 1941: 385-387; 1769: 472-466 (page 473 is numbered 465).

39. Printed in full in Cohen, 1943*a*: 406.

40. Printed in full, *ibid.*

41. See Boerhaave, 1727: **1**: 229-230.

42. See Cohen, 1955*a*.

43. Metzger, 1930: 191.

44. Boerhaave, 1727: **1**: 62n; 1741: **1**: 72n; 1741: **1**: 364n.

45. See Gibbs, 1951.

46. Guerlac, 1951.

47. Quoted in Cassirer, 1943: 369.

48. Boerhaave, 1741: **1**: 173n.

49. Boerhaave, 1735: **1**: 44.

50. Boerhaave, 1741: **1**: 156.

51. *Ibid.*, 166n.

52. *Ibid.*, 155n-156n.

53. *Ibid.*, 206.

54. *Ibid.*, 206n.

55. *Ibid.*, 207-208.

56. *Ibid.*, 172-173.

57. *Ibid.*, 210.

58. *Ibid.*, 210-211.

59. *Ibid.*, 211.

60. *Ibid.*, 212.

61. *Ibid.*, 213.

62. *Ibid.*, 214.

63. *Ibid.*, 217.

64. *Ibid.*, 219-220.

65. *Ibid.*, 236.

66. *Ibid.*, 238 and 238n-240n.

67. *Ibid.*, 296.

68. *Ibid.*, 284.

69. *Ibid.*, 273-274.

70. *Ibid.*, 298.

71. *Ibid.*, 300.

72. *Ibid.*, 335, 336, 342, 349, 350, 353.
73. *Ibid.*, 286.
74. *Ibid.*, 357.
75. *Ibid.*, 359.
76. *Ibid.*, 360.
77. *Ibid.*, 361.
78. *Ibid.*, 362.
79. *Ibid.*, 362.
80. *Ibid.*, 363-364.
81. *Ibid.*, 363n-364n.
82. See Brunet, 1926: 41 ff.; Torlais, 1937: 18-22.
83. 'sGravesande, 1747: 1: ii; the preface to the earlier editions are reprinted in this sixth edition, the edition which was in Franklin's library.
84. *Ibid.*, 2-3.
85. *Ibid.*, v, vii.
86. *Ibid.*, ix.
87. *Ibid.*, xii.
88. 'sGravesande, 1726: 2: bk. III, pt. I, pp. 1-2.
89. 'sGravesande, 1747: 2: bk. V, pt. II, ch. VIII, p. 63.
90. Whittaker, 1951: 39, n. 5.
91. Mazéas, 1752.
92. See Torlais, 1937; Barles, 1937.
93. Desaguliers, 1734-1744: 2: 561.
94. Musschenbroek, 1744.
95. Torlais, 1937: 22-23.
96. Franklin, 1907: 2: 264.
97. Brett-James, 1926.
98. Desaguliers, 1734-1744: 1: 4.
99. *Ibid.*, 6, 10.
100. *Ibid.*, preface p. [xvi].
101. *Ibid.*, 42.
102. *Ibid.*, preface, p. [xv]-[xvi].
103. *Ibid.*, 354.
104. *Ibid.*, 7.
105. *Ibid.*, 16.
106. *Ibid.*, 41.
107. *Ibid.*, 17.
108. *Ibid.*, 450-451.
109. *Ibid.*, 21.
110. Desaguliers, 1734-1744: 2: 403.
111. *Ibid.*, 36.
112. *Ibid.*, 37.
113. *Ibid.*, 262.
114. *Ibid.*, 311.
115. *Ibid.*, 312.
116. *Ibid.*, 336.
117. *Ibid.*, 343.
118. *Ibid.*, 344.
119. *Ibid.*, 349.
120. *Ibid.*, 296; see p. 367.
121. *Ibid.*, 368.
122. *Ibid.*, 369.
123. *Ibid.*, 316-336.
124. Franklin, 1907: 2: 249, 249n, 253-254.
125. Gauger, 1736: 3.
126. *Ibid.*, 46.
127. *Ibid.*, 62-63.
128. *Ibid.*, 38.

129. Franklin, 1907: 2: 252n.
130. Clare, 1737.
131. *Ibid.*, 302.
132. *Ibid.*, 294.
133. Reprinted from Franklin, 1840: 2: 9n-10n.
134. Clare, 1737: 320.
135. *Ibid.*, 290-308.
136. *Ibid.*, 366; see pp. 362-363, 365.
137. *Ibid.*, 240-248.
138. *Ibid.*, 115; see p. 242.
139. Guerlac, 1951.
140. See Clark-Kennedy, 1929.
141. Singer, 1931: 364.
142. See Sarton, 1930*b*.
143. Hales, 1743: 23.
144. *Ibid.*, 24.
145. *Ibid.*, 40.
146. Franklin, 1907: 4: 109.
147. Hales, 1750: 680. See Franklin, 1941: intro., pp. 83, 83n; p. 242.
148. See Cohen, 1952*b*.
149. Colden, 1919-1920: 43-47, 139-140; Franklin, 1907: 2: 284-285, 290-294.
150. Hales, 1738: vi.
151. *Ibid.*, x.
152. *Ibid.*, ix.
153. *Ibid.*, intro. (prec. ch. I), p. 1.
154. Franklin, 1941: 214-215; 1769: 56.
155. Hales, 1738: 162-163.
156. Harris, 1736: 2, *s.v.* "subtile."
157. Hales, 1738: 172.
158. *Ibid.*, 208.
159. *Ibid.*, 212-213.
160. *Ibid.*, 285.
161. *Ibid.*, 286-287.
162. *Ibid.*, 263.
163. See Fulton, 1935; Patterson, 1931; Guerlac, 1954*a*; 1954*b*.
164. Hales, 1738: 234.
165. *Ibid.*, 283.
166. *Ibid.*, 300.
167. *Ibid.*, 261-262.
168. Hales, 1740: 284-288.
169. *Ibid.*, 56-57.
170. *Ibid.*, 87.
171. *Ibid.*, 90.
172. *Ibid.*, 92.
173. *Ibid.*, 93-94.
174. Beccaria, 1793: v.
175. Hales, 1740: 287-288.
176. "Opinions and Conjectures . . . 1749," Franklin, 1941: 230, §33; 1769: 76.

CHAPTER EIGHT

BENJAMIN FRANKLIN'S CONTRIBUTION TO THE NEWTONIAN NATURAL PHILOSOPHY

> From the point of view of the physicist, a theory of matter is a policy rather than a creed; its object is to connect or co-ordinate apparently diverse phenomena, and above all to suggest, stimulate and direct experiment. It ought to furnish a compass which, if followed, will lead the observer further and further into previously unexplored regions.
>
> J. J. THOMSON (1907)

THE primary test of Franklin's place in the history of scientific thought is the degree to which his work illuminated fundamental problems. The major subject of his research was electricity and so his primary aim was to discover new electrical phenomena and to devise sound principles on which to explain, correlate, and predict electrical events. In following out this program he enlarged the boundaries of the Newtonian natural philosophy, because his investigations led to a new point of view respecting the constitution of matter, the composition of bodies in relation to their physical properties, and the behavior of different varieties of matter when subjected to controlled conditions in the laboratory. Franklin's scientific reputation derived only in part from his having made of electricity a kind of exact science, as Newton before him had made an exact corpuscular philosophy. Franklin's contemporaries esteemed his work because he had explicitly framed new general principles of matter that accorded with the Newtonian natural philosophy. By showing the importance of the concept of conservation in a variety of physical phenomena, Franklin indicated to his contemporaries the possibility of a complete mechanical explanation of the universe.

The physical scientist of today takes it for granted that electricity is the indispensable tool for investigating atomic and nuclear structures and forces, that most of the building blocks of matter are electrically charged or give signs of their existence through electrical effects. Yet a little more than two hundred years ago it was not even certain that electricity might be of primary importance in the normal or " natural " operations of the external world. Galileo and Newton had constructed what they considered to be near-complete systems of the universe without giving electricity more than a passing comment.* To Franklin was reserved the honor of bringing to the scientific world the first demonstration that there are naturally occurring electrical phenomena of significance in the world. From then onwards, no account of physical events could be considered complete if electricity were left out. It is easy to understand why such a point of view had to wait a long time for its full statement and general acceptance: why, for example, the prenatal history of electricity as a part of serious science begins only at about the time of Galileo and Newton,† in contrast to chemistry, light, heat, sound, and mechanics, which were considerably advanced in antiquity and the Middle Ages. The reason is that the basic gross phenomena of electrical attraction and repulsion are not usually observed as a result of spontaneous action but only as a secondary effect to deliberate manual operations, such as rubbing a piece of glass or amber. Electrical phenomena not only seemed to appear to be a result of man's artifice, but the consequence of a very special condition—being rubbed. When Franklin began his research in the 1740's, there was no certainty that a state of electrification might ever arise from any other of the familiar physical processes which produce changes in a body's situation or condition, such as falling, being squeezed, fracturing, undergoing chemical reaction, being heated or cooled, and the like.‡ It took Franklin's experiments on lightning to prove that nature had been producing electric charges and discharges since the beginning of the world, but that until 1752 man had had no positive knowledge of it.

The Franklinian experiments demonstrating that the lightning discharge is an electrical phenomenon thus had a more profound significance than is usually recognized. They constituted the first empirical proof that electrifications occur constantly in nature without the direct intervention of man. If anyone might suppose the lightning discharge to be an extra-ordinary rather than an ordinary natural event—a supposition in agreement with the belief that thunder and lightning are signs of the divine wrath—then Franklin could reply with his further experiments which indicated that the clouds passing overhead are apt to show signs of electrification even in the absence of a storm. The scientists of the mid-eighteenth century said that, after the Franklinian experiments on atmospheric electricity, the whole subject of electricity became " interesting." ¹ They meant,

* Newton performed some electrical experiments and mentioned the subject here and there.

† In antiquity it had been observed that straws and chaff would collect on rubbed amber (and perhaps another substance, the " lyncurium "), but it is an historical error to say in retrospect that " electrical attraction " was known in antiquity.

‡ Such effects were discovered only after Franklin's basic work.

of course, that, since Franklin had shown them that electrical effects are part of the regular happenings of the world of nature, a complete rational explanation of the universe must embrace electricity along with heat or light or gravity. Electrical experiments performed in the laboratory could reveal aspects of the frame of nature, some essential features of the Creator's plan. Thereafter, every experimenter rubbing glass tubes in his laboratory knew that he was studying cosmic forces on a small scale.

Throughout his writings, Franklin stressed the possible role of electricity in the whole economy of nature, not only atmospheric electricity. He sought electrical explanations of cloud formation, rain, and so on. He even indicated the just proportions of all things in a universe created according to weight and measure because he showed what dreadful things would happen if there had been given to the earth a greater quantity of electric fluid than the divine providence had ordained.[2] In his eagerness to show that electrification is an ordinary physical manifestation, Franklin sought by experiment the possible connections between electricity and other varieties of ordinary physical phenomena like heat, light, magnetism, and change of state.

Franklin's theory of electricity was based on the primary postulate that the substances out of which bodies are made include an electric matter as well as ponderable matter and that electrification in the usual sense means only that a body has undergone a loss or gain of its normal quantity of electrical matter. Hence for Franklin even a non-electrified body contains within it the matter of electricity. There are, he said, three possible states of electrification: *null*, when a body has its natural quantity of electric matter; *minus*, when a body has a deficiency of electric matter; and *plus*, when a body gains an excess of electric matter—and every body in the universe must be in one of these three states. When a body does not electrically attract or repel neighboring bodies, said Franklin, it is in the null state of electrification but it contains more electric matter than it would if it were negatively charged. Since electricity is an element of matter, it is neither manufactured by man's artifice nor produced by divine intervention in natural events. The electrifications we observe in our laboratory objects and in the clouds must be merely a result of transferring the electric matter from one body to another or causing a redistribution of the electric matter within a body. Under such circumstances the electric matter manifests itself in attractions and repulsions, but according to Franklin the electric matter is always present and is a universal component of the matter which we encounter in our experience. Dr. John Fothergill, who wrote the preface to Franklin's book on electricity, insisted on this point. Franklin, he said, exhibits to the reader's consideration " an invisible, subtle matter, disseminated through all nature in various proportions, equally unobserved, and . . . inoffensive," but which under certain circumstances may manifest itself and which can even become " perhaps the most formidable and irresistible agent in the universe." [3]

Fothergill was aware of some of the attempts to " ascribe every grand or unusual operation of nature, such as lightning and earth-quakes, to electricity." Such was " the fashion " of late. In contrast to Franklin, the authors of such " schemes " had not " discovered any connection betwixt the cause and effect, or saw in what manner they were related "; it would seem that they had merely been " un-acquainted with any other agent, of which it could not be positively said the connection was impossible." We have no way of telling exactly what Fothergill had in mind but we do know something about the contemporaneous speculations concerning a possible rela-tion of electricity to natural phenomena. It is not surprising that there had been some suspicion that " electricity " might play a role in the lightning discharge; after all, every spark produced in the laboratory has the appearance of lightning in miniature.§

Scientists did not place much reliance on such an analogy, at least in the absence of experimental proof—most likely because the effects in a thunderstorm and in the production of sparks in the laboratory are on such a vastly different scale. So great is the dis-parity between sparks and lightning that when Franklin showed a variety of reasons for supposing lightning to be an electrical discharge from clouds and even devised an experiment to prove it, there was little reaction in scientific circles (save for some derision!) until three French experimenters agreed to carry out the steps Franklin had suggested.* Some indication of the skepticism about those ex-periments is shown in the report to the Royal Society about similar experiments in England. The author of this report concluded by

---

§ In a letter of 1716 Newton wrote that he had been " much amused by the singular φενομενα [phenomena] resulting from bringing a needle into contact with a piece of amber or resin fricated on silke clothe. The flame putteth me in mind of sheet lightning on a small—how very small—scale." Hauksbee had described electric sparks as appearing " like flashes of lightning." In the 1740's Gray, Du Fay, Freke, Winckler, and Nollet had also written about the similarity in appearance between the lightning discharge and electric sparks—but none of them had conceived a way of making a test by experiment, nor do their writings even give the reader a firm assurance that such an experimental test might be possible. Nollet, for example, had expressed (1748) the hope that someone would prove that the thunder is in the hands of nature what electricity is in ours, but he conceived the proof to be limited to " une comparaison bien suivie des phénomènes." [4]

* D'Alibard, De Lor, Buffon.[5] See, below, page 488.

calling attention to the fact that the effects observed in England had
been on a small scale and might appear " trifling " when compared
with those reported from the Continent. Even so, since the British
experiments " were made by persons worthy of credit, they tend to
establish the authenticity of those transmitted from our [Conti-
nental] correspondents." [6]

One of the first British scientists to applaud Franklin's remarks
about lightning was the Reverend William Stukeley, F. R. S., an
advocate of the doctrine that lightning may accumulate in the earth
and produce an earthquake. Stukeley approved Franklin's ideas because they seemed to advance his own view: if electric fluid may
accumulate in clouds to produce a concussion, why cannot the same
electric fluid accumulate in the earth to cause a quake? [7] Stukeley
was aware that Hales and others had also made " an approach toward
electricity being the cause of earthquakes," but said these scientists
did not " directly attribute " earthquakes to electricity. [8] Such speculations were groundless, and were properly castigated by Fothergill;
although based on, or implemented by, Franklin's discussion of
lightning, they did not truly advance knowledge of the function of
electrical phenomena in the economy of nature. They could produce only a " philosophical romance."

Prior to Franklin's experiments, there had been some speculations
about the electrical aspects of natural phenomena. Newton, in Query
31 of the *Opticks*, had raised the question of the possibility of short-
range electrical forces between corpuscles of matter. It had been
suggested that the repulsion between the particles of elastic fluids
might be electrical in origin. Others had supposed that certain
chemical reactions might be caused by electrical forces between the
particles of different kinds of matter.† Hales had thought that the
blood corpuscles might be electrified. But history does not show
that this line of speculation was fruitful or convincing. Soon after
Franklin had shown that clouds are electrified, however, another
source of " natural " electricity was discovered: pyro-electricity, produced in tourmaline crystals that are heated. Later on, " animal "
electricity was discovered, being found in the electric ray or torpedo
and in the electric eel. Franklin welcomed these discoveries and even
suggested experiments to ascertain the identity of such " electricities " and the " electricity " of rubbing. So strong was prejudice,
however, that the names " natural " and " artificial " electricity continued into the nineteenth century. Faraday, for example, found it
necessary to devote considerable research to proving by actual ex-

† See Chapter Nine.

periment that all electrical effects—no matter what the source—are identical.

Electricity in Relation to the Fundamental Problems of Matter

In Franklin's day it was well known that matter could be classified according to electrical properties, although there was no unanimity on the interpretation to be given such properties in relation to the composition and structure of bodies. To say, for example, that most bodies that become electrified on rubbing contain " unctuous " or " sulphureous " particles was not particularly helpful to the " electrician." ‡ The one major property that produced a dichotomy between all kinds of bodies was the possibility of electrification by rubbing. For instance, an iron rod held in one hand and rubbed with the other shows no sign of being electrified; thus it will not attract a nearby pith ball suspended on a silk string, in the way that a glass rod or a piece of amber will under the same circumstances. In terms of their electrical behavior bodies could thus be classified into two broad categories: those that like glass and amber could be electrified by rubbing (electrics) and those that like the metals could not (non-electrics) : non-conductors and conductors. Then it was shown that the electrics could be subdivided into two groups, those that exhibit the vitreous electrification and those that exhibit the resinous electrification. Such physical properties must be related to the structure or composition of bodies, to be sure, but it was not of any great advantage to divide substances into three categories that had no marked bearing on the chemical composition or molecular arrangement—especially since nature quite obviously presents to our eyes more than a hundred times three varieties of matter! This situation in electricity would be analogous to optics if we could determine only two major optical properties of bodies, opacity and non-opacity, and could classify non-opaque substances only as transparent and translucent.

Franklin's explanation of electrical phenomena in relation to the composition and structure of bodies was therefore a contribution to a fundamental problem, comparable in its way to Newton's studies of the particle-size within bodies by their optical properties. In Newton's day and in Franklin's, the fundamental problems in physical science were still " matter " and " motion." Under these two rubrics one could consider all the observable properties of objects in the external world. " Motion " (and its special state, rest)

‡ This idea, cited on the authority of Newton, lost all value once Du Fay had discovered that there are two quite different kinds of electrification, vitreous and resinous.

embraced the regularities of movement (real or apparent) of the celestial bodies—sun, planets, moons, stars, and the earth itself—and of objects on the earth, whether falling freely, being pushed or pulled, moving against a resisting medium or force, colliding with other objects, and so on. By analyzing the kinds of motions and uncovering the kinematical relations, it was hoped that all of the underlying forces of nature producing or changing motion would be found. "Matter" embraced the alterations produced in bodies by chemical and physical operations, the varieties of matter of which bodies are composed, the interactions of one kind of matter with another, and the relation of the physical and chemical properties of bodies to their composition and structure. Able thinkers hoped to see a universal science—one that would simultaneously embrace the physics of the large and of the small so as to produce a rational understanding, based on mechanical principles, of such seemingly disparate phenomena as the motion of planets around the sun, of satellites around planets, the falling of stones, chemical reactions, the production of heat and light, and eventually electrical phenomena.

Such problems had been the concern of thinking men for at least two millennia. The ancient Greeks had posed questions of systems of the universe, varieties of matter or elements, the motion of winds and rocks and sun and stars, properties of heat and light, and even the possible atomic constitution of matter. They had produced general laws of mathematics and exact laws of physics and had speculated on the causes of phenomena. And even before the Greeks, the exact scientists of Mesopotamia had studied the regularities and near-regularities of the appearances of heavenly bodies and had devised methods of computation that yielded reliable predictions of the phenomena, *and* that could be corrected to agree with new data of observation. Thus the history of the search for quantitative relations between appearances, for exact laws of nature, and for systems of cause and effect, was a long one.

The revolutionary quality of the science of the seventeenth century had not lain in the subject matter or the fundamental questions, but in the methods of attack and solutions. Up until the time of Galileo, the problems of matter and the problems of motion had been too closely related by a philosophical prejudice. There had been a belief that a wholly different set of physical laws must govern the motion of earthy objects (made of sublunary matter which is subject to change) and celestial objects (made of celestial matter which is immutable)—each according to its nature. Galileo's telescope had indicated that the "matter" of heavens and the "matter" of earth are most likely the same, and men came to believe that there

might be a single or universal system of mechanics that would embrace the motion of apples, rocks, planets, and moons—and possibly
atoms. Thereafter, any research which uncovered laws of motion of
general applicability to heaven and earth had an obvious importance
in relation to the fundamental problem of the mechanism of the
universe as a whole and the action of its parts. Huygens' studies on
centrifugal forces, such as those that produce the circular paths of
weights whirled around at the end of strings, were seen at once to
bear an obvious implication for the problem of planets whirling
around the sun, or moons whirling around planets. Whether or not
one liked the implications of the doctrine expounded in Newton's
Principia, or some of its basic presuppositions, there could never be
any question of the fundamental character of that book, simply
because of the kind of problem that was presented for solution. In
Franklin's day the situation with respect to electricity was quite
different in that there was no certainty of electrical research illuminating fundamental problems.

Newtonian science was premised on the possibility of producing a
mechanical explanation of the universe in terms of attraction (between gross bodies and also between particles of matter) and repulsion (between particles of matter and also between æther particles)
—so that the study of all types of forces of attraction and repulsion
was of some importance. Plainly, even electricity might reveal information or reinforce conjectures about the properties of repulsive
and attractive forces in general. In the opening chapter of Desaguliers's *Course of Experimental Philosophy,* which Franklin was reading in the 1740's, the subject of electricity was introduced only to
illustrate the subject of forces, in particular to show that attractions
and repulsions need not be " occult qualities or supposed virtues "
but " really exist and are by experiments and observations made the
objects of our senses." [9]

Today we are aware that in nature we never observe " forces."
All " attractions " and " repulsions " and " stresses " are merely concepts invented in the mind of an observer to simplify the description
and explanation of such phenomena as motions of bodies toward and
away from one another or conditions of strain. In Franklin's day
men still believed that forces have an objective reality and they
sought to make their apparently abstract constructions concrete.
But how could one make gravitation seem real? Everyone is aware
of his own weight and the weight of the objects he tries to lift. Yet
such weights seem fixed, as if they are properties of the physical
objects (like their masses or inertias) and do not also depend on
the mass and radius of the earth. If the gravitational force exerted on

an object could easily be varied to a readily discernible degree, say by carrying it from one place to another, the concept of that force as determined by more than the body itself would have presented no problem to the eighteenth-century expositors of the Newtonian natural philsosphy. But we cannot so easily alter the earth's gravitational attraction on a body. We have no system of control in which the gravitational attraction can be turned on and off, say by the interposition of an " anti-gravitational " screen between the body and the earth.§

Weight was real enough, but it was not obviously an inverse-square force. Yet there was a force that appeared equally real and one that did depend inversely on some power of the distance: magnetism. Place a lodestone in one hand and a piece of iron in the other and there is no question of the reality of the force. Nor can there be any doubt that this force becomes greater as the hands are brought closer and closer together. But in one sense magnetism was misleading to the eighteenth-century student of gravitation. After all, a major novelty about gravitation was its universality: one and the same attractive force to keep the planets in their regular orbits about the sun, produce weight on earth, cause bodies to fall to the earth with uniformly accelerated motion, and keep the moon going around the earth. Magnetic forces, despite their apparent reality, do not help us to believe that gravitational forces are real, because magnetic forces are not in any sense universal; they arise in and affect only materials containing iron (at least so far as was known in the eighteenth century). Electrical forces, however, may be produced in and affect a wide variety of substances.* A common piece of amber brought near a pith ball on a silk string does not visibly affect it; the Newtonians could explain that the force of gravitation is too

§ The phenomenon of variation in the length of a seconds pendulum as a function of the latitude was too complex to be easily convincing.

Late in life Franklin conceived an experiment to test variations in the gravitational force acting on a body. His idea was to hang " a weight on a spiral spring, to discover if bodies gravitated differently to the earth during the conjunctions of the sun and moon, compared with other times. . . . We suppose that, by the force of gravity in those luminaries, the water of the ocean, an immense weight, is elevated so as to form the tides; if that be so, might we not expect that an iron ball of a pound suspended by a fine spiral spring should, when the sun and moon are together both above it, be a little attracted upwards or rendered lighter, so as to be drawn up a little by the spring on which it depends, and the contrary when they are both below it. The quantity, tho' very small, might perhaps be rendered visible by a contrivance like the above. It is not difficult to make this experiment, but I have never made it." [10]

* In the opening chapter of the first volume of his book, Desaguliers discussed electricity at length, but only mentioned magnetism in passing. The reason he gave is that " magnetism is a particular virtue that affects only load-stones and iron and steel," so that " we shall refer a fuller account of it to another place; because we are now only considering general properties of bodies."

small to cause any motion. But if the amber is rubbed, the pith ball will fly to it at once; if the pith ball is shaken off the amber it will now fly away from it—and as we bring the amber near the ball, the ball will dart away with a violent motion. The same effects would ensue if wax or sulphur were rubbed instead of amber, or glass or diamond or any one of a vast number of common substances. And the electrical force resulting from rubbing did not have to be indicated by a pith ball, since bits of straw, paper, hair, metal foil, or string would serve equally well; anything light could be used. Could anyone who observed such experiments doubt the reality of universal forces of attraction and repulsion in ordinary bodies?

At about the middle of the eighteenth century there was a paradoxical situation because of a seeming universality of electricity. So many different kinds of substances could be easily made to exhibit electrical attraction or be attracted electrically that extravagant speculations arose concerning electrical explanations of almost every kind of phenomenon. At the same time, the absence of any proof that electrical effects should be included in the list of regular natural operations increased the caution of those who believed that the unrestrained enthusiasm of some " electricians " might lead only to the construction of " philosophical romances." This situation caused the initial lack of enthusiasm, on the part of many scientists, for Franklin's suggestion of an experimental test of the electrical character of the lightning discharge and it also explains why Fothergill, in his preface to Franklin's book, was at such pains to distinguish Franklin's ideas about the electric fluid from the many statements in print about supposed electrical causes of natural phenomena.

Electricity and the Newtonian Philosophy

In orthodox Newtonian fashion Franklin's mentor, Desaguliers, held that forces are real and not imagined, and that they arise spontaneously in nature. The force of gravitation between gross bodies, and the force of cohesion between the parts of bodies, he held to be examples of naturally occurring attractions. As instances of the effects of a repellent power in small bodies, he pointed to the dissolution of salts and the expansion of air and vapors, explaining that under some circumstances the repulsion could be transformed into an attractive power. This point of view agreed with Newton's, as expressed primarily in the *Opticks* when he had explained how heat or fermentation could force particles outside of a sphere of attraction so that they would recede from one another with great force.

The ability of one and the same body in varied circumstances to attract or repel another body might seem strange, Desaguliers argued, but those who doubted the possibility of such action had only to examine the behavior of rubbed pieces of amber or glass as they attract nearby bodies and then repel them. In the 1740's, then, it was plain that electrical forces might serve to illustrate varieties of attraction and repulsion, even if there existed no conception of how this particular type of attraction and repulsion was related to the regular occurrences in the external world. Newton himself had used electrical forces for purposes of illustration in the *Opticks* when he wanted to show that it is not unreasonable to conceive an æther " 700,000 times more elastick than our air, and above 700,000 times more rare." Newton said that whoever doubted the possibility of such a rare and subtle æther might try to explain how electrified bodies emit a potent " exhalation " which attracts a bit of leaf gold or copper one foot away even though this emission is so rare that it produces no observable change in weight. But Newton was not implying here that electrical forces have any major role in so far as our understanding of the universe is concerned.

Speculations about electrical phenomena are not conspicuous in either the *Opticks* or the *Principia*, although in the final General Scholium to Book Three of the *Principia*, Newton hinted that the æther might be the material agent responsible for electrical phenomena.† From Newton and from Boyle the scientists of the eighteenth century had inherited the doctrine of effluvia, particles coming from rubbed bodies which caused other bodies to be attracted or repelled, and a hint that the source of such attraction and repulsion might be sought in variations in the density of the all-pervading æther. As we saw in Chapter Four, the doctrine of effluvia, small material particles produced from bodies by rubbing, seemed to fit the requirements of " matter and motion " and agreed with the well-known fact that friction or attrition wears down matter or breaks off small parts and also produces heat which, under other circumstances, causes bodies to send forth " steams." The explanations of electrical phenomena produced in the early eighteenth century are quite remarkable, but they failed to keep abreast of the new discoveries. When it seemed that the effluvia need not return to the parent body there was raised the problem of how such a body might be an inexhaustible source of effluvia. Furthermore, this concept left unresolved the whole question of why some bodies could be electrified under given conditions while others could not.

A careful reading of the literature on electricity between 1675,

† See Chapters Five and Six.

the year of publication of Boyle's tract, and the 1740's shows that the simple doctrine of effluvia had become a poor substitute for a workable conceptual scheme for the whole range of electrical phenomena. During this period, many notable new phenomena were discovered—phenomena, it must be said, which were to become the foundations of a new approach to the whole subject. But each such phenomenon at first only added to general bewilderment: it was either something else that could not be explained or something that confuted the *ad hoc* hypotheses invented to explain some previously discovered phenomenon. The constant note sounded by every writer on electricity before the mid-1740's is one of chagrin that there are no regularities discoverable in electrical experiments, that this is a subject apparently governed by chance or caprice. Small wonder, then, that electricity was not universally considered the major area in which the natural philosophy of matter would be forwarded!

An important new era in electrical science began when Gray's beautiful experiments in the 1730's indicated that some bodies are able to conduct " electricity " while others cannot. As an empiricist whose ability lay in uncovering many new sorts of phenomena, Gray did not make any notable contributions to electrical theory. His writings can in a sense be characterized as showing the want of a theory of electrical action rather than displaying an inadequate theory. When Du Fay next discovered that there are two kinds of electrification, he too was limited by inadequate concepts and lapsed into a form of Cartesianism. Nollet, the most popular electrical theorist and experimenter in Franklin's day, carried the Cartesian explanation a step further by imagining a curious construction in all bodies, two sets of wholly distinct pores. A kind of æther was supposed to leave through one and simultaneously enter through the other. When in the 1740's the new German electrical machines and the Leyden jar (or condenser, capacitor) permitted larger-scale laboratory phenomena than had been possible before, facts accumulated so rapidly that there was an almost complete bewilderment. Not only was there a want of an all-embracing conceptual scheme, but it seemed as if there might not be a single principle that could be successfully applied to all the known facts. Musschenbroek, one of the discoverers of the Leyden jar, wrote in his treatise on natural philosophy that enduring fame awaited the first man to bring together the fragments of electrical knowledge into a sound theory.[11] When, just before Franklin began his research in electricity, he read Desaguliers's book on natural philosophy, he encountered the statement that " electricity " is only the name given to the attracting or repelling force excited in bodies by friction. Such forces are " properties of bodies "; like gravity, cohesion, and other attractions and repulsions, they serve to " explain several phænomena." We cannot doubt, he read, that in some regular fashion, " these properties produce effects "; that is, there must be discoverable laws of forces which relate all effects to their causes, even though the " causes of those causes are not known." [12]

Franklin's philosophy of science derives from Newton and his disciples—Desaguliers, 'sGravesande, Hales—and was therefore based on the firm conviction that the invention of fanciful hypotheses does not forward the job of scientific explanation. While all scientific theories are based on axioms or postulates which are hypotheses in the sense of being untestable by direct experience, the number of such axioms was required to be as small as possible. These axioms, furthermore, had to be simple, widely applicable, and capable of leading by logic to the facts of experience: new and old. Franklin's scientific attitude represents, in one aspect, a later stage of development than Newton's because he recognized the limits of men's understanding of the external world and was content with the seemingly limited goal of finding exact laws of nature without overly concerning himself about why bodies seem to obey such laws. Newton abhorred the idea of gross bodies acting on one another (gravitationally, for example) over a great distance, and of matter having the innate property of gravitation simply because of its mass. We have seen that he suggested that variations in density of a subtle æther might cause gravitation, and that the æther might also be the material agent causing electrical and other phenomena. Since Newton believed that causes are knowable, he thus implied the possibility of a knowledge of the æther's properties. From Newton's writings some physicists of the eighteenth century gained the hope of learning the laws of the æther, so to reach an understanding of the action of particles of light and of electrical forces and gravitational forces, along with the nervous impulses, and the rest. Students of electricity following this line were led quickly into an almost impossible situation because there was no way of determining directly or indirectly the state of the æther in a given body. Neither the chemical composition, the physical state, nor the history of the operations performed on that body would yield such information. The end-result was that these scientists could describe the changes in æther density only by knowing in advance the effects that they had supposed would accompany these very changes in density. Thus they could invent explanations but could not predict accurately the outcome of experiments. Premised on variations in a mysterious all-pervading æther, these theories seem much like the fables of alchemists, based on the principle of *obscurum per obscurius, ignotum per ignotius.* In Newtonian terms the forces of gravitation and electrical attraction and repulsion are " deduced " from phenomena and are not hypotheses, but the subtle æther is hypothetical. The properties attributed to the æther are not only subtlety but elasticity, supposedly due to a mutual repulsion of its particles. Thus even if we could discover the laws of its variations in density and its interactions with matter, would we then know how nature acts to produce gravitational and electrical phenomena? Not at all! Franklin said that we would only be led to make the hypothesis of another, more subtle substance which causes the æther particles to repel one another and to cause variations in its density. Presumably the new substance would also prove to be elastic, and so we would need yet another substance, and so on. There is no apparent end to such a causal chain, no hope of ever attaining a final state of knowledge of what Desaguliers had called " causes of causes."

So far as electricity is concerned Franklin was closer to the spirit of Newton's writings than were many of his contemporaries and immediate predecessors. His mind, prepared by extensive scientific reading in the 1740's, was certainly conditioned in the Newtonian philosophy. For him the basic principles of nature had to be mechanical,‡ reducing the observed properties of bodies to the forces and motions and other mechanical properties of their constituent parts. His goal was to use experiment and reflection to construct a conceptual scheme for electricity that would require the smallest possible alteration of the Newtonian doctrine of matter, introducing only such new concepts as were necessary to correlate and predict observed phenomena—concepts, furthermore, closely related to laboratory operations. If electrical effects were to be reduced to the two " catholick principles " of matter and motion, Franklin needed to decide which " matter " is involved in electrical phenomena and the kinds of " motion " that it may have.

A valid scientific theory, as Einstein once observed, leads to tests by experiment, but there is no path that " leads from experiment to the birth of a theory." In this latter process the imagination is what counts most. Often, once a theory has proved successful, jealous

---

‡ Franklin found a mechanical explanation of the rending of trees by lightning in the phenomenon of water being " exploded, that is, blown into vapour," whereby a great " force is generated " because water " reduced to vapour " occupies (it is " said ") " 14,000 times its former space." The experiment of exploding water electrically, according to Franklin, " was first made by that most ingenious electrician, Father Beccaria," and it " may account for what we sometimes see in a tree struck by lightning, when part of it is reduced to fine splinters like a broom; the sap vessels being so many tubes containing a watry fluid, which when reduced to vapour, rends every tube lengthways." [18]

contemporaries (like later historians) can show how each part of the theory had already been stated; yet it is to be noted that such prior statements achieve at this later date a significance they never had before. Many of the elements of Franklin's theory and a number of the new facts he and his Philadelphia friends discovered could be found in the literature of the 1740's—but found more easily after Franklin's work than before it. Such is almost always the character of scientific progress and it does not detract in the slightest from the greatness of Franklin's achievements. Rutherford, the Newton of nuclear physics, explained this aspect of the history of science as follows: ". . . it is not in the nature of things for any one man to make a sudden violent discovery; science goes step by step, and every man depends on the work of his predecessors. When you hear of a sudden unexpected discovery—a bolt from the blue, as it were—you can always be sure that it has grown up by the influence of one man on another, and it is this mutual influence which makes the enormous possibility of scientific advance. Scientists are not dependent on the ideas of a single man, but on the combined wisdom of thousands of men, all thinking of the same problem, and each doing his little bit to add to the great structure of knowledge which is gradually being erected." With this sentiment as our guide we may ignore for the moment the problem of Franklin's indebtedness for this or that aspect of his theory and concentrate on the broad features of the theory as a whole. In the next two chapters information will be presented on the growth and clarification of Franklin's concepts in relation to the reports from Europe which he was reading.

The Role of Conservation in Franklin's Physics

The key word to the Franklinian innovation in electricity is " conservation." The great German-American philosopher of science, J. B. Stallo, once observed that a mechanical theory of the universe must be based on the postulate of there being " some constant amid all phenomenal variations," that there can be no science if all change is not considered merely as a transformation. The aim of science is thus " to apprehend all phenomenal diversities in the material world as varieties in the grouping of primordial units of mass, to recognize all phenomenal changes as movements of unchangeable elements, and thus to exhibit all apparent qualitative heterogeneity as mere quantitative difference." [14] Franklin's theory of matter offers such a construction for simple electrical events. An ordinary (uncharged) glass rod differs qualitatively from a rubbed (charged) glass rod in that the latter attracts to itself any light bodies in the neighborhood and repels another rubbed glass rod. Franklin explained the qualitative difference between the rods in the charged and uncharged states by supposing a quantitative difference in the amount of an electric matter in each. The change in the amount of electric matter is a mechanical one in that it is originally produced by a mechanical operation, rubbing. If rubbing is an operation that implies no more than a transfer of electric matter, then the gain or loss of such electric matter by one body must be accompanied by an equal and opposite loss or gain of electric matter by another body or bodies. The concept of electric charge is, therefore, in Franklin's theory merely a quantitative description of the amount of electric matter that a body has either gained or lost. This is an absolute or determinate quantity in that it is independent of the size of the body or the total magnitude of the electric matter in that body. The loss or gain of electric matter must alter the "electric density" of that body, conceived in terms of the ratio of quantity of electric matter in the charged state to quantity of electric matter in the uncharged state or the ratio of quantity of electric matter to the mass of the body. Franklin's theory does not take account of such density because he conceived no possible measure of the total quantity of electric matter in a body. The theory is limited to the "quantitative difference" in electric matter, the supposed effect of rubbing or of transfer, a quantity that can be measured or compared to other quantities.

This conceptual scheme for electricity, then, attributes the observed effect of electrification (manifested in the acquired ability of a body to attract or repel electrically) to a material cause, a change in the total amount of electric matter in that body. Presumably there is a way to explain why the loss or gain of electric matter should cause such attraction or repulsion, and Franklin applied himself to finding it. But before examining that problem, we must observe that Franklin's theory of electricity was based on an exact quantitative concept, charge, which had previously been absent (at least, in this sense) from writings on this subject and which has been one of the fundamental electrical concepts ever since. This is an invented concept, because we do not observe "charge" in nature; by its use Franklin was able—and for the first time—to distinguish between the state of electrification and the effects produced by or in a body in that state. By its very definition, charge (the amount of electric matter a body has gained or lost) must be conserved; thus we cannot make a distinction between Franklin's invention of the concept of charge and his adoption of a principle of conservation of charge. On the other hand, this principle agreed with the new facts of electrification which

Franklin had discovered: that under a variety of observable conditions in the laboratory, positive and negative charges were produced in equal amounts. Even the Leyden jar, the major electrical mystery of the late 1740's, proved to be explainable in a simple way once Franklin had found that the inner and outer conductors—separated by the glass of the bottle—have always equal charges of opposite sign.

Two of the implications of Franklin's theory were surprising. First of all, there was the principle of conservation, which was not the rule in physical phenomena. The only prior example of such a general principle had been the conservation of momentum, enunciated by Newton; in the restricted conditions of falling bodies Leibniz had postulated a conservation of energy. For instance, heat is not conserved as such, but may be augmented by the same processes that produce electrification, notably rubbing. But in this case, one of the rubbed bodies does not become cold while the other becomes hot, but both become hot. Thus electrical phenomena bore no apparent resemblance to heat phenomena or even optical phenomena. Heat became a subject of exact conservation principles at the end of the century when Joseph Black showed how to compute the temperature changes in mixtures, using the concepts of specific and latent heat. But the heat generated by friction was not part of a conservation principle until the middle of the nineteenth century, when it was found that by considering heat as energy a description of conservative systems could be made in terms of the total energy of all sorts. Nor was there in Franklin's day a generally recognized principle of conservation of matter. Newton had held that matter is convertible into light, which implied that ponderable matter might be transformed into the matter of light. Although Lavoisier is credited with the explicit statement of the principle of conservation of matter, chemists had—for at least two centuries before Lavoisier—sought to explain changes of weight in chemical reactions by additions or losses of some kind of matter. Confusion had arisen in part from lack of a clear distinction between weight and density and the supposition that alterations of weight did not necessarily proceed from the gain or loss of *ponderable* matter. Lavoisier's clear recognition and systematic application of the latter aspect of chemical change entitle him to the credit for this discovery, which is the third great conservation principle in physical science.§

§ Lavoisier's ideas were in accord with the Newtonian natural philosophy to the extent that Newton had suggested a permanence in the original atoms of matter—they " are incomparably harder than any porous bodies compounded of them; even so very hard, as never to wear or break in pieces. . . ." [15] Franklin too had espoused a kind of doctrine of conservation of matter, discussed below on pages 336-337.

Lavoisier's principle marks the beginning of modern chemistry in the sense of calling attention to the need of examining all the material in a closed system in which a chemical reaction occurs. It implies that the total quantity of matter in the universe is constant, that none may be created or destroyed, and that in chemical reactions the original matter is only regrouped. In Stallo's terms, Lavoisier brought chemistry into the domain of mechanistic science. Franklin's principle implies that the total quantity of electric matter in the universe is also constant and that the only alterations possible by the arts of man or the operations of nature are redistributions of this electric matter in some way, regroupings of "primordial units."

Now there is of course no way of proving that the total quantity of electrical matter (or charge) in the universe is constant. Hence, the law of conservation of charge is an hypothesis, in the sense of being an unprovable statement in physics, a basic axiom or postulate like the law of inertia. It can be proved only in particular examples of isolated systems. Yet, like Newton's law of inertia, the law of conservation of charge has been continually applied to physical situations for two hundred years and has never, in any situation, led to a result that was inconsistent with observation. Whenever we rub a glass rod with silk, the glass acquires a positive charge exactly equal in magnitude to the negative charge on the silk. The disappearance of a positive charge unit in positron annihilation, to cite a modern example, is accompanied by the simultaneous disappearance of a negative charge unit, an electron; and the production of a positron is always part of a pair-production, one negative and one positive charge unit appearing together. Neither on the atomic or sub-atomic level, nor on the scale of gross bodies, has an experiment ever indicated either the production or complete disappearance of a positive or negative charge without the equal production or disappearance of a charge of the opposite sign but of the identical magnitude.

In our century it has been found that the principle of conservation of matter and the principle of conservation of energy are only approximations and that neither one by itself can predict accurately the outcome of all experiments. It is thus curious to reflect that in the middle of the twentieth century the only conservation principles that have survived as accurate independent descriptions of phenomena are the first two to have been discovered: Newton's law of conservation of momentum and Franklin's law of conservation of charge. No theory of atomic structure, for example, that violated either of these two principles would be acceptable to the physicists of the mid-twentieth century. As a broad generalization that has withstood the test of two hundred years of fruitful application, Franklin's law of conservation of charge must be considered to be of the same fundamental importance to physical science as Newton's law of conservation of momentum. It certainly encouraged men of science to look for other conservation principles and to seek for explanations of the universe as a complete or closed system.

All ideas of conservation, as Ernst Mach once pointed out, " have a solid foundation in the economy of thought " because a " mere unrelated change, without fixed point of support, or reference, is not comprehensible, not mentally reconstructible." [16] The conservation of charge relates the change in objects to a constant reference and thus provides a basis for prediction. For example, it enables us to explain and to predict accurately what happens in a large variety of electrical phenomena and with a minimum of auxilliary postulates. The electric matter is a constituent part of all matter in its normal state, so that matter may be said to be composed of ponderable matter (or, to use Franklin's words, " common matter ") and electric matter. In keeping with the Newtonian philosophy, Franklin conceived that the electric matter, like common matter, is atomic or composed of particles. The particles of common matter have a cohesive force of attraction for one another, and a strong force of attraction for particles of electric matter, although the latter repel one another. These forces of attraction and repulsion were considered by Franklin to be the primitive or unanalyzable concepts in his system and he never, therefore, saw any need of exploring them further. Franklin's natural philosophy was thus based on matter in the form of particles and on force as a property of the different particles. From that point on, all the phenomena and laws of electricity were to be deduced from the basic axioms in conformity with the data of experiment and observation. There were, of course, subsidiary properties of matter necessary to a complete account of the subject. For example, some bodies—conductors—permit the electric matter to move freely within them, but others—non-conductors—do not. Since all bodies have a " normal " quantity of electric matter, as much as they can hold, any excess that they receive must be outside their exterior surface or collect around that surface to form a loosely bound " electrical atmosphere." Hence, if a positively charged body were brought near a negatively charged body, there would be an attractive force between the unsaturated common matter in the negatively charged body and the excess electric matter bound to the positively charged body. Obviously such a mechanical explanation was superior to those based on a doctrine of effluvia which arise from all rubbed bodies. Yet there was no particular virtue to an explanation of this single fact or of similar facts; what gave Franklin's theory so great a prestige was the great number and variety of different kinds of phenomena it embraced and the important new effects it predicted. A few typical examples from Franklin's writings will show the power of the new concepts.

An insulated tin tube may be set up with a pair of pith balls hanging from the far end of the tube, side by side, by conducting threads. A positively charged glass rod is brought close to the near end of the tube, but not close enough for a spark to jump between them. Observation shows that the two pith balls will diverge, indicating a force of repulsion between them. Yet when the glass rod is withdrawn the divergence ceases, indicating that the tin tube has not acquired a net charge. What does Franklin's theory predict? The positively charged glass rod has an " electric atmosphere " or an excess over its normal quantity of electric matter. Hence it will repel some of the electric matter in the tube which, like all bodies, contains some electric matter. This force of repulsion is deduced from the primary axiom that particles of electric matter repel one another. The motion of electric matter in or along the tube is deduced from the property of all metals to conduct electric matter, a generalization from experience interpreted in terms of the primary concepts. Thus the theory tells us that as long as the glass rod is near the tin tube, there will be an accumulation of more than the usual amount of electric matter at the far end, in the threads and pith balls. Owing to its property of repulsion, this excess electric matter will cause the balls to diverge. As the rod is withdrawn, the amount of excess electric matter at the far end of the tin tube will gradually decrease until there is no divergence of the balls whatever. Franklin's exposition of the process that we call today electrostatic induction agrees perfectly with the data of experiment, a signal victory for any theory. Here is an example of Newtonian " synthesis," in which the facts of experience are deduced from fundamental principles. An analogous situation is one in which a conductor acquires by contact a positive charge while a nearby conductor is temporarily grounded. In Franklin's theory, the earth may be considered a practically inexhaustible electrical reservoir, either a source of supply or a recipient for the electric matter needed or released in any experiment. Hence, if a positive charge accumulates on one conductor, it will repel some of the electric matter in the nearby conductor; and if the latter is grounded, some of the electric matter it originally contained will flow into the ground. Break the connection with ground and that conductor would, according to Franklin's predictions, be found to be in a negative state. This deduction from theory was verified by experiment.

Now it may seem to the reader who is not acquainted with the subject of electricity that such effects as have just been described are perhaps " curious " but without significance. That this is not the case may be seen in Franklin's application of them to the analysis of the condenser, just discovered as he was embarking on his research in electricity, the greatest single mystery in the subject at that time. The condenser is a vital component of every electronic device, which —whether radio or radar set or automatic control system—is composed of only four elements joined by wires: vacuum tubes (or other electric " valves ") , resistors, inductances, and condensers (or " capacitors "). In the condenser as it existed in Franklin's day, there were two conductors separated by glass (a non-conductor). The condenser was charged by making a contact between one of the conductors and a positively charged object, while the other was grounded. If contact were then made with only one of the conductors of a charged condenser, there was little or no effect. But if a wire or animal tissue were to make a continuous external circuit from one conductor to the other, the discharge would be on a very large scale, sufficient to kill a small animal or to produce a marked physiological effect on a large number of human beings. The deductions from Franklin's postulates are as follows. During charging, the positive charge on one conductor induces a negative charge on the other because it is grounded. The attraction between the unsaturated common matter on the negatively charged conductor and the excess electric matter on the positively charged conductor is strong enough to permit that conductor to have a greater positive charge than would be possible if it were isolated and not part of a condenser system. The positive charge on one conductor must be quantitatively equal to the negative charge induced on the other. A discharge through an external circuit, say a man's arms and chest, is more powerful than that a man would experience if he touched a single positively (or negatively) charged conductor. The reason is that in the latter case the contact is from positive (or negative) charge to ground or neutral condition, while in the condenser the contact is from positive charge to negative charge.* Each of these

---

* Writing before the concept of electrical potential had been invented, Franklin could only compare such differences as the relative amounts of electrification of two objects. He could also compare an object with an excess of fluid and one in the normal state, an object with a deficiency of fluid and one in the normal state, and an object with an excess of fluid and one with a deficiency of fluid. Arguing only from a mechanistic analogy sufficed to yield a correct (i. e., experimentally verifiable) answer in the cases he considered.

deductions was found to conform to known facts of observation or the new facts of experiment discovered by Franklin. And it is no exaggeration to say that this brilliant analysis of the condenser constituted, in the minds of many of his contemporaries, one of his greatest scientific achievements, rivalled only by his discovery of the natural electrification in clouds and the electrical character of the lightning discharge.

Franklin's discussion of the condenser, like the two preceding examples drawn from his writings, indicates the importance of distinguishing between a charged state and the effects of such a state. No *electric matter* passes through the glass when a condenser is charged, although the *force* produced by the electric matter does go through the glass. Franklin pointed out that if electric matter could pass through glass, then a condenser could never remain charged; the excess electric matter in the positively charged conductor would immediately supply the deficiency in the negatively charged conductor. But, as Franklin observed, this does not happen unless there is a small hole or crack in the glass. (Later on, it was found that very hot glass is a conductor.) In Chapter Ten and Chapter Eleven, we shall see the steps whereby Franklin arrived at these and other results in the course of his investigations, but at this point the intention is only to indicate the kinds of important exact results in the science of electrostatics of which his theory was capable.

The Electric Fluid as a Form of Matter

In formulating his theory of electricity, Franklin introduced a postulate of two kinds of matter, electric and ponderable, each particulate, one kind attracting the other. We have seen how his reading in Newton's *Opticks* and such books as Desaguliers's and Hales's prepared him for the view that particles of different sorts of matter may attract one another while particles of the same kind may repel each other or attract each other as the case may be. Franklin reduced electricity to matter and motion by postulates about the forces between the particles he supposed matter made of, and the motion of one kind of particle within conducting bodies and in transfer from one body to another. The necessity of an electric matter or substance was made clear in the conditions of conservation of charge, in the observed fact of simultaneous production of equal resinous and vitreous electrifications. Although rubbing might be conceived as simply a process that imparted motion to the particles of the two bodies rubbed together—as Boyle had thought of heat—one could not explain in this way the production of contrary electrical states in the two rubbed bodies. This is the basic fact that suggests the existence of a material substance. Hence we may see that Franklin's postulate of electric matter in bodies was not a fanciful creation of a free imagination but was derived from experience, which showed the impossibility of applying the principles of matter and motion to the particles of ordinary matter alone.†

Franklin's conceptual scheme for electricity required the emendation of ideas about the composition of matter in supposing that bodies contain electric matter as well as ponderable matter. Newton had held that the particles of light could penetrate between the particles of matter and had devised a method for estimating the size of particles of which bodies are made. Franklin's theory also implied a loose construction of matter, since there must be room between the particles of ponderable matter for the particles of electric matter all bodies contain. Newton had suggested that particle size and perhaps arrangement could explain why some bodies reflect or transmit light of certain colors. Franklin's theory demanded an explanation of the property of some bodies to transmit the electric matter and of others to be impervious to it and the varying ease of conduction of electric matter in different substances. Finally, the composition of matter of different sorts and the various possible arrangements of the particles must be related to the observed electrical property of a given substance to gain or lose electric matter (or to become positively or negatively charged) when rubbed with a suitable material. Since the electrical properties of the different types of matter might be correlated with the varieties and conditions of matter, Franklin's theory implied that electrical investigation could provide an important tool for exploring matter itself—a conclusion that has been continuously exemplified ever since his time. This is the sense in which we may say that Franklin's theory of electricity was more than a device for predicting the outcome of electrical experiments, that it was based on a doctrine of the particulate construc-

---

† Franklin was not the first person ever to write about an "electric matter"—in the sense of their being some kind of substance which is the material cause of electrical phenomena. Boyle and Hauksbee (and even Gilbert) had written about material effluvia, as Gray did also. Du Fay used the expression "matière électrique," and so did his disciple Nollet, when he wrote of emanations or currents ("écoulements") of "matière effluente" and "matière affluente"—"Je conviens que la matière électrique s'élance réellement du dedans au dehors des corps électrisés . . . [&] qu'une matière semblable se porte de toutes parts au corps électrisés. . . ." [17] Although Franklin had not invented, entirely on his own, a new type of matter, his precise concept of "electric matter" was as original as new concepts are apt to be in science. Thus in the very strict sense of being conserved in every case as shown by experiment, Franklin's concept differed markedly from the more primitive ideas of his contemporaries and predecessors. The question is discussed at further length in Chapter Nine.

tion of matter that had a productive influence on the course of thought in the physical sciences.

The prehistory of the concept of a distinct kind of electric matter or electric fluid tends to place the importance of Franklin's concept in high relief. The doctrine of effluvia—found in the writings of Gilbert, Boyle, Newton, Hauksbee, and others—may be likened to a vapor which arises from bodies heated by rubbing in a way reminiscent of steam coming out of sufficiently heated water. Dr. N. H. de V. Heathcote, whose profound studies have illuminated many aspects of the growth of physical science since Newton, suggests (in a letter to the writer) that in the late seventeenth and early eighteenth centuries " the emphasis is almost always on the *bodies*; in fact, it is only toward the latter part of the period that the word ' electricity ' tends to be dissociated from the bodies and to denote the cause, whatever it might be, of the phenomena, though then as now it frequently occurred in titles of papers, etc., to denote the subject." Even beyond the middle of the eighteenth century, many scientists wrote of electricity as the property of being like amber, an " amberishness," to use Dr. Heathcote's term. We shall see in Chapter Nine that such men as Gray and Du Fay considered electricity as a " virtue " with which bodies became endowed and which could be transferred from one body to another. Thus Du Fay's two " electricities " (vitreous and resinous) were not necessarily two distinct kinds of electric matter, two fluids, but were considered primarily in relation to types of bodies. Thus he wrote of " a body of the resinous electricity," meaning a body that behaves electrically as resin does, and also discussed " the two classes of electricity [to which] any body belongs."

This pre-Franklin usage of " electricity " bears a resemblance to the concept of heat. We observe bodies to gain or lose heat, but we cannot readily study heat in empty space as it moves from body to body. Newton suggested that radiant heat consists of vibrations in the æther, thus excluding the possibility of heat as an entity that might have an existence in the absence of any form of matter, say, in a truly empty space, or of heat as a form of matter. In the early eighteenth century, when the concept of a matter of heat was being advanced, it was only natural that experiments were undertaken to see whether heat has weight. Similarly, in the 1740's, the concept developed of electrical phenomena having some causal relation to a form of matter, and experiments were undertaken by Le Monnier and Watson to discover whether the transmission of electrical effects required time—since all forms of matter must move with finite, even if enormous, speeds. The " matière électrique " of Nollet, which was

" effluente " and " affluente," and the " electrical æther " of Watson, which could vary in density within bodies, may be considered as the first primitive views that electricity is due to " something " in bodies which could change in amount or in distribution.

Franklin's concept of a distinct electric matter was an enormous improvement on these antecedent views. Perhaps, as Dr. Heathcote has suggested to me, the Leyden jar or condenser was of particular importance in the development of the concept of electric fluid or matter because it provided a device in which it seemed that something could be accumulated and stored, as water may be collected in a bottle and kept there. If this point of view is correct, then Franklin's experiment of electrical convection is of special importance because for the first time it showed that an electric discharge could be produced in a series of little steps over a relatively long period of time, and not only in an instantaneous uncontrollable explosion. As the little ball, in Franklin's convection experiment, traveled back and forth between the positively and negatively charged conductors in the Leyden jar, it must have appeared to have been transferring some substance in a sequence of finite amounts rather than weakening a state of " virtue " in successive steps. (Franklin's experiment on " electrical convection " is described, below, in Chapter Ten.)

Evaluations of Franklin's Theory

In 1746, just as Franklin's research in electricity was getting under way, a report on the state of electrical science, written from Paris by Turbervill Needham, was published in the *Philosophical Transactions* of the Royal Society. Like many others who were interested in electrical phenomena during the '40's, Needham was struck by the fact that electricity was not a science. There are so many of what the French call " *bizarreries,* or unaccountable phænomena, in the course of electrical experiments," Needham wrote, " that a man can scarce assert any thing in consequence of any experiment which is not contradicted by some unexpected occurrence in another." Needham felt " confident " about this statement since he had discovered that the great naturalist, Buffon, had held the same opinion: " I remember he told me one day, when I had the honour of waiting upon him, that he thought the whole subject of electricity, though illustrated with so great a variety of experiments, very far from being yet sufficiently ripe for the establishment of a course of laws, or indeed of any certain one, fixed and determined in all its circumstances." [18]

Statements like Needham's and Buffon's are characteristic of the literature of electricity in the 1740's; they indicate the proportions of Franklin's achievement in science. Canton, one of the major electricians of the Franklinian era, reported in the *Philosophical Transactions* in 1754 that the discovery of resinous and vitreous electrification by Du Fay had " received no light till the publication of the second part of Mr. Franklin's experiments." [19] Buffon, who maintained his interest in electrical phenomena, recognized at once the clarity of Franklin's explanations and urged his friend, D'Alibard, to issue a French translation of Franklin's book. We have seen, earlier, that Diderot, immediately after the publication of the French edition, described it as the best example of the experimental art with which he was acquainted. Laudatory notices of Franklin's book on electricity appeared in England, France, Germany, and Italy, and although his ideas were attacked as well as supported, there were strong and enthusiastic supporters everywhere to defend him. Franklin asked Musschenbroek, discoverer of the Leyden jar, for information about European authors who had written on electricity. Musschenbroek replied in 1759, pointing out that, if Franklin were to survey the literature produced in Europe, he would discover that " nobody has discovered more recondite mysteries of electricity than Franklin." He therefore advised Franklin to ignore the European literature and to go on making experiments entirely on his own, pursuing a path that would be quite different from any that had been followed by Europeans, " for then you shall certainly find many other things which have been hidden to natural philosophers throughout the space of centuries." [20]

In 1773 Barbeu-Dubourg described Franklin's theory of electricity as one which indicated the route to be taken to make new discoveries. Franklin, says Dubourg, wrote, " Do this, and that is what will happen; change this circumstance, and that is what will result from it; . . ." [21] In Italy, Father Beccaria demonstrated " the truth of the Franklinian theory " by appealing to " the two masters of true learning, observation and experiment." [22] Two hundred years after Franklin stated his theory, J. J. Thomson, who discovered the nature of the electric charge and was a great admirer of Franklin, repeated the sentiments of Barbeu-Dubourg almost word for word as he explained that we still account for the major facts of electrostatics in precisely the way Franklin proposed. After describing the general character of Franklin's one-fluid theory, Thomson said:

The service which the one-fluid theory has rendered to the science of electricity, by suggesting and co-ordinating researches, can hardly be overestimated. It is still used by many of us when working in the laboratory. If we move a piece of brass and want to know whether that will increase or decrease the effect we are observing, we do not fly to the higher mathematics, but use the simple conception of the electric fluid which would tell us as much as we wanted to know in a few seconds.[23]

Franklin would have been particularly delighted by J. J. Thomson's remarks, because Thomson's use of Franklin's methods rather than higher mathematics was a matter of free choice, not of ignorance; although a gifted experimenter, Thomson was a skilled mathematician who had devoted one of his early major publications to an exposition of the mathematical theory of electricity. Franklin himself had had no choice in the matter, because he was ignorant of higher mathematics. On one occasion he boasted that if his " method of accounting for the principal phænomena," or his " hypothesis, is not the truth itself, it is [at] least as naked. For I have not with some of our learned moderns disguised my nonsense in Greek, clothed it in algebra or adorned it with fluxions. You have it in *puris naturalibus*." [24]

One of the reasons that today we look a little condescendingly at physics that is not mathematical is that the conceptual models from which physical equations derive have often been abandoned, even though the equations themselves remain valid. The models we envisage are, therefore, apt to be considered only as stages in the development of equations. Maxwell's electromagnetic theory remains a cornerstone of our structure of physics, even with the disappearance of the æther on which it was based, and may be said to be epitomized by " Maxwell's equations." But Maxwell himself, recognizing the origin of his ideas in Faraday's pictorial concepts of " lines of force," held that " scientific truth should be presented in different forms and should be regarded as equally scientific whether it appears in the robust form and vivid colouring of a physical illustration or in the tenuity and paleness of a symbolical expression." [25] This statement may serve as a reminder of the danger of reading contemporary physics into the science of the past.

Even though Franklin did not produce a set of equations, his theory can hardly be described as qualitative, in the older sense of merely postulating qualities of matter and believing them to constitute an explanation. It was an exact theory in that it predicted unique results of operations, which were verifiable by means of experiments. This theory, furthermore, led to one form of quantification, the use of order of magnitude. Despite the fact that Franklin never assigned numbers to the main parameters—charge, conductivity, electric force—he was able to classify conductors according to their relative conductivity; he estimated by experiment whether one charge appeared to be greater than another; he devised ingenious tests to show when two charges are equal; and he used his own body to determine relative " forces " of electric discharges.

Whenever possible, Franklin made quantitative estimates. For example, he compared two electrical machines by the number of turns required to charge a given jar. An electrical machine with a globe of nine inches diameter took 2000 turns to charge fully two Leyden jars of six-gallon capacity coated; a half-pint jar could be charged with only 50 turns.[26] Franklin had no electrometer at his disposal; this valuable instrument was perfected only after his research had been completed. It must be pointed out, however, that at first it was used only to indicate the presence of charges and to compare charges. A system of units to permit charge measurements could not be developed until the force law had been effectively discovered by Coulomb. The striking aspect of Franklin's theory is that it works and does so simply. With but one modification, to explain the repulsion between negatively charged bodies, it is applicable to a wide range of important phenomena. Its predictions are always unequivocal and generally in accord with observations, and its basic postulate of conservation has remained the unchallenged fundamental principle of electricity for two hundred years.

Franklin's Knowledge of Newtonian Principles

No one who reads critically the scientific writings of Benjamin Franklin could ever believe that such profound experiments and gifted explanations were produced by a man who was wholly without scientific training. Genius in science is powerless without education, without that special preparation which sharpens the mind to a razor-edge of acuteness, enabling it to penetrate the mysteries of nature. A romantic view of Franklin holds that he received a gift of electrical apparatus and directions for using it, and within a few years had created a new science of electricity, without his having had any prior knowledge of science. Such a view ignores the facts and runs counter to everything we know about how scientific discoveries are usually made. Presumably this erroneous impression derives from a confusion between scientific training and formal schooling. Franklin attended no courses in science, but the books he studied in the 1740's provided a sound scientific education that was very likely superior to that received by most college graduates at that time. After having studied the analysis of many experiments, he essayed some of his own in the subject of heat. Having seen experimental demonstrations performed by such men as Spencer and Greenwood, his native skill in experimental science was prepared for the great investigations. He had absorbed the precepts of experimental Newtonian science and had followed their application by such masters as Hales, 'sGravesande, Desaguliers, and Newton himself.

Furthermore, the books Franklin had been reading in the 1740's introduced him to the principles of Newtonian dynamics, even though he lacked the mathematical prerequisites to follow the arguments in Newton's *Principia*. The main principles and applications of Newton's mechanics were displayed by Pemberton and Desaguliers for the non-mathematical reader. It was one of the axioms of eighteenth-century Newtonianism that men unskilled in mathematics could learn the physical principles of the *Principia* without needing to follow the complex mathematical niceties of proof and example. We are not surprised, therefore, to find that Franklin's preparation for research in the 1740's included some physical aspects of Newtonian dynamics.

On the very eve of Franklin's first electrical experiments he was busy with problems of motion. Franklin's discussions of dynamics at this time are of particular relevance to a general consideration of his doctrine of physical explanation because they show us his acquaintance with the first great conservation principle in the history of science: Newton's law of conservation of momentum. Franklin's essay into dynamics shows us his solid grasp of this conservation principle in its simplest aspect, together with a partial failure (one that we would surely expect) in its more complex application. Furthermore, we shall see how a good scientific mind like Franklin's takes an original turn, even in subjects of which it is not the complete master.

The main problem that Franklin set himself in dynamics is related to one of the difficulties that had faced all Copernicans: to explain how a falling object could descend vertically on a rotating earth. For instance, at the equator, an object let fall from a 400-foot tower will reach the ground in about five seconds. During this time the earth will rotate eastward so that the tower will be a little more than a mile east of the place it occupied when the object was let fall. Should not the object then reach the ground at a point a mile west of the tower? Copernicus had provided no satisfactory answer to this problem. Galileo had explained that it would fall at the foot of the tower whether the earth were rotating or at rest, on the basis of a brilliant concept of a kind of " circular inertia " that would always carry a falling object along with the earth. Today we analyze the problem in its simplest aspects by applying the Newtonian principle of the conservation of *angular* momentum, a cognate principle to the conservation of linear momentum. For a particle or small object, the angular momentum is *mvr* where *m* is the mass of the object, v its speed along a circular path, and r the radius of the path. As an object falls to the earth through 400 feet, the radius of the circular path r decreases by about $\frac{2}{10}$ [5] and there must be a correspondingly small increase in its velocity along the new smaller circular path, if the angular momentum is conserved.‡ Hence, neglecting air friction and wind, we may predict on simple Newtonian principles that the falling object will fall neither directly down nor be left behind, but will descend so as to get ahead of the tower. It will strike the ground a little bit to the east of a point directly underneath the place from which it was let fall. This account of falling bodies was a little beyond the average eighteenth-century Newtonian; Desaguliers, for example, explained why objects fall almost vertically by using an argument similar to Galileo's.

Franklin posed a nice question related to the one just presented. In this case, the body changes its radius of rotation by being shifted suddenly on the earth from one latitude to another. In 1746 he wrote to Colden: " I wish I had mathematics enough to satisfy myself whether the much shorter voyages made by ships bound hence to England, than by those from England hither, are not in some degree owing to the diurnal motion of the Earth; and if so, in what degree? 'Tis a notion that has lately entered my mind; I know not if ever any other's." He knew that on the equator, a becalmed ship moves " with the sea " at 15 mi/min, neglecting any ocean currents. For the sake of argument we may suppose, said Franklin, that " at our capes " such a ship would rotate with the earth at the rate of 12 mi/min and in the British Channel 10 mi/min. A difference in velocity of 2 mi/min is " no small matter in so weighty a body as a laden ship swimming in a fluid! " How is this velocity lost in the voyage from America to England, he asked. By " the resistance of the water." In other words, " the water, which resisted in part, must have given way in part to the ship, from time to time, as she proceeded continually out of parallels of latitude where the earth's motion or rotation was quicker, into others where it was slower." And thus as her velocity tends eastward with the Earth's motion, she perhaps makes her " easting sooner." Suppose, for example, that a vessel were becalmed " at our cape," wrote Franklin, and that she were instantaneously picked up and dropped in a place of equal calm in the English Channel, " would not the difference of velocity between her and the sea she was placed in, appear plainly by a violent motion of the ship thro' the water eastward? " [27]

‡ Since the quantity mvr is conserved or remains constant, where m is the mass which does not change, a decrease in the radius r must imply an increase in the velocity v.

Franklin's problem was to compute the effect of the earth's diurnal rotation on the respective times for an ocean crossing from England to Pennsylvania and from Pennsylvania to England: " Suppose a ship sails on a N. East line from Lat. 39° to Lat. 52° in 30 days, how long will she be returning on the same line, winds, currents, etc., being equal? " His partial solution was to apply the Newtonian principle of conservation of momentum which in this special case becomes a problem of velocity, assuming the same mass (ship, cargo, and crew) on both voyages. Franklin saw that the linear velocity of a point on the earth's surface depends on the latitude, being a maximum at the equator and zero at the poles.§ In 24^h of mean time, a day of 1440^m, a body at latitude λ will move around on a circle of approximately radius $R \cos \lambda$, where R is the equatorial radius of the earth (say, in miles), or will move at a linear velocity of $2\pi R \cos \lambda/1440$ mi/min. The latitude of Philadelphia is 39° 57′ N (he used 39°) and that of Bristol is 51° 27′ N (he used 52°). A check on his computation shows that the difference in linear (tangential) velocities at the two latitudes is a little less than 2.5 mi/min, assuming $R = 3,960$ mi.; a good enough agreement with his estimate of about 2 mi/min, or about 105 knots, an enormous magnitude for a sailing vessel.

From a point of view of " higher criticism," we would have to observe that the problem posed by Franklin is not one that can be treated from the point of view of conservation of linear momentum. The gain in velocity of an object translated instantaneously to a greater latitude is not simply the difference between the velocity of rotation at the two latitudes. We must apply the principle of conservation of *angular* momentum, as in the case of the falling body. Just as a body falling downward to the earth's surface gains in its velocity of rotation because it moves to a circle of smaller radius, so a ship translated from the latitude of Philadelphia to the latitude of Bristol will undergo an increase in its velocity of rotation because it too will then move along a smaller circle.* Franklin oversimplified

§ Franklin, in other words, computed the linear velocities V_1 and V_2 with which a becalmed ship moves in a circular orbit at latitudes λ_1 and λ_2. Then assuming the mass M of the ship (with its cargo and crew) to be constant, he computed the difference between the linear momentum MV_1 at latitude λ_1 and MV_2 at latitude λ_2 and found a difference of velocities $|V_1-V_2|$ which the ship must gain or lose, depending on whether $\lambda_1 > \lambda_2$ or $\lambda_1 < \lambda_2$.

* In the linear case, the assumption of a constant mass of ship, cargo, and crew, led us to draw from the principle of conservation of momentum the conclusion that linear velocity is conserved.

With respect to the earth, the ship may be considered a mass point of constant mass M, with angular momentum MVR where the orbital velocity V at latitude λ is $2\pi R \cos \lambda/1440$, corresponding to a radius of rotation of $R \cos \lambda$. If, then, the angular momentum of a becalmed ship at latitude λ_1 is MV_1R_1 at latitude λ_2 it is MV_2R_2.

the case and the true answer to his problem would be almost 20 per cent greater than the linear difference of 2.5 mi/min.

Yet we must not criticize Franklin overly since his contemporaries, such as Desaguliers, would have treated the problem in just the same way. It is of far greater importance to observe that this particular problem is—so far as we know—original with Franklin: and it indicates a shrewdness in stating physical problems. That he saw at once the application of a principle of conservation is also of interest, even if he thought the approximation to the linear case would suffice. For it prepares us to appreciate his recognition of the fundamental role of conservation principles in nature and we are, therefore, less surprised when we find him discovering a conservation principle of his own, and seeking for others.

Franklin returned to this problem in a paper on meteorology read at the Royal Society on 3 June 1756. He pointed out that the rotation of the earth implies a different velocity for its parts depending on the latitude, and that therefore even in " a general calm over the face of the globe " the air must be in motion since it must move " as fast as the earth or sea it covers "—15 mi/min at the equator and " nothing " at the poles. Then, without proof or explanation, he asserted that " He that travels, by sea or land, towards the equinoctial, gradually acquires motion; from it loses." If the air " under the equator, and between the tropics," is heated and rises, its place will be taken by cooler air " from the Northern and Southern latitudes, which coming from parts where the earth and air had less motion, and not suddenly acquiring the quicker motion of the equatorial earth, appears an East wind blowing Westward; the earth moving from West to East, and slipping under the air." [28] Again a shift from the linear case assumed by Franklin to the rotational case is required by the circumstances.†

The angular momentum of a becalmed ship translated from latitude λ_1 to λ_2 remains, according to the principle of conservation of angular momentum, MV_1R_1. The difference between the angular momentum of a ship becalmed at latitude λ_2 and the angular momentum of the ship instantaneously translated from latitude λ_1 to λ_2 is $|MV_1R_1-MV_2R_2|$, from which the gain or loss in orbital velocity Δv may be computed. If the ship were to be translated from latitude λ_1 to λ_2, where $\lambda_1<\lambda_2$, then $\Delta v = (V_1R_1-V_2R_2)/R_2$.

† The problem raised by Franklin is not one whose solution is obvious—as I have proved by trying it out on several of my graduate assistants who were completing their doctorates in physics and astronomy. Franklin included this topic in his " Maritime Observations," addressed to David Le Roy, and read at a meeting of the American Philosophical Society in 1785: " Suppose a ship to make a voyage eastward from a place in latitude 40° north, to a place in latitude 50° north, distance in longitude 75 degrees. In sailing from 40 to 50, she goes from a place where a degree of longitude is about eight miles greater than in the place she is going to. A degree is equal to four minutes of time; consequently the ship in the harbour she leaves, partaking of the diurnal motion of the earth, moves two miles in a minute faster, than when in the

There are obvious limitations to a comprehension of Newtonian dynamics without mathematics. For instance, if rotational problems are reduced to linear problems, the central issue turns out to be merely conservation of velocity or motion, if the mass is assumed constant. One could reach the same results as Franklin's by thinking that what was conserved was always velocity, invoking a Galilean type of inertia that applies to the motion of the earth and to objects moving in relation to the moving earth. And it is by no means clear that Franklin, and other men of his day, always appreciated the subtle difference between effects of inertia and of momentum. In the very discussion of winds at the Royal Society, he explained that " He that sails, or rides, has insensibly the same degree of motion as the ship or coach with which he is connected. If the ship strikes the shore, or the coach stops suddenly, the motion continuing in the man, he is thrown forward. If the man were to jump from the land into a swift sailing ship, he would be thrown backwards (or towards the stern) not having at first the motion of the ship." [31] Here is a problem, seemingly similar to the ship changing in latitude, but all the effects described are owing to inertia, and do not require for their explanation the principle of conservation of momentum.

Franklin and the Tradition of Experimental Newtonianism

One of Franklin's most intemperate critics compared Franklin's book on electricity to Newton's *Principia*, with what results the reader may imagine. The critic, who preferred to remain anonymous,[32] was not " entirely against illustrating propositions in Natural Philosophy by particular experiments." After all, he observed, " the weakness of the human mind often requires such assistance." [33] This critic did not once refer to the *Opticks*, arguing that only in the *Principia* can one find an accurate view of science, its methods and principles. We are not surprised to learn that the anonymous gentleman had not found time to read about electricity, that he was " not very fond of novelties." Franklin might " very easily believe that a man who has spent the greatest part of his time in the study of Newton's *Principles*, and the sciences necessary for understanding that book, might hear of people rubbing glass tubes with-

port she is going to; which is one hundred and twenty miles in an hour. . . . Query. In returning, does the contrary happen, and is her voyage thereby retarded and lengthened? " [29] A footnote by Franklin contains this comment: " Since this paper was read at the Society, an ingenious member, Mr. Patterson, has convinced the writer that the returning voyage would not, from this cause, be retarded." This discussion may be found in the printing of this paper in the Sparks edition of Franklin, but not in the Smyth edition. Smyth omitted the letter to Colden on this topic, and also the " paragraph relating to this mistaken theory in the ' Maritime Observations.' " [30]

out any violent curiosity about the consequences. But more especially if he had persuaded himself that Newton reaped so compleat an
harvest, as to leave but poor gleanings for posterity." Alas! Newton's
great book, he was sorry to say, " seems to be but little regarded or
understood by the present race of Philosophers." [34] Unwittingly, he
was paying Franklin and his fellow scientists a high compliment,
saying that the natural philosophers of this age were not content to
study the *Principia* but had used experimental techniques to explore vast areas of science in a wholly new way.

Franklin was proud to belong to the great Bacon-Boyle tradition
of experimental science, to which he publicly affirmed his allegiance
at the height of his scientific creativity. "Poor Richard," in the
issue for 1749, paid tribute in Franklin's name to Bacon, "justly
esteemed the father of the modern experimental philosophy," and
to Boyle, "one of the greatest philosophers the last age produced."
The previous year, he had remembered the death of Newton,
" prince of astronomers and philosophers," and of Locke, " the Newton of the microcosm." [35] As Franklin sought to relate his primary
subject—electricity—to one after another of the domains of physical
science, he remained aware of the need for keeping in mind those two
cardinal principles of matter and motion. On the lookout for ways
in which experiment might reveal new aspects of heat, light, sound,
and chemical reactions, he was especially interested in unsuspected
connections between these types of natural phenomena and electrical phenomena. And in every subject of physical science, he tested
some conservation principle or used the general concept of conservation to challenge accepted doctrines. By successfully invoking
analogies with electricity, he even made a minor but significant
addition to the subject of heat.

As we explore Franklin's scientific thinking in fields other than
electricity, we shall find a unity of concept, a systematic application
of mechanistic ideas to all varieties of natural phenomena. Hence
we may understand Franklin's concern about Newton's " particles
of light," because the basic principles of matter and motion seemed
to lead to contradictions. The velocity of light is about 186,000
miles per second; conceive the " particles of matter called light "
to be as small as you like, Franklin said, and yet their momentum—
hence force on impact—must be enormous, " exceeding that of a
twenty-four pounder, discharged from a cannon." Franklin's empiricist scientific attitude would not permit him to believe in a
physical property that did not produce a sensible effect. These
supposed particles, he noted, despite their " amazing " momentum,
" will not drive before them, or remove, the least and lightest dust

they meet with." [36] A second problem arose from Newton's view that particles of matter might be convertible into particles of light. Franklin said that in this case the sun's production of light would be accompanied by a constant diminution in mass: would not " the planets, instead of drawing nearer to him, as some have feared, recede to greater distances through the lessened attraction? " [37] Yet " the sun, for aught we know, continues of his antient dimensions, and his attendants move in their antient orbits." ‡

Franklin's rejection of the hypothesis of particles of light on the principles of Newtonian mechanics was for a long time considered to be the primary statement of the mechanical inadequacy of the " emission " theory. It was still cited as late as 1835 in a report on optical theories prepared for the British Association for the Advancement of Science by Humphrey Lloyd, discoverer of conical refraction.[38]

Almost as soon as Franklin had published his views in the 1769 edition of his book on electricity, the strict Newtonians rose to the defense. Bishop Horsley, editor of the only major collection of Newton's writings,[39] published an article in the *Philosophical Transactions* called " Difficulties in the Newtonian Theory of Light, considered and Removed." In it he showed that the momentum (or force of motion) of a particle of light is probably much less than that of a twenty-four pounder. He assumed that the average particle of light could be considered as approximately a sphere of one millionth part of a millionth part of an inch in diameter (10^{-12} in), having a density one-third that of iron. He concluded that the differences in mass between iron balls and the average light-particle were far greater than the differences in velocity—that " the force of the motion in each particle of light " is equal to the " force of motion " in an iron ball of ¼ in. diameter moving only $1 / (13,666 \times 10^{21})$ yards per second. " Dr. Franklin's first question is answered," Horsley concluded, " A particle of matter, which is probably larger than any particle of light, moving with the velocity of light, has a force of motion, which, instead of exceeding the force of a twenty-four pounder discharged from a cannon, is infinitely less than that of the smallest shot discharged from a pocket pistol, or less than any that art can create." [40] Horsley's answer, of course, misses the point. It is not of great importance that Franklin's guess about the twenty-four pounder was wide of the mark; what matters is only whether one can assert that matter is in motion even in the absence of an observable phenomenon arising from the impact of that supposed

‡ Franklin later thought of a way in which the sun could produce light without loss of mass. See below, page 336.

matter. From Franklin's empiricist point of view a momentum attributed to matter with unobservable effects must have implied that the particular matter could be hypothetical at best and perhaps have self-contradictory properties.§ Furthermore, however small the mass of a single particle might be, an extraordinarily large number of them must certainly strike a piece of paper in every second, especially in very bright sunlight. Thus although the force of an individual particle might be tiny, should not the effect of the aggregate be discernible?

Franklin's views had been expressed in a letter to Colden of 1752, read at the Royal Society in 1756. In the same year in which Franklin wrote this letter, the celebrated mathematician, Euler, wrote a short work entitled *Nova Theoria Lucis et Colorum,* published in the Berlin *Acta,* in which he too objected to the exhaustion of the sun " by such a copious emission of material particles." [42] He held, furthermore, that such particles would interfere with the motion of planets and comets. Franklin's friend, Priestley, in his history of optics, reviewed these objections to the Newtonian hypothesis and devoted a whole chapter to the many unsuccessful eighteenth-century attempts to discover and perhaps measure the force or pressure of light.[43]

Franklin's Views on Light

Franklin's objections to the Newtonian doctrine of light are especially interesting from yet another point of view, in relation to his outlook on the general problem of scientific explanation. We have seen earlier in this chapter that a particular virtue of Franklin's theory of electricity was that in it a distinction could be made between variations in quantity of electric matter and the propagation of electric forces or disturbances. Thus Franklin's theory could explain electrostatic induction, whereby an alteration in the distribution of electric matter in a conductor (or the total quantity, if the conductor is grounded) can be produced by a nearby insulated charged body even though the electric matter in that insulated charged body remains constant. That a charged body can be a source of electrical effects without any motion or transfer of its electric matter is part of a large category of natural occurrences which Franklin presented in his book. In all of them an effect is transmitted but the matter does not move with the effect.

§ Newton had allowed for unobservable physical phenomena. In Query 31 of the *Opticks,* he had said: " The attractions of gravity, magnetism, and electricity, reach to very sensible distances, and so have been observed by vulgar eyes, and there may be others which reach to so small distances as hitherto escape observation; and perhaps electrical attraction may reach to such small distances, even without being excited by friction." [41]

If we see " the swell or top of a wave " on the surface of water moving at the rate of 20 miles an hour, he wrote, we are apt to suppose that " the current or water itself, of which the wave is composed, runs at that rate." Yet the " water does not proceed with the wave, it only rises and falls to form it in the different parts of its course." [44] If a stone is dropped in the middle of a stagnant pond, the waves spread out in all directions, all making " use of the same water with their predecessors." [45] Franklin also presented the example of standing waves produced in a cord fastened to a window at one end; the parts of the rope do not move along the rope although the waves do.[46] Again, his discovery that northeast storms move toward the southwest invoked a distinction between the direction of motion of an air disturbance and the direction in which the air is blown by the wind.[47]

The motion of an electrical effect is to be distinguished from the motion of the electric matter, the motion of a storm disturbance from the motion of the disturbed air, and the motion of waves on water from the motion of water. Although sound reaches our ears from a ringing bell, we do not have to imagine " sonorous particles " flying " in strait lines to the ear," he wrote; we can explain the observed acoustical phenomena by vibrations of the air.[48] Thus by a careful analysis we may avoid an endless multiplication of hypotheses or supposed material or physical causes of phenomena. In conformity with the Newtonian precept, " We are to admit no more causes of natural things than such as are true and sufficient to explain their appearances," * Franklin sought to account for optical phenomena by eliminating the matter of light and referring all the properties of light to vibrations of the æther, which presumably had other functions in nature as well. Hence, the introduction of the electric matter into considerations of the physics of bodies was compensated for by the elimination of the matter of light. The æther-vibration theory was also Newtonian, and Franklin paid no attention to Newton's objections to it as the sole explanation of phenomena, ignoring such problems as rectilinear propagation and " polarity " or " sides."

In optics Franklin particularly addressed himself to the relations between light and electricity. An electric spark can be as big as a candle flame and brighter, but " without fuel." [50] " I am persuaded," he said, " no part of the electric fluid flies off in such case to distant places, but all goes directly and is to be found in the place to which I destine it." If a spark discharge is produced between equally

---

* Franklin paraphrased Newton when he said, " We should not, indeed, multiply causes in philosophy without necessity." [49]

charged positive and negative bodies, they both end up with no charge, the negative body having absorbed the excess fluid of the positive body. These sparks might possibly excite vibrations in the æther, just as " different degrees of vibration given to the air produce . . . different sounds "; experiments had indicated that the " strongest sparks " are white and the " weakest " red, and that others are blue or purple—could not the strength of such sparks be related to the " degree of vibration " in the æther? [51]

Early in his research, Franklin had studied various ways of discharging a positively charged insulated conductor: by sprinkling sand on it, breathing on it, enveloping it in smoke, bringing a lighted candle near it, and so on. The explanation he advanced was that sand, moisture, and smoke consist of material particles which are attracted by the charged body, on contact receive a small amount of the electric matter, and are then repelled—each one carrying away a small amount of the electric matter until the positive charge has disappeared.† But while candlelight discharged such a body, sunlight did not—a difference that " seems new and extraordinary." [53] Later on, Franklin added a note explaining that this " different effect " probably implied no " difference in the light." He suspected that it arose " from the particles separated from the candle, being first attracted and then repelled, carrying off the electric matter with them." ‡ These experiments seemed to show that, despite the supposed Newtonian interconvertibility of the matter of light and ordinary matter, the particles of light do not have the properties of other kinds of material particles. Franklin, from the point of view of homogeneous properties of matter and motion, could reject the hypothesis of particles of light because in the domain of electricity it was found that these supposed particles did not produce the effect one would expect from particles.

The challenges raised by Franklin and by Euler to Newton's hypothesis of particles of light had to be answered because of the important place of Franklin and Euler in the science of the mid-eighteenth century. Franklin's criticism has, in this sense, a greater interest than just exhibiting the juxtaposition of the exact corpuscular philosophy and the theory of electricity in relation to optical phenomena: the language used in the replies is a measure of his

---

† It is interesting to speculate on the possible outcome of this experiment had Franklin also tried it with a clean polished metal plate with a *negative* charge. Sir Arthur Schuster suggested that Franklin might, in that case, have discovered the photoelectric effect. [52]

‡ This note first appeared in the 1769 edition; there is in Franklin's manuscript copy of these letters (the " Bowdoin MS ") an addendum in which a draught of this note appears.

stature as a scientist. Horsley, for example, began his discussion in the *Philosophical Transactions* by saying that "Dr. Franklin's questions are of some importance, and deserve a strict discussion." Midway in his argument he paused for this observation: "Dr. Franklin's character is not more distinguished by his superior talents, than by a candor truly philosophical. And upon this circumstance I build the strongest confidence that he will not be offended that I differ from him: that, as a friend to inquiry, he will be pleased that I take the liberty to communicate my own notions, however opposite they may be to his." [54]

Franklin's Doctrine of Fire

Franklin's ideas on light had only a critical value, but his views on heat led to new concepts and helped to influence the growth of thought in heat from the point of view of both chemistry and physics.§ That the subjects of heat and electricity must be closely related was clear before Franklin, if only from the obvious fact that the friction producing electrification also warms the rubbed bodies. 'sGravesande, as we saw in Chapter Seven, had introduced the subject of electricity as a sub-section of the part of his book treating "of fire." He believed that the property of having electrical attraction was given to bodies "when they are heated by attrition." [56] He did not say, however, that electrical phenomena are caused by the "fire" in bodies, only that "several remarkable phenomena . . . are ascribed to the fire contained in bodies . . . amongst which there are such as have a near relation to electricity." [57] "Experiments confirm my conclusions," he said, that although there is a "connexion between the cause of electricity and the cause of fire," yet "these two ought really to be distinguished." [58] 'sGravesande held that in glass and around its surface there is "a certain atmosphere" which may be "excited" by friction and "put into a vibratory motion" which causes attraction and repulsion. The motion of this atmosphere produces an expulsion of the fire contained in glass; at least that fire moves with the atmosphere, producing light or a luminous

§ The only statement of Franklin's on light to be taken seriously was a curious observation relating to light and flame. Priestley records: "Dr. Franklin shewed me that the flames of two candles joined give a very much stronger light than both of them separate; as is made very evident by a person holding the two candles near his face, first separate, and then joined in one. For immediately upon the junction, his face will be observed to be much more strongly illuminated than it was before. It is conjectured that the union of the two flames produces a greater degree of *heat*, and that this causes a farther attenuation of the vapour, and a more copious emission of the particles of which light consists." Plainly, Franklin might have endorsed the view that the greater heat of the two candles might produce more than twice the light of each burning separately, but he did not subscribe to an hypothesis "of the particles of which light consists." [55]

glow. Such conjectures, "though they have a great many experiments for their foundation," were to be laid aside, however, since they were peripheral to the primary purpose of investigating "fire." [59]

Some of the properties of Franklin's "electric matter" and 'sGravesande's "fire" are similar, as that "fire is attracted by bodies," [60] "fire unites itself to bodies," [61] and all bodies "contain fire in them." [62] In a much revised form, Franklin's final ideas about light and heat agreed with the words, if not the spirit, of 'sGravesande's statement that "heat and light proceed from the same cause." [63]

As we read Franklin's earliest electrical writings, we cannot help noticing his use of the phrase "electrical fire," which was later replaced by "electrical matter"—and eventually became the "electric fluid." Yet, although Franklin's thoughts on the electric matter were conditioned in part by analogy to some of the properties of the material heat-particles, as expounded by Boerhaave and to some degree by 'sGravesande, he never committed himself to an identification of the two, as so many of his contemporaries were prone to do. Although, in his first four scientific papers, he used the phrase "electrical fire" or "fire," he did write that water will rise "in vapours more copiously" when it becomes electrified, just as when "heated by common fire." [64] The reason is that both sorts of fire give "repulsion" to water particles and thus overcome their normal "attraction of cohesion." Franklin saw that the two kinds of fire have many properties in common. Since both are to be found in all bodies, he was willing to admit the possibility of their being only "modifications of the same element"; but he preferred to believe that they "may be different elements." [65] An electric spark could inflame a substance, a fact interpreted by Franklin to mean that the passage of "electrical fire" could put the "common fire" in motion. [66] This "effect" seemed to him to follow a fixed relation between the quantities of the two kinds of fire; a cold body could be inflamed only by a large quantity of "electrical fire," but increase the quantity of "common fire" (i. e., warm the spirits to be fired) and a small spark would do the job.

Franklin had at first believed that lightning melts metals by a "cold fusion," but he later admitted that the melting was always accompanied by the production of heat. He had, of course, been misled by stories he had read about lightning melting money in purses and swords in their scabbards, without any burning of the purses or scabbards.* His collaborator, Ebenezer Kinnersley, had

---

* Franklin said that "if a sword can be melted in the scabbard, and money in a man's pocket, by lightning, without burning either, it must be a cold fusion." A footnote, added to the 1769 edition of his book, corrected this statement: "These facts,

put the question out of all doubt by a series of beautiful experiments in which wires were so heated by " the electric explosion " that they fired gunpowder.[69] To the conclusion that " heat is produced by our artificial electricity," [70] Franklin added evidence that natural electricity—lightning—also melts metals by heating them..

" How many ways there are of kindling fire, or producing heat in bodies! " he wrote. " By the sun's rays, by collision, by friction, by hammering, by putrefaction, by fermentation, by mixtures of fluids, by mixtures of solids with fluids, and by electricity." [71] And yet, Franklin concluded, despite the difference " in circumstances, as in colour, vehemence, etc.," in the same bodies fire seems generally the same. Thus he was led to suggest that in such cases " fire " exists in the body in a quiescent state and that the actions producing heat or burning, which he had enumerated, only excite the " fire," disengage it, or bring it " forth to action and to view." [72] It seemed, therefore, as if fire might be a " principal part " of the ordinary solid substance of bodies, just as the electric matter is. Franklin supposed that kindling fire in a body is a process in which this " inflammable principle " is liberated and then acts to separate the parts of the body, causing the appearance of the customary signs of scorching, melting, or burning. When a spark ignites a magazine of gunpowder, he argued, it is difficult to conceive that all the fire producing that immensely violent explosion could have existed at first in such a tiny spark.[73]

If his hypothesis were valid, then Franklin could explain the heat produced by the passage of electricity through bodies. The electric fluid might liberate the fire within them, or separate the parts of those bodies, so that there would be " the immediate appearances of fire." [74] He could then dispense with such needless hypotheses as that the electric fluid " heats itself " in its swift motion, or that the resistance it encounters in bodies is the source of the heat.[75]

Ebenezer Kinnersley in America, and John Canton and Benjamin Wilson in England, had shown that when glass is heated it is no

though related in several accounts, are now doubted; since it has been observed that the parts of a bell-wire which fell on the floor being broken and partly melted by lightning, did actually burn into the boards. (See *Philos. Trans.* vol. LI, part 1, and Mr. Kinnersley has found that a fine iron wire, melted by electricity, has had the same effect.) " [67] In a letter to Kinnersley, Franklin explained how he had been led into error " by accounts given, even in philosophical books, and from remote ages downwards, of melting money in purses, swords in scabbards, etc., without burning the inflammable matters that were so near those melted metals." He concluded that " men are, in general, such careless observers that a philosopher cannot be too much on his guard in crediting their relations of things extraordinary, and should never build an hypothesis on any thing but clear facts and experiments, or it will be in danger of soon falling, as this does, like a house of cards." [68]

longer impermeable to the electric fluid, but becomes a kind of conductor, a phenomenon confirmed by the experiments of Lord Charles
Cavendish.[76] Æpinus found yet another relation between heat and
electricity in the tourmaline crystal, which becomes charged when
heated. This phenomenon, confirmed by Franklin's experiments on
such crystals,† was particularly satisfying to him in that at different
places on the heated crystal there would be a positive and a negative
charge, thus indicating that what had occurred was merely a redistribution of the normal quantity of electric matter in the original
crystal: another instance of the generality of the principle of conservation of charge.

An Electrician's Views on Heat

In a paper read at the Royal Society in 1756, Franklin observed
that damp winds " give a more uneasy sensation of cold than dry
ones," but they are " not colder by the thermometer." [78] He admitted that he could not help speaking " like an electrician ": damp
winds " *conduct* better " than dry ones, they are " better fitted to
convey away the heat from our bodies." Sensations of heat and cold
must always arise in our bodies, he said, not in the surrounding air;
the air merely deprives exposed parts of our bodies of their heat and
causes the sensation of cold. Franklin then explained that if a piece
of wood and a piece of metal were at room temperature, they would
not seem equally cool to his hand, which is at body heat, somewhat
higher than room temperature. The metal is a good conductor and
can " receive and convey away the heat from my skin and the adjacent flesh," but wood is a poor conductor and does not remove heat
as efficiently as the metal; hence the metal will " seem " colder.[79]
This explanation, with little change, still appears in every textbook.
As a control experiment, Franklin fashioned a piece of wood " of the
size and shape of a dollar," which was to be held at its edge between
the thumb and forefinger of one hand while the dollar was to be
held similarly in the other hand. Simultaneously, the far edges of
both were to be placed in a candle flame. The heat would then be

† In a letter to Dr. William Heberden, London, 7 June 1759, Franklin described a
series of experiments which satisfied him " that M. Æpinus's account of the positive
and negative states of the opposite sides of the heated tourmalin is well founded."
Some reports indicated that these experiments did not succeed, Franklin said, " Possibly
the tourmalins they have tried were not properly cut; so that the positive and negative
powers were obliquely placed, or in some manner whereby their effects were confused,
or the negative part more easily supplied by the positive. Perhaps the lapidaries who
have hitherto cut these stones had no regard to the situation of the two powers, but
chose to make the faces of the stone where they could obtain the greatest breadth, or
some other advantage in the form." [77]

conducted through the metal to the hand so quickly that it could not long be held, but the wooden disc could be held without pain even though it burst into flame.[80]

When Franklin said that in his discussion of heat he was speaking as an electrician, he meant that electrical experimenters always had to keep in mind the conducting properties of every substance present during an electrical experiment—not only the objects rubbed, or charged by contact or induction, but the bodies on which those objects were supported. Lack of care about proper insulation and possible grounding had been the cause of failure of many an experiment and had undoubtedly been a contributory cause to the apparent caprices or irregularities in observing electrical effects, the failure to be able to produce exactly the same phenomenon again and again under seemingly identical conditions. Furthermore, the two problems of conduction and grounding were of obvious importance in planning lightning protection—the field in which Franklin pioneered. Franklin established his claim that metal rods " of sufficient thickness, and extending from the highest part of an edifice to the ground, being of the best materials and compleat conductors, will, I think, secure the building from damage, either by restoring the equilibrium so fast as to prevent a stroke, or by conducting it in the substance of the rod as far as the rod goes. . . ."[81] But the question raised immediately was: ". . . what thickness of a metal-line rod may be supposed sufficient? " Franklin's experiments showed that an electric discharge would follow the best conducting path. For example, a discharge from five Leyden jars was found to " be all conducted round the corner of a book, by the fine filleting of gold on the cover, it following the gold the farthest way about, rather than take the shorter course through the cover, that not being so good a conductor." Franklin supposed that a length of iron wire of one-quarter inch diameter would contain as much conducting metal as an equal length of gold filleting, " and if so, it will conduct the charge of 25,000 such glass [Leyden] jarrs, which is a quantity, I imagine, far beyond what was ever contained in any one stroke of natural lightning." Fine wires are apt to be melted and destroyed by a discharge, whereas coarser ones are not.[82]

It may be observed that the whole foundation of lightning protection by conductors or rods rests on the difference in electrical conductivity of various materials. Over and over again, Franklin showed by analyses of the destruction wrought when houses were struck by lightning, that the discharge always followed the best conducting path. If two alternative paths were the timbers of a building and a metal rod going into the ground, the charge would choose the metal rod because metal is a better conductor than wood.

Franklin and his co-experimenter, Ebenezer Kinnersley, were particularly concerned with degrees of electrical conductivity in different conducting materials, not just the two extremes of a substance being a conductor or a non-conductor, and Franklin was led to apply this concept to problems of heat transfer. Kinnersley had contrived a particularly revealing experiment on electrical conductivity in which a pair of parallel external circuits was made between the two coatings of a Leyden jar: one through a trough of water 10 feet long and 36 square inches in cross-section, and the other through 20 feet of wire.[83] The discharge took place almost entirely through the wire, a better conductor than the water, even though that path was much longer.‡ This experiment was an obvious improvement on Franklin's. Franklin noted " that, generally, those [substances] which are the best conductors of the electrical fluid are also the best conductors of this [common fire]; and *e. contra*." [85]

Franklin was able to find a number of similarities in effects observed in heat and in electricity and he showed that analogous theoretical explanations were possible in the two subjects. To be sure, there was no " normal quantity " of common fire for a given body, as there was for electric matter. Yet common fire, like electric matter, could permeate bodies and it did seem to act as if " seeking an equilibrium." [86] By this statement Franklin meant that if two conducting bodies at different temperatures were in contact, heat (common fire) would flow from the hot body to the cold one, until an equilibrium was reached, just as electric fluid would flow from a positively charged conductor to a negatively charged conductor if they were brought into contact with one another. Electric fluid

‡ Franklin's co-experimenter, Ebenezer Kinnersley, devised a beautiful instrument which he called " an electrical air thermometer," in which sparks are produced across a gap enclosed in a glass tube; the pressure of the air in the tube could be set at atmospheric pressure or higher and the pressure could be determined by an open-ended manometer, so that changes in the temperature of the enclosed air were manifested by changes in pressure. Kinnersley showed that when the points of the spark-gap were brought together, the passage of electricity produced no alteration in the surrounding air, but when the points were separated so that there would be a spark, the air was heated and rarefied, or expanded. Kinnersley also heated wires until they were red hot and could ignite tinder and gunpowder. Thus Kinnersley assumed that " lightning does not melt by a cold fusion, as we formerly supposed," but like electricity it produces heat. Since " electric fire " will produce heat in passing through a small wire when the same quantity will not produce heat in a large body, Kinnersley concluded that the heat arises from resistance to the passage of the " electric fire." The latter has no heat in itself, so that an electrified body does not feel warm to the touch. But " the electric fire must produce heat in itself, as well as in the air, by its rapid motion." In the same way, Kinnersley argued, trees and houses are set on fire by lightning which, " by its rapid motion, produces heat in *itself*, as well as in other bodies," and which in " combustible matter " generates heat because of the resistance of that matter to the " lightning's violent motion." [84]

would also move from a positively charged body to a neutral one; similarly, " if two bodies, both good conductors, one heated, the other in its common state [i. e., at room temperature], are brought into contact with each other, the body which has most fire readily communicates of it to that which had least, and that which had least readily receives it, till an equilibrium is produced." [87]

" This fluid " of heat, or " fire," had the postulated property that as it enters solid bodies it expands them.§ It then separates their parts so as to change solids to liquids, and finally dissipates those parts in the form of a vapor or gas. But, Franklin said, if " fluid " can be removed from a liquid, the liquid will cool and become

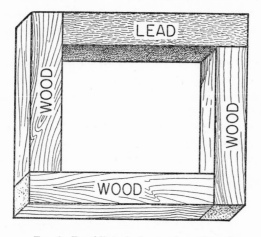

FIG. 6. Franklin's device to show the relative " conductivity " (with respect to heat) of wood and lead.

solid.[88] From these properties of the " fluid " of common fire, Franklin was led to a testable deduction. Since lead is a better conductor of heat (and electricity) than wood, a lead bar should conduct away the common fire of a hot body more rapidly than one of wood. If a piece of lead and a piece of wood were to be brought into contact with a mass of molten metal, Franklin argued, the lead would conduct away the common fire from the molten metal (and thus induce solidification) much more rapidly than the wood. Franklin's experiment employed a square hollow frame consisting of three pieces of wood and a bar of lead, each 4 inches long and 1 square inch in cross-section, set on a smooth board. Some molten lead was poured

§ This property of heat was considered then to have been established by the experiments of Boerhaave.

into the frame and was observed to "chill and become firm" on the "side next the leaden bar" long before it chilled on the "sides in contact with the wooden bars," even though all four bars were originally at the same temperature as the air in the room. Furthermore, the lead bar obtained so much heat in a short time from the molten lead that it melted a little.[89]

Franklin devised another experiment on "heat conductivity" which was intended to provide a scale of conductivity for different metals. This is the familiar experiment, still performed in almost all introductory courses, in which a number of rods of different metals are joined at one end and fanned out at the other, with little wax rings placed on them in a regular spacing. The ends joined together are placed in a flame, and the "conductivity" is indicated by the relative speeds with which the wax rings melt and fall off. Although Franklin obtained the necessary materials for performing such an experiment while in France, he never found time to carry it out. He suggested that his friend, Ingen-Housz, and he might do it together, but in the end he merely turned the materials over to Ingen-Housz to do the experiment by himself. This experiment differed slightly from the one performed in physics courses today. There were seven rods of equal length and cross-section mounted horizontally, parallel to one another in a wooden frame. The rods projected by an equal amount at both ends. The projecting portions of the rods at one end were coated with wax and then heat was applied at the other end by dipping the non-coated projecting parts into warm oil; * the order of melting was found to be silver,

---

* Franklin's comments on this experiment are as follows: "Your account of the experiments you made with the wires gave me a great deal of pleasure. I have shown it to several persons here, who think it exceedingly curious. If you should ever repeat those experiments, I wish your attention to one circumstance. I think it possible, that, in dipping them into the wax, and taking them out suddenly, the metal which attracts heat most readily may chill and draw out with it a thicker coat of wax; and this thicker coat might, in the progress of the experiment, be longer melting. They should therefore be kept so long in the wax, as to be all well and equally heated. Perhaps you may thus find the progress of heat in the silver quicker and greater. I think, also, that, if the hot oil in which you dipped the ends was not stagnant, but in motion, the experiment would be more complete, because the wire which quickest diminishes the heat of the oil next to it, finds soonest the difficulty of getting more heat from the oil farther distant, which depends on the nature of the oil as a conductor of heat, that which is already cooled interfering between the hotter oil and the wire. In reversing the experiment also, to try which of the metals cools fastest, I think the wires should be dipped in *running* cold water; for, when stagnant, the hot wires, by communicating heat to the water that is near them, will make it less capable of receiving more heat; and, as the metals which communicate their heat most freely and readily will soonest warm the water round them, the operation of such metals may therefore soonest stop; not because they naturally longer withhold their heat, but because the water near them is not in a state to receive it. I do not know that these hints are founded; I suggest them only as meriting a little consideration. Every one is surprised that the

brass or tin, iron, steel, lead.[91] This experiment was thought by
Franklin to yield the relative speed of transmission of heat (related
to ease of transmission, or conductivity), but after the work of
Joseph Black became known, it was seen that the results could not
properly be interpreted without the introduction of the concept of
specific heat.†

In problems of heat transfer such as Franklin had been considering, heat may be considered as a fluid. Our common language for
this subject—including terms like heat capacity, heat flow, heat conductivity, and the like—is a language of fluids. Whenever we deal
with problems of mixtures of substances at different temperatures,
we do not attempt to use higher mathematics or the dynamical theory
of heat, but continue to use this fluid theory, just as we still use
Franklin's theory of electricity in somewhat similar circumstances.
Difficulties in this theory of heat arise only when we have to take
into account the heat losses in machines, or other cases of heat produced by friction; all of which were wisely avoided by Franklin. On
the level of heat theory he explored, correct results follow from considering heat as a fluid, one which acts in conformity to a conservation principle, as Franklin knew. It may be observed that even today
we use the fluid theory of heat in problems of mixtures or calori-
metry, of heat flow and conductivity, because this theory gives the
proper answer with the minimum of mathematical complexity.

The conservation of heat was implied in Franklin's major supposition that temperature changes are caused by heat transfer, a
motion of an indestructible element from one body to another.
Frictional heat is not conserved because it appears to be producible
in limitless quantities, just as if it were being created in the process.
When Rumford observed the "inexhaustible" heat issuing from
the metal of cannon being bored, he concluded that heat "cannot
possibly be a material substance"; he could conceive of nothing
"capable of being excited and communicated in the manner heat
was excited and communicated in these experiments, except it be

progress of the heat seems to have no connexion with the gravity or the levity of
the metals." [90]

   † In their analysis of this experiment, Poynting and Thomson point out that "the
propagation of the high temperature along the rods depends not only on their conductivity, but also on their specific heats. If, for example, a cubic centimetre of one
rod has twice the heat capacity of the same volume of another, it requires twice the
quantity of heat to raise its temperature to the same extent, and if the melting
extends equally quickly along the two rods, the conductivity must be twice as great in
the one case as it is in the other; that is, we must consider not only the conductivity,
but the ratio . . . [of conductivity to heat capacity per cubic centimetre]. This quantity
is termed the *diffusivity* of the substance. We may regard it as the conductivity for
temperature as distinguished from the conductivity for heat." [92]

motion." [93] Heat produced by friction was not brought into a conservation principle until the middle of the nineteenth century when James Prescott Joule proved by experiment that there is a fixed heat equivalent to all mechanical work. In a paper read at the Royal Society on 4 November 1756, Franklin explored the possibility of the " heat . . . of friction by the dashing on the surface of the water " being sufficient to " render a bubble of water . . . specifically lighter than air." He concluded that such friction was not important in causing the vaporization of water. In any event, he reminded his listeners, " water agitated ever so violently produces no heat, as has been found by accurate experiments." [94]

Franklin returned to this subject in a letter to Mary Stevenson, written from London, 13 Sept. 1760, which was published in the fourth English edition of his book on electricity. His correspondent had asked him why the water at the place she was staying was cool as it came out of the spring but became warm by pumping. Franklin's elegant reply began: " It will be most prudent in me to forbear attempting to answer, till, by a more circumstantial account, you assure me of the fact. I own I should expect that operation to warm, not so much the water pumped, as the person pumping." Then he explained that although the production of heat by rubbing solids together had been well known for a long time, " the like effect has never yet, that I have heard, been produced by the mere agitation of fluids, or friction of fluids with solids. Water in a bottle shook for hours by a mill hopper, it is said, discovered no sensible addition of heat." [95] Those who have performed experiments on increasing the temperature of water by mechanical means, as with a " Jouler," will readily appreciate the difficulties that beset the eighteenth-century experimenters.

The failure to observe heat production by fluid friction implied, said Franklin, that the " production of animal heat by exercise " must " be accounted for in another manner." [96] Franklin was more than a little troubled by the problem of animal heat, especially in relation to conservation. The air surrounding an animal is generally at a lower temperature than the animal and so cools it, continually taking away some of the animal's common fire. But the animal does not grow cold; he does not even attain a state of thermal equilibrium (or common temperature) with his environment. Hence, from the point of view of conservation, the animal must be constantly acquiring heat—otherwise, he could maintain his temperature only by creating common fire, in contravention of any possible doctrine of conservation. To solve this problem Franklin supposed in 1757 that in their growth, plants absorb air, which " becomes consolidated with the other materials of which they are formed, and makes a great part of their substance "—a conclusion that would come naturally to a student of the writings of Stephen Hales—and that along with that air they attract " the fluid fire," which also becomes an element in their composition.[97] When the plants are digested by an animal, they " suffer . . . a kind of fermentation," in which not only does some of the air recover " its fluid active state again " (Hales, once more), but part of the " fire " is also released " and diffuses itself in the body digesting it and separating it." ‡

The principle of conservation and the distinction between conductors and non-conductors of heat allowed Franklin to explain why a woolen outer garment keeps a man warm in winter; it provides no heat, but as a non-conductor it prevents a loss of body heat to the surrounding air and thus allows the body to maintain its temperature. But Franklin discerned that the suppositions of this theory of heat could not explain why mixing snow and salt produced cold, which is " the absence of heat or fire." [99] Neither the air nor the containing vessel showed any sign of the fire that the theory said must be released when the snow and mixture lowered in temperature, and the vessel itself was cold to the touch! [100]

In 1762 Franklin pointed out that a candle flame will melt a fine wire but not a coarse one, even though both were made of the same metal. Evidently, he said, in the coarse wire, the flame that tended to separate the parts of the wire (to make it fluid) was resisted much more than in the fine wire. He thought that possibly the force of the flame was weaker in the coarse wire because it had to be divided among a larger number of parts. The effect of size on thermal properties was similar to what Franklin had observed in some ingenious experiments on electrical conduction, which had been devised to discover " the different effects of the same quantity of electric fluid passing through different quantities of [the same] metal." [101] Franklin had taken a strip of tinfoil three inches long, tapering gradually

‡ " I have been rather inclined to think that . . . whatever quickens the motion of the fluids in an animal, quickens the separation, and reproduces more of the fire, as exercise. That all the fire emitted by wood and other combustibles when burning existed in them before in a solid state, being only discovered when separating. That some fossils, as sulphur, sea-coal, &c., contain a great deal of solid fire. . . . in short, what escapes and is dissipated in the burning of bodies, besides water and earth, is generally the air and fire that before made parts of the solid. Thus I imagine that animal heat arises by or from a kind of fermentation in the juices of the body, in the same manner as heat arises in the liquors prepared for distillation, wherein there is a separation of the spirituous, from the watery and earthy parts. And it is remarkable, that the liquor in a distillers' vat, when in its highest and best state of fermentation, as I have been informed, has the same degree of heat with the human body, that is about 94 or 96." [98]

from a quarter of an inch at one end to a point at the other, and fixed it between two pieces of glass. When a Leyden jar was discharged through this conductor, the broad end was undisturbed, but the middle section appeared " melted in spots," the adjacent narrower section was " quite melted," but the narrowest part—at the point—was " reduced to smoke." This subject had also been explored fruitfully by Kinnersley.

Franklin's experiments on conductivity may seem trivial because we take them for granted today, but in the 1750's and 1760's they were new additions to natural philosophy. Although Desaguliers had suggested the names " conductor " and " non-conductor " for electricity in the 1730's, these names do not appear to have been applied to heat prior to Franklin. Very likely, the reason why investigators did not at once draw an analogy between heat and electricity in respect to conduction is the fact that Desaguliers's terms " conductor " and " non-conductor " had not been generally accepted by electricians, and there is no obvious analogue to " electric *per se* " in thermal phenomena.§ Both Boerhaave and 'sGravesande had discussed the penetration of heat in bodies of different substances in connection with thermal capacity and thermal transfer, but Franklin focussed attention on heat conduction, as distinct from convection and radiation. A recent investigator of this subject concludes that Franklin not only had " as a result of experiment, rather accurate ideas concerning electric conduction," but " was apparently the first to invoke the heat-electricity analogy," particularly " in connection with conduction." [103] What made his contribution to this subject particularly striking was his recognition that in an important range of phenomena the fluid of heat, like the fluid of electricity, followed a conservation principle and could, therefore, be studied quantitatively in terms of transfer as if heat were a substance.

Possible Influence of Franklin's Ideas on Heat

In presenting Franklin's ideas on heat, in relation to conservation and conduction, I have not attempted to state at each point the degree of anticipation to be found in the writings of his contemporaries and his predecessors—the aim being to show the quality of Franklin's reasoning and experiments and the way in which he made a fruitful transfer of concepts which has proved their worth in electricity to the domain of thermal phenomena. The major ad-

§ In a letter to Cadwallader Colden in 1751, Franklin indicated that " the terms *electric per se*, and *non-electric*, should be laid aside as improper: and (the only difference being this, that some bodies will conduct electric matter, and others will not) the terms *conductor* and *non-conductor* may supply their place." [102]

vances in this subject in the latter half of the eighteenth century were associated with quantitative calorimetric experiments, notably the work of Black, Wilcke (who translated Franklin's book on electricity into German), and Lavoisier (a friend and admirer of Franklin's) in collaboration with Laplace. The development of the concepts of specific and latent heats rendered much of the earlier speculation useless. In an exemplary monograph on the discovery of specific and latent heats, Douglas McKie and N. H. de V. Heathcote have shown how all previous ideas on thermal equilibrium were outmoded by the discovery of specific heats.[104] For example, Black himself pointed out Boerhaave's error in supposing that because bodies had reached thermal equilibrium (as indicated by the same thermometric temperature) there would be in each volume of space precisely the same quantity of heat. Ever since Black's day it has been a fundamental axiom that equal changes in temperature in different bodies of the same mass are not accompanied by the absorption or emission of the same quantity of heat unless the bodies are identical.

Apart from the specific contribution of thermal conduction, Franklin's place in the growth of ideas about heat is largely that he helped to make precise the concept of conservation and its area of applicability. With or without Franklin, there would undoubtedly have been the same development of a fluid theory of heat. Nevertheless, since Franklin did write on this subject and since his writings were widely read, there can be no question but that it was easier for men afterwards to create a fluid theory of heat on mechanical principles than if he had not dealt with the subject at all. Lavoisier, in a memoir of 1777 on the " matter of fire," described a subtle fluid which penetrates all bodies, sometimes existing in matter in a " free state " and sometimes combined with matter. He called it the " igneous fluid, matter of fire, of heat and of light." [105] In another memoir of the same year, on " combustion in general," Lavoisier stated as the primary " phenomenon " that in every case of combustion, there is liberated " matter of heat or light." If one were to ask him, he said, what he understood by " matter of fire," he would reply " with Franklin, Boerhaave,* and some of the older philosophers, that the matter of fire or of light is a very subtle and very elastic fluid, which surrounds every part of the planet we inhabit, which penetrates with more or less ease the bodies which compose

---

* The opening sentence of the first chapter of Lavoisier's *Elements of chemistry* describes a " physical axiom, or universal proposition, [established] by the celebrated Boerhaave," that ". . . every body, whether solid or fluid, is augmented in all its dimensions by any increase of its sensible heat."

it, and which tends when it is free, to put itself in equilibrium in all of them." [106] We may conclude, without further question, that Lavoisier had read carefully Franklin's statements on the equilibrium of the subtle fluid of heat. I cannot help feeling, furthermore, that Lavoisier placed Franklin's name at the head of his list of authorities because Franklin had played a major role in showing that subtle elastic fluids, both electricity and fire, could be treated in terms of mechanical principles, with a conservation law. This particular aspect of Franklin's natural philosophy in general must have held a special appeal for Lavoisier, whose own great chemical system was based on explicit conservation principles—applied to matter and to heat—which mark a new age in chemical philosophy. Because both electricity and heat are conserved, they appeared to Franklin as a kind of matter, whereas light did not appear to be a kind of matter since it is not conserved. This conclusion agreed with the observed fact that pieces of matter and heat would discharge an electrified body, whereas light would not do so. Lavoisier referred to " caloric " in his *Elements of Chemistry* as an " igneous fluid " or " matter of fire and of heat." Like Franklin's electric fluid in many respects, it particularly had the properties " of a real and material substance, or very subtile fluid, which, insinuating itself between the particles of bodies, separates them from each other. . . ." Because, like Franklin's electric fluid, this caloric was endowed with the property of repulsion, a sufficient quantity of caloric added to matter would make that matter into an " aeriform fluid." In Franklin's book, as a matter of fact, Lavoisier would have found a discussion of the action of heat or fire in separating particles of matter but never destroying them, and it was accompanied by a kind of anticipatory statement of the doctrine of conservation of matter in combustion.

The occasion was Franklin's discussion of the origin of solar radiation: part of a letter of 1752 to Cadwallader Colden, read at the Royal Society in 1756. According to Franklin, light is not a kind of matter; hence the mass of the sun is not diminished by the emission of light. He then asked whether we could conceive the mass of the sun remaining constant, even if it should be a flaming mass of sulphur. Franklin's answer is based on the axiom that the " action of fire only *separates* the particles of matter, it does not *annihilate* them." [107] During combustion, a process of chemical change, matter is not destroyed, he said. Using a familiar analogy he reminded his readers that water, raised up from the earth by heat in the form of vapors, returns to the earth as rain; hence the total mass of water on the earth and in the clouds is constant. During combustion, we always observe changes in weight, but Franklin wondered whether such changes would occur in a closed system: " If we could collect all the particles of burning matter that go off in smoak, perhaps they might, with the ashes, weigh as much as the body before it was fired: And if we could put them into the same position with regard to each other, the mass would be the same as before, and might be burnt over again." [108] Franklin was obviously misled by the idea that fire does no more than separate the particles of matter, confusing two quite distinct processes: the evaporation of liquids and the combustion of liquids and solids—the former a reversible process but not the latter. The comparison to cloud-formation and rain was not, therefore, felicitous. Experiments, such as those of Lavoisier, show that a closed retort containing air and combustible matter weighs just as much before that matter is burnt as afterwards—providing the retort has remained sealed. But the ashes and " smoak " will weigh more than the original combustible material if by " smoak " we mean not only smoke particles as such but the water vapor and gases that are ordinarily produced by a chemical combination of the combustible matter and the oxygen in the air.

Franklin made a number of remarks on chemical subjects, most of them reminiscent of the Queries in Newton's *Opticks* and their development in Hales's *Vegetable Staticks*. Hales and others had written on the attractive force between particles of different kinds of matter; thus Franklin could observe in a paper read at the Royal Society on 4 Nov. 1756 that to suppose a mutual attraction between air particles and water particles is hardly to introduce " a new law of nature; such attractions taking place in many other known instances." [109] In one of his early papers, Franklin remarked that the particles of " sundry menstrua " (acids) can insinuate themselves " between the particles of metals, and overcome the attraction by which they cohere " [110]—a statement in accord with Newtonian chemistry, expounded in Query 31 of the *Opticks*. From the same source Franklin gained the information he presented about the particles of salt of tartar being deliquescent because of an attraction between them and the " particles of the water which float in the air in the form of vapours." [111]

Joseph Black, in his posthumously published book on chemistry (which contains his discoveries in the field of heat), does not acknowledge a direct influence of Franklin, although he frequently cited Franklin's writings with evident approval. Black had little interest in speculations and spoke of theories as " a mere waste of time and ingenuity." [112] Although he admired Lavoisier's discoveries, he argued that " chemistry is not yet a science," so that " we should avoid every thing that has the pretensions of a full system. The whole of chemical science should, as yet, be analytical, like Newton's *Opticks*. . . ." [113] Black, therefore, presented more than one concept of heat, as if to let his readers (or listeners) choose amongst them. There was the Bacon-Boyle view of heat as a motion of the particles of which bodies are made (of which motion Black acknowledged he could not form " a conception . . . that has any tendency to explain even the more simple effects of heat.") .[114] Then there was the view of the greater number of the German and French " philosophers and Dr. Boerhaave " that heat is a motion of " the particles of a subtile, highly elastic, and penetrating fluid matter." This " matter " is supposed to be " diffused through the whole universe, pervading with ease the densest bodies "; when it is " modified in different ways," this matter also " produces light, and the phenomena of electricity." [115] Black rather liked the " ingenious " suppositions of the late Dr. Cleghorn,† especially because they readily explained the transmission of heat through a vacuum. We must, incidentally, observe that even as good a man as Black did not carefully distinguish between conduction, convection, and radiation of heat.

Cleghorn advanced a fluid theory of heat, too, but it differed from those other fluid theories, according to Black, in that it postulated an attraction between the particles of subtle matter and those of ordinary matter in addition to a force of repulsion between its own particles. In the words used by Black to describe the postulates of Cleghorn's theory, we encounter what seems like Franklin's own statement of the postulates of his electrical theory, with only a change of the word " electricity " to " heat." Cleghorn supposes, wrote Black, " that the common grosser kinds of matter consist of attracting particles, or particles which have a strong attraction for one another, and for the matter of heat; while the subtile elastic matter of heat is self-repelling matter, the particles of which have a strong repulsion for one another, while they are attracted by the other kinds of matter. . . ." [116]

Black was attracted to this " opinion or supposition " because it could be applied " to explain many of the remarkable facts relating to heat; and it is conformable to those experiments of Dr. Franklin and of Sir Benjamin Thompson [Count Rumford]." [117] The experiments in question were " made by the celebrated Dr. Franklin and some of his friends at Paris." [118] Two " similar " bodies were employed, both heated equally. One was suspended in the exhausted

---

† Despite Black's favorable opinion of Cleghorn, history has passed him by. No account of him is to be found in Poggendorff's *Biographisch-literarisches Handwörterbuch* nor in the *Dictionary of national biography*.

receiver of an air pump while the other hung in the open air, " these bodies being such as to shew exactly the variations of heat that happened in them." As the temperatures fell to that of the room, it was found that the body in air " lost its heat " more rapidly than the body in vacuo in times " nearly in the proportion of 5 to 2." ‡

The thermometers fell from 60° (Réaumur)		
	IN VACUO	IN THE AIR
to 50°	in 17 min.	in 7 min.
37°	54 "	22 "
30°	85 "	29 "
20°	167 "	63 "

These experiments were variations on cruder ones reported by Newton in Query 18 of the *Opticks,* in which Newton had been interested in the general problem of the passage of heat through a space devoid of air, but still containing a subtle material through which heat may pass.

That a major thermal experiment of Franklin's should be related to Query 18 of the *Opticks* is of more than passing interest. Newton's ideas on heat were never unambiguously presented to the reader. There was almost the same duality as in his theory of light. For all that he considered heat as a mode of motion in the particles of ordinary matter, as Bacon and Boyle had done before him, he had shifted his position somewhat when he had to explain the transmission of heat through a vacuum. Should he deny the basic axiom of heat as a motion of matter or deny the existence of the vacuum? He chose the latter course. Light as well as heat may be transmitted through a space devoid of air, he said, but such space is not truly empty; it is filled with a subtle matter, an æthereal medium, and *its* motion is responsible for the transmission of heat (we should say radiation).

Black's comment on Newton's conclusion, that a vacuum contains " in it some subtle matter by which the heat is transmitted," is most interesting. According to Black, " This opinion probably was founded on a very general association in our minds, between the ideas of heat and matter; for, when we think of heat, we always conceive it as residing in some kind of matter; or possibly this notion of Sir Isaac might be founded on some opinion which he had formed

‡ Franklin's data were given by Black, who referred the reader to a confirmation " by a set of similar experiments, made by Sir Benjamin Thompson. (*Phil. Trans.* for the year 1786)." [119]

concerning the nature of heat." [120] Black was undoubtedly correct in assuming that Newton denied the existence of a vacuum because heat transmission through empty space would contravene the fundamental axiom of mechanistic physics and remove heat from the category of the phenomena of " matter and motion." Newton was led to the æther in order to account for heat radiation in much the same way that Franklin was led to the concept of a mobile electric matter when he found he could not explain electrical phenomena in terms of the motion of the particles of " common matter." §

Franklin on the Æther

In one of his last scientific papers, written at Passy on 25 June 1784, Franklin set down some " Loose thoughts on a universal fluid." * This subtle fluid is said to fill up universal space and its " motion or vibration is called light." In his old age Franklin, like his master, Newton, unburdened himself of those speculations about the æther which had been a continuous thread through his scientific thinking for about four decades. We have seen, earlier in this chapter, the bases on which Franklin rejected the hypothesis of particles of light, or a matter of light, traveling out from luminous objects, and his conclusion that the æther waves—which Newton had said accompanied the motion of the particles of light—might produce the light itself. Franklin, like Newton, believed that " Nature . . . affects not the pomp of superfluous causes." [122] So, like Newton, he was convinced that the æther is not only the medium in which light-producing vibrations arise, but also is active in other types of physical events.

Franklin suggested that the subtle fluid producing light " may possibly be the same " as that producing heat. Entering solid matter, this fluid dilates bodies by " separating the constituent particles," thus eventually making them fluid; it also maintains " the fluidity " of bodies in the liquid state and even in the gaseous state. Earlier, Franklin had declared that the repulsion between particles of gases (elastic fluids) must be referred to a material cause, since the primary quality of ponderable or common matter is attraction and not repulsion.[123] In 1784 he returned to this point of view, by asking whether this same æther or subtle fluid does not keep " asunder the particles of air, permitting them to approach, or separating them more, in proportion as its quantity is diminished or augmented? " [124]

---

§ See above, page 168.

* Addressed to David Rittenhouse, this paper was read at a meeting of the American Philosophical Society at Philadelphia on 20 June 1788.[121] It was apparently written at Passy, 25 June 1784.

Vapors rise because this fluid seems to have "a great affinity with water." The solid from which vapors rise is cooled in the process, being not only " cold to the touch " but cold to a " degree measureable by the thermometer." The well-known fact that clouds of water vapor condense into rain, snow, and hail, must therefore imply a separation of the subtle fluid from the water particles. The general doctrine of conservation thus required of Franklin the query, " What becomes of that fluid? "

Does it rise above our atmosphere, and mix with the universal mass of the same kind? Or does a spherical stratum of it, denser, or less mixed with air, attracted by this globe, and repelled or pushed up only to a certain height from its surface, by the greater weight of air, remain there, surrounding the globe, and proceeding with it round the sun?

His speculations as to an envelope of this subtle matter took him into questions of meteors that acquire " fire " and burn as they approach the earth, and kindred matters. He supposed that when the earth was first formed, the " original particles took their place at certain distances from the center in proportion to their greater or less gravity." The " fluid fire, attracted toward that centre, might in great part be obliged, as lightest, to take place above the rest, and thus form the sphere of fire above supposed, which would afterwards be continually diminishing by the substance it afforded to organize bodies, and the quantity restored to it again by the burning or other separating of the parts of those bodies." The union of this matter and common matter might occur when " infinitely small vibrations " strike common matter " with a certain force," enter " its substance," and are " held there by attraction, and augmented by succeeding vibrations, till the matter has received as much as their force can drive into it."

Now at first reading it may seem that Franklin was guilty of failing to make that very distinction which marked his discussions of electricity and of water waves: between the motion of a disturbance and the motion of a kind of matter. Sunlight transmits motion to the envelope of subtle matter around the earth, thus making the whole sky bright. But if light is merely a vibration, how could it move the subtle matter itself? Franklin apparently conceived that there was a motion of this matter as well as a vibratory motion within it, and that the possibility of these two kinds of activity enabled the same subtle matter to operate so as to produce heat and light.

In these speculations of 1784, Franklin repeated his earlier ideas about the cause of the sensations of hotness and coldness being the loss or gain of the fluid of heat, and the way that plants " attract and consolidate " this fluid while they grow. Thus he was led to insist again on that great and universal principle of conservation. "The power of man relative to matter seems limited," Franklin declared. Man can divide matter, he can mix together different varieties, he can change the form and appearance of matter by making different compositions of it. But he can never create new matter, nor can he annihilate the old. "Thus," Franklin said, "if fire be an original element, or kind of matter, its quantity is fixed and permanent in the universe. We cannot destroy any part of it, or make addition to it; we can only separate it from that which confines it, and so set it at liberty, as when we put wood in a situation to be burnt; or transfer it from one solid to another, as when we make lime by burning stone, a part of the fire dislodged from the wood being left in the stone."

Such speculations show us something of the uniform natural philosophy of Benjamin Franklin; they are not particularly important additions to our understanding of the behavior of matter, nor did they suggest new ways of exploring or explaining the occurrences in the external world. But they indicate to us that at the end of his scientific career, as at its inception, Franklin sought to unify all scientific explanations within a single comprehensive framework of material causes and conservation principles. As such, Franklin was a leading exponent in his age of the general idea that the universe was an intelligible machine that could be completely described in terms of varieties of matter interacting with one another according to simple principles of attraction and repulsion and in agreement with exact proportions of weight and measure. The over-all doctrine of conservation implied, furthermore, that the universe was complete and everlasting: nothing was ever destroyed or created, and the great machine that we call the world could function in its regular way forever without the need of supernatural intervention.† We may call such a point of view "materialist" or "rationalist" if we wish, but in Franklin's eyes it merely was a reflection of the superior intelligence of the divine craftsman who had made the universe complete.

---

† It should be observed that conservation of matter, heat, and the like is not a sufficient reason for the everlastingness of the universe. At the height of belief in the principle of conservation of energy (latter half of the nineteenth century), it was recognized that energy could become degraded and that the universe could slowly run down. In Franklin's day, however, for the universe to continue running without divine intervention, the heavenly bodies needed to maintain their masses. But all men did not agree with Franklin that a diminution of the mass of the sun owing to emanations of particles of light was absurd since the solar system would not then continue forever to maintain its present state. Franklin's friend, James Bowdoin, for example, held "that if the material system, in its present form, was not intended by its creator to be perpetual, then the waste of the sun's matter, and the consequent disorder of the system, arising from the altered state of its gravitation, will only be a proof of that intention, and not operate against the truth of the doctrine." [125]

Franklin's Experimental Philosophy

Joseph Priestley, one of Franklin's major philosophical disciples, once said that, " if the simple electric shock would have appeared so extraordinary to Sir Isaac Newton," what would that great man have said " upon seeing the effects of a modern electrical battery [Franklin's term for a combination of condensers or Leyden jars], and an apparatus for drawing lightning from the clouds! " [126] Priestley had in mind that the " electric shock " from a Leyden jar, " if it be considered attentively," would be as surprising to Newton as " any discovery that he had made." The new science of electricity was not " a small object "; it was not, " like magnetism, confined to one kind of bodies." The discoveries of Franklin and his successors had shown that the " electric fluid " is not a " local or occasional agent in the theatre of the world," but that " its presence and effects are every where, and that it acts a principal part in the grandest and most interesting scenes of nature." Since every body possesses electric fluid, and since all bodies can be classified electrically as conductors and non-conductors, the electrical properties of bodies must be " as essential and important as any they are possessed of. . . ." Up until now, Priestley said, " philosophy has been chiefly conversant about the more sensible properties of bodies; electricity, together with chymistry, and the doctrine of light and colours, seems to be giving us an inlet into their internal structure, on which all their sensible properties depend. By pursuing this new light, therefore, the bounds of natural science may possibly be extended beyond what we can form an idea of. New worlds may open to our view, and the glory of the great Sir Isaac Newton himself, and all his contemporaries, be eclipsed by a new set of philosophers in quite a new field of speculation." [127] This point of view prepares us for Priestley's many descriptions of Franklin as the Newton of electrical science. Priestley was particularly impressed by the fact that Franklin, like Newton before him, was able to explain so many diverse and apparently unrelated phenomena by the consistent application of simple principles. Franklin's great merit, according to Priestley, is " independent of all hypotheses," and stands " upon the firm basis of the discovery of many new and import[ant] facts, and, what is more, applied to the greatest uses." [128] Furthermore, as Priestley indicated, the electric fluid, according to Franklin's postulates, differed in many important respects from the æther of Sir Isaac Newton, even though like the æther it was subtle and elastic. Hence it could be seen at once that Franklin had followed his own course as he explored the phenomena of electricity and, by differing from Newton, had gone beyond him.

Like Newton, Franklin had always expressed himself with modesty. He had not adopted the strict form of " Queries," but he always introduced his own speculations, hypotheses, and his theory of electrical action as a whole with the utmost diffidence. Recognizing the clear distinction between observations and statements about observations, he had displayed what Priestley called " a truly philosophical greatness of mind to which few persons have ever attained," [129] and was always ready to abandon a working hypothesis when a better one was presented or when new facts were uncovered which rendered it unacceptable without modification.

Priestley began the third part of his account of the present state and origins of our knowledge of electricity with a methodological discussion " of philosophical theories in general," as a prelude to presenting in final form the theory of Dr. Franklin. His methodological precepts were necessary, he said, because of the completely *a priori* quality of most electrical hypotheses. The imagination may have " full play in conceiving the manner in which an invisible agent produces an almost infinite variety of visible effects," because " the agent is invisible." Hence, " every philosopher is at liberty to make it whatever he pleases, and ascribe to it such properties and powers as are most convenient for his purpose." [130]

In every branch of science, according to Priestley, we observe particular facts; " all general propositions, as well as general terms, are artificial things, being contrived for the ease of our conception and memory: in order to comprehend things clearly, and to comprise as much knowledge as possible in the smallest compass." [131] Here we have an early statement of a modern positivist attitude: practically Ernst Mach's doctrine of science as the " economy of thought." The late Sir Philip Hartog first called attention to Priestley's modern philosophical point of view, and indicated its sources in Newton's *Opticks* and Franklin's *Experiments and Observations on Electricity*.[132] But Hartog could not appreciate the point of view of Priestley's philosophic mentor, Franklin, who was willing to use the word " effect " without its correlative " cause." Hartog apparently had little sympathy with the idea that science is primarily concerned with linking observable phenomena, " effects," while maintaining a skeptical attitude towards any supposed " cause " which must by its nature be unobservable, an " artificial thing." [133]

Franklin's views on " causes " and " effects " were stated most explicitly in a paper read at the Royal Society on 4 Nov. 1756. The opening sentence of this paper contained the declaration " that it seems absurd to suppose that a body can act where it is not," followed by the correlative statement, " I have no idea of bodies at a distance attracting or repelling one another without the assistance of some medium, though I know not what that medium is, or how it operates." [134] Franklin's position was somewhat analogous to Newton's, when Newton proposed his grand hypothesis of an all-pervading æther, with variations in its density as the source of gravitational attraction between bodies; discussing this subtle medium (in the Queries of the *Opticks*) Newton had said that he did not know what the æther is. But Newton, despite his disclaimer, had considered the æther particulate, elastic (because of the mutual repulsion of its particles), and varying gradually in density at each point in space in a fixed but unspecified relation to neighboring bodies. Franklin had no patience with speculations on æther density in spaces so distant from us that we have no way of testing any statement we might make about them. Writing out some critical comments about Hoadly and Wilson's book on electricity in 1751,‡ Franklin expressed his dislike of Newton's hypothesis. According to Hoadly and Wilson: " This æther is much rarer within the dense bodies of the sun, stars, planets, and comets, than in the empty celestial space between them; and in passing from them to great distances, it grows denser and denser perpetually. . . ." [135] " How is it discovered," asked Franklin, " that the æther grows denser in proportion to its distance from the sun, planets, etc.? " In the second edition of the book, a footnote was added that Newton had only " supposed " a subtle ætherial fluid, and had not " asserted " its existence.

Franklin's philosophic attitude seems very modern. The question of how bodies " come to fall " was for him as for most scientists today a matter of unnecessary speculation; he was content to know the laws of falling bodies and to be aware that these laws could be derived from the Newtonian law of universal gravitation and the three Newtonian laws of motion. Although he wrote out in old age his own " loose thoughts " about the æther in relation to attractive and repulsive forces, the tone of that document indicates his lack of conviction that anything positive could come from such a line of

‡ Franklin's views on the nature of scientific explanation are displayed in some hitherto unpublished critical comments which he wrote out for Benjamin Wilson on 28 January 1759. These notes in Franklin's hand are at present in the Library of the American Philosophical Society and consist of a long series of questions and short paragraphs, introduced by numbers which are not continuous (as 2, 13, 35, . . .), and a final statement that he had given Wilson a copy. In the Mason-Franklin Collection in the Yale University Library there is a copy of Hoadly and Wilson's *Observations on a series of electrical experiments* (London, printed for T. Payne, 1756), formerly in Franklin's personal library. The paragraphs were numbered by Franklin in his own hand and there are marks in the margin here and there throughout the book. The association of Franklin's comments with this copy of the book is made certain by the fact that there is a one-to-one correspondence between the marginal marks and the comments.

thought. His sentiment that in the realm of science " it is enough to know the laws themselves " undoubtedly was derived from a belief that we never can really know " the manner in which nature executes her laws." §

Such words as " attraction " and " repulsion," Franklin said, were poor words; they are. Even today they are apt to have overtones of occult grasping or pushing powers in bodies that make them draw other bodies to them or send other bodies away from them. These words imply the notion of a " cause " of action of one body on another through space, when in fact they should be descriptive only of the observable motion of one body either toward or away from another. Yet Franklin did use the words " attraction " and " repulsion," but only " for want of others more proper." His intention, he said, was " only to express *effects* which I see, and not *causes* of which I am ignorant." [136] The phenomena of electricity were explained by Franklin on the assumption of the existence of particles of electric matter and particles of common matter, forces of repulsion between the electric particles and of attraction between them and the particles of common matter. Franklin was not overly concerned that he could not well envisage a " cause " of such attractions and repulsions, although he probably thought there must be some material process involved.* As a sample of the way in which his mind conceived the impossibility of ever knowing such " causes," we may examine his own discussion of action at a distance in relation to air pressure.

Like all good Newtonians, he held that a body cannot " act where

§ See Chapter Four.

* Franklin's ideas about physical " cause " may have been one of the bases for Hume's admiration of the American philosopher. Similar ideas to Franklin's and Priestley's were held by Hume's countryman, the Scottish chemist, Joseph Black. Black said that Newton's theory of chemistry was not " very well received at first by the chemists abroad," who preferred to use the term " affinity " in place of " attraction." " They objected to the word attraction, as implying either an active quality in matter, which we cannot conceive to be possessed of activity, or some connecting intermediate substance, by which the particles of bodies were drawn together, and for the existence of which no proof is offered."

Black's position was that " their objections to the word *attraction* were certainly unreasonable. Sir Isaac, in the beginning of these queries, expressly declares, that when he uses this word, he does not pretend to assign the causes, natures, or manners of acting, of those forces by which bodies are disposed to rush together into union. He only means the forces themselves, or the disposition to join, manifested by the fact itself, leaving it to others to discover the cause, and observing that it is improper to attempt it, until we become better acquainted with its manner of acting, by studying the facts. And when the word is used with this precaution, merely as a term expressing a fact, a phenomenon, I do not see any advantage in preferring *affinity* to it. It would sound very ill, to speak of the affinity of gravitation, of electrictiy, or of magnetism. Attraction is more expressive; and affinity implies, or suggests, some similarity, which, in most cases, is not agreeable to fact, seeing that we generally observe the greatest dissimilarity in those bodies which are eminently prone to unite." [137]

it is not," save through the assistance of " some medium ": but we cannot know " what the medium is, or how it operates." Franklin explained that if he tried to press between his knees a sealed bladder full of air, he would find that he could not bring the sides of the bladder together, that his knees would " feel a springy matter, pushing them back to a greater distance, or repelling them." [138] Since this phenomenon would not occur if the bladder were empty, and would be of a lesser magnitude if the bladder contained a smaller quantity of air, he could legitimately conclude that the air the bladder contains " is the cause " of the effect he feels. Experiments on air show that we " cannot by pressure force its particles into contact"; the air particles will always " spring back against the pressure." Franklin apparently conceived that ponderable matter can have no " innate " powers of attraction or repulsion, thus show-ing himself a good Newtonian.† Hence the only possible conclusion about the air was that " there must be some medium between its particles that prevents their closing, though I cannot tell what it is." Suppose that somehow or other he " were acquainted with that medium, and found its particles to approach and recede from each other according to the pressure they suffered." Then he could not help but " imagine there must be some finer medium between them, by which these operations were performed." In other words, Frank-lin did not envisage any stage in which an ultimate cause would be found as a principle within a particle to explain its apparent repul-

† In a paper sent to Dr. John Mitchel, 29 April 1749, Franklin wrote, " The particles of air are said to be hard, round, separate and distant from each other; every particle strongly repelling every other particle, whereby they recede from each other, as far as common gravity will permit." This repulsion, to which no cause was assigned, was said to be increased by " common fire joined with air," just as both electrical and common fire can " assist in raising vapours " by giving " repulsion to the particles of water " to destroy " their attraction of cohesion." In a paper read at the Royal Society on 3 June 1756, Franklin repeated his conviction, " The particles of air are kept at a distance from each other by their mutual repulsion." It was to explain such " mutual repulsion " of air particles and the " mutual attraction between the particles of water and air " [139] that Franklin would conceive a " medium " between the particles; but to deduce consequences from the supposition of such attractions and repulsions requires no explanation or further hypothesis of cause. Since Franklin's theory of electrical action needed no ancillary hypothesis to explain the mutual repulsion between particles of electric matter and their attraction by common matter, Franklin has often seemed to have been adopting a doctrine of action-at-a-distance for particles as a means of avoiding action-at-a-distance in gross bodies. Whether or not he really thought there might be a fine medium that made particles of electric matter repel one another, he never made use of it in his theory of electricity. His procedure thus reminds us of Newton in the *Opticks*, where he allowed particles of matter and of light to act on one another at a distance, supposed forces of attraction and repulsion between particles of matter, and even suggested that the æther might be composed of mutually repelling particles—but without any apparent concern for the cause of such particulate action-at-a-distance.

sion of a like particle.‡ There would always remain an ultimate unknowable. He believed only that each type of phenomenon, whether attributable to the particles of matter or the particles of some medium in which matter exists, and so on, must arise mechanically. In this sense, it would be fruitless to search for some ultimate cause of " why " phenomena occur. We must be content to form concepts and laws on which to base primary axioms from which we can derive statements about phenomena which agree with experience. Thus we may correlate the events of the external world in a unique way, and predict the outcome of operations which we perform in the laboratory or of natural occurrences in the universe around us.

Franklin as a Newtonian Experimental Scientist

Following his teacher Franklin, Priestley held that the only causes in nature are conditions which seem to yield the same effects. We may illustrate this proposition of Priestley's by an example taken from Franklin. If we bring one of the conductors of a Leyden jar into contact with a charged glass rod and ground the other conductor, we have a condition in every way similar to bringing a charged glass rod near a grounded tin tube suspended by silk threads. In both cases, the grounded object becomes negatively charged, so that—to use Priestley's words—we can " predict other similar appearances from similar previous situations of things." [140]

The hypothesis of a single electric fluid, with constant laws of

---

‡ Franklin's discussion is related to the problem posed by Newton in the final Query of the *Opticks*. Newton had asked how the " parts " of " homogeneal hard bodies " stick together. He rejected the concept of " hooked atoms " and the notion that " bodies are glued together by rest, that is, by an occult quality, or rather by nothing." Newton preferred to think of a force " which in immediate contact is exceeding strong, at small distances performs the chymical operations . . . , and reaches not far from the particles with any sensible effect." All bodies " seem to be composed of hard particles," and " even the rays of light seem to be hard bodies." Hardness, " reckoned the property of all uncompounded matter," seems " to be as evident as the universal impenetrability of matter." If compound bodies are " hard," and yet " very porous," and " consist of parts which are only laid together," then surely " the simple particles which are void of pores, and were never yet divided, must be much harder. For such hard particles being heaped up together, can scarce touch one another in more than a few points, and therefore must be separable by much less force than is requisite to break a solid particle, whose parts touch in all the space between them, without any pores or interstices to weaken their cohesion. And how such very hard particles which are only laid together and touch only in a few points, can stick together, and that so firmly as they do, without the assistance of something which causes them to be attracted or pressed towards one another, is very difficult to conceive." If this " something " were æther, then the immediate question would be—as Franklin said—to find out what produces the interaction between æther particles, thus getting to an ultra-æther, an ultra-ultra-æther, etc.

behavior and fixed properties, enables us to predict the observable outcome of our manipulations more exactly than we could without such an hypothesis. The hypothesis proposed by Franklin had much in its favor. It is simple; it reduces complex variations of phenomena to an understandable quintessence that enables us to classify and predict them and it leads to testable results, such as the equal production—in a variety of different situations—of positive and negative charges. Furthermore, it does not contravene other established scientific principles, such as Newtonian mechanics, nor does it demand too many ancillary hypotheses.

Despite Franklin's conviction that his hypothesis of a single electric fluid with its postulated properties was adequate to explain practically all the phenomena of electricity, he was ever willing to admit his readiness to surrender it if a better one were to be produced. He stated again and again his preference for the truth rather than the mere " correctness " of his suppositions. Unlike the Abbé Nollet and his disciples, he was always on guard against his vanity. Thus Franklin remained safe from what Priestley called " the only danger in the use of hypotheses." [141]

Priestley had in mind the delicate transition from speculation to supposed fact. Every experiment, he said, " in which there is any design, is made to ascertain some *hypothesis*. For an hypothesis is nothing more than a preconceived idea of an event, as supposed to arise from certain circumstances, which must have been imagined to have produced the same, or a similar effect, upon other occasions. An hypothesis absolutely verified ceases to be termed such, and is considered as a fact. . . ." [142] We may observe such a transition in relation to Franklin's principle of conservation of charge. Originally a deduction from the particular hypothesis of a single fluid, it has been tested for two hundred years in a multiplicity of conditions on the macroscopic and microscopic scale of physical events, without ever a departure from it having been observed. It has, therefore, become independent of any particular hypothesis about the nature of electric charges, and has the status of a " fact " in the description of physical events.

As Priestley pointed out, if an hypothesis is too soon given the status of a fact rather than being considered " a mere probable supposition,"

. . . a philosopher not only acquiesces in it, and thereby mistakes the cause of one particular appearance; but, . . . he mistakes the cause of other appearances too, and is led into a whole system of error. A philosopher who has been long attached to a favourite hypothesis, and especially if he have distinguished himself by his ingenuity in discovering or pursuing it, will not sometimes be convinced of its falsity by the plainest evidence of fact. Thus both himself and all his followers are put upon false pursuits, and seem determined to warp the whole course of nature, to suit their manner of conceiving of its operations.[143]

Just like Newton, Priestley conceived that hypotheses are useful "while they are considered merely as such," because they "lead persons to try a variety of experiments in order to ascertain them." § In the course of making these experiments, "new facts generally arise," and they may "serve to correct the hypothesis which gave occasion to them." [144] This wise counsel of Priestley's reminds us of Franklin's statement that "a bad solution [i. e., explanation] read, and its faults discovered, has often given rise to a good one, in the mind of an ingenious reader." [145] Franklin's experiments were almost all made to test some working hypothesis. For instance, he explained the impermeability of glass to the electric fluid on the hypothesis that the pores in the middle sections of a piece of glass are too fine to admit the passage of electric matter. This led to an experimental test. He "ground away five-sixths of the thickness of the glass from the side of one of my [Leyden] phials, expecting that the supposed denser part being so removed, the electric fluid might come through the remainder of the glass, which I had imagined more open; but I found myself mistaken." [146] The jar charged as well as ever.*

Whenever possible in scientific matters, Franklin made his working hypotheses explicit. Whether the subject was the electrification of clouds, the evaporation of water, the conduction of heat, or the charging and discharging of Leyden jars, Franklin's fertile imagination led him to propose a working hypothesis and an experimental test of its validity. Franklin thus indulged in hypotheses, as he said, but in every case, such hypotheses were either a premise in a philosophical proposition or a mechanism supposed in order to explain laws of phenomena or simple working hypotheses, and in Newtonian fashion, he put them always to the test. Unlike Newton, he had no concern for other varieties of hypotheses—as systems of the world (Copernican or Ptolemaic), premises in mathematical theorems, or general propositions in mathematics that he could not

§ See Newton's statement to Pardies, pages 155-156, above.
* Franklin had first advanced the hypothesis about the pores of glass in 1749.[147] Soon after, he wrote in 1755, "I did, in order to *confirm* the hypothesis, (which indeed I ought to have done before I wrote it) make an experiment." He thus admitted in 1755 that he was "now, as much as ever, at a loss to know how or where the quantity of electric fluid, on the positive side of the glass, is disposed of," and that as to "the pores of glass, I cannot answer otherwise, than that I know nothing of their nature; and suppositions, however ingenious, are often mere mistakes." [148]

prove.† But all hypotheses—those used by Newton as well as those used by Franklin—partake of the character of " working hypotheses " when they are employed as a guide to an experiment or observation. This successful combination of speculation and experiment has characterized the growth of physical science during the last two centuries. Both the speculations or working hypotheses and the design of experimental tests require the exercise of a keen imagination. We may therefore agree with Einstein's strictures against " the faith that facts by themselves can and should yield scientific knowledge without free conceptual construction." [149]

Franklin's theory of electricity may be said to rest on his hypothesis of a single electric fluid, just as Newton's theory of light may be said to rest on his hypothesis of particles of light and their interaction with the æther. But certainly Franklin would never have built a purely hypothetical structure any more than Newton would have. Franklin liked to frame hypotheses because they led to experiments and observations and so helped to increase knowledge. But he approved the sentiment that " too much said on a merely speculative matter is but a robbery committed on practical knowledge." [150]

Typical of Franklin's caution in this regard is the closing sentiment in a letter of 1760, devoted to his explanation that " our North-East storms in North America begin first, in point of time, in the South-West parts." The hypothesis he offered was not meant to be general, but was " only . . . an hypothesis to account for this particular fact; and, perhaps, on farther examination, a better and truer may be found." [151] In 1755 he admitted to Dr. John Lining that in the matter of the way in which clouds " become charged with electricity," he was " still at a loss . . . no hypothesis I have yet formed perfectly satisfying me." [152] Three years earlier, in a letter of 24 Jan. 1752 (read at the Royal Society in 1756), he said he had already grown " more doubtful of my former supposition," and wished he could make further experiments to help solve the problem. " In the mean time, before we part with this hypothesis, let us think what to substitute in its place." [153] On another occasion, he wrote concerning a working hypothesis, ". . . it may not be a true one, and I shall be obliged to him that affords me a better." [154]

I have said in Chapter Three that the major difference between Franklin and Newton as speculative experimental philosophers lay in their personalities. Newton gave to the world highly polished results or imperfect speculations, but he only rarely, if ever, allowed the outsider a glimpse of the route by which his ideas developed:

† See the types of Newtonian hypotheses on pages 138-140, above.

those tentative working hypotheses which are a necessary condition to systematic experiment.‡ Franklin, on the other hand, gave every reader of his book the story of many of the major experiments he made: what he had had in mind at the planning stage, the actual operations he performed and the apparatus employed, and how the working hypothesis had been justified or contradicted. Franklin's readers could easily find the stages of progress of Franklin's knowledge, and could also see the many slips and downright errors which were corrected as time went on.

From the point of view of the speculative Newtonian experimental scientists of the eighteenth century, Franklin's book was the perfect testimony that in the domain of experiment, theory is never as final as it is in mathematics. For as a theory goes through progressive stages, it becomes better and better, comprehending more and more types of phenomena under fewer and fewer untestable assumptions—as Franklin's record of research and thought amply demonstrated. Priestley went a step further when he said that new facts " serve to correct the hypothesis which gave occasion to them," so that a " perfect theory " arises—a " system of propositions, accurately defining all the circumstances of every appearance, the separate effect of each circumstance, and the manner of its operation." [155] Yet even Priestley knew that this was the description of an ideal and not an encountered situation, save perhaps in dynamics. In most realms of physical science we are more likely to encounter what Priestley called a " progressive state, or method of approximation," [156] each discovery leading to an increase in knowledge and " an *increase* of new objects and new difficulties." [157]

As we look back to the science of the last three hundred years from today's vantage point, we may recognize the illusion—once cherished —that there is a terminus to scientific research, a recognizable state of knowledge which indicates what Priestley called a " perfect theory." Newton helped to create this illusion by the supreme qualities of the *Principia*, when he said in the Preface that he wished " we could derive the rest of the phenomena of Nature by the same kind of reasoning from mechanical principles " which had proved to be so successful in the realm of dynamics. Although the *Opticks* was imperfect in this regard, Newton and his disciples had believed that his successors might achieve such perfection by following along the lines he had laid down.§ Perhaps in part because he was no mathematician, Franklin never held out any hopes of a completely

‡ Some clue was available to anyone who collated the several editions of the *Principia* or the *Opticks*, but then as now, such information was not sought.

§ See, for example, Pemberton's statements, quoted on pages 211 ff., above.

worked out subject of electricity. " There are no bounds (but what expence and labour give) to the force man may raise and use in the electrical way," [158] he wrote and, as it has been said so well, he held the human mind in sufficient respect to set no limitations on its ingenuity.

Many a Newtonian believed that Newton's mind was so great that he had left practically no discoveries to be made by his successors, but Priestley said that anyone who thought " nothing had been done to any purpose in natural philosophy . . . since the time of Sir Isaac Newton " [159] had only to read his *History . . . of Electricity*. Franklin was delighted as new phenomena arose because they enlarged the boundaries of human knowledge and implied an evergrowing control of the forces of nature for man's use. He hoped, as all scientists do, that the new facts would always be conformable to his theory, but he was ready for the possibility that they might not. Because the ultimate value of any theory in science is the harmony of its predictions and the observed phenomena, we can understand why Franklin naturally was willing to provide electrical apparatus to Symmer in 1759, even though Symmer's aim was to upset Franklin's one-fluid theory of electricity and to substitute in its place his own two-fluid theory.

To see the kind of insight that characterizes the good experimenter, we may examine Franklin's instructions to Dr. John Walsh in 1772. Walsh studied the torpedo, a kind of sting ray, and proved that its " power of benumbing the touch " is of electrical origin, thus increasing our knowledge of sources of naturally produced electricity. Walsh's publication of his results in the *Philosophical Transactions* for 1773 was addressed to Franklin and was accompanied by an anatomical description of the torpedo by John Hunter.[160] Franklin's instructions to Walsh are printed below from the original manuscript in the Library of the American Philosophical Society. The final paragraph is of particular interest because it shows that even in the realm of animal electricity Franklin sought an instance of conservation in the simultaneous production of positive and negative charges.

Franklin's Instructions to try if the stroke of the Torpedo be Electrical

It has long been supposed that the Stroke given by the Torpedo was the Effect of sudden violent muscular Motion. It is now suspected to be an Effect of the electric or some similar subtil Fluid, which that Fish has a Power of acting upon and agitating at Pleasure.

To discover whether it be the Effect of a subtil Fluid or of muscular Motion, let the Fish be touch'd with the usual Conductors of Electricity, viz. Iron or other Metals; and with the known Non-conductors of Electricity, dry Wood, Glass, Wax, &c.

If the Stroke be communicated thro' the first and not thro' the latter, there is so far a Similarity with the electric Fluid; and at the same time a Proof that the Stroke is not an Effect of mere muscular Motion.

Let it be observed whether the Stroke is some times given on the *near Approach* of a conducting Body without actual Contact; if so, that is another similar Circumstance. Then observe whether in that Case any Snap is heard; and in the Dark whether any Light or Spark is seen between the Fish and the approaching Body. If not, then the Fluids differ.

Let a Number of Persons standing on the Ground, join Hands, and let one touch the Fish so as to receive the Stroke. If all feel it, then let him be laid with his Belly on a Plate of Metal; let one of the Persons so joining Hands touch that Plate, while the farthest from the Plate with a Rod of Metal touches the Back of the Fish; and then observe whether the Force of the Stroke seems to be the same to all in the Circuit as it was before, or stronger.

Repeat the last Experiment with this Variation. Let two of the Persons in the Circuit hold each an uncharg'd electric Phial, the Knobs at the Ends of their Wires touching. After the Stroke, let it be observ'd whether those Wires will attract and repel light Bodies; and whether a Cork Ball suspended by a long silk String so as to hang between the Wires at a small Distance from the Knob of each, will be attracted and repell'd alternately to and from each Knob; if so, the Back & Belly of the Fish are at the Time of the Stroke in *different States* of Electricity.

London, Aug. 12. 1772.　　　　　　　　　　　　　　　B. FRANKLIN

In the eighteenth century, Franklin's kind of science—a combination of insight, imagination, ingenuity, and hard facts of experiment and observation—opened up a limitless world of phenomena; at least, no man could see an end to it. In the nineteenth century new triumphs were added when mathematical theories also proved capable of predicting new phenomena, such as the existence of unknown planets and a new type of radiation. And today, in the middle of the twentieth century, we are still far from a complete science of matter, one in which the unchained experimental imagination does not constantly throw before our eyes new facts which render the current systems untenable without emendation.

The Dangers of Speculative Natural Philosophy

Again and again in the course of this monograph, we have had occasion to make a contrast between mathematics and experimental physical science. In both fields there is the same order of creativity, each requiring a special temperament, a particular sort of genius.

Yet, as Newton himself said, and as his predecessors had known for ages, a theory of nature can never be proved true in the sense of a mathematical theory being shown consistent with itself. It is true in the mathematical sense that Kepler's laws can be derived from the axioms of Newtonian mechanics, but there is no absolute sense in which the Newtonian system is a true statement about the external world.

The scientists of the eighteenth century who were engaged in constructing conceptual schemes for explaining or coordinating the data of experience were just as apt to pervert speculative experimental natural philosophy into a philosophical romance as to advance our understanding of natural phenomena. It would be a mistake to assume that all theories of the eighteenth century, however in harmony they may have been with the general climate of Newtonian atomism, were of merit. The doctrine of corpuscles of gross and subtle matter, subject to forces of mutual attraction and repulsion, had to be applied with great skill by masters if the results were to be useful. We can appreciate the skill of men like Franklin and Lavoisier only by being aware of the abysmal failures of some of their contemporaries. "Every thing has its fashions," said the eighteenth-century naturalist, Réaumur, "nor is philosophy itself an exception to it." What Réaumur had in mind was that "those occult qualities, those sympathies and antipathies which no body would have dared to name in physicks fifty years ago, have, since that time, shewed themselves again with splendor under the name of attraction." Although the doctrine of attraction had served well "with regard to the motions of the celestial bodies," Réaumur did not approve of the "great efforts [which] have been made likewise to make it serve in general to explain all the phenomena in nature." Some people had attempted to use this doctrine "to disentangle all the materials which are to enter into the prolifick liquors," and it had even been "deemed capable of operating the miracle of the formation of the foetus." All that had been thought necessary was "to suppose that the similar parts of one and the same kind had the property of mutually attracting one another, and that there were different laws of attraction for similar parts of different kinds." [161]

The extravagances of the age were apt to take their departure from the Queries of the *Opticks*, the final scholium to Book III of the *Principia*, *De natura Acidorum*, Newton's famous letter to Boyle, and his grand hypothesis published in the mid-eighteenth century in Birch's *History of the Royal Society*. Essays were written on the cause of muscular motion "founded on the Newtonian philosophy of attraction and repulsion," on the æther as the cause of phenomena of heat, electricity, gravitation, magnetism, nervous impulses, and so on. Newton had linked these topics in his discussions of the æther, and it was only natural therefore for men to follow in the steps of the master. Furthermore, there has always been a tendency in natural science to atempt to link together the apparently separate areas of phenomena, either by showing they may be produced from one another or affected by one another, or even that they are members of a single larger class. We may note, in this regard, the nineteenth-century discovery that changing magnetic fields may produce an electric current and that an electric current always gives rise to a magnetic field, and the invention of an electro-magnetic theory of light.

In the eighteenth century it was found that an electric discharge produces heat as well as light, and there was a natural inclination to suppose that the electric fluid was either the Newtonian æther or the matter of heat, even phlogiston. Franklin studied experimentally the relations between electrical phenomena and heat, light, magnetism, and so on. Yet he wisely forebore identifying the causes of these effects. He was willing to speculate in a general way about the æther, as in his " Loose Thoughts on a Universal Fluid," but he never confounded scientific theories with such speculative extravagances, broad hypotheses which were not susceptible of experimental test. In a spirit somewhat reminiscent of Newton, he referred to " my *Queries* upon light," recognizing that he knew very little on that subject.[162]

In 1751 Franklin wrote to Colden that he had magnetized needles by the electric discharge.[163] Yet he never went so far as to identify the cause of electricity and of magnetism. " I am very little acquainted with the nature of magnetism," he wrote to James Bowdoin in 1752.[164] He was pleased to read Æpinus' theory of magnetism based on a single magnetic fluid, he told Professor John Winthrop in 1764, " perhaps . . . the more readily on account of the relation he has given it to mine of electricity." [165] Yet, in 1773, reviewing the whole subject in a letter to Barbeu-Dubourg, who was preparing a new French edition of the book on electricity he said of " the magnetism, which seems produced by electricity, my real opinion is that these two powers of nature have no affinity with each other, and that the apparent production of magnetism is purely accidental." Franklin's views were derived, he said, from the hypothesis of " that excellent philosopher of Petersburg, M. Æpinus," an hypothesis " which appears to me equally ingenious and solid." Franklin admitted the possibility of a subtle magnetic fluid which exists in all ferruginous bodies. He supposed that the fluid might be put into motion so as to become condensed in one part of a body and rarefied in another part, thus producing two poles. Thus the magnetic fluid acted according to a conservation principle. But this fluid " cannot be withdrawn by any force that we are yet made acquainted with, so as to leave the whole in a negative state, at least relatively to its natural quantity; neither can it be introduced so as to put the iron into a positive state, or render it *plus*. In this respect, therefore, magnetism differs from electricity." [166] Following a discussion of the earth's magnetism and the processes by which heat destroys the magnetism of a steel bar, by which hammering a bar allows the earth's magnetism to make a magnet of the bar, and so on, Franklin showed how an electric shock might magnetize a needle. The shock, " passing through a needle . . . and dilating it for an instant," renders the needle a " permanent magnet." The electric shock does not impart magnetism to the needle, but only allows the needle's " own magnetic fluid to put itself into motion." Despite the analogies between such a supposed magnetic fluid and the electric fluid, Franklin was no more willing to consider them the same than he had been in the case of the electric fluid and the matter of heat.

After Barbeu-Dubourg had published Franklin's letter on magnetism (in the 1773 French edition of Franklin's book on electricity), an otherwise friendly and laudatory book review in de Rozier's journal, *Observations sur la Physique*, contained a criticism of Franklin's conservatism with respect to the identity of the electric and magnetic fluid.* In the absence of conclusive evidence to the contrary, Franklin stuck to the position advanced by Æpinus. He would probably have agreed with the conclusions of Sigaud de la Fond in 1776, who, after reviewing the evidence and opinions on this subject, concluded that much additional research was needed before any final opinion could be reached.[168] On the basis of the knowledge of magnetism in Franklin's day, it was far from clear that the theory based on the hypothesis of a magnetic fluid had much merit. There was not yet available either the quantity or variety of experiential data to tell whether this theory could or could not correlate the known facts and predict the outcome of experiments. It would, under such circumstances, have been rash to postulate that this fluid was the same as the electric fluid.

Benjamin Franklin trusted his own science sufficiently to put it to the test of experience; he had been daring enough to suggest an

---

* According to the anonymous author, Franklin had alleged that electricity and magnetism have no relation to each other and that the apparent production of magnetism by electricity is only accidental. " We leave to the physicists the task of examining this idea," he said. " However ingenious it may seem, it does not appear to have been sufficiently demonstrated." [167]

experiment on lightning once he was convinced that the direction of
his research was proving fruitful in terrestrial or laboratory tests.
But to have ventured into the realm of magnetic theory without
considerable research would have been foolhardy. The stern discipline of the controlled scientific imagination is apt to be the mark
of a first-rate scientist. Franklin displays that paradoxical combination of traits that, to an even greater degree, made Newton the
foremost scientist of his age. He had the creative capacity to invent
new concepts, to explore new areas of experience, to find new regularities of nature, and to conceive imaginative schemes on a large
scale that gave a unity and a meaning to otherwise unrelated phenomena. At the same time he had the scientific humility to overcome the pride in his own mental inventions, to accept the modifications of theory required by experiential tests, to discard cherished
concepts and laws that were contravened by experiments and observations, and—above all—to refrain from ever taking too seriously
any speculations that did not at once lead to a confrontation of
conceptual scheme by experience. He was fortunate in having dexterity in his hands to perform the experiments that his mind devised
and in having a nimble and acute enough mind to produce ideas
worthy of experimental exploration.

SOURCES

The major accounts of the growth of physics in the eighteenth century are Rosenberger (1882-1890) and Wolf (1952). Also of value are Cajori (1938), Crew (1935), Gerland (1892), Hall (1954), Heller (1882), Hoppe (1928), Poggendorff (1883), and Ramsauer (1953). For the development of ideas concerning heat, see McKie and Heathcote (1935), Lilley (1948), Ramsay (1918), Roller (1950), and Rosenfeld (1941); Bachelard (1927), while useful, ignores the eighteenth century and should be supplemented by Burr (1933) and Cajori (1922a). Mach (1911 and 1919) are of interest from a general point of view, as are Bridgman (1941) and Poynting and Thomson (1919). For Lavoisier's ideas on heat, see Partington and McKie (1937-1939) and McKie (1936b). For eighteenth-century theories of light, see Hoppe (1926b), Mach (1926), Priestley (1772), Ronchi (1939), and Wilde (1843). Some of Priestley's views on the philosophy of science are presented in Hartog (1941); on this subject I have profited greatly from discussions with Professor Robert E. Schofield and with Professor Duane Roller. My own points of view on the subjects treated in this chapter have been corrected, reinforced, and implemented by suggestions made by Dr. N. H. de V. Heathcote of University College, London, in articles, book reviews, and private correspondence.

REFERENCES

1. See Canton, 1754: 780.
2. "Opinions and Conjectures, . . . 1749," §10, Franklin, 1941: 214; 1769: 56. See also Franklin, 1769: 231.
3. Franklin, 1941: 166; 1769: iv.
4. See Franklin, 1941: intro., pp. 33, 106-109; also Brunet, 1947.
5. Mazéas, 1752, reprinted in Franklin, 1941: 256-257; Franklin, 1769: 106-107.
6. Watson, 1752, reprinted in Franklin, 1941: 264; Franklin, 1769: 110.
7. See Franklin, 1941: intro., p. 81-83, 89-91.
8. See Cohen, 1954b: 44-45, 44n.
9. Desaguliers, 1734-1744: ch. 1.
10. Benjamin Franklin to Jan Ingen-Housz, 29 April 1785, Franklin, 1907: 9: 317.
11. Musschenbroek, 1744: 1: 197.
12. Desaguliers, 1734-1744: ch. 1.
13. Benjamin Franklin to E. Kinnersley, 20 Feb. 1762, Franklin, 1941: 373; 1769: 415.
14. Stallo, 1882: 25.
15. *Opticks*. Qu. 31; Newton, 1952: 400.
16. Mach, 1919: 504.
17. See Brunet, 1947: 122.
18. Needham, 1746: 258.
19. Canton, 1754.
20. See Franklin, 1941: intro., p. 71; 1840: 7: 186-187.
21. Franklin, 1773: translator's comment, 1: 335-338.
22. Beccaria, 1776: 1, 18.
23. Thomson, 1936: 252-253.
24. Benjamin Franklin to John Perkins, 4 Feb. 1753, Franklin, 1907: 3: 121; this paragraph omitted in Franklin, 1769.

25. Maxwell, 1890: **2**: 220.

26. Franklin to Collinson, 4 Feb. 1750/51. Church, 1908: 11.

27. Colden, 1919-1920: **3**: 185; Franklin, 1840: **6**: 74-75.

28. " Physical and meteorological observations, conjectures, and suppositions," Franklin, 1769: 189.

29. Franklin, 1840: **6**: 488-489.

30. See Franklin, 1907: **1**: 82-83.

31. Franklin, 1769: 189.

32. I have been unable to ascertain the name of this critic.

33. Franklin, 1941: appendix II, p. 433.

34. *Ibid.*, 424, 432.

35. See Jorgenson, 1935.

36. Benjamin Franklin to Cadwallader Colden, 23 April 1752, Franklin, 1941: 325; 1769: 264-265.

37. *Idem.*

38. Lloyd, 1834.

39. Newton, 1779-1785.

40. Horsley, 1770.

41. Newton, 1952: 376.

42. See Priestley, 1772: 358.

43. *Ibid.*, 383 ff.

44. Benjamin Franklin to Miss Stevenson, 13 Sept. 1760, Franklin, 1769: 452.

45. *Ibid.*, 453.

46. *Idem.*

47. Benjamin Franklin to Alexander Small, 12 May 1760, Franklin, 1769: 381.

48. Franklin to C. Colden, 23 Apr. 1752, Franklin, 1941: 326; 1769: 265.

49. Franklin to E. Kinnersley, 20 Feb. 1762, Franklin, 1941: 367; 1769: 406.

50. Franklin to C. Colden, 23 Apr. 1752, Franklin, 1941: 326; 1769: 265.

51. *Idem.*

52. Schuster, 1894-1895.

53. Letter II, Franklin to P. Collinson, 25 May [11 July], 1747, Franklin, 1941: 173; 1769: 5-6.

54. Horsley, 1770.

55. Priestley, 1772: 807.

56. 'sGravesande, 1747: **2**: 72.

57. *Idem.*

58. *Idem.*

59. *Ibid.*, 76-77.

60. *Ibid.*, 63.

61. *Idem.*

62. *Idem.*

63. *Idem.*

64. " Observations and Suppositions . . . for explaining . . . thunder-gusts," to John Mitchel, 29 Apr. 1749, Franklin, 1941: 202; 1769: 40.

65. Observations and Suppositions, Franklin, 1941: 210; 1769: 50.

66. *Idem.*

67. Franklin, 1941: 211n; Franklin, 1769: 52n.

68. Franklin to E. Kinnersley, 20 Feb. 1762, Franklin, 1941: 370-371; 1769: 411-412.

69. E. Kinnersley to Franklin, 12 March 1761, Franklin, 1941: 355; 1769: 392.

70. Franklin to E. Kinnersley, 20 Feb. 1762, Franklin, 1941: 370-372; 1769: 411-413.

71. *Idem.*

72. *Idem.*

73. *Idem.*

74. *Idem.*

75. *Idem.*

76. Same letter, Franklin, 1941: 362-363; 1769: 401-404.

77. Letter XXXIV, Franklin, 1769: 375.

78. *Ibid.*, 259.
79. *Ibid.*, 260.
80. *Idem*; see Franklin to John Lining, 14 Apr. 1757, Franklin, 1941: 340; 1769: 343.
81. Franklin to P. Collinson, Sept. 1753, Franklin, 1941: 277-288; 1769: 124-125.
82. *Idem.*
83. Franklin to J. Lining, 18 Mar. 1755, Franklin, 1941: 333; 1769: 322.
84. E. Kinnersley to Franklin, 12 Mar. 1761, Franklin, 1941: 351-356; 1769: 389-393.
85. Franklin to J. Lining, 14 Apr. 1757, Franklin, 1941: 340-341; 1769: 343-345.
86. *Idem.*
87. *Idem.*
88. *Idem.*
89. *Idem.*
90. Franklin, 1840: **6**: 439-440.
91. *Ingen-Housz*, 1789, also in Ingen-Housz, 1785.
92. Poynting and Thomson, 1919: 94.
93. Rumford, 1798.
94. Franklin, 1769: 251.
95. Franklin, 1769: 449.
96. *Idem.*
97. Franklin to J. Lining, 14 Apr. 1757, Franklin, 1941: 342-343; 1769: 346-347.
98. *Idem.*
99. Same letter, Franklin, 1941: 344; 1769: 348.
100. *Idem.*
101. Franklin to E. Kinnersley, 20 Feb. 1762, Franklin, 1941: 372; 1769: 413.
102. Franklin, 1941: 247; 1769: 96.
103. Burr, 1933: 249.
104. McKie and Heathcote, 1935.
105. Lavoisier, 1862: **2**: 212.
106. *Ibid.*, 228; see Partington and McKie, 1937-1939: pt. III.
107. Franklin to C. Colden, 23 Apr. 1752, Franklin, 1941: 326; 1769: 266.
108. *Idem.*
109. Franklin, 1769: 251.
110. Franklin 1941: 211; 1769: 51-52.
111. Newton 1952: 376.
112. Black, 1803: 1: p. vii.
113. *Ibid.*, 547.
114. *Ibid.*, 33.
115. *Idem.*
116. *Ibid.*, 34.
117. *Idem.*
118. *Ibid.*, 24.
119. *Idem.*
120. *Ibid.*, 24-25.
121. Franklin, 1907: **9**: 227.
122. Newton, 1729*b*: **2**: 202.
123. E. g., Opinions and Conjectures . . . 1749, Franklin, 1941: 213; 1769: 54; also Franklin, 1769: 258.
124. Franklin, 1907: **9**: 229.
125. Bowdoin, 1783: 201.
126. Priestley, 1775: **1**: pref., p. xv.
127. *Idem.*
128. Priestley, 1775: **2**: 39.
129. *Idem.*
130. *Ibid.*, 16.
131. *Ibid.*, 12.
132. Hartog, 1941: § ix.
133. *Ibid.*, § x.

134. Franklin, 1769: 258.
135. Hoadly and Wilson, 1756: 1.
136. Franklin, 1769: 258.
137. Black, 1803: 1: 266-267.
138. Franklin, 1769: 258.
139. *Ibid.*, 42, 182.
140. Priestley, 1775: 2: 12.
141. *Ibid.*, 15.
142. *Ibid.*, 14.
143. *Ibid.*, 15.
144. *Idem.*
145. Opinions and Conjectures . . . 1749, Franklin, 1941: 219; 1769: 62.
146. Franklin to J. Lining, 18 Mar. 1755, Franklin, 1941: 333; 1769: 321.
147. Opinions and Conjectures . . . 1749, Franklin, 1941: 234; 1769: 82.
148. Franklin, 1941: 333; 1769: 321.
149. Autobiography, Schilpp, 1949.
150. Franklin, 1769: 210.
151. Franklin to A. Small, 12 May 1760, Franklin, 1769: 383.
152. Franklin, 1941: 334; 1769: 323.
153. Franklin to J. Bowdoin, Franklin, 1941: 318; 1769: 176.
154. Opinions and Conjectures . . . 1749, Franklin, 1941: 233; 1769: 81.
155. Priestley, 1775: 2: 15-16.
156. *Ibid.*, 16.
157. Priestley, 1781: pref., p. viii.
158. Franklin to C. Colden, 1751, Franklin, 1941: 246; 1769: 94.
159. Priestley, 1775: 2: 53.
160. Walsh, 1773; Hunter, 1773.
161. Reaumur, 1750: 462-463.
162. Franklin to J. Bowdoin, 1 Jan. 1786, Franklin, 1907: 9: 479.
163. Franklin, 1941: 245; 1769: 93.
164. Franklin, 1941: 316; 1769: 173.
165. Franklin, 1907: 4: 250.
166. Franklin, 1773: 1: 227; trans. in Franklin, 1907: 6: 23.
167. [Anon.] (1773).
168. Sigaud de la Fond, 1781: 586; ed. princ. 1776.

PART FOUR

Franklin:
The Rise of Electricity as a
Newtonian Science

CHAPTER NINE

ELECTRICITY—THE NEW NATURAL PHILOSOPHY OF THE EIGHTEENTH CENTURY

> Voilà les principes, ou, si l'on veut, les faits simples &
> primitifs auxquels se peuvent réduire toutes les expériences
> sur l'électricité, qui sont connuës; le nombre de ces principes
> diminuera vraisemblablement à mesure que l'on parviendra
> à une connoissance plus exacte de cette merveilleuse propriété
> de la matière, qui jusqu' à présent n'étoit indiquée que par
> quelques expériences très-compliquées qui l'avoient fait juger
> particulière à certaines matières, & dépendante de circon-
> stances bisarres, & dans lesquelles il ne se trouvoit presque rien
> d'assûré ni de positif.
>
> —CHARLES FRANÇOIS DE CISTERNAY DU FAY (1734)

ALTHOUGH the textbooks of Newtonian physics in the 1730's
contained only passing references to electrical phenomena, the
treatises written at the century's end without exception contained
whole sections devoted to this subject. Thomas Young's popular
Course of Lectures on Natural Philosophy (1807), for example, had
two chapters or " lectures " dealing with electricity (" On electricity
in equilibrium " and " On electricity in motion ") ; the Abbé René-
Just Haüy's *Elementary Treatise on Natural Philosophy* (1804;
English translation, 1807) had seven major sections, of which one
was devoted entirely to electricity.* As an exact subject and a fully
recognized branch of natural philosophy, electricity may be said to
have come of age in the middle decades of the eighteenth century.

An examination of the learned journals during the fourth, fifth,
and sixth decades of the century quickly shows the extensive interest
in this subject at that time. The Royal Society published in its
Philosophical Transactions the latest news about electrical research
on the Continent and in America, as well as at home, while the
Journal des Sçavans and the annual volumes of the Académie Royale
des Sciences (Paris) regularly contained reports on novelties in this
field from Germany, Italy, Britain, America, Holland, Scandinavia,
and Russia. Articles on electrical subjects from the *Philosophical*

---

* The others were: I: " The most general properties of bodies "; II: " Properties
relative to certain forces that solicit or impel bodies " (mobility, hardness, elasticity
and ductility, gravity, crystallisation, heat) ; III: " Water " (including change of state
and steam engines) ; IV: " Air " (including sound) ; VI: " Magnetism "; VII: " Light."

Transactions in the 1740's were often reprinted as pamphlets, and English pamphlets on electricity were apt to be speedily translated into French along with German pamphlets. This great intellectual turmoil caught up with Benjamin Franklin in the mid-1740's and swept him along with countless others all over the world who were trying to comprehend the mysterious powers of electrical attraction and repulsion. The times were ripe for a man of superior insight and experimental imagination to create sound principles that would transform the congeries of miscellaneous unrelated facts into a science. If ever there was the right time for a man of Franklin's talents, it was this period in the late 1740's when many basic facts were known, when all was in readiness for their correlation by ideas that were " in the air " and all but grasped.

As we examine the thinking with respect to electricity on the eve of Franklin's research, we shall find that many writers were at the point of recognition of the conservative property of electrification and the significance of the two types of electrification: " resinous " and " vitreous." That these men failed to see the " obvious " next step should not be considered a disparagement of their abilities so much as a measure of the degree to which the concepts of Franklin were not so obvious after all—either in their complete formulation or their implications. " The seeds of great discoveries are constantly floating around us," Joseph Henry once said, " but they only take root in minds well prepared to receive them." Franklin's preparation of mind, in this sense, may be only the defining quality of his scientific genius, but we must not forget that like all great men of science he owed an incalculable debt to his heroic contemporaries and immediate predecessors. It is, in fact, their very greatness that provides the full measure of his achievement.

The Franklinian Electric Fluid

Franklin's theory of electrical action depends on the supposition that there is in nature an " electric fluid,''' composed of particles that mutually repel one another while being attracted by the particles of " common matter ": in eighteenth-century terms, an " elastic " fluid. This electric fluid was postulated as " subtle," in that it can penetrate the empty spaces between the particles of matter in bodies, and it is weightless. The program of Franklin's research was to explain all observed electrical phenomena in terms of a fundamental conservation principle: the law of conservation of charge. In this chapter, we shall see the antecedents of Franklin's concept of the electric fluid and his theory of electrical action by examining the growth of knowledge of electrical phenomena during the years prior to his research.

In earlier chapters, we saw that the attribution of " elasticity " to mutually repellent particles had been developed by such men as Desaguliers and Hales out of the suggestions made by Newton in the *Opticks* and in one place in the *Principia*. Thus there arose the notion that gases, " air," or " elastic fluids " have the property of elasticity because of a repulsive force between their particles, and that this " elasticity " could be increased by heat. Hales had made the additional suggestion that air is a mixture of elastic and inelastic particles, and that the two might combine with a resultant non-elasticity. In some sense, then, here was a model of Franklin's theory, since Franklin supposed the existence of inelastic particles (of common matter) and elastic particles (of electric fluid) which attracted one another to produce neutral (uncharged or non-electrified) bodies which did not have elastic (mutually repellent) properties. It is to be observed, however, that Franklin's concept of the electric fluid differed in one essential respect from the elastic fluids (gases) discussed by Desaguliers and Hales: the electric fluid was postulated as subtle and weightless. We may observe, therefore, a resemblance in this regard to the concept of a material substance of " fire " presented by Boerhaave, which was apparently subtle and probably weightless,† and which had the property of spreading out in all directions, forming an " atmosphere " around bodies under the proper circumstances: a concept often employed by Franklin in a doctrine of " electric atmospheres."

Despite the resemblance between Boerhaave's ideas on heat and the later ideas about the electric fluid, there are important differences between them. The electric fluid and Boerhaave's matter of heat are both particulate or granular in structure. Both are extremely subtle, able to penetrate the pores between the solid particles of bodies, and capable of spreading out to large distances in all directions. But whereas, in Franklin's conception, the particles that compose the electric fluid are mutually repellent, this property was not specifically attributed by Boerhaave to the particles of heat. Boerhaave suggested, though by no means asserted, that perhaps— like Newton's particles of light—the particles of heat may have variations among them. Franklin supposed that the electric fluid has but one kind of particle. And, although Boerhaave was not overly concerned with the difference between those bodies that easily conduct heat and those that do not, this consideration became important in

† Many experiments were made in the eighteenth century to test the " ponderability " of heat.

discussions of electricity. The difference between the two states of electrification—resinous and vitreous—did not suggest an obvious correlation with coldness and hotness as being due to an excess or deficiency of the matter of fire. The reason is that in problems of heat, unlike electricity, there is apparently nothing such as a " normal " (unelectrified) state. Hence grounding seemed to the eighteenth-century scientist to have no obvious role in heat as it does in electricity.‡ Even so, speculations on the nature of the matter of electricity were influenced by prior speculations on the matter of heat, and both were to some degree conditioned by Newton's views on the " matter " of light.

From Newton's speculations, or hypotheses, of a universal æther, Franklin learned of a subtle, weightless, elastic fluid that was particulate. But Franklin's concept of the electric fluid differed from Newton's æther. The æther was supposed to fill all of space, whereas the electric fluid was confined to bodies or surrounded bodies in an electric atmosphere. Furthermore, the æther produces gravitational attraction in bodies by a difference in " density," whereas the electric fluid produces attraction and repulsion according to a wholly independent set of principles—at least in Franklin's theory.§

Even though the particular concept of electric fluid Franklin advanced was attuned to the general Newtonian framework of scientific thought, there were novel aspects of Franklin's concepts (such as conservation) that mark his creation as original. Since—like all creations in science—Franklin's concepts depended on the ideas of his predecessors, I shall, in describing the growth of electrical science prior to Franklin, lay special emphasis on the development of those ideas which can be considered in any sense as related to Franklin's concept of the electric fluid.

Gray's Concept of " Electric Virtue "

A convenient starting point for any discussion of electrical theory is the discovery of conduction by Stephen Gray, in about 1730. Stephen Gray was born in 1666 (or 1667), spent most of his life in Canterbury, lived for a while with Desaguliers in London, and be-

‡ This is true from the point of view of the eighteenth century. From a more recent standpoint, we may say that bringing two conductors in contact will cause them both to have the same potential and that contact with the earth produces zero or ground potential reckoned with respect to the earth, which actually has a net negative charge. Hence we see a similarity between heat and electricity: two conducting bodies in contact will arrive at the same electrical potential or the same temperature. There is an analogy between high and low temperature and positive and negative potential, and also between room temperature and ground or zero potential.

§ See the end of this chapter, and the beginning of Chapter Twelve, for a comparison between Franklin's theory and the theories based on variations in " density."

came, a " poor brother " of the Charterhouse, where he made many of his electrical experiments. He was elected a Fellow of the Royal Society in 1732 and died in 1736. For a brief period he was assistant to Roger Cotes (editor of the third edition of the *Principia* under Newton's supervision) at the new astronomical observatory in Trinity College, Cambridge. Gray's earliest publications in the *Philosophical Transactions* dealt with the " water microscope " and astronomy.[1] The only field, however, to which Gray made a contribution of any magnitude is electricity. The modern reader of Gray's work cannot help but wonder why Gray's experiments did not " naturally " lead at once to a dichotomy of all bodies into conductors and non-conductors. Yet the general usage that grew up tended, instead, to use a distinction between " electrics *per se* " (i. e., those substances which, like amber [or " elektron "], can be charged when held in the hand and rubbed) and " non-electrics " (i. e., those substances which do not become charged when held and rubbed, notably the metals).

Prior to Gray's experiments (performed often in concert with Granville Wheler), not very much attention had been given to the transmission of " electrick vertue " through bodies, although observations had been made from time to time of such phenomena as the electrification of threads. Gray's experiments showed that the electric attractive virtue or " effluvia " may pass from one body to another; from today's point of view we would note that many of the effects described by Gray were produced by electrostatic induction. In some of Gray's experiments, there was a physical contact between the charged body and a conductor (or set of linked conductors). In others, the charged body was merely brought near one end of a long conductor without any contact wherever, and the far end exhibited the familiar attraction of electricity. Such experiments indicated that it was not necessary to suppose that electric effluvia must always return to the parent body.

Gray was an ingenious and skilled experimenter, but we have no evidence that he created a consistent theory to account for his own discoveries, or those facts of electrical action known in his day. He related that in 1729 he had communicated to J. T. Desaguliers and others his discovery " that the electrick vertue of a [rubbed, or charged, or electrified] glass tube may be conveyed to any other bodies, so as to give them the same property of attracting and repelling light bodies, as the tube does, when excited by rubbing. . . ."[2] In the same communication, he referred to " several bodies " that " had an electricity communicated to them " and also to bodies that had " an electrick vertue communicated to them." We may observe here the obscurity of concept that underlies the many expressions for electrification. Gray's important discovery, that some substances are conductors of electricity while others are not, was never stated by him as a universal law, nor did he use the terms " conductor " and " non-conductor." He had been using packthread to transmit the " electrick vertue " and had supported the pack-thread " line, by which the electrick vertue was to pass," by silk threads; he had not at first appreciated the insulating action of the silk but had imagined that the " effluvia " would not move along a silk line in the same easy manner as along the packthread, " upon the account of . . . [the] smallness " of the silk lines. But when, following the logical implications of his supposition, he substituted fine brass wires for the silk supporting threads, the experiment failed; the packthread no longer would transmit the " electrick vertue." Success, as Gray noted, " depended upon the lines that supported the [packthread] line of communication being silk, and not upon their being small, as before trial I imagined it might be; the same effect happening here as it did when the line that is to convey the electrick vertue is supported by packthread; *viz.* that when the efflu-via come to the wire or packthread that supports the line, it passes by them to the timber, to which each end of them is fixed. . . ." [3] The same type of " explanation," or rough description was used by Gray in his discussion of what we would call " induced charges." He had suspended a lead weight from the ceiling by an iron ring at the end of a " hair-line, such as linnen-cloaths are dried on." When he brought an electrified glass tube near the hair line, but not in contact with it, the lead weight attracted some " leaf brass," showing that " electrick vertue may be carried from the tube, without touch-ing the line of communication, by only being held near it." [4]

While Gray introduced new experimental data that had impor-tant theoretical consequences, his theory was limited to the crude notion of electrification being due to the transmitted " electrick vertue " or " electricity " that was related in an unspecified way to a motion of " effluvia." Gray was a simple empiricist who reported his findings without overmuch concern for their theoretical implica-tions. He expressed himself in the language of his day without any effort to specify the sense of the terms he employed even so far as they were related to his own discoveries.* Nor did Gray's successor, Charles Du Fay, go much further with regard to a theory of electrical action as such.

---

* Shortly before his death, Gray had come to believe that perhaps the motion of the planets might be caused by an electric force, and hoped to illustrate this notion by constructing an apparatus in which a sphere could be made to move around an electrified body in the laboratory, thus simulating the motion of the planets around the sun.

Du Fay's Discovery of the Two " Electricities "

Charles François de Cisternay Du Fay, born in 1698, began his research in electricity at the age of thirty-five, and died six years later in 1739. Educated as a soldier, he became a lieutenant at fourteen and tried diplomacy before devoting himself to science. He appears to have been interested in many aspects of science and could claim to be an astronomer, anatomist, botanist, chemist, geometer, physicist, and antiquary. His biographer, Fontenelle, said that Du Fay was the only man of his time to submit contributions to the Académie Royale des Sciences in every one of the then recognized areas: anatomy, astronomy, botany, chemistry, geometry, mechanics, and general physics; he had originally been elected to the Académie as a chemist, and after 1732 was a professional botanist, superintendent (*intendant*) of the royal Jardin des Plantes.[5] Known for his studies of phosphorescence, Du Fay was also a pioneer in the study of crystals. His last scientific paper, not quite finished at the time of his death, dealt with birefringent crystals: rock crystal and iceland spar (calcite). After criticizing Bartholinus (discoverer of double refraction), Newton, and Huygens for inexact measurements, he presented his own careful work, culminating in the great discovery " that all transparent stones which have right angles are but singly refracting, whereas those whose angles are not right angles are doubly refracting and that the measure of their double refraction depends on the inclination of their angles." [6] These principles † have been described recently by Adolf Pabst as " the first steps toward a correlation of crystal form and optical properties "; they may be fairly said to mark the first major achievements in scientific crystallography.

Du Fay began his electrical research by repeating and verifying Gray's experiments on conduction.[8] He found that the " electrick virtue was . . . communicated " better if the packthread was wet, and that glass tubes might serve as insulating supports for the conductor, in place of the silk lines.[9] (Gray himself had indicated that a person might be charged while standing on a resin cake.) The totally inadequate state of electrical theory at that time is made clear in Du Fay's description of one of his discoveries as " a very simple principle, which accounts for a great part of the irregularities, and if I may use the term, of the caprices that seem to accompany most of the experiments on electricity." [10] The new principle may be stated as follows: ". . . Electrick bodies [i. e., those that are charged, or have the attractive power or " virtue "] attract all those

---

† In modern terms, we may say that Du Fay discovered " the optically isotropic character of isometric crystals, the anisotropic character of all other crystals, and the fact that the amount of birefringence is, in general, different for each species." [7]

that are not so, and repel them as soon as they are become electrick, by the vicinity or contact of the electrick body." Thus a piece of gold leaf is attracted by the electrified tube, " acquires an electricity by approaching it," and is then repelled. It is not re-attracted as long as " it retains its electrick quality," but if it comes into contact with another body it " loses its electricity " and may then be re-attracted by the tube; and so on.[11] All of this had been well known to Gray, but not stated by him in such specific terms.

The " principle " just described, however, was less important, Du Fay noted, than " another principle, more universal and remarkable," which " chance has thrown in my way " and " which casts a new light on the subject of electricity." According to Du Fay, " This principle is that there are two distinct electricities, very different from one another; one of which I call *vitreous electricity*, and the other *resinous electricity*." To tell whether a given electrified body has one or the other, Du Fay recommended the use of an electrified silk thread, which " is known to be of the *resinous electricity*." If the silk thread is attracted by an electrified body, then that body must have the " *vitreous electricity*," but, if repelled, then that body must have the " *resinous electricity*." [12] Bodies with the same electrification always repel each other, while bodies with different electrifications attract each other.

It should be noted that the two " electricities " postulated by Du Fay appear to be two modes of electrification, and there is certainly no indication of a belief in two kinds of electrical matter as such. Furthermore, Du Fay held that the two electricities or the two modes of electrification are related directly to the kind of body that had been rubbed and in a manner wholly independent of the substance used in rubbing, i. e., the " rubber." The effect of the latter, he said, was only to control the degree of electrification, but not the type, i. e., vitreous (like that of glass) or resinous (like that of amber).

Almost any discussion of two types of electrification or charge is apt to appear to be an endorsement of the theory that there are two kinds of " electricity, " two varieties of electric matter, or two electric fluids. A little more than a century after Du Fay's discovery, Lord Kelvin (then Sir William Thomson) was careful to declare that he " could not conclude without guarding himself against any imputation of having assumed the existence of two electric fluids or substances, because he had frequently spoken of the vitreous and resinous electricities." He noted, too, that " Du Fay's very important discovery of two modes or qualities of electrification, led his followers too readily to admit his supposition of two distinct electric fluids." And he added the sagacious observation that " Franklin, Æpinus, and Cavendish, with an hypothesis of one electric fluid, opened the way for a juster appreciation of the *unity* of nature in electric phenomena." [13] This judicious opinion accords with the documentary evidence. But in the closing years of the eighteenth century and opening years of the nineteenth, at the height of the active controversy over whether there were two electric fluids or one, it seemed to many scientists that " the original opinion of Du Fay " was " the existence of two distinct fluids, a vitreous and a resinous electricity." These quoted phrases, typical of the period, come from Thomas Young,[14] who was usually careful in historical matters. In the revised edition of Young's book (1845), the editor referred the reader to Du Fay's summary of his work in the *Philosophical Transactions* (for 1733) and his " Quatrième mémoire " in the annual volumes of the Académie Royale des Sciences (1733). But in both of these cited works Du Fay spoke only of a " resinous electricity " and a " vitreous electricity " in the sense of two distinct and contrary forces or modes of electrification.

One set of experiments performed by both Gray and Du Fay is of great interest in showing the attempt to correlate electrical and optical phenomena. Gray had observed a difference between the electrical attractive properties of differently colored materials. Red, orange, and yellow objects seemed to be more effective attractors than green, blue, or purple ones.[15] This type of investigation was natural enough in a day when experimental scientists were still a little over-awed by Newton's investigations of color. We have already seen Boerhaave's suggestion as to the effect of color on the absorption of solar heat. Gray's experiments may be considered as a kind of electrical variation of the experiments being performed at about the same time by Franklin and Breintnal. Du Fay showed himself a master of experimental philosophy by adapting to this experiment Newton's own device for producing spectral colors: the prism. In this way he showed that Gray's observed differences in electrical properties had been the result only of the several substances used in dyeing the cloth. He had only to moisten pieces of cloth dyed in different colors to render them all equally good conductors.‡

‡ Du Fay's experiments on color in relation to electricity indicate his sure experimental hand. "I . . . cut out nine square pieces of gause, of the same colours with the ribbons, and having put them one after another on a hoop of wood with leaf-gold under them, the leaf-gold was attracted thro' all the coloured pieces of gause, but not thro' the white or black. This inclined me at first to think that the colours contributed much to electricity. But three experiments convinced me of the contrary: The first, that by warming the pieces of gause, neither the black nor white pieces

In his first memoir on electricity, Du Fay defined "electricity" as a "property common to several substances"; it consists of an "attraction of light bodies of all kinds placed at a certain distance from the electric body," after it has been suitably rubbed.[17] In his third memoir, containing the experiments on color in relation to electrification, he wrote of conduction as the "passage of the action of an electric body,"[18] and also of "electric matter" (*matière électrique*) passing from one place to another.[19] On a single page he used these terms: *la vertu électrique, la matière électrique, l'électricité, les écoulements électriques*—all of which were stopped or conducted by different materials.[20] He explained that by *vertu électrique* he meant "not only the virtue which electric bodies have to attract, but also that of repelling bodies which they have attracted."[21] In discussing repulsion, he added yet another expression —*le tourbillon électrique*. Such *tourbillons* could be of various dimensions. Because the *tourbillon* surrounding an "electric" (electrified) body could be communicated to a second body which it had attracted until the two were in contact, the subsequent repulsion could be explained by the interaction of the two *tourbillons*.[22] Apparently Du Fay used the term *la matière électrique* much as Gray had used "electric effluvia," and the *tourbillons* were intended to convey the sense of some kind of envelope or atmosphere surrounding repelling charged bodies. Du Fay did not discuss the nature or physical properties of either the *matière électrique* or the *tourbillons*, and the latter have inescapable Cartesian overtones.§

obstructed the action of the electrical tube more than those of the other colours. In like manner, the ribbons being warmed, the black and white are not more strongly attracted than the rest. The second is, the gauses and ribbons being wetted, the ribbons are all attracted equally, and all the pieces of gause equally intercept the action of electrick bodies. The third is, that the colours of a prism being thrown on a piece of white gause, there appear no differences of attraction. Whence it follows that this difference proceeds not from the colour, as a colour, but from the substances that are employed in the dying. For when I coloured ribbons, by rubbing them with charcoal, carmine, and such other substances, the differences no longer proved the same."[16]

§ Du Fay's "fourth memoir" is devoted in large part to explanations of electrical attraction and repulsion in terms of vortices. He believed that around an electrified body there is formed a vortex of exceedingly fine matter in a state of agitation, which urges towards the body such light substances as lie within its sphere of activity. The existence of this vortex Du Fay held to be more than a mere conjecture, on the basis of his observation that an electrified body brought close to the face causes a sensation like that of encountering a cobweb. This phenomenon was well known at this time, having been often observed since at least the writings of Hauksbee, but the inference that it gave evidence of a "vortex" rather than a mere motion of "effluvia" indicates the degree of Cartesianism then prevalent in French scientific circles. There is no point in making a close study of the mechanisms invented by Du Fay for the production of vortices and the interaction between vortices, since these mechanisms are of interest chiefly for the history of eighteenth-century Cartesian thought rather than the growth of electrical concepts.

The "vitreous" and "resinous" electricities of Du Fay were said by their discoverer to be "two different natures of electricity [electrification]," or "two electricities [kinds of electrification] of a totally different nature." [23] When he announced their names, Du Fay insisted that "vitreous electricity" and "resinous electricity" derived only from the fact that glass and resin (copal) were the two substances in which he had discovered "the two different electricities." He did not for a moment believe that bodies "of the nature of glass" were endowed with one and "resinous substances" with the other; as a matter of fact he claimed to have "strong proofs to the contrary." [24] Thus it is plain that Du Fay did not suggest two kinds of electric matter or a two-fluid theory of electricity.

In his "sixth memoir" on electricity, Du Fay made a convenient summary of his discoveries and the principles he had announced in his previous publications. Here he restated the laws of the two "electricities" or modes of electrification, such as the attraction between a neutral body and a body with either vitreous or resinous "electricity," and the repulsion between two bodies having the same "electricity"—whether vitreous or resinous. One of the statements in this summary indicated that "electric bodies placed in a vacuum will exert their force [action] there, but the matter of electricity moves out sooner in vacuo than in air. . . ." This phrase again implies that perhaps the *matière électrique* corresponds to the electric effluvia of Gray, Hauksbee, and Boyle.* Commenting on the light produced by electrified bodies in vacuo (actually the triboluminescence in air at low pressure), he suggested that "the matter of this kind of light is NOT the same as that of electricity, one of these two properties [*propriétés*] being able to subsist independently of the other." [27]

In his penultimate memoir, Du Fay allowed himself to speculate a little on the cause of the electrical phenomena he had been describing. With true modesty, he called attention to the fact that he had not attempted a full explanation because he was still far from

* Du Fay gave credit for these observations to Boyle, Hauksbee, and Gray. Throughout his memoirs, Du Fay wrote in the most praiseworthy terms of these three British investigators, often giving extensive summaries or quotations so that French readers would know of their achievements. Although Du Fay encountered the necessity of correcting Gray from time to time, there was never any acrimony between them. In Du Fay's memoirs we find a continuous laudation of Gray. Du Fay was also an admirer of Stephen Hales, as were Beccaria, Franklin, and other electricians of the eighteenth century; in his "sixth memoir," he spoke of "le livre de M. Halès sur l'Analyse de l'Air." [25] Du Fay also seems to have been the first writer on electricity in the eighteenth century to have noticed the work of Guericke and he wrote as if he had been the rediscoverer of Guericke, whose discoveries relating to electricity had apparently been ignored during the intervening years.[26]

finding one. Yet he hoped that he had at least " given an idea of the way in which things could happen," which " did not badly agree with " the experiments he had reported. His idea was that there is a special atmosphere (*une atmosphère particulière*) that surrounds metals as well as animate bodies. " This atmosphere retains, so to speak, the electric matter diffused around these bodies by the approach of the [rubbed glass] tube." When the experimenter " brings into this atmosphere another metal or another animate body, the electric matter with effort, violence and noise, leaves this first atmosphere which retained it in order to pass into that which is presented to it." The " passing from one atmosphere to another, manifests itself by the appearance of that piercing spark which we see and which we feel." [28] In such statements, we may see Du Fay in a rare moment of speculation. He believed in emanations of electric matter, restrained by surrounding atmospheres—but of what substance the atmospheres are composed he did not say. Electric vortices or *tourbillons* were also suggested, but not much was said about them. He found that it was easy to draw a spark from vitreously electrified bodies and difficult to draw a spark from resinously electrified bodies, a kind of observation which later gave Franklin his clue that the vitreous electrification corresponded to a positive charge and the resinous electrification to a negative charge, but Du Fay merely reported " cette petite irrégularité " and admitted his difficulty to " rendre raison de ce fait." [29] Electricity, he said, is " perhaps a quality of matter in general dependent on invariable principles, subject to exact laws, and which may influence the economy of the globe far more than we think." The modern reader is struck chiefly by the word " perhaps " and by the accompanying statement that Du Fay hoped physicists would not neglect so fertile a field of enquiry, " a new world, so to speak, in which there very likely remain so many interesting discoveries to be made." [30]

Desaguliers's Views on " Effluvia " and on Electric Forces among Particles of Elastic Fluids

The low state of electrical theory at the time of Du Fay is indicated in the latter's statement about the irregularities or caprices that occur in making electrical experiments. A similar sentiment introduced J. T. Desaguliers's first paper † on electricity: " The

---

† In Number 454 of the *Philosophical Transactions* (" For the months of July, August, September, and October, 1739 ") Desaguliers published a paper on the cause of elasticity and four separate papers on electricity. This sudden outburst of publication was occasioned by the recent death of Stephen Gray. Desaguliers said that he had not hitherto presented anything to the Royal Society on electricity even though " I can excite as strong an electricity in glass, by rubbing it with my hand, as any

phænomena of electricity are so odd, that though we have a great many experiments upon that subject; we have not yet been able from their comparison to settle such a theory as to lead us to the cause of that property of bodies, or even to judge of all its effects, or find out what useful influence electricity has in nature: Though certainly, from what we have seen of it, we may conjecture that it must be of great use, because it is so extensive." [31] Desaguliers set forth a number of propositions (in the form of queries,‡ with experiments to support them) such as: (1) that all bodies are capable of receiving the electricity which has been given to a tube by friction, although some cannot be electrified by " heat, or friction, or any other operation on the bodies themselves "; (2) that to communicate electrification to a body hanging by a string, the string should be " of such bodies as are capable of having electricity excited in them by friction, heating, beating, or patting, or some immediate operation on the bodies themselves." Desaguliers, in successive paragraphs, wrote of bodies " receiving the electricity which has been given to a tube by friction "; the " electrical virtue " which is " excited " in bodies and which some bodies will pass along to others but which yet other bodies stop from " passing any further "; the " electrical stream " with which bodies may be saturated; and also " the *effluvia*, or *virtue*," and the " electrical virtue," and " effluvia." Such confusion, or multiplicity of expression indicates the then-existing want of a clear concept of electrical action. Every one of these expressions invokes the primary quality of a material effluvium, but with somewhat different overtones.

After describing experiments in transmitting " electricity " along suspended threads, Desaguliers introduced a new terminology: he would call " *conductors* those strings, to one end of which the rubbed tube is applied; and *supporters* such horizontal bodies as the *conductor* rests upon." [32] These terms were applied only to the functions of the two during the experiments at hand; Desaguliers was not yet willing to make a universal dichotomy of substances into conductors and non-conductors. He preferred the distinction of " electrical *per se* " (a body in which " electricity " may be " excited " by rubbing, patting, hammering, melting, warming, or any other action on the body itself) and " *non-electrical* " (a body that cannot be " made electrical " by " any action upon the body itself immediately,"

body can," because he had been " unwilling to interfere with the late Mr. Stephen Gray, who had wholly turned his thoughts that way; but was of a temper to give it intirely over, if he imagined that any thing was done in opposition to him."

‡ Once again, we may see the stylistic influence of Newton's *Opticks*.

though it can receive "that virtue" on contact with an excited §
electrical per se) .[33]

His experiments seem (to us) to have indicated that a non-electrical can be charged by rubbing because it is not a conductor, while an electrical *per se* cannot be so charged because it is a conductor. That he should, therefore, have chosen the distinction of electrical *per se* and non-electrical rather than conductor and non-conductor is a token of his primary concern with the production of charge rather than the effects of charges once produced. Desaguliers soon shortened these names to "non-electric" and "electric *per se*," in which form they became standard and, for example, were used by Franklin.

"Virtue," in the eighteenth-century sense of the word, implied "power" or "strength" or "force," i. e., "puissance," in terms of the etymology of the word—from the Latin "vir" or man, as in "virile." This was the traditional meaning of the word in the Middle Ages. Most writers on natural science during the eighteenth century did not observe the nice distinctions of precision among force, work, energy, power, potency, and strength, which became the rule in physics during the nineteenth century. When Galvani entitled his treatise *De Viribus Electricitatis in Motu Musculari, Commentarii*, he meant a commentary on the "force" of electricity on muscular motion only in the most general sense: almost as if he were concerned with "causes." Helmholtz, even in the nineteenth century, called his book on the conservation of energy (or perhaps work) *Die Erhaltung der Kraft*, but "Kraft" is really "force" or "strength," "power" or "vigor"—and has generally the same connotations as "puissance" or "vis" or "virtue." The communication of "electric virtue" from one body to another meant that one body which has acquired the electric attractive (or repulsive) "power" has transmitted some of it to a second body. No observable physical alteration seems to occur in a body that has become "electrical," i. e., one that has acquired the "electric virtue" or attractive (or repulsive) power; this changed state is discernible only in the defining terms of its becoming able to attract or repel in an electrical way. This acquisition of "electric virtue" is practically always a product of observable physical operations, such as rubbing, heating, patting, or contact (or even "near-contact," i. e., proximity) with a second body that already has "electric virtue." Sometimes this state was described by saying that a body had become "electric."

§ It should be observed that in defining "non-electrical" and "electrical *per se*" Desaguliers used three different expressions for what we should describe today as "charging."

The use of these terms may be further illustrated by the arguments of Stephen Hales, presented in Chapter Seven, about the electrification of blood-globules which appeared to be repelled from the "cut orifices of the blood-vessels" and attracted by adjoining blood vessels. Hales also observed other globules "rolling round their centre" and repelling one another. He concluded that bodies may acquire "both attractive and repulsive virtue or electricity" in a watery fluid by rubbing and twirling about. The passage from Hales's *Hæmastaticks* in which these observations were described was quoted in full in an article in the *Philosophical Transactions* by Granville Wheler, who had been associated with Stephen Gray in the latter's experiments. Wheler had repeated Hales's examination of blood globules and had concluded that the "globules of the blood, if by friction they acquire an electrical attractive virtue, must of necessity repel one another, and that electricity is not so properly called an attractive and repulsive virtue, as a virtue attractive of those bodies that are not attractive themselves, and repulsive of those that are. . . ." [34]

The preceding statement is similar to another one in which Desaguliers pointed out that " bodies electric *per se* " have inherent in them "a virtue of attracting and repelling small bodies at a distance," although this "virtue" is "not always in action, so as to produce that effect"; such bodies "are in a non-electric state" until rubbed, warmed, hammered, etc.[35] A substance which is a " non-electric " is to be distinguished from a body in a " non-electric state," the latter referring to an electric *per se* that does not have an electric virtue, or that is not electrified. As a type of substance, " non-electric " refers to all bodies which cannot be charged by ordinary rubbing, warming, hammering, etc., i. e., conducting bodies. Desaguliers observed that substance as such, in the sense of chemical composition, is not sufficient to determine the category of a given body. One and the same body will be a conductor or non-conductor, depending on its physical state: whether it is dry or damp. In Desaguliers's description of how a " non-electric, having received electricity, will communicate [it] to another body . . . losing . . . all its own electricity," he apparently was using the word " electricity " to describe the state of having active an " electric attractive virtue " which he called " a state of electricity."

According to Desaguliers, when a " non-electric " which has received " electricity " (i. e., " electric virtue ") communicates its " electricity " to another body, it loses its " electricity at once," and as it does, " the effluvia, in coming out strike the new body. . . ." The " excited electricity exerts itself in a sphere round the electric *per se*;

or rather a cylinder, if the body be cylindric," and the "electricity which a non-electric of great length (for example, a hempen string 800 or 900 feet long) receives, runs from one end to the other in a sphere of electrical effluvia." [36]

Desaguliers wrote of the effluvia of electricity in the same terms as the "effluvia" of sulphur which spread out in a room and which combine with particles of air whenever sulphur burns. The implication is that "effluvia" of sulphur are tiny mutually repellent particles, but we cannot assume that the electric effluvia were supposed to have such specific properties. Desaguliers never discussed the physical composition of electric effluvia, nor did he ever make it perfectly clear as to whether the two kinds of electrification—vitreous and resinous—were due to two distinct types of effluvia or only one that might act in one of two ways according to the circumstances. Even the "shape" of the atmosphere of the effluvia was only vaguely specified as a sphere, rather like the ancient "spheres of influence." Although in one case he did indicate that the atmosphere around a cylindrical object might be a cylinder, he also wrote of the "electricity" running in a "sphere" of electric effluvia along eight or nine-hundred feet of hempen string. Nor did Desaguliers ever conceive that the effluvia around an irregular object (like a man's head) might form an atmosphere of a similar shape, or even be subject to varying degrees of intensity. Furthermore, there is no indication that the electric effluvia were thought to be an elastic fluid in the sense of a collection of mutually repellent particles. Probably, the difference between electric effluvia and other manifestations like heat (which spreads out in all directions from a hot body) or gases and vapors (which likewise spread out to fill any containing vessel, including a room, etc.) lay in the fact that the electric effluvia never stray far from bodies, and they move out only to strike other bodies.

It seems surprising that Desaguliers did not attribute repulsion to particles of the electric effluvia; he surely was one of the chief advocates of the general doctrine of particle repulsion in matter. In Chapter Seven we saw that he had explained in his *Course* that the properties of gases (elastic fluids) arise from the mutual repulsion of the particles. In the same year in which he published his first articles on electricity in the *Philosophical Transactions*, he published a description of elasticity which he later reprinted in the *Course*. "Attraction and repulsion," he wrote, "seem to be settled by the Great C r e a t o r as first principles in nature; that is, as the first of second causes; so that we are not solicitous about their causes, and think it enough to deduce other things from them" [37]—a doctrine in full harmony with the natural philosophy of the *Opticks*. The primary postulate was "that the same particles that repel each other strongly, will attract other particles very strongly; as appears by many chemical dissolutions, especially by the alternate dissolution and precipitation of metals in acid menstruums. The Reverend and Learned Dr. Hales has proved this many ways, in his *Vegetable Statics* and *Hæmastatics*." [38] Following the Newton-Hales line, Desaguliers explained first that the elasticity of the air consists "wholly in the repulsive power of its particles," then that the "effluvia" of burning sulphur consist of particles that repel one another. But since the two kinds of particles attract, a mixture of the two destroys the repulsion of each kind and may produce a solid out of two elastic fluids. When Desaguliers presented this material in his article on elasticity, as also when he discussed the subject in his book, no reference was made to electricity. He merely explained that when "brimstone matches" are burned, "the effluvia of the sulphur repel each other to great distances" (proof was to be seen in the "sulphureous smell" spreading out in all directions). No cause was assigned to explain why air particles repel air particles, sulphur particles repel sulphur particles, nor why the two types of particles attract one another.

In 1742 Desaguliers sought to explain the elastic property of air and its chemical affinity for sulphur in electrical terms, making use of the "two electricities" discovered by Du Fay. "Pure" dry air, Desaguliers noted, is to be included among the electrics *per se* "because it repels all bodies in a state of electricity [i. e., all electrified bodies], whether they have been excited to it by wax or glass; that is, by either of the two sorts of electricity." [39] What meaning can we give to this statement? There are two types of "electricity," vitreous and resinous, and all bodies endowed with the same kind of electricity repel one another. Air particles can be supposed to repel both the vitreously and the resinously electrified bodies if they are normally non-electrified, for then the air particles will be attracted by any electrified body and gain one or the other kind of electricity *on contact*; repulsion will then ensue between the newly electrified air particles and the electrified body to which they have been attracted and which has given up some of its electricity on contact; such behavior would be in accordance with the well-known law that like electricities repel one another. The situation just described is like that of an unelectrified feather which is attracted to a rubbed glass tube or piece of charged wax; on contact, the feather gains either the vitreous electricity of the charged tube and is then repelled by the tube, or it gains the resinous electricity of the wax and is then repelled by the wax. (Such a series of phenomena had been fully described by Du Fay and was well known to Desaguliers.)

But if we suppose the particles of air to be always electrified—and invariably with the same kind of electricity—then the above explanation cannot be applied. Now Desaguliers did suppose the " particles of pure air to be electric bodies always in a state of electricity, and that vitreous electricity." In this event, however, the air particles would *attract* bodies with a resinous electricity and could not then repel *all* electrified bodies—as he claimed—whether " excited by glass or wax." Furthermore, if air particles attract both resinously and vitreously electrified particles, because they are originally non-electrified, they could hardly repel one another by virtue of electric force alone. It would seem as if Desaguliers's logic were faulty.*

In order to support his view that air particles have a vitreous electrification, Desaguliers advanced three chief arguments: (1) air particles exert a mutual repulsion upon one another, " as has been deduced from experiments and observations"; (2) dry air drives back to a rubbed glass tube the effluvia which the tube throws out, " from whence they [effluvia] dart out . . . with a vibratory motion, which continues their electricity"; (3) a vitreously charged feather will keep its charge in dry air, but not in moist, since the moist particles—which are non-electric (i. e., which are conductors—are attracted by the feather and soon make it lose all its charge. (Did not Desaguliers know that this would also happen to a resinously charged feather?)

Referring again to Hales's experiments (in *Vegetable Staticks*) in which " air is absorbed, and loses its elasticity by the mixture of sulphureous vapours, so that four quarts of air in a glass vessel will be reduced to three," Desaguliers now offered an explanation based on the supposition that the particles of sulphur have a resinous electrification, and are therefore attracted by the oppositely electrified air particles.[40] " The effluvia of sulphur, being electric, repel one another " and form an elastic fluid in the manner of air particles, which also repel one another because they too are " electric." † But in a mixture of air and sulphur, some particles are resinously electrified and the others are vitreously electrified; the two kinds of particle attract one another to produce " moleculæ compounded of them [which], becoming non-electric, lose their repulsive force." ‡

* Du Fay had shown that a body strongly electrified (either vitreously or resinously) would attract a body with the same electricity, if the second body were very weakly electrified. Hence, Desaguliers's statements can possibly be made reasonable by additional assumptions about the strength of electrification in the various particles. But it must be said that such assumptions do not appear as part of Desaguliers's argument.

† " Air being electrical of a vitreous electricity, and sulphur of a resinous electricity."
‡ Precisely the same argument was advanced by Desaguliers in his *Dissertation*

I have referred to the fact that Desaguliers did not make any attempt to explain in a physical way—i. e., in terms of specific physical properties of effluvia—the difference between the vitreous and resinous electrification. Practically every one of his experiments was performed with the glass tube; hence he had but little occasion to study resinous electricity. We shall see in a moment that the tradition of performing electrical experiments almost exclusively with glass rods, spheres, or cylinders was a handicap to other experimenters, including Franklin. I suspect that the greater ease in rubbing glass was responsible for the neglect of phenomena of resinous electricity; rubbing a sulphur cake is apt to break it and resins and waxes are so much softer than glass that rubbing bodies made of them is more difficult than rubbing glass tubes. But by confining his experiments to vitreous electricity, Desaguliers missed the obvious crucial experiment with regard to the supposed vitreous electrification of air: the relative times required for an electrified piece of glass and an electrified piece of wax to return to the neutral state in dry air. Plainly, if the electrifications of the glass and wax were more or less equal, a resinously electrified piece of wax would attract the vitreously electrified air particles and thereby lose its electric virtue in a short time, whereas the vitreously electrified glass rod would in this case repel the vitreously electrified air particles and the effect would be quite different.

One gathers that according to Desaguliers's conception, the effluvia are " thrown out " of glass tubes by rubbing, thereby producing a state of vitreous electrification in the glass. The eventual loss of these effluvia destroys the electrification, as, for instance, when the tube is surrounded by moist air. Hence, a body which has a vitreous electrification is one which has the effluvia around it. When the effluvia have been carried away, the body is in the same state as it was before having been rubbed—even though during the process it may have lost forever the effluvia which were in it prior to the rubbing. This conceptual system is, therefore, not the same as one in which a charge is thought to be due to a material substance that comes out of bodies and leaves them in an altered state—minus that material substance—once it is taken away. Nor is any distinction made between two possible " states " of bodies having a vitreous electrification: one a glass body from which effluvia have been evoked by rubbing, the other a body of any substance whatever which has received effluvia from a second body which has been rubbed.

All in all, the explanations are not very satisfying. Although

concerning electricity (1742), which won the prize of the Academy of Bordeaux and which was reprinted in volume 2 of his Course of experimental philosophy (1744).

Desaguliers received various prizes and honors for his contributions to electricity, it is plain that the subject remained—in spite of his efforts—in a rather primitive state. He admitted that he did "not pretend to know the cause of electricity in general," but he did "hope from a few laws of electricity deduced from known phænomena, to solve most other phænomena (tho' seeming quite unaccountable) so far as to shew what law of electricity they depend upon; and to be able to foretel what will happen to most bodies, before the experiments are tried upon them in an electrical way." However, except in the restricted domain of conduction, the predictive quality —which is the *sine qua non* of any physical theory—was still largely lacking in electrical science.

Electrical Machines and the Leyden Jar

Two great innovations marked the development of the study of electricity in the early part of the fifth decade of the century. While both of them were contributions to practice rather than to theory, they stimulated theory by providing a complex variety of new phenomena to challenge concepts that were inadequate. The improved "electrical machines," or electrostatic generators, and the condenser, or "Leyden jar," made it possible to produce electrical effects on a far larger scale than had ever before been possible, thus affording the means for making wholly new types of experiments and also spectacular public demonstrations which drew considerable attention to the subject of electricity. These innovations came chiefly from Germany and Holland. Volume forty-three of the *Philosophical Transactions* (for the years 1744-1745) for example, contains a number of papers describing the recent German developments, chief among them the invention of large electrical machines with their whirling glass globes and cylinders.[41] There can be little doubt but that the new electrical machines designed or improved by such men as Bose, Winkler, Gralath, Gordon, Krüger, and Hausen, beginning about 1743, created a great stir; experiments in which great crackling noises and awesome sparks were produced were of value in transforming the budding science of electricity from a kind of "toy physics" to a subject of commanding importance. Presumably these innovations were the source of Professor John Winthrop's remarks to his Harvard students in 1746: "This electricity since the year 1743 has made a considerable noise in the world; upon which it's supposed several of the (at present hidden) phænomina of nature depend."[42] No longer was experimental electricity limited to effects produced by rubbing glass tubes or pieces of amber, wax and resin—attracting bits of feather, paper, gold leaf, or investigating the transfer of "electric virtue"—but now spirits could be ignited by powerful sparks. Human beings could be given such powerful shocks that the pain seemed almost unbearable.§

The electrical machines of the mid-forties usually consisted of a wooden frame with huge globes or cylinders on axles which were rotated by a cord passing around an axle pulley and a large wheel with a crank. The ratio of the diameter of the wheel to that of the axle was great enough to permit one or more globes or spheres to be rotated at a very high speed; William Watson estimated that the globes on a machine which he used in 1746 rotated with a mean speed of about 1100 rpm. The sphere (s) or globe (s) were excited by having an experimenter hold his hand against them while they whirled; later a stuffed leather cushion was introduced to replace the hand and became known as the "rubber." To facilitate the making of experiments, a gun-barrel was suspended near the globe by insulating strings and received a charge from the globe through "metallic fringes" inserted into the barrel and which hung down in contact with the globe. Later machines established contact between the globe and the gun-barrel by means of a chain. After a while, the metal "comb" was introduced to "draw off" the charge from the globe or cylinder. The gun-barrel was eventually called the "prime conductor."

An innovation which further increased the magnitude of electrical effects was the condenser, or Leyden jar, as it was called after the place of one of its independent discoverers, Pieter van Musschenbroek, professor of physics at Leyden, who announced his discovery in a very dramatic letter to Réaumur in 1746. The story of this discovery is well enough known to enable us to dispense here with all save the barest outline. Musschenbroek was investigating the "force of electricity" and had suspended from the gun-barrel a wire which was inserted into a glass flask or vial, partly filled with water, held in his right hand. After the globe of the electrical machine had been whirled (so that the gun-barrel and water had become charged), Musschenbroek attempted to draw sparks from the gun-barrel and received so great a shock that he thought "it was all up" with him. He noted that the effect would follow only if one and the same experimenter held the flask in one hand while touching the gun-barrel with the other; not if one man held the flask and another touched the gun-barrel. The shape of the flask did not seem to make much difference, although the kind of glass was very important.

---

§ Musschenbroek's original letter to Réaumur, announcing the discovery of the condenser, begins, "I wish to communicate to you a new, but terrible, experiment that I would advise you never to attempt yourself." [43]

Some idea of the interest aroused by the " experiment of Leyden "
may be seen in the remarks of the Abbé Nollet, accompanying the
publication of Musschenbroek's letter, to the effect that " this experiment . . . has excited admiration for the last three months, so
that everybody flocks to see it, and . . . [it] has resulted in making
electricity so celebrated that it has been made a show of for the
world." The mystery of the Leyden jar, from the scientific point
of view, was how it was possible to put so fantastically large an
amount of electricity into a glass of water that was held in the hand
of an experimenter, when under other circumstances so little electricity could be put into the same glass of water.[44]

Nollet's Doctrine of " Effluences " and " Affluences "

Great as the need had been for a satisfactory electrical theory in
the '30's, the new electrical machines of the '40's and the discovery
of the Leyden jar made the want of such a theory even more acute.
Two major theories were advanced in the '40's; one was the creation
of the Abbé Nollet, and another was put forward by William Watson. These two theories must be considered in some detail because
Nollet's was thought by its inventor and his partisans to be the chief
rival to Franklin's, while Watson's was said by its inventor to be
identical to Franklin's, although the latter might have been conceived independently. Watson's claim at first convinced Franklin,
although Franklin soon saw the basic differences between his own
primary concepts and Watson's. They were, of course, very similar
and the distinctions between them became apparent only in their
implications. This difference was seen most plainly when Watson,
reviewing a book written by Nollet to attack Franklin's theory,
endorsed the French point of view, thereby disavowing any effective
claim to the Franklin theory.

All eighteenth-century discussions of the respective merits of the
Franklin and Nollet theories were bound to be partisan, and the
tone of Nollet's publications invited a good fight. Nollet's attack on
Franklin was answered by David Colden,[45] and also by the French
physicist, Le Roy,[46] and others. Priestley, in his history of electricity,
lauded Franklin at the expense of Nollet, but the French translator
of the history, that same " Monsieur B——— " (Brisson) described
by Franklin in his autobiography as the " last élève " of Nollet,
introduced, in the footnotes to the French edition a running rebuttal which was carried over into the German edition as well. In
defense of Nollet Krünitz, the German translator, pointed out that
a distinction must be made, as Newton had done, between a theory
and an hypothesis.[47] Nollet had produced a theory, not an hypothe-

FIG. 7. William Watson's electrical machine or tribo-electric generator.

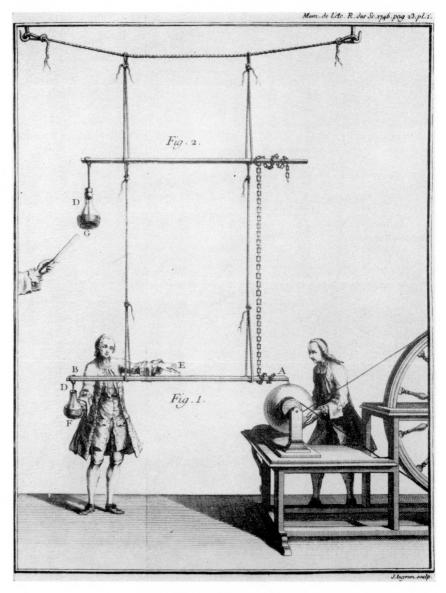

Mem. de l'Ac. R. des Sc. 1746. pag. 23. pl. 1.

Fig. 2.

D

G

Fig. 1.

B   E

D   A

F

J. Ingram sculp.

FIG. 8. The "Leyden experiment."

sis, and in fact the only true theory, the only theory based on experiments, on " proven events that have been repeated thousands and thousands of times without any divergence." Franklin and his disciples, Krünitz warned, have had to alter their theories by constantly introducing new assumptions; here is ample proof that this kind of theory had been badly conceived. " But M. Nollet's theory has never been changed. It is still the same as ever. It has not been altered in the slightest degree because the facts on which it is based are ever-lasting." [48]

The bitterness of the quarrel between Nollet and Franklin, and between their respective followers, indicates, as Rosenberger has suggested, a profound chasm between the metaphysical bases of the two theories: the Cartesian and the Newtonian.[49] Nollet, following the ideas of Descartes, was not a believer in a subtle fluid whose particles repel one another through empty space while being attracted by particles of ponderable matter. Nollet was proud to have been a pupil and quondam assistant of Du Fay's and he undoubtedly inherited some of Du Fay's Cartesianism.[50] But whatever the merits (or lack of merits) of Nollet's theory might have been, the world of science owes him a debt of gratitude. He was a master showman and the success of his public demonstrations of electrical phenomena stimulated an interest in the subject. He was particularly well known in the world of " physique du salon," the presentation of experimental physics to the fashionable ladies of the French court; he eventually became " preceptor in natural philosophy " to the French royal family. A prolific writer of books and articles, Nollet wrote more about electricity than any other branch of physics. Many of his communications were printed in the annual volumes of the Académie Royale des Sciences (Paris) and he held an important position in the scientific circles of his day. Nollet wrote a number of books about his experiments and his electrical theory, each sufficiently popular to warrant several editions. Two such volumes were devoted to an attack on Franklin's writings. Another was an " Essay on the Electricity of Bodies." One was called " Researches on the Particular Causes of Electrical Phenomena," and yet another was the sixth volume of his famous " Lessons on experimental physical science," a major part of which dealt with electricity.[51] Nollet's books contain a vast accumulation of curious and ingenious experiments, in which plants, birds, animals, human beings, water fountains, etc., were electrified. Many of these performances were spectacular and arresting, and clearly they could entertain as well as instruct a courtly audience. Considerable space was always devoted to a frontal attack on those who disagreed openly with Nollet's theory or who advanced a theory in any way contrary to his own. Although he claimed he was not a Cartesian, he boasted that he was not a Newtonian.[52]

The Nollet theory of electrical action is characterized by two principles: effluence and affluence. It may best be presented in his own words, under 18 fundamental propositions * which may be translated as follows:

FUNDAMENTAL PROPOSITIONS, drawn from experience, & with the aid of which one can account for all the electrical phenomena known until now:

1. Electricity is the effect of a fluid matter which moves around or within the electrised body.

2. This fluid is neither the real matter of the electrised body, nor the coarse air which we breathe.

3. There is every ground to believe that the electric matter is the same as that of elementary fire and light, united to some other substance which gives it an odor.

4. This matter is present everywhere, in the interior of bodies as well as in the air which surrounds them.

5. The electric matter, excited or put in action, moves, as much as it can, in a right line, & its movement ordinarily is a progressive movement that transports its parts.

6. The electric matter is sufficiently subtle to penetrate through the hardest and most compact bodies.

7. But it does not penetrate them all with the same ease. Living bodies, the metals & water are those in which it passes most easily; sulphur, sealing wax, glass, resins, & silk are those in which it has the most difficulty penetrating, unless these bodies are rubbed or heated.

8. The air of our atmosphere is not as permeable to the electric matter as the metals, living bodies, water, etc.

9. When the electric matter leaves a body with great impetuosity and issues forth into the air, whether it be visible or not, it divides up into several divergent jets, which form a kind of spray or plume [brush].

10. A body electrised by friction or by communication emits, from all sides, rays of electric matter which extend in straight lines in the air or in the other bodies in the vicinity.

11. While these emanations continue, a like matter comes from all sides to the electrised body, in the form of convergent rays.

12. These two currents of electric matter, which go in contrary directions, perform their movements at the same time; & one of the two is stronger than the other.

---

* Nollet also presented his theory in a set of 33 " Fundamental propositions drawn from experience," [53] but I have chosen the shorter version.

13. The pores by which the electric matter leaves electrised bodies are not so numerous as those by which it re-enters them.

14. The matter which comes to the electrised body is not furnished to it by the air alone, but by all the other bodies in the vicinity which are capable of becoming electrised by communication.

15. The matter which leaves the insulated conductor through the different parts of its surface, which never ends up at the globe, comes in good part from this globe and from the body which rubs it.

16. The electric matter which comes from all sides to the insulated conductor makes its way to the globe and to the body which rubs it, whence it goes into the neighbouring air or into other contiguous bodies.

17. Bodies electrised by communication easily lose their virtue on contact with another body [that is] non-insulated.

18. Glass electrised by friction or by communication does not dielectrise by itself, & can keep its electricity very much longer than ordinary conductors.[54]

In other words, Nollet's theory was postulated on the existence of a subtle matter which penetrates all solid bodies, liquids, and the air, but with differing degrees of ease. It is a fluid matter that is probably identical with elementary fire and light; when combined with some other matter it has an odor. An electrified body emits rectilinear divergent rays of electric matter but simultaneously receives convergent rays of the same electric matter. Bodies have two sets of pores, one for the emission of electric matter, the other for receiving it—and more of the former than the latter. Yet, independent of the number of pores, some bodies at some times have a stronger current of efflux than of afflux, and hence there may be both resinous and vitreous electrification.

Nollet's theory is Cartesian rather than Newtonian to the degree that the electric fluid is not elastic in the sense of Newton's æther, but was more like the " elementary matter " of Descartes. Descartes had explained magnetic and electric attraction and repulsion by the supposition of a subtle matter leaving bodies and returning to them, or passing through pores or ducts in bodies. This matter was supposed to spread out from rubbed pieces of glass in right lines in the shape of threads, but since air has no pores adjusted to receive them, these threads return to the parent body bringing with them small pieces of hair, straw, and so on.[55] Nollet introduced a second set of pores, and supposed that the returning matter was not necessarily that very matter which had left the electrified body, but different matter—although of the identical kind. To me, as to Joseph Priestley in the eighteenth century, Nollet's theory appears to be little else but a multiplication of hypotheses that neither coordinate the observed phenomena nor predict the outcome of any but the simplest experiments. To a non-Cartesian, such a theory could hardly fulfill the expectations of the day, and it would seem that the only reason for its popularity must have been the all but complete absence of any other theory even remotely satisfying the demand.†

William Watson: Franklin's Mentor

William Watson, the greatest of Franklin's immediate predecessors, was a physician and naturalist, who began as an apothecary, published a number of botanical and medical papers, was knighted in 1786, but is remembered today chiefly for the electrical research he conducted in the 1740's. He was awarded the Copley Medal of the Royal Society in 1753, and was the leading "electrician" in England at the time when Franklin began his research. It is no exaggeration to say that Watson was Franklin's master and guide in the study of electricity; Franklin studied each of Watson's writings with care and they influenced his own concept of electrical action in a variety of ways that will be described in the next two chapters. Although Watson claimed at one point that Franklin's theory of electrical action was the same as his own, it is pleasant to be able to report a complete absence of acrimony between Franklin and Watson. Watson, in fact, referred to Franklin's work in the highest of terms from the very beginning. The first notice in print of Franklin's research was in the articles written by Watson, which included long extracts from Franklin's letters—the first publication of any of his scientific discoveries. When Franklin's book on electricity was published in London in 1751, Watson wrote an enthusiastic review for the *Philosophical Transactions*. We have only fragmentary remains of any correspondence between them, but they certainly were in contact in person during Franklin's later visits to England.‡ It was Watson who introduced the motion that Franklin be elected a Fellow of the Royal Society.

---

† It is difficult to comprehend the positive virtue of Nollet's theory today—a fact which may be taken to be a measure of the conceptual changes that have occurred in physics since Nollet's day. Even his most recent biographer fails to convey the worth of this theory although he does demonstrate Nollet's other achievements.[56]

‡ For example in 1772 Watson and Franklin, together with Cavendish and Robertson, served on a committee of the Royal Society and the Board of Ordnance to study the subject of "the propriety of fixing conductors for securing the powder magazines at Purfleet." Watson was one of the signers of the report drawn up by Franklin. Portions of Franklin's first letter to Watson are printed in Chapter Eleven. Watson and Franklin were co-signers of the certificate supporting Priestley for the Royal Society and they joined together in helping Priestley to write his history of electricity. They had many friends in common in Birmingham and were fellow members of the Club of Honest Whigs.

Watson's papers in the *Philosophical Transactions* dealt with medicine, meteorology, lightning and lightning rods, applications of electricity to medicine, and botany. He appears to have suggested the metal coating on the inside of the Leyden jar, following Bevis's suggestion of an outer metal coating, and he performed important experiments to try to ascertain the velocity of the discharge from a jar. These experiments were an improvement on earlier ones performed by Le Monnier in France in 1746, in which a discharge circuit had been formed partly of chains of men holding hands and partly of bodies of water (the lakes at the Tuileries and the Jardin du Roi) and moist earth.[57] In one of Watson's experiments, the discharge circuit was composed of three men, of whom two were on opposite sides of the Thames River dipping an iron rod into the water, and an insulated wire carried along Westminster Bridge. Such an experiment indicated only that the discharge was instantaneous, or really that it was too rapid to be measured over so short a distance by crude means; but Watson had shown the possibility of a discharge through about twelve hundred feet of water, a distance he later surpassed. Franklin, it will be recalled, performed similar experiments across the Schuylkill River. Other experiments of Watson's showed that a discharge could be obtained if two conducting chains were each grounded at one end and put into contact with the inner and outer surface, respectively, of a charged Leyden jar. Watson interpreted these results to mean that "electricity" could be transmitted through even relatively dry earth.§

Watson's major contributions to electricity were reprinted from the *Philosophical Transactions* in three pamphlets, each of which went through several editions; their titles are *Experiments and Observations tending to illustrate the Nature and Properties of Electricity* (1745, 1746); *A Sequel to the Experiments and Observations . . .* (1746); *An Account of the Experiments made . . . in order to discover whether the Electrical Power would be sensible at great distances . . .* [&] *Some Further Inquiries into the Nature and Properties of Electricity* (1748). Since Franklin had been reading these publications while performing his own experiments and developing his own ideas, a rather complete analysis of their contents is necessary to any judgment of Franklin's originality.

In the preface to his *Experiments and Observations,** Watson re-

---

§ Franklin carried this experiment a step further by ramming some "simple dry earth" into a glass tube open at both ends to see whether electricity would pass through it. It would not, but he pointed out that "the ground is never so dry."[58]

* This book is most often encountered in the so-called "third edition" of 1746. The communications that it contains were read at meetings of the Royal Society. Watson tells us that he printed them separately in a pamphlet before publication in

ported that his " experiments were all made with glass tubes of about two foot long; the bore about an inch in diameter." On one occasion he " used a glass sphere as well as a tube; but . . . [found himself] capable of sending forth much more fire from the tube than from the sphere, probably from not being sufficiently used to the last." Later, he became skilled at using the electrical machine with whirling globes, in the German style. The bulk of the book is composed of three letters, the first addressed to Martin Folkes, President of the Royal Society, dated 27 March 1746. This letter reports Watson's success in having set on fire some " spirits of wine " by electricity, a notable feat since his early efforts to produce this effect had been failures, even though the Royal Society had " heard from some of their correspondents in Germany, that what they call a vegetable quintessence had been fired by electricity." [59] There can be little doubt that these are the German experiments which Franklin tells us were described in an account of electrical novelties sent to Philadelphia by Peter Collinson in 1746 or 1747.†

Following Desaguliers, Watson divided bodies into two classes: (1) " *Electrics per se* or *originally-electrics*," bodies in which the attractive power can be excited by friction (including glass, amber, sulfur, sealing wax, and " most dry parts of animals, as silk, hair, . . .") and (2) " *non-electrics*, or conductors of electricity," bodies in which the above property is not found or is only " very slightly perceptible " (as in wood, dead and living animals, metals and vegetable substances) .[60] He described electrified bodies as " bodies made electrical " which might lose " that electricity." He also wrote of the " electricity " of electrified bodies as " this fire," and " the very subtle fire of electricity," as well as " effluvia from the tube."

By means of an electric discharge, Watson was able to ignite " not only the ætherial liquor or phlogiston of Frobenius [61] and rectified spirit of wine, but even common proof spirit." [62] Watson had observed a difference in the kind of discharge he could obtain from a pointed end of a conductor and a blunt end.‡ Franklin and his

the *Philosophical Transactions* " to satisfy . . . the impatience of several learned and very valuable friends, to whose importunities I have neither will nor inclination to deny any thing in my power to grant." Only " a few copies " were printed in an edition of 1745, presumably the first edition. I have not been able to find a " second edition," and I suppose that Watson implied that publication in the *Philosophical Transactions* constituted a second edition. The continuing demand was so great that a " third edition " was printed in 1746, by C. Davis, who was also the printer of the *Philosophical Transactions*. The " third edition " was also published in 1746 in Dublin, and a French translation appeared in 1748, in a collection which included books by Winckler, Freke and Martin.

† This point is discussed at the beginning of the next chapter.

‡ The Abbé Nollet pointed out that Jallabert had noticed that a body round at one end and pointed at the other would produce different effects depending on which

Philadelphia associates explored even further the electrical effects depending on the shape (pointed or blunt) of conductors, and probably received their first hint of such differences from Watson, who had written: " When you transmit the electrical fire along a sword or other instrument, whose point is sharp, it often appears as a number of disseminated sparks, like wet gunpowder or wild-fire; but if the instrument has no point, you generally perceive a pure bright flame, like what is vulgarly called the blue-ball, which gives the appearance of stars to fired rockets." [64]

Watson quoted in full the statement of Desaguliers concerning the capriciousness observed in electrical experiments [65] and indicated that the source of this unpredictability is the variation in the moistness or dryness of the air. He reasoned as follows: (1) since air is an " electric *per se*, and of the vitreous kind," it repels " the electricity arising from the glass tube, and disposes it to electrify whatever non-electrical bodies receive the effluvia from the tube; " (2) " water is a non-electric, and of consequence a conductor of electricity." Thus a coating of moisture will render a non-conductor conducting, as when you " only blow through a dry glass tube, the moisture from your breath will cause that tube to be a conductor of electricity." Hence, if " the air is replete with watery vapours, the electricity arising from the tube . . . is, by means of these vapours, communicated to the circumambient atmosphere and dissipated as fast as excited," a phenomenon of which Du Fay and Desaguliers had been aware. Anyone who has taught elementary physics and who has had to perform demonstration experiments in electrostatics, will agree that moisture or humidity produces effects which a lecturer finds painful to explain to his students.

Watson at first ignited spirit by electrifying a poker suspended by silk lines and then having an assistant bring a spoon full of warm spirit near the end of the electrified poker; a spark discharge ignited the spirit. If the spoon actually touched the poker, the " electricity without any flashing is communicated to the spoon, and to the assistant in whose hand it is held, and so is lost to the floor." [66] We

end was presented to an electrified body; these experiments were made in the presence of the Abbé Nollet, who found the effect to be not constant. Nollet acknowledged that it was Franklin who first showed the property of pointed bodies to " draw off " electricity at greater distances and with greater ease than bodies of other shapes. As we shall see in the next chapter, in the fourth and fifth editions of Franklin's book on electricity, Franklin added a note stating that this particular discovery had not been made by him but by Hopkinson. The German Bose had also studied the kinds of discharge obtained from conductors of different shapes and had named the two major types the " female " and " male " fire: the " female " is the " heavy disruptive discharge " obtained when the electrodes are smooth and blunt or round and the " male " is the " more silent brush or corona discharge from pointed conductors." [63]

may observe that this sentence does not imply that " electricity " is a substance, or that it is not a substance. Yet, when Watson wrote of the effect " produced by non-electrical [conducting] substances impregnated with electricity received from the exciting electrics *per se* [non-conductors]," he plainly implied the existence of some kind of fine matter or " effluvia." Watson's method of electrifying the poker (insulated by being suspended by silk threads) was to hang from the handle " several little bundles of white thread, the extremities of which were about a foot at right angles from the poker. Among these threads, which were all attracted by the rubbed [i. e., electrified] glass tube, I excited the greatest electrical fire [of which] I was capable."

In one of his experiments, Watson " placed a man upon a cake of wax, who held in one of his hands a spoon with the warm spirits, and in the other a poker with the thread. I rubbed the [glass] tube amongst the thread, and electrified him as before. I then ordered a person not electrified to bring his finger near the middle of the spoon." The " flash from the spoon and spirit was violent enough to fire the spirit. This experiment I then repeated three times. In this method, the person by whose finger the spirit of wine is fired, feels the stroke more violent, than when the . . . fire goes from him to the spoon." [67] Watson called this the " repulsive " method of firing spirit electrically as opposed to the more customary " attractive " method introduced by the Germans who had originated the experiment.§ The sense in which the experiment can be described as " repulsive " is that the insulated man holding the spoon with warmed spirit is electrified and, by repelling the " electrical fire " away from himself (and the spoon) , produces the spark that ignites the spirit. In this case, Watson observed, the effect was to be compared to that of the " attractive " method, in which the spoon with warmed spirit is held by the man on the ground. In the latter case, the " electrical fire " is attracted by the spoon from the electrified insulated man; in the former the " electrical fire " is repelled from the spoon to the uncharged grounded man. These statements of Watson indicate a belief in the existence of an electrical matter (" fire ") ; but, since he also described the transmission by water of " the electrical effluvia," we see that he had not fully worked out as yet the nature and properties of the electric matter or electric fire. Watson later specified the properties of electric fire, but at this point he declared an unwillingness " to introduce more terms into any demonstration than what are absolutely necessary for the more ready conception

§ ". . . those German gentlemen, to whom the world is obliged for many surprizing discoveries in this part of natural philosophy." [68]

thereof." In other words, Watson felt free to write of " an excited non-electric [that] emits almost all its fire, if once touched by a non-electric not excited," [69] without implying anything more than the barest suggestion that the state of excitation and the later return to non-electrification were owing to a gain or loss of some kind of " fire." Yet it should be observed that although Watson used the term " electrical fire " in describing spark discharges, he did not use it in discussing how certain electrics *per se* do " not permit the electricity to pass through them." [70] He wrote of " the electricity [that] floats only upon the surface of bodies," and said that a wet body is " a conductor of electricity." Watson had no doubt that when an insulating cake of wax or resin is wet, the water " hanging about it " transmits " the electrical effluvia." But on the fundamental question of the " effluvia " or the " electrical fire " being particulate, he was not ready to make a positive commitment. It would appear that Watson was primarily concerned with reporting ingenious variations he had made of the German ignition experiments, and that he was not even aware that his terms might be interpreted in various senses, each possibly implying a wholly different concept of " electricity."

Watson read the results of these experiments before the Royal Society on 24 Oct. 1745; on the following 6 Feb. 1745/6, he read a " continuation " in which he devoted himself, in part, to a statement of fundamental propositions regarding " the several properties that electricity is possessed of peculiar to itself " and those it has " in common with magnetism and light." [71] He had observed that the appearance of fire from electrified substances seemed to differ " in colour and form according to the substances from which they proceed." Newton's optical discoveries had made all physical scientists particularly aware of color, and we have seen that both Gray and Du Fay had experimented on the relation of color to conducting power in cloth. Franklin, too, studied the relation of light and electricity in a particularly fruitful way. Of course, the visible spark discharges in electrical experiments aroused an optical concern since plainly light was being produced by an electrical phenomenon. Watson concluded that the luminous rays in which the electrical fire appeared in a discharge from sword-points, a silver probe, the points of scissors, and the edges of magnetized steel bars, differed in color from the more reddish discharge " from unpolished bodies, as the end of a poker, a rusty nail, or such-like." The cause, he said, was only " the different reflection of the electrical fire from the surface of the body from which it is emitted," and was not a result of " any difference in the fire itself." [72]

Watson's first proposition is that, like magnetism, "electricity" can counteract and even overcome (in light bodies) the force of gravity; like magnetism, "electricity" exerts a force in vacuo as powerful as the force it exerts in air, and this force extends "through various substances of different textures and densities" to a considerable distance. The second proposition is that, like light, "electricity pervades glass," but it is not refracted. Of course, as Watson noted, the "rectilinear direction is observable only as far as the electricity can penetrate through unexcited originally-electrics, and those perfectly dry"; nor did it seem to matter very much whether the substances were transparent, "semidiaphanous" (translucent), or opaque, so long as they were not conductors. With "non-electrics" (conductors), the situation is markedly different, for in such case "the direction, given to the electricity by the excited originally-electric, is altered as soon as it touches the surface of a non-electric [conductor], and is propagated with a degree of swiftness, scarcely to be measured, in all possible directions, to impregnate the whole non-electric mass in contact with it, or nearly so, . . . and which must of necessity be terminated by an originally electric before the electricity exerts the least attraction, and then this power is observed first at that part of the non-electric the most remote from the originally-electric." [73] To illustrate the rectilinear action of "electricity" and the differential effect of conductors and non-conductors, Watson conceived an ingenious experiment. A man holds an "excited" tube horizontally in one hand, and finds that pieces of leaf gold underneath the tube will be attracted straight upwards to the tube even though glass, cloth, or other "original electrics" be interposed, and that this attraction "is exerted to a considerable distance." However, if "silver, tin, the thinnest board, paper, or any other non-electric [be]held in the manner before-mentioned," the rubbed tube will not attract "leaf gold or other light bodies." Du Fay and others had also experimented on effects of shielding.

In another experiment, Watson put some pieces of gold leaf and "the seed of cotton-grass" under an inverted glass jar that had previously been warmed. On top of the jar he "placed books and several other non-electrics." When he moved the rubbed glass tube over the books, the motion of the light bodies in the jar seemed to follow exactly the motion of the tube, "the electricity seeming instantaneously to pass through the books and the glass." [74]

When Watson wrote of "electricity" penetrating through unexcited "originally-electrics," [75] or "electricity" seeming to pass through glass and books, what did he mean? It is apparent from his text that the word "electricity" was being used to denote attractive

power similar to the sense of " electric virtue," which has been discussed previously. For example, there was no perceptible time-lag
between the motion of the rubbed tube and the corresponding motion of the bodies in the jar—hence the " electricity " moved through
the glass back and forth with the rod. The word " electricity " was
being used loosely, however, and had at least one other meaning.
Watson wrote of a condition existing " before the electricity exerts
the least attraction," which sounds almost as if the " virtue " were
due to " the electricity," which he then called " this power." [76]
Hence, the word " electricity " has the sense used by Desaguliers, as
the power causing the attraction. When Watson described the experiment of holding a rubbed glass rod over the books which were on
top of the inverted bottle, he noted that while the " electricity "
seemed " instantaneously to pass through the books and glass," the
effects noted do not occur " till the electricity has fully impregnated
the non-electrics, which lie upon the glass, which received electricity
is stopped by the glass; and then these non-electrics dart their power
directly through the upper part of the glass after the manner of
originally-electrics." [77] The first part of this quotation certainly
seems to indicate that " electricity " was being used in the sense of
a substance impregnating bodies, but the latter part indicates the
sense of " power " or " virtue." In a footnote Watson tried to clarify
matters by saying that the motion of " effluvia " explains why " electrical attraction through glass is much more powerful when the glass
is made warm, than when cold." First, warm glass does not produce
as much condensation of water vapor on its surface as cold glass does,
and the moisture " makes the glass, as has been before demonstrated,
a conductor of electricity." Second, heat enlarges bodies and " consequently causes their constituent parts to recede from each other,"
with the result that " the electrical effluvia, passing in straight lines,
find probably a more ready passage through their pores " when
bodies are hot than when they are cold. But the reader's confusion
is aggravated by the fact that in his statement about the rod waved
over a bottle, as in his discussion of the first two fundamental propositions, Watson no longer used the term " electrical fire," but now
used the terms, " electricity," " electrical attraction," and " electrical
power," and reverted to the old expression " effluvia " in a footnote.

Watson's third and final proposition [78] states that electricity is like
light; for " when its forces are collected, and a proper direction given
thereto upon a proper object, [it] produces fire and flame." The
" corollary " to this proposition contains further information about
Watson's conception of electricity. He now introduced the term,
" the fire of electricity," apparently a variation of " electrical fire."

It is, he observed, " extremely delicate, and sets on fire . . . only inflammable vapours." The " flame " so produced is not increased by being " superinduced " on an iron rod that has been made " red hot with coarser culinary fire," nor is it diminished " by being directed upon cold water." Thus Watson implied that the " delicate " electrical fire is to be compared with " coarser culinary fire," although the sense of delicateness and coarseness is not specified. Perhaps he meant no more than the degree of ease in penetrating bodies. One of his experiments, using " an artificial cold " (30 degrees below the freezing point in the Fahrenheit scale), seemed to indicate that " the fire of electricity is affected neither by the presence nor the absence of other fire." A " vast difference " in temperature apparently " makes no alteration in the appearance of the electrical flame." [79]

Watson's *Experiments and Observations* concludes with a defense against those who might think him " too minute in some of the before-mentioned particulars." These inquiries are " abstruse," he pointed out, and we have little " à priori " to guide us. Hence, " the greatest attention must be had to every circumstance, if we are truly desirous of investigating the laws of this surprizing power." [80] Watson appears to have been groping towards a unified conceptual scheme, but evidently he had not found it. The occasional use of " electrical fire " suggests an insight into a concept of subtle fluid, but the only physical property specifically attributed to " electrical fire " was a less degree of coarseness than " culinary fire." Thus, we have no way of being sure that he had a genuine concept of an elastic fluid of electricity. Certainly, the absence of any consideration of resinous electricity prevented him from arriving at a concept of a body's gaining or losing " electrical fire " in the sense of Franklin's " negative " and " positive " states of electrification. Furthermore, we must note that Watson paid no attention whatever to the possible mechanisms by which a body became charged; his interest began only with a state of electrification, with a glass rod already excited by having been rubbed. An awareness of this aspect of his investigations helps us to explain his failure to pursue the lead given by a beautiful experiment which appears to be wholly isolated in the book, unconnected with the rest of the text, and with no conclusions drawn from it. Let two men *A* and *B* stand on insulating cakes, he said. *A* is electrified and *B* is not. *A* touches *B* and " loses almost all his electricity at that touch only." This " electricity " is received by *B* and " stopped by the electrical cake." Once again, *A* is electrified " to the same degree as before," touches *B*, and the " snapping " is now less than before. With each successive electrification of A, the "snapping" between A and B "grows less and less, till B being impregnated with electricity, though received at intervals, the snapping will no longer be sensible." [81] The implications of this experiment for a theory based on a concept of electric matter seem so plain to us that we cannot easily understand how Watson failed to follow them to their "logical" conclusion. But the very fact that as good a man as Watson did not do so must be interpreted as signifying that creation in retrospect is vastly simpler and more "logical" than the actual production of new scientific ideas.

Even so, there is no doubt that the empirical observations made by Watson helped in considerable measure to explain a part of the capriciousness of electrical experiments. For example, he studied the degree of "penetration" of the "electrical power" through a dry "originally-electric" and "found by repeated trials, that either in a cake of wax alone, or of wax and resin mixed, when the electricity is very powerful, it has passed, I say, in straight lines through these cakes of the thickness of 2 inches and $\frac{4}{10}$ but I never could make it act through 2 inches $\frac{8}{10}$, for in this it was perfectly stopped." The conclusion drawn by Watson is that "the cakes commonly made use of to stop the electricity [insulators], by being too thin, suffer a considerable quantity of the electrical power to pervade them, and be lost in the floor." In other words, this "penetration of the electrical power through "originally-electrics is much greater than has hitherto been imagined, and has caused the want of success to great numbers of experiments." [82] Experimenters thereafter knew that care must be taken in the choice of adequate insulators.

Watson's Explanation of the Leyden Jar and the Circulation of Electricity

Watson's next publication was his widely read *Sequel*,* to which Franklin made reference in his first communication on the subject of electricity. Watson had now adopted the German type of electrical machine, which he described at length in the first pages of the *Sequel*. He thus had become master of a "greater electrical power than heretofore." [83] With the new apparatus he quickly found the

---

* Watson's *Sequel* was published as a pamphlet in 1746 by C. Davis, printer to the Royal Society, who had printed his previous pamphlet. The *Sequel* consists of a long paper dated 20 October 1746, addressed to the Royal Society, and read at a weekly meeting of 30 October 1746. The printed pamphlet of 1746 is described as "the second edition," presumably with the intention that the publication of the *Philosophical Transactions* be considered the "first edition." This paper was published belatedly in an appendix to volume 44 of the *Philosophical Transactions*, No. 484 (for the months of October, November, December, 1747) "containing some papers, which were not ready to be inserted in the order of their date."

" electricity [to] pervade . . . originally-electrics of above four inches diameter [i. e., thickness]." [84] In a darkened room, he brought a " black non-electric unexcited " near a large blunt wire hanging from the gun barrel or prime conductor (but not near enough to produce a " snap "), and noticed a " brush of blue lambent flame," accompanied by a " phosphoreal smell " that could be perceived at a considerable distance. By a pair of ingenious experiments he then showed " that flame conducts the electricity, and does not perceptibly diminish its force," a phenomenon previously studied by Winkler, and further explored by Franklin. Thus, it was demonstrated that the electrical effluvia themselves do not have a " sulphureous " nature, and that they do not burn. If " effluvia " could burn, they would be destroyed by a flame, which is contrary to the experiments on the conduction of effluvia by flame.[85]

Watson next turned to the famous experiment of Leyden " first discovered by professor Muschenbroek ":

The experiment is, that a vial of water is suspended to a gun-barrel by a wire let down a few inches into the water through the cork; and this gun-barrel, suspended in silk lines, is applied so near an excited glass globe that some metallic fringes inserted into the gun-barrel touch the globe in motion. Under these circumstances a man grasps the vial with one hand and touches the gun-barrel with a finger of the other. Upon which he receives a violent shock through both his arms, especially at his elbows and wrists, and a-cross his breast. This experiment succeeds best, *ceteris paribus*,

1. When the air is dry.
2. When the vial containing the water is of the thinnest glass.
3. When the outside of the vial is perfectly dry.
4. In proportion to the number of points of non-electric contact. Thus if you hold the vial only with your thumb and finger, the snap is small; larger when you apply another finger, and increases in proportion to the grasp of your whole hand.
5. When the water in the vial is heated; which being then warmer than the circumambient air, may not occasion the condensing the floating vapour therein upon the surface of the glass.[86]

Watson explained that " this effect arises from electrifying the non-electric water, included in the originally-electric glass." Thus, anything that makes the glass less originally-electric (more conducting), for example wetting the outside, " defeats the experiment by preventing the requisite accumulation of the electrical power." † Wat-

---

† Watson found it necessary to confute certain popular delusions about the Leyden jar: a fact which tends to show how great a mystery the action of the jar was at the time that Franklin made his initial electrical experiments. For example, Watson demonstrated that a gun barrel is not necessary in the performance of the experiment;

son found that the Leyden jar can be charged directly from the globe of the electrical machine. If one grasps the jar in the hand and removes it without touching the wire, " the electrified water ‡ will contain its force many hours, may be conveyed several miles, and afterwards exert its force upon touching the wire." Watson hung two vials from the gun barrel, grasped one in each hand and brought his forehead near the gun barrel; the shock was so violent that he never repeated the experiment again.[87] He noted that the increase of " the electrical force " arose from the addition of a second vial " whereby the points of non-electric contact were augmented." Dr. Bevis improved the form of the Leyden jar by wrapping the outside of the vial in very thin lead, so as to give a better contact between the non-electric (conductor) and the glass than could be provided by a hand holding the bottle. In agreeable conformity to Watson's theory, the new device produced a stronger stroke than had been possible in the old way.[88]

By a series of experiments, Watson showed " that the electrical force always describes a circuit." A man who discharges a Leyden jar by holding the electrified vial in one hand and touching the gun-barrel with the other will feel the shock only in his arms and " a-cross his breast. So that here we see the electrical power darts *rectissimo cursu* between the gun-barrel and vial." [89] An ingenious experiment involved two lines of persons, four to a line, each standing on wax. Persons *A*, *B*, *C*, *D*, formed a chain by grasping hands, as did persons *W*, *X*, *Y*, *Z*. *A* grasped the vial and *Z* the gun-barrel; if *D* then touched *W*, all eight felt the shock. But if *D* touched *X*, then *W* was not in the circuit (although *W* was in contact with *X*) and did not feel the shock. Or, *D* could touch *Y*, leaving *W* and *X* out of the circuit; or *D* could touch *Z*, leaving *W*, *X*, and *Y* out of the circuit; in each case the individuals left out felt no shock, although they remained in contact with those who did. In another demon-

the prime conductor could equally well be a sword, a solid piece of metal, or six men standing on wax cakes and touching each other. He also showed that iron filings can replace the water in the jar, but in this case the effect is lessened; if mercury is used to replace the water, the effect is the same, even though it might " have been imagined " that the " stroke " would increase in proportion to the specific gravities of the conducting material inside the bottle. A dry wood twig, inserted into the water through the cork (instead of a wire), was found to reduce the stroke to that of ordinary contact with an electrified gun barrel; the stroke was also greatly lessened when the hand of the experimenter was gloved.

‡ One of Franklin's discoveries was that when a Leyden jar is charged, the water itself is not electrified. It was, of course, natural enough to believe that the action of charging a Leyden jar was to put " electricity " into the water, because one merely grasped the jar in one hand and brought an insulated wire, which dipped into the water, to the prime conductor of the electrical machine; thus it would seem as if one were merely leading the accumulated " electricity " from the prime conductor into the water of the jar.

stration of the same phenomenon, a number of insulated persons were joined together by wires going from the left hand of one to the right hand of another, save for the two persons at the end. If one end-person grasped the vial with his free hand while the other end-person grasped the gun-barrel with his free hand, all would feel the shock. But if one member of the chain brought the wire in his left hand into contact with the wire in his right, the circuit would not include his body, and therefore he would not receive the shock when the other members of the chain did.[90] In the account of " circuits," Watson was using the term to express a path of action. He did not imply that there was a transmission of anything more than a force or " virtue " through the circuit or path from the outside of the vial to the gun-barrel or prime conductor.

Watson next showed the steps (of his " inquiries into the nature of electricity ") by which he had discovered " that the glass tubes and globes had not the electrical power in themselves, but only served as the first movers and determiners of that power." [91] A few months earlier, he had insulated himself on a cake of wax prior to rubbing a tube, hoping in this way " to prevent any of the electrical power from discharging itself through me onto the floor." But the opposite had happened; the charge produced was less than usual and not greater. A similar occurence, he noted, had been described by Bose:[92] an electrical machine was placed upon " originally electrics " (it is not specified whether they were glass, wax, or resin) and then the person whose hands were rubbed by the rotating globe gave " no sign of being electrified, when touched by an unexcited non-electric." But if the second experimenter, standing on the bare floor, touched the globe in motion with a finger, the person rubbing the globe became " instantly electrified, and that very strongly." Bose gave what " he modestly calls [according to Watson] a plausible subterfuge rather than a solution," really an analogic § explanation. Watson referred also to an account by " Mr. Allamand, lately printed at the Hague," in which the same type of phenomenon had been

§ This " explanation " was presented by Watson as follows: ". . . that a power cannot act at the same time with all its vigour, when one part of it is already employed; as a horse, who already draws an hundred pounds, cannot draw an additional weight as freely as if he had not been loaded at all. That the hand excites the virtue already in the sphere; therefore if the same power impregnates the man, there remains none for the globe. That the virtue of the globe then cannot be communicated at the same time to the man, by whom it is created. That he, who gives it, cannot receive it himself. From these, and such like considerations, it appears to him; that the man upon the ground, who holds his fingers to the globe in motion, instead of his diminishing its electrical force, throws that force back again over the man, who excited it. That the finger in this case seems to operate as an electric *per se*, and drives back the electrical power." [93] This extract is a valuable index to what might pass for an explanation of electrical phenomena prior to Franklin.

observed. A machine and the man who rubbed the globe were both placed upon pitch in order to prevent the dissipation of the electrical power of the globes (which " passes off by the frame, upon which the globes are mounted, into the floor and [is] dissipated thereby "). Contrary to expectations, the electrical power was found to be " considered diminished, and sometimes there is even none at all." [94]

Watson repeated Allamand's experiment with similar results; he placed the electrical machine and the man turning the wheel on insulating " electrical cakes," and found that the gun-barrel in contact with the globes would, " after one or two small snaps," no longer attract light substances or " emit any fire." He was thereby led " to conceive, that the electrical power was not inherent in the glass, but came from the floor of the room." If this explanation were correct, Watson reasoned, then if a second experimenter standing on the floor should merely touch any part of the insulated electrical machine, while the globes were turning, the gun-barrel would " snap." Watson himself stood on the floor next to the insulated electrical machine with its insulated " operator " and " put one hand upon the frame of the machine, and touched the gun-barrel with one of the fingers of my other [hand]. Upon this fire issued, and the snapping continued as long as I held my hand upon the machine, but ceased upon taking it off." When the machine and the man who turned the wheel were both placed on insulating cakes, did the electrical power actually go through his body to the machine? If so, Watson reasoned, then " a fine wire held in my hand at a few inches distance ought to be attracted by any part of the machine." While the test seemed to have worked out according to the theory, " the attraction lasted a very small space of time. After that the wire hung from his hand vertically even though the globes continued to be rotated. This action could be explained, however, by a further supposition or working hypothesis, viz. " that the gun-barrel, and the other non-electrics suspended in contact with the globes, would only contain a certain quantity of the electrical æther," and no more. Thus, to make the wire be steadily attracted to the frame of the insulated electrical machine (by the action of the electrical power going from the floor through Watson and then through the wire to the machine) a means had to be provided so that the electrical power might find " again a communication between the floor and the machine."

The above explanation contains what seems to have been Watson's first use of the term " electrical æther." It thus provides an occasion for inquiring whether Watson had at this point a genuine concept of the electric fluid such as Franklin later had. Had this been the case, then an obvious experiment for Watson to have performed next would have been to stand on an insulating " electrical cake " alongside the insulated machine and the insulated man turning the globes, and touch the gun-barrel with one hand while holding the wire near the frame of the machine with the other hand. In the terms of the single-fluid theory of Franklin, charging the globe by rubbing would be nothing but a transfer of electric fluid from the leather or human " rubber " to the globes (or, possibly, *vice versa*) which could not go on indefinitely unless the fluid accumulating on the globe were enabled to return to the machine and the rubber, as through the insulated man and the wire.* But Watson performed the experiment standing on the floor (i. e., grounded, not insulated). He found that if he placed one finger on the gun-barrel while holding a wire in the other hand near the machine, the wire was attracted so long as his " finger continued upon the gun-barrel . . . but no longer." To his mind this afforded a satisfactory proof that " one cause of the electrical attraction is the current of the electrical æther setting [!] to the machine through the wire." This current may be stopped by either of two causes: (1) if there is no discharge from the gun-barrel, so that the accumulation reaches the maximum possible —then the current of electrical æther (from the floor [earth] through the machine to the gun-barrel) ceases; (2) if " other currents [i. e., paths] are opened," as would be the case when " the machine is touched in other parts." [95]

Watson also performed the above experiment, so to speak, in reverse. With the machine and the operator who rotated the globes insulated as before, a second man stood on the machine itself; although the globes were rotated, not much sign of electrification was observed in the second man. But if a third man, standing on the floor, were to touch the gun-barrel (or, if a " wire hanging to the wainscot of the room " were to touch the gun-barrel), then " the man on the machine emits fire copiously; and either himself, or the man who turns the wheel of the machine, fires inflammable substances." The " usual course of the electricity," remarked Watson, was inverted in this experiment. " That power " which is usually brought to the globes by the " wood-work " of the machine, and from the globes " discharged " upon the gun-barrel, was in this instance brought to the gun-barrel by the wire. From the gun-barrel the globes " throw it all over, not only the machine, but any non-electric in contact with it, if the electricity is stopped." [96]

* Watson later performed such an experiment as I have indicated, but he did so in a quite different context. We shall see that he proved by it that the current of

Watson's explanation of the preceding experiment shows clearly that he did not have in mind a conception of the electric fluid such as characterized Franklin's theory. Although Watson had referred (at least once) to " electrical æther," he wrote of " the electricity " in his account of this experiment, using the latter term in a loose and general way, as he had done previously. It is, in other words, not clear from the text whether Watson had always in mind an elastic subtle fluid or æther or merely " electrical power " or a kind of " virtue." Later on, Watson felt the need of specifying some properties of an electrical æther as an elastic subtle fluid and attempted to explain the observed phenomena in terms of currents of this æther.

The " electricity " manifested in experiments with an electrical machine comes, Watson said, from the ground through the building (floor or wainscoting). It can either enter the wooden framework of the machine and proceed through the globes to the gun-barrel, or—according to Watson—it can enter the gun-barrel and proceed through the globes to the wooden framework of the machine. The Franklinian type of electric fluid, by contrast, is unidirectional; it accumulates on glass (which becomes positively charged) and can come from the floor to the machine and proceed thence to the globes and gun-barrel; or it can go from the machine to the globes and gun-barrel and proceed thence to the wainscoting; but it can *not* move in different ways as Watson's " electricity " is able to do. Yet Watson was at times very near to Franklin's ideas, as may be seen in his statement that " the glass globes circulate the electrical fire, which they receive from their friction against the cushions or the hand of a man, and which is constantly supplied to these last from the floor." From this sentence, there can be no doubt that Watson had in mind some kind of genuine substance of electricity that the globes tend to circulate, or redistribute in some way, in much the same manner that circulation is produced by a water pump or the heart of an animal.

The gun-barrel may receive electricity from the globes but, Watson said, its presence gives no sign whatever unless " the electricity " is " stopped," i. e., unless the gun-barrel is insulated from and has no contact with ground—such as through a wire from the wainscoting, or a man standing on the floor touching the gun-barrel, or through a wetting and dampening of the silk threads that suspend the gun-barrel. Otherwise " the electricity" passes " *pleno rivo* to the floor from whence it came." If the gun-barrel is not grounded, " the elec-

electrical æther may be driven through a circuit by an electrical machine in either of the two possible directions, depending on the circumstances.

tricity " is " stopped " and can go no further. Then it accumulates—
but only up to a certain degree (as he had demonstrated previously)
—and may make its presence manifest " either by fire or attraction."
A " snap " will ensue when a man standing on the floor touches the
gun-barrel, but while " the fire is always observable " as it leaves
the gun-barrel, there is not always an observable " snap." For example, if a piece of blunt wire is fastened to the suspended gun-
barrel, and the hand brought near but not quite touching it, " the
electrical power becomes visible like a fine blue cone of flame, with
its point towards the wire. When the hand is placed at a proper
distance, the blast, like that of cold air, is therefrom very manifest."
But if one does not " determine the electricity by these means to a
point," it is dissipated in a general manner from all parts of the
charged gun-barrel.[97]

Watson's Theory of the " Electrical Æther "

Watson had to specify what he meant by the " electrical æther."
" What I here call the electrical æther, is that atmosphere which
surrounds both excited originally-electrics and excited non-electrics." [98] This " atmosphere " would seem to resemble the " sphere of
effluvia " in the Desaguliers conception; its extent to a considerable
distance from charged bodies is supposedly manifested by the attraction of a piece of thread or " cotton-grass-seed " at several feet from
a charged body, by the " blast of cold wind " from the wire in the
previous experiment, and so on. If there is not an unelectrified
(" unexcited ") non-electric (conducting body) in the neighborhood, this " atmosphere seems to be determined equally over all the
excited non-electrics in contact with the machine," but if an " unexcited " non-electric is brought near, most of the " atmosphere "
or " æther " is " determined that way " and the attraction in any
other region is diminished. Repulsion does not operate until " the
electrical æther is sufficiently accumulated "; in this accumulation
we are to see " the cause of the repulsion of electricity."

A comparison with common air shows the " electrical æther " to
be " much more subtile," since the latter passes to a certain depth
through all known bodies." Its greater " subtility " is " demonstrated by its passing through several glasses at the same time;
through any one of which, though ever so thin, air cannot pass." [99]
It passes most readily through the metals, water and other fluids
(but not " resinous " ones) : next, in order, through moist animal
bodies (dead or alive), stones, wood, and earths. Resins, dry animal
substances, wax, and glass, permit the passage of this " æther " only
to a limited extent. Like common air, the " electrical æther " has

the property of being able to move light bodies. Another property that this æther has in common with air is elasticity; the " electrical æther " is thus to be included in the category of " elastic fluids " in the sense (described earlier) in which the men of the eighteenth century used the word. Evidence for its elasticity is provided in its property of " extending itself round excited electrics " and non-electrics to a considerable distance, and the property of over-coming the " attraction of cohesion " in the siphon experiment. The latter was a popular experiment in the 1740's and consisted of elec-trifying an ingeniously contrived siphon in which the water would begin to flow upon electrification; a variation was the electrical foun-tain in which the rate of flow of the water and the degree of spread-ing out was vastly increased upon electrification of the water. The elasticity of this æther was also to be deduced " from the violent shock we feel in our bodies in the experiments with water."

All bodies contain " a quantity of this æther." [100] Thus, said Watson, we may explain why one or two snaps can be obtained from the gun-barrel in the experiment of the insulated machine and operator, but not many more. The machine loses æther in each snap, and can give out no further snaps from the gun-barrel unless an additional supply of æther is brought to the machine so as to be pumped by the globe onto the gun-barrel; this happens " as soon as any non-electric unexcited touches the machine." The æther is an elastic fluid; therefore, if there is an accumulation of it, there must be an endeavour " by the nearest unexcited non-electric to restore the æquilibrium." Watson supposed that the restoration of the equilibrium was " the cause of the attraction of excited glass tubes and globes, as well as that of excited non-electrics." From what has gone before, we should expect that the restoration of equilibrium might have been supposed to occur by a blast of electrical æther from the globe or the gun-barrel to a neighboring unexcited non-electric (conductor). This conclusion would certainly accord with the idea of an excited state being caused by an accumulation of æther. But the lack of clarity (or consistency) in Watson's conceptions is shown by his adoption of the opposite view, viz. " the blast of electrical æther constantly sets in from the nearest unexcited non-electric towards those excited, and carries with it whatever light bodies lie in its course." The reason why the blast had to be directed *toward* the globes or tube or charged body is clear, even if simple logic would seem to demand that the blast must proceed in the other direction: Watson had to explain that light uncharged bodies are *attracted toward* the charged body and are not repelled from it.†

† Plainly Watson, at this point, had no concern with the two modes of electrification: vitreous and resinous.

Watson attempted to show that there is evidence for this " setting in of the current of electrical æther towards excited non-electrics," that it is " very perceptible to your feeling as a blast of cold wind; if when you are electrified, you hold your hand over a plate with some bran in it, by which blast the bran is carried against your hand."

No hint was given by Watson as to the mechanics of the process of æther accumulation or the flow of current of electrical æther. The excited globes or gun-barrel, in terms of his theory, accumulate a quantity of electrical æther from the woodwork of the electrical machine and the floor. This accumulated æther is said to stand around such charged bodies in the form of an atmosphere. The atmosphere arises from the elasticity of the fluid or æther, whose parts repel one another. Hence there would seem to be some tendency for the electrical æther to leave charged bodies in a blast towards an uncharged non-electric (conductor). This is not only a conclusion from theory; Watson had previously dwelt at length on the empirical evidence to support this view: the glow or brush discharge from the gun-barrel with a wire affixed to it and also the motion of æther away from that wire which becomes " manifest to your feeling as a blast of cold wind." [101]

The reader's bewilderment is soon increased. Watson established —at least to his own satisfaction—the existence of a blast of æther toward excited or electrified bodies from non-excited non-electrics, accompanied by a motion of light substances toward the excited bodies. And then he showed how " these light substances are again repelled by the blast from [!] the excited bodies, as soon as they come in contact and sometimes before."

Watson found no inconsistency in the fact that theory and empirical evidence seemed to indicate two æther blasts: one away from charged bodies and the other toward charged bodies. Electrical phenomena, in other words, must involve a simultaneous motion of æther in two opposite directions. Such was Watson's firm belief at this time, and he presented an experimental demonstration that " the restoring this æquilibrium is not imaginary." [102]

The experiment in question was due to Benjamin Wilson. Two metal plates, very clean and dry, whose surfaces were " nearly equal," were placed horizontally, one above the other, to form what we call today a parallel-plate air condenser. The upper plate was hung from an excited non-electric (such as the gun-barrel or prime conductor of an electrical machine) and the lower plate was grounded, being held in the hand of a man standing on the floor. A " whole leaf " of silver was placed on the lower plate, which was then slowly brought nearer and nearer to the upper one; a number of trials would determine the proper separation for the silver leaf to become perfectly suspended at right angles to the two plates, but touching neither one.‡ " You frequently observe, both at the top and bottom of the silver, the electrical fire "; the same effect was produced when the lower plate was charged and the upper one grounded.[103] According to Watson, " the space occupied by this leaf of silver, is that, where the *æquilibrium* of the electrical æther is restored." The reason he gave for this conclusion is that the silver leaf was " blown away " when he removed the lower plate " through which from the floor the flux of this æther is furnished." The leaf was also " blown away " if he placed the lower plate on an electric *per se* (non-conductor) " by which this flux is prevented likewise." So far, the explanation seems merely to involve the flow of æther from the ground to the charged gun-barrel or other non-electric. But Watson immediately added the following commentary:

No body can be suspended *in æquilibrio* but from the joint action of two different directions of power: so here, the blast of electrical æther from the excited plate blows the silver towards the plate unexcited. This last in its turn, by the blast of electrical æther from the floor setting through it, drives the silver towards the plate electrified. We find from hence likewise, that the draught of electrical æther from the floor, is always in proportion to the quantity thrown by the globes over the gun-barrel; or the *æquilibrium*, by which the silver is suspended, could not be maintained.[104]

This explanation is surely not an " obvious " inference from the observed facts. Therefore, after describing how dry shoes worn by the holder of the lower plate would prevent the experiment from succeeding, and similar matters, Watson returned to the doubts that might be aroused by his explanation:

It may be imagined, that it is possible for the silver to be suspended, without supposing a flux of the electrical æther from the nearest unexcited non-electric, as well as from excited one; that is, by the simple electrical attraction. But to obviate this, it must be remembered; that the electrified gun-barrel both attracts and repels light substances at the same time. Can this attraction and repulsion be conceived without the operation of the electrical æther both to and from the gun-barrel at the same time? Does not this point out an afflux as well as an efflux? Are not the electrical repulsions as strong at least as the attractions? Do not we see light bodies, either between excited originally-electrics or excited non-

‡ So far as I know, Wilson's device is the first parallel-plate condenser with air separation, a device usually attributed to Æpinus who described one in the memoirs of the Berlin Academy of Sciences for 1756, a decade later. Franklin studied the air condenser of Wilson in the 1740's and altered the shape of the metal leaf so that it would move like a fish.

electrics, and unexcited non-electrics, dart like a ball between two rackets of equal force?

There follow two objections to this theory of electrical action, each of which can be answered so long as there is no doubt about the possibility of a simultaneous " afflux " and " efflux," but the whole argument has begun to remind us of the hypothesis of the Abbé Nollet. And surely it must have seemed that Watson was a partisan of Nollet when he said that he was " able to prove the afflux experimentally, as well as the efflux. . . ." [105] There is no doubt of Watson's approval of Nollet. The penultimate paragraph of the *Sequel* begins: " I cannot conclude these papers without congratulating that excellent philosopher and learned member of this Society, the Abbé Nollet of Paris." [106] The latter had apparently stated two years earlier a number of principles for which the experiments had yet to be made. Watson said that these principles agreed closely with his own conclusions from experiments. It was all the more remarkable, he said, in that Nollet's principles had been stated (so far as Watson knew) before there was much valid empirical evidence to support them. The evidence was apparently provided for the first time in Watson's own experiments as described in the *Sequel*. Nollet's list of principles included the statement " that when electrics were excited and brought near non-electrics unexcited, the electricity moved in opposite directions." [107]

Immediately after describing how the electrical æther is simultaneously in efflux and afflux,§ Watson presented another experiment in which he believed the electrical æther went in one direction under one set of circumstances and in the opposite direction when the circumstances were but slightly altered. In this experiment, the electrical machine and operator are both insulated and the experimenter is likewise insulated by being on an originally-electric or non-conductor. The experimenter receives a snap or two on touching the gun-barrel and no more, even though the operator continues to rotate the globes. If he then " touches the wood-work of the machine with one hand, and applies a finger of his other near the gun-barrel, at that instant he receives the electrical strokes." Here, Watson remarked (and it could almost have been Franklin writing instead of Watson)

we see a circulation of part of this man's electrical fire, which operates in the following manner. First, the man by applying one of his hands to the machine becomes a part thereof; and by the motion of the globes,

§ We shall see in the next chapter that Franklin had a brief Nolletian moment in the first stages of his research and thought he had observed the " efflux " and " afflux " described by Watson.

part of the electrical fire, inherent in his body, is driven upon the gun-barrel; but it is instantly restored to him again upon his touching the gun-barrel with his other hand. Thus he continues communicating the fire with one hand, and having it restored to him with the other, as long as he pleases.

But the next experiment has a different conclusion. The machine and operator are insulated from the floor as before, and one experimenter stands on wax and touches the machine to supply the electrical fire. A second experimenter, standing on the floor, " constantly or by turns " touches the gun-barrel to remove the accumulated electrical fire. Since the insulated man can receive no supply of electrical fire from the floor, Watson remarked, it might be supposed that he would be divested of all of his normal supply of electrical fire. " But the contrary proves true, and after a considerable time, the strokes are as strong as at first . . ." Therefore, Watson concluded, " I conceive, that, as soon as this man has parted with any portion of his necessary, his determined quantity, to the gun-barrel by the motion of the globes, he has it restored to him upon any unexcited non-electric's touching the gun-barrel, by having the usual course of the electricity inverted." [108] In other words, the rubbed globes—which Watson compared to pumps or the heart in animals—were supposed to have the curious property of transmitting the electrical fluid at times in one direction and at times in the opposite direction.*

Watson concluded his *Sequel* in the style of Newton's *Opticks* with a series of " queries " which I will now summarize in the form of statements.[109] (1) Electrical attraction and repulsion may be attributed to the flux of electrical æther. (2) Electricity or electrical æther may be elementary fire. (3) This fire appears in different forms; as air when diffused, as lambent flame when brought towards a point; it explodes and becomes the object of feeling as well as hearing; and although it does not provide the sensation of heat on the skin, it is truly fire because it ignites inflammable substances. (4) This fire is always intimately connected with all bodies (least with pure dry air) and has been separated from and found in water, flame, smoke, red-hot iron, and mixtures colder than freezing water. (5) Its subtilty is proved by its passing through all known bodies. (6) Its elasticity may be inferred from a number of observations. (7) The electrical machine may be called a fire-pump in the same sense that the instrument of Guericke and Boyle is called an air-pump. (8) The separation of fire from bodies by motion, and its restoration to them after that motion has ceased, inclines us to the opinion that

---

* In this case apparently, there was no simultaneous afflux and efflux.

fire is "an original, a distinct, principle, formed by the Creator himself," rather than the opinion held by Bacon, Boyle, and Newton that it is "mechanically producible from other bodies." (9) Caution must be used in connecting the elementary fire which we see issue from a man with the "vital flame and *calidum innatum* of the ancients," since this fire is equally producible from dead and live animals. (10) By increasing the number and sizes of the water-filled Leyden jars we can probably kill instantly even large animals. (Le Monnier had killed birds and Watson himself had killed a linnet and a "rat much more than half grown"; Franklin tried the experiment and killed a turkey by the electric shock, roasted it, and found it very tender).

Watson referred in Qu. 1 to "the flux of electrical æther," but in Qu. 2 he suggested that what "we call electricity, electrical æther, electrical power, etc.," might be only "elementary fire." This fire appears in various forms, is subtle and elastic. Since it is separated from bodies by motion and is restored to them after motion has ceased, Watson suggested, furthermore, the rejection of the concept of his British predecessors (Bacon, Boyle, and Newton) who had not conceived "fire" as an "original, a distinct principle," as Boerhaave had done, but rather as being "mechanically producible from other bodies." The reader was referred to Newton's discussion of this subject in the *Opticks*, from which Watson also took the quotation with which he terminated his book. For the contrary view to Newton's, he cited, with brief quotations, two articles in the memoirs of the French Academy of Science (1705 and 1709), 'sGravesande's book on Newtonian philosophy, and Boerhaave's *Elements of Chemistry*.† Although, like Nollet whom he so admired, Watson identified the matter producing electrical effects with fire, he did not state explicitly that this matter was identical to that of light, as Nollet had done. Watson's view that glass tubes or globes "had not the electrical power in themselves" and that they were merely "the first movers and determiners of that power" is similar to Nollet's general principles. But what is far more important—at least from the general view of eighteenth-century physics presented in this study as a whole—is that Watson concluded his *Sequel* with a general defense of his method based on "that excellent maxim of Sir Isaac Newton laid down in his *Opticks*," i. e., Newton's own final statement about the method of investigating difficult things by proceeding from analysis to composition, and having no regard for hypotheses in experimental philosophy. Forsooth!

Watson then added a final modest note:

† See Chapter Seven.

I am desirous, that what is contained in these papers, you will be pleased to regard, rather as the rude outlines of a system, than as a system itself; which I am in hopes, men of better heads and more leisure will prosecute: and if hereafter from being possessed of more observations than we at present are masters of, any opinions in these papers shall be found erroneous; I at all times shall be willing readily to retract them. I rely upon your wonted candour.

I have described Watson's ideas and their development at great length so that the reader may judge the novelties in Franklin's theory by viewing them against the background of Watson's ideas with which Franklin was acquainted. Franklin had been reading the *Sequel* at the time of completing his first letter on electricity, and he was conscious of the fact that he was adding something to what had been previously stated by Watson. No one can read Watson's publications and Franklin's without appreciating Franklin's enormous debt to Watson—in experiments, concepts, and even style and expression. Without a full presentation of Watson's ideas there is no possibility of judging Watson's belief that he was an independent discoverer of the so-called Franklinian theory of electrical action.

The preceding pages may seem to contain too great an emphasis on the shortcomings of Watson's explanations. This was done not so much to disparage Watson as to indicate the need for revision and extension which Franklin saw and, in great measure, devoted himself to supplying. But we must not forget that without Watson's work as a starting point, Franklin could never have made the speedy progress that altered the whole subject of electricity to the first stages of being an exact science.

Benjamin Martin on the " Electrical Æther "

Watson's ideas about the " electrical æther " were related to the material concept of fire expounded by Boerhaave, 'sGravesande, and others, and to Newton's views on the æther. The association of the " cause " of electricity with the Newtonian æther was presented in the works of two other authors, published in the same year as Watson's *Sequel*, 1746: a little essay by Benjamin Martin, the famous instrument maker and writer on natural philosophy (whose point of view has been presented in earlier chapters), and a book by Benjamin Wilson. In the manuscript version of Franklin's first communication on electricity, addressed to Peter Collinson in London from Philadelphia, 25 May 1747, he acknowledged that " Watson's first Part and Sequel " and " Martin's Electricity " had been received.[110]

Benjamin Martin, whose little tract on electricity Franklin read at about the same time that he read Watson's *Sequel*, has the illuminating title: *An Essay on Electricity: being an enquiry into the nature, cause and properties thereof, on the principles of Sir Isaac Newton's theory of vibrating motion, light and fire. . . .* The preface contains an attack on Dr. John Freke, the author of a recently published pamphlet who—according to Martin—disagreed with the principles of Isaac Newton. Newton has many opponents, Martin observed, and he regretted that Freke should prove to be one of them; as far as Martin was concerned, " forsaking Sir Isaac is as bad, if not worse, than opposing him; and I look upon error in philosophy to be hurtful." [111] Martin seems to have been particularly disturbed by the fact that many of the writings on electricity were written " as if Sir Isaac, and his philosophy, had never been heard of, or read." But, unless " we pursue our enquiries by the clue given us by that great man," we shall never understand the cause of electricity, because the " nature, cause, properties, and effects of electric virtue, are explicable only on the principles of the *Newtonian doctrine of light and fire.*"

Martin explained that a sensation of warmth or heat is produced whenever the parts of bodies are agitated, as in the case of friction, percussion, fermentation, vital motion, or the action of light. When bodies are agitated or heated beyond a certain limit, they " emit or throw off such fine subtle particles, or effluvia, which shine or excite the idea of light; and which therefore we generally call particles of light." When the parts of bodies are agitated to emit light and heat, the motion is " of the vibrating kind." [112] This was the way, supposedly, that Isaac Newton had explained a number of different phenomena, including one electrical experiment. Martin's idea was to apply Newton's theory of light and fire to solve the phenomena of electricity.

We may observe the transformation or perversion of the Newtonian categories, in Martin's statement of a series of " Phænomena." The first of these is that the " electric virtue consists in a fine subtile matter, omitted from some sorts of bodies under the circumstances of attrition, which bodies are called electrics *per se.*" [113] Certainly, Newton would never have considered such a statement to be a " phenomenon." Martin explained that this " virtue " repels all light bodies which lie on the surface of the excited body, attracts light substances " within the space of its action," and then repels them again, not allowing them to approach the " electrized body " again until they have touched some other body.

The experiments presented by Martin are all explained in terms of " this subtle matter, or spirit," which " appears to be of an elastic nature, and acts by the reciprocations of its tremours, or pulses, which are occasioned by the vibrating motion of the parts of an electric body, excited by friction." [114] The experiments themselves are ingenious, invoking repulsion and attraction, and illustrating some of the elementary principles of insulation. Yet, save for the title itself, it is difficult to see in what way Martin's explanations, based on effluvia and virtue, are in any sense related to Sir Isaac Newton's philosophy, in any of its forms.

Martin published a supplement to his book on electricity, which was devoted to an even more complete attack on Freke, but which has in it an interesting " postscript," devoted to Watson's *Sequel*. This postscript begins by comparing Freke and Watson: " Having now done with the *worst* writer on electricity that ever was, I shall beg leave to make a few observations on what we have just now proposed to us from the *best*; I mean the *Sequel* of the ingenious and industrious Mr. Watson. . . ." [115] Martin addressed himself primarily to the " queries " of Watson. First of all, he said, Watson had asked whether one could not attribute electrical attraction and repulsion to the flux of æther or " ætherial particles of matter." Martin objected; he could not understand why Watson had used the word " electrical," since Newton had plainly shown that " this ætherial matter is the common subject of all kinds of light and fire, as well as that of electricity." [116] In the second query, Watson had asked whether the electrical æther is distinct from elementary fire. Martin replied that a distinction should be made between " electrical æther " and " electricity." As to " electricity," it is " undoubtedly fire." But the " electrical æther " is evidently not " fire " and is certainly not " elementary fire." Martin wanted to understand a little bit more exactly what is meant by the word " fire." Before one could ask whether " fire " is an " element," the sense of the word " element " would have to be specified.

Martin addressed himself chiefly to the eighth query, whether or not electrical experiments do not make us incline to the opinions of 'sGravesande and Boerhaave, " who held fire to be an original, distinct principle," rather than believing with Bacon, Boyle, and Newton that it is simply a mechanical production. Martin's argument is chiefly based on the fact that there is an important difference " between *separating fire from bodies*, and a *setting in of fire*, (*i. e., æther*) *to those bodies* from the air." This fire should be considered as easily pervading the pores of all bodies and thrown out by the vibration of their elastic particles, whenever these particles are excited to vibration by friction. Neither Boerhaave nor anyone else has ever " proved fire to be an element." [117]

Furthermore it is "plain from phænomena" that bodies whose parts are most inflammable are saturated more than others with "this electrical matter," and that this matter is kept in them by a very great attracting power so that they cannot easily transmit it. Bodies whose parts are very elastic will throw out this "electric matter" whenever they are excited by friction, and then "electric matter" will set in "from all other parts and bodies to restore the equilibrium." This suggestion, sounding exactly like the theory of the Abbé Nollet, is said to account for what is called "the attracting power of electricity." As for "the repulsive power," experiment shows that a light body is never repelled until it has first become "impregnated with the electric matter." If a body is insulated, and then receives "electric matter," it will—according to Martin—be repelled by another electrified body, so long as neither one becomes discharged. This statement seems to indicate that Martin was not aware of the two kinds of electricity or electrification, a subject to which neither he nor Watson particularly addressed themselves.

The action of the globe, according to Martin, is merely to put this "electrical matter" into motion, and to condense it to such a degree that it will begin to shine, or will "become flame, and will in a small degree burn; and then, and not till then, is it properly called fire. So that the Newtonian theory is still worthy of its superior author, and consistent with every experiment and phænomenon of nature; and, I doubt not, will at last be universally received, when the mists that have obscured it, shall be all dispelled by the irresistible beams and radiance of culminating truth." [118]

Martin's book certainly did not contribute greatly to the advance of electrical theory, and the appeals in the name of Newton and the Newtonian philosophy seem to have been made in name only, and not in fact. Wholly apart from the presentation of obvious hypotheses as "phænomena," Martin's little tract can at best be described as a travesty of the whole Newtonian point of view. We shall see in the final chapter of this monograph that others at this time were writing loosely about all sorts of phenomena in the name of Newton, and that many of their attempts ended up by being very little more than "philosophical romances"—springing from the exact corpuscular philosophy expounded by Newton in the *Opticks*. In considering the achievement of Benjamin Franklin, therefore, we must keep in the forefront of our mind that the application of the Newtonian natural philosophy to new areas, such as electrical phenomena, was not purely mechanical, but required deep insight into the operations of nature. Yet we must also take note that Martin was one of the European writers who can be described in Franklin's terms as saying that whatever might be the substance causing electrical attraction and repulsion, it is certainly not " created " by friction.

Benjamin Wilson on Electricity and the Æther

The other book published in 1746 was based upon papers read at the Royal Society by Benjamin Wilson. This little book, printed by C. Davis, printer to the Royal Society, who was also the printer of Watson's pamphlets, was dedicated to Martin Folkes, President of the Royal Society, and was entitled *An Essay towards an Explanation of the Phænomena of Electricity deduced from the Æther of Sir Isaac Newton*. In the manuscript version of Franklin's second communication on electricity, a letter addressed to Peter Collinson of London from Philadelphia, 28 July 1747, Franklin acknowledged that " we have received . . . Wilson's Electricity." [119] Benjamin Wilson was a man of many parts, equally famous in his day as a scientist and a painter. A portrait of Franklin by him graced the walls of the Franklins' living room in Philadelphia until it was removed when the British evacuated the city during the Revolution. Author of many books and articles,‡ Wilson achieved a certain notoriety in science because of the violence of his attack on the pointed lightning rods advocated by Franklin. Wilson preferred blunt lightning rods and persuaded some of his contemporaries at the time of the Revolution that Franklinian rods should be replaced by anti-American rods ending in knobs. Because Franklin's friend, Sir John Pringle, a conservative in politics, would not acquiesce in political legislation of scientific laws, he was said to have retired as President of the Royal Society.§

‡ Franklin's comments on the book by Hoadly and Wilson have been mentioned in Chapter Eight.

§ In his biography of Sir John Pringle, Andrew Kippis mentioned that during Sir John's presidency of the Royal Society he suffered an accident, falling " in the area of the back part of his house, from which he received considerable hurt, and which, in its consequences, affected his health, and weakened his spirits. Such being the state of his body and mind, he began to entertain thoughts of resigning the President's chair. It hath been said likewise, and believed, that he was much hurt by the disputes introduced into the Society, concerning the question, whether pointed or blunted electrical conductors are the most efficacious in preserving buildings from the pernicious effects of lightning." Andrew Kippis could " assert nothing from personal knowledge " on this subject for he " never heard from him any suggestion of the kind that has been mentioned." [120]

In a volume containing manuscripts and correspondence written by Benjamin Wilson, chief advocate of the blunted conductors, there is a page on which Wilson gives his own version of the affair. (This volume is in the British Musem, and the following selection is reproduced through the courtesy of the Trustees.)

" In 1778, he quitted the presidency of the Royal Society. A fall which he considered as the effect of a palsy, appeared to him a notice to think no longer of anything but repose; besides, a discussion which had arisen in the bosom of the Society, lively

In the preface, Wilson said that it is the custom of " experimental philosophers to frame no hypotheses " in deriving the " causes of things from their effects." Experimental philosophers do not admit hypotheses into philosophy, except as " questions whose truth may be disputed." The job of the experimenter is to derive the cause of things from the simplest principles possible, and to assume no principle that is not " proved from experiments." This admirable way of philosophizing enabled Sir Isaac Newton to give us an explication of the system of the world, " most happily deduced from the theory of gravity." In a similar manner, said Wilson, he hoped " to be able, from the phænomena of electricity, to shew by experiments, how far it agrees with that most general of all material causes the *æther*: the properties of which have been lately, and very learnedly treated, by Dr. Bryan Robinson of Dublin." The basic problem, as Wilson saw it, was to determine how electrics *per se* (like glass, wax, pitch, resin, sulphur, silk, and so on) have the particular property of being able, after friction, " to emit a certain fluid called the electric matter." [121] To determine also what the electric matter is, and how it acts upon bodies.

Wilson believed that the precise nature and properties of the æther are " not universally known." Thus he had found it necessary to insert " some quotations from Sir Isaac Newton, to explain what his notions of it were; particularly an extract of his letter to Mr. Boyle, and likewise some propositions from a dissertation on the æther by Dr. Bryan Robinson." The conclusion to which Wilson's thoughts had led him was " that the æther and electric matter are the same, or productive of the same effects."

In 1745 Robinson had published a work entitled *Sir Isaac Newton's Account of the Æther*, a pamphlet of fifty-one pages, of which the first twenty-one contain a reprint of Newton's famous letter to Boyle of 28 February 1678/9, which had just been published for the first time in the life of Boyle prefixed to the edition of Boyle's works. Pages 22 to 32 consist of extracts relating to the æther, taken from the Queries in Book Three of Newton's *Opticks*. The re-

afflicted him: the use of electrical conductors, constructed according to the principles of Mr. Franklin, had been greedily adopted in England, at the time when Mr. Franklin was an Englishman; he had ceased to be so, he was become one of the Chiefs of a revolution, perhaps more humiliating to British pride, than on the contrary to the true interests of the nation: they appeared to have repented that they had received the discovery of an enemy: a question on the form of electrical conductors, became a party affair between the enemies of America and the numerous partizans which it had retained in England. Friend of Mr. Franklin, more friend to truth, Mr. Pringle supported their cause with courage, and he gained the victory; but he saw with grief the Society divided in opinion, and the spirit of political factions profane the sanctuary of the Sciences."

mainder comprises an appendix in which Robinson tried to explain at further length the applications of Newton's ideas to the explanation of muscular motion and sensation. Several propositions were developed mathematically, in a manner similar to a previous publication of Robinson's, entitled a *Dissertation on the Æther of Sir Isaac Newton*, which had appeared in Dublin in 1743. This earlier work, of 124 pages, led to a General Scholium in which Robinson asked how the æther, which " causes a great part of the phænomena of nature," has such "great activity and power." Its particles do not touch one another, although they repel one another with great force. Hence, Robinson argued, there must be " some cause interceding the particles which gives them this repulsive power." [122] He then explained that such a cause * must be either " matter " or " spirit," because man knows of nothing in the universe other than matter or spirit. In the case of the æther particles, the cause cannot be matter, since matter is, according to the Newtonian philosophy, " in its own nature inert, and has not any activity in itself." Because inert matter cannot communicate any " power " to the æther, the cause of the activity and power of the æther must be spirit.

Since spirit gives æther particles their repulsive powers, it " ordains and executes the laws by which æther and bodies act mutually on one another." Spirit must, in other words, be " present in all parts of space where there is æther." Since æther exists in all parts of space where we find attraction, gravity, light, or any of the great phenomena " which I have shewn to be caused by an æther," Robinson concluded spirit must be " in every part of infinite space." [123] Apparently Robinson's enthusiasm for the Newtonian doctrine had led him dangerously close to building a " philosophical romance," instead of a useful explication and correlation of physical phenomena.

Wilson was greatly inspired by the works of Robinson, and mentioned experiments which he had performed in concert with Robinson.[124] One of the major experiments which had led Wilson to what may " amount to a discovery of the cause of electricity " employed the parallel-plate air condenser. He placed two polished metal plates closely parallel to each other and electrified one of them by an electrical machine containing a globe thirteen inches in diameter. He found that " sparks of light " seemed to issue from one plate and pass to the other, and as readily from the non-electrified plate as the one in direct contact with the electrical machine. After studying carefully the circumstances of such experiments, he said,

---

* This discussion is reminiscent of Franklin's remarks about the elasticity of air, mentioned in Chapter Eight. Franklin, however, came to a conclusion exactly the opposite of Robinson's.

" I framed [!] an hypothesis, which I confirmed every day more and more to my own satisfaction." [125] His basic hypothesis was

that the electric matter was in all bodies, in reciprocal proportion to their densities, luminous, sulphureous, and unctuous bodies only excepted; that it issued from all bodies, as well from those that were not electrified, as from such bodies as were electrified. Further, when any body was electrified, I called that quantity of electric matter, by which it was electrified, the excess of electric matter in that particular body, above its natural original quantity; from which, in an experiment of suspending a light body between two planes, I endeavoured to account for the cause of gravity.†

Wilson fell into the trap, as did so many other students of electricity at this time, of following too closely the Newtonian ideas of " density."

According to Wilson, it is now " agreed " that the density of æther in bodies varies inversely with the densities of bodies, with the exception that in sulphureous and unctuous bodies, the æther has a greater density than it has in any other kind of bodies.‡ If " there is electric matter in all bodies," he claimed he would prove it to exist in bodies in inverse proportion to their density, save that in sulphureous and unctuous bodies, there must be more electric matter than in any other bodies of the same density. Rubbing bodies alters the density of the electric matter, so that bodies may attract or repel electrically.[126] Wilson was led to some propositions for which the evidence was at best doubtful. For example, since electrics *per se* are insulators (" prevent the electric matter from passing into the earth "), he concluded that such bodies " will repel the electric matter." [127]

In one of his experiments, Wilson employed bodies which do not abound with " luminous, sulphureous and unctuous particles," but which may be " replete with electricity." [128] Wilson wanted to prove that the flame, or sensation and snap, which is " produced upon the approach of bodies not electrified " is greater or less depending on their density. In the experiment to illustrate this proposition, there were three bodies of the same size, but made of wood, stone, and

---

† Although Wilson used the phrase " the excess of electric matter . . . above its natural original quantity," it is plain from the context that he intended it to mean an increase in æther density rather than the motion of a fluid from one body to another in accordance with a conservation principle. Newton's suggestion that the phenomena of electricity and gravitation might both be explained by the action of the æther was developed by Wilson in a natural enough way; after all, the two phenomena seemed to be related since charged bodies appear to exhibit electrical forces which overcome gravitational forces.

‡ For Franklin's criticism of Wilson's views on the variations in the density of the æther, see page 345.

iron, so that they would be of different density. The three bodies were electrified, and the experimenter would present to each of them, one after the other, a body " of the same kind (not electrified) ." In this case the effect of snapping was greatest from the densest body, and weakest from the rarest.[129] So, too, if the densest body touched the rarest, there would be a greater effect than if the densest body approached the middle one.§

In relation to density, Wilson developed a number of propositions that implied variations in the quantity or distribution of electric matter in bodies. Like Watson, whose work he had followed closely, Wilson had reached the point where he was explaining some of the facts of electrification by a subtle matter. If he had not stuck so closely to the aim of relating variations in the electric matter in bodies to their density and had been able to free himself from the influence of Robinson, he might have arrived at Franklin's position. He was quite aware that the electric matter must be " elastic " but he did not envisage an attractive force between particles of the electric matter and particles of ordinary matter. Yet he did write that " this electric matter " will collect around bodies " that are capable of being made replete with this electric fluid, which is elastic," and which will form " an atmosphere." [131] One of his propositions was that if " two equally electric atmospheres are brought so near as to touch, they will repel each other." In this case the force which moves the bodies " will be equal in both, if the densities are equal." [132] The electric atmosphere was also described by Wilson as an " elastic atmosphere." [133]

§ Wilson's studies of " density " were related to Newton's ideas in two different ways. First of all there was Newton's view of the æther as varying in density in bodies of different sorts. Then there was Newton's attempt (in Book Two of the *Opticks*) to correlate the density of bodies and the size of their particles with the index of refraction, with the notable exception—similar to that found by Wilson in electrical effects—of bodies containing sulphureous or unctuous particles. (See page 161, above.) Watson also had tried to correlate electrical properties of substances with their densities. Wilson and Watson probably were drawn to this topic by the obvious fact that the best conductors are metals and that metals generally have a high density (bismuth and zinc were thought to be semi-metals). Watson reported in his *Sequel* (§XVI) that he had tried to increase the effect of the Leyden jar " by increasing the quantity of water in glasses of different sizes, as high as four gallons, without in the least increasing the stroke. If filings of iron are substituted in the room of water, the effect is considerably lessened. If mercury, much the same as water; the stroke is by no means increased in proportion to their specific gravities, as might have been imagined." [130] Evidently Watson had supposed, like Wilson, that the amount of " electricity " a non-electric (conductor) can contain should be directly proportional to the density. This experiment should have proved the incorrectness of such an assumption; or it might have implied that charging a Leyden jar was a more complex process than merely accumulating " electricity " in the inner conductor. Watson, we saw, came to believe that the power of the jar could generally be increased by a larger number of " points of contact of non-electrics to the glass."

The " electric matter," according to Wilson, is " composed of æther, light, and other particles of matter that are of a sulphureous nature," evidently not homogeneous.[134] The particles move with great speed and, if they are suddenly stopped, explosions may be produced, and light may be seen. That there actually is " light " in the electric matter may be seen from the fact of its " being re-fracted through a prism of glass," and " suffering the same laws with the solar light." [135] Then, without any particular experiments, Wil-son simply concluded with a General Scholium that the electric matter " causes such various and surprizing phænomena," and " seems to be the great desideratum to account for many of the wonderful operations in nature, particularly muscular motion, and an universal attraction and gravity."

To support his position, Wilson printed the major part of New-ton's letter to Boyle about the æther, and then appended a long series of extracts from the Queries to the *Opticks*. Wilson's book was written in the style of the *Opticks*. A proposition would be stated, and then would follow " *Proof by* EXPERIMENT." * There was included an extract from the preface to the *Principia* to show that Newton really believed in a " repulsive force of certain particles of matter, which . . . produces most of the phænomena in nature." Thus Wilson could have the authority of Newton for the action of both the æther and the electric matter in terms of " an elastic and repulsive power." Wilson laid particular stress on the fact that in the preface to the *Principia* Newton had pointed out that the particles of bodies " by some unknown cause are either impelled mutually towards one another to cohere in regular figures or are repelled and recede from one another." He also explained that at the end of the *Principia*, Newton had mentioned explicitly a " most subtle matter," which pervades and lies hidden in all gross bodies, and which pro-duces many different phenomena of nature.[136]

Plainly then, Wilson was basing his electrical ideas on the major hypothesis outlined by Newton in his letter to Boyle, the hypotheti-cal portions of the Queries in the *Opticks*, and on the Newtonian hypothesis embodied in the final paragraph to the last General Scholium of the *Principia*.

The second part of Wilson's book contains a paper read at the Royal Society on 13 November 1746. Having restudied his earlier communication (printed in the first part of the book) and having carefully studied Dr. Robinson's treatise on the æther, he was willing to state that the electric matter and the æther " have a great affinity, as far as can be judged from reason and experiments, if they are

* See Chapter Six.

not one and the same thing." [137] He now wanted it understood that the electric matter issuing from bodies is not itself " luminous and sulphureous," although our senses of sight and smell might tell us so. Wilson's opinion, conforming to " that of the Doctor [Robinson] when I was with him in Dublin," is now that " the vibrations of the æther, or electric matter (caused by friction) " make " the loose particles of light, and sulphur, or other subtle matter lodged within the pores of bodies " be " thrown off, or emitted along with that subtle matter which I have called the electric matter." [138] Wilson believed that the " æther seems to be the sole cause of the electrical phænomena," and could only be understood by the principles expounded by Dr. Robinson. But the latter's book was available to " few in this kingdom," so Wilson summarized it and quoted a number of propositions from it.[139] Wilson found that identifying the æther and electric matter did not cause any significant alterations of his earlier work.[140] But we now encounter such propositions as this: " When a non-electric body is electrified, the accumulated matter will cause a light body, which is placed within the sphere of its vibrations, to approach it, and that by an elastic, or repulsive force; which is the property of the æther given in the propositions before quoted." [141]

Buried away in these many speculations are two observations of great importance. Wilson found that the power of the Leyden jar could be increased by (1) using a larger jar and increasing the area of the conductors in contact with the glass, and (2) making the glass itself thinner.[142] We have already seen that similar observations were made at this time by Watson.

The treatises by Martin and Wilson are of interest to us primarily because they show the nature of the attempts to develop a concept of " electrical matter " that was based on the Newtonian æther. In neither book was any effort made to explain the two kinds of electrification, or the existence of an attractive force between two bodies if one is electrified vitreously and the other resinously. Although Wilson was rather explicit in his statement of " electric atmospheres," he never used this concept effectively; there is no indication that the concept of a subtle matter, put into vibration and changing in density, could be used to predict the outcome of electrical manipulations in the laboratory.

Undoubtedly the references to Newton's speculations in relation to electricity made an impression upon Franklin, but he never tried to apply to electrical phenomena this unfruitful line of thought. Without question, the most important of the works that he received during 1747 were the two books of Watson, and not those of Martin or Wilson. From all three authors Franklin learned that there was a possibility of explaining electric phenomena by some kind of elastic subtle fluid, without having to assume that friction creates some kind of matter. But as to the elastic fluid itself, he could not learn from books if it was merely the Newtonian æther, or possibly the matter of heat, or a kind of matter *sui generis*. Only experiments and the exercise of the imagination could tell him the specific properties and laws of action with which an " electric fluid " needed to be endowed in order to account for the phenomena described by Watson, Wilson, and Martin and the additional phenomena that were being discovered in Philadelphia. The particular concept of the electric fluid which Franklin used in his theory of electrical action had many properties in common with the electric æther, matter, or fire described in the books published in 1746, but it had other properties which differentiated it from them and which serve to define Franklin's unique contribution to the science of electricity. In this sense we can appreciate the reasons why Franklin's contemporaries referred to the one-fluid theory as the Franklinian theory. There was no intention of playing down the work of the " giants " on whose shoulders he stood, to use Newton's phrase, but rather a desire to single out the major contribution which had made of electricity a kind of exact science.

SOURCES

The major fonts of information about mid-eighteenth electricity are the *Philosophical Transactions* of the Royal Society of London, the annual *Histoire de l'Académie Royale des Sciences* (with the *Mémoires* for the same year), and other serial publications. The outstanding source is Priestley (1775). Hoppe (1884), and Rosenberger (1898) are extremely valuable. A useful general survey may be found in Wolf (1952), and much information is contained in Mottelay (1922). The catalogues of two great collections of books on electricity are useful introductions to the literature: Ronalds (1880) and Wheeler Gift (1909), the latter based on the Latimer Clark Collection in the library of the American Institute of Electrical Engineers. Other histories of electricity are Benjamin (1898), Daujat (1945), Gliozzi (1937), Miller (1939), Potamian and Walsh (1909), Turner (1927), Whittaker (1951). An interesting account of the German and Dutch work in the 1740's may be found in Espenschied (1955). Roller and Roller (1954) is extremely perceptive and sound.

For biographical materials concerning Gray, see Chipman (1954), Cohen (1954b). For Desaguliers, see " Sources " for Chapter Seven. A biographical study of Du Fay is greatly needed to supplement the *Éloge* by Fontenelle; Du Fay's work in crystallography is described in Pabst (1932) and a general account is given in Brunet (1940). Nollet is a neglected figure; a study of his reputation would reveal much information about the teaching and dissemination of science in the eighteenth century. Benjamin Wilson, painter and scientist, merits a biographical study. So does B. Martin, prolific writer on many aspects of science, and scientific instrument-maker without peer in his day; on the latter score some information is available in Daumas (1953) and Cohen (1950a). Known today chiefly for his work in electricity in relation to Franklin's theory, William Watson also needs a critical study. The lack of any critical scholarly appreciations of Du Fay, Nollet, Wilson, and Martin indicates the primitive state of our knowledge of eighteenth-century science. [A biography of Nollet, (Torlais, 1954), was received just as the typescript of this monograph was being sent to the printer.]

REFERENCES

1. See Cohen, 1954b, and Chipman, 1954. For information on the Trinity College Observatory, see Price, 1952.
2. Gray, 1731-1732a: 18.
3. *Ibid.*, 29.
4. *Ibid.*, 33.
5. Fontenelle 1766.
6. *Idem*, trans. in Pabst, 1932.
7. Pabst, 1932.
8. Du Fay, 1733-1734: 258-259.
9. *Ibid.*, 260.

10. *Ibid.*, 262.
11. *Ibid.*, 263.
12. *Ibid.*, 263-264.
13. Thomson, 1872: §288.
14. Young, 1807: Lecture LIV.
15. Gray, 1731-1732a: 44.
16. Du Fay, 1733-1734: 260; 1733c: 234 ff.
17. Du Fay, 1733a: 23.
18. Du Fay, 1733c: 240
19. *Idem.*
20. *Ibid.*, 241.
21. Du Fay, 1733d: 457.
22. *Ibid.*, 459-460.
23. *Ibid.*, 466, 467.
24. *Ibid.*, 469.
25. Du Fay, 1734a: 355.
26. Du Fay, 1733a; 1733-1734; cf. Cohen, 1951, and Heathcote, 1950.
27. Du Fay, 1734b: 525.
28. Du Fay, 1737a: 95.
29. *Ibid.*, 99-100.
30. Du Fay, 1734b: 526.
31. Desaguliers, 1739-1740b: 186.
32. *Ibid.*, 193.
33. *Ibid.*, 203.
34. Wheler, 1739-1740: 110-111.
35. Desaguliers, 1740-1741a: 634-635.
36. *Ibid.*, prop. 11-prop. 13.
37. Desaguliers, 1739-1740a: 175.
38. *Ibid.*, 176.
39. Desaguliers, 1742-1743a: 16.
40. Desaguliers, 1742-1743b: 142; see a similar point of view in Wheler, 1739-1740.
41. See Priestley, 1775: 1: " Period VII," pp. 87 ff., " Period VIII," pp. 102 ff.; Espenschied, 1955; Benjamin, 1898: ch. 15.
42. See Cohen, 1950a: 43.
43. Nollet, 1746b.
44. *Ibid.*
45. " Remarks on the Abbé Nollet's letters on electricity," Franklin, 1941: 283-292; 1769: 130-142.
46. Le Roy, 1753.
47. See Rosenberger, 1898: 21.
48. *Ibid.*, 22.
49. *Ibid.*, 23.
50. Nollet, 1764c: 1: 26.
51. Nollet, 1746a; 1754; 1764.
52. Nollet, 1752: preface, pp. xvi-xvii.
53. Nollet, 1746a: 141-146.
54. Nollet, 1764: Leçon XXI.
55. See Scott (1952) .
56. Torlais, 1954.
57. Le Monnier 1746.
58. Franklin, 1941: Letter IV, §27; 1769: Letter IV, §27.
59. Watson, 1746a: 3.
60. *Ibid.*, 4n.
61. See Frobenius, 1740-1741.
62. Watson, 1746a: 7.
63. Quoted from Espenschied, 1955.
64. Watson, 1746a: 6:

65. *Ibid.*, 11-12.
66. *Ibid.*, 7.
67. *Ibid.*, 11.
68. *Ibid.*, 16.
69. *Ibid.*, 17, 21.
70. *Ibid.*, 24.
71. *Ibid.*, 46.
72. *Ibid.*, 45.
73. *Ibid.*, 50-51.
74. *Ibid.*, 52-53.
75. *Ibid.*, 54.
76. *Ibid.*, 51; see also p. 54.
77. *Ibid.*, 53.
78. *Ibid.*, 55.
79. *Ibid.*, 57.
80. *Ibid.*, 58.
81. *Ibid.*, 26.
82. *Ibid.*, 54-55.
83. Watson, 1746*b*: 4, §6.
84. *Ibid.*, 6, §8, n.
85. *Ibid.*, 9, §§11, 12; 7, §8.
86. *Ibid.*, 10-11, §13.
87. *Ibid.*, 17, §26.
88. *Ibid.*, 19, §28.
89. *Ibid.*, 26, §36.
90. *Ibid.*, 27-28, §§37, 38.
91. *Ibid.*, 31, §44.
92. *Ibid.*, 32, §45.
93. *Ibid.*, 33-34, §45.
94. *Ibid.*, 34, §46.
95. *Ibid.*, 35-38, §47-49.
96. *Ibid.*, 39, §51.
97. *Ibid.*, 42-43, §52.
98. *Ibid.*, 45, §53.
99. *Ibid.*, 50, §55; 51, §56.
100. *Ibid.*, 54, §57.
101. *Ibid.*, 55, §57.
102. *Ibid.*, 57, §58.
103. *Ibid.*, 58, §58.
104. *Ibid.*, 59, §59.
105. *Ibid.*, 62, §60.
106. *Ibid.*, 76, §66.
107. *Ibid.*, 77, §66.
108. *Ibid.*, 65, §62.
109. *Ibid.*, 70-75, §65.
110. See Franklin, 1941: 178n.
111. Martin, 1746: preface, p. 4.
112. *Ibid.*, 7-8.
113. *Ibid.*, 9.
114. *Ibid.*, 11.
115. *Ibid.*, supplement, p. 33.
116. *Ibid.*, supplement, p. 34.
117. *Ibid.*, supplement, p. 36.
118. *Ibid.*, supplement, p. 38.
119. See Franklin, 1941: 179n.
120. Pringle, 1783: lvi-lvii.
121. Wilson, 1746: vi.

122. Robinson, 1743: 122.
123. *Ibid.*, 123.
124. Wilson, 1746: xii.
125. *Ibid.*, ix.
126. *Ibid.*, x, 5.
127. *Ibid.*, 7, prop. III and corollary.
128. *Ibid.*, 9, prop. V.
129. *Ibid.*, 10.
130. Watson, 1746*b*: 12-13.
131. Wilson, 1746: 18-19.
132. *Ibid.*, 19, prop. X.
133. *Ibid.*, 20, prop. XI.
134. *Ibid.*, 25.
135. *Ibid.*, 25-26.
136. *Ibid.*, 49.
137. *Ibid.*, 51.
138. *Ibid.*, 52.
139. *Ibid.*, 53.
140. *Ibid.*, 79.
141. *Ibid.*, 64, prop. II.
142. *Ibid.*, 88.

CHAPTER TEN

THE FRANKLINIAN THEORY OF ELECTRICITY

> The first theory of electricity which connected the phenomena
> in a satisfactory manner and enabled the electricians to fore-
> tell the results, was that of Dr. Franklin.
>
> THOMAS THOMSON (1830)

AFTER having traced the rise of knowledge concerning electricity, Joseph Priestley presented a critical review of the current state of the science. In his discussion of Franklin's concept of a single fluid of electricity, or the "theory of positive and negative electricity," Priestley found it "a little remarkable" that the "hypotheses" or fundamental properties of the electric fluid "should so much re-semble the ether of Sir Isaac Newton in some respects, and yet differ from it so essentially in others." Joseph Priestley's value judgments are notable because he was a great scientist and a splendid historian. His *History and Present State of Electricity* was based on the study of articles and books—that is, original sources—to a degree that puts many later scholars to shame by comparison. He was an honest scholar and in his bibliography distinguished between the books which he "had seen, and made use of in compiling this work," and those which he knew only by title and at second-hand. William Watson, John Canton, and Benjamin Franklin supplied him with books and personal information and read much of the manuscript.[1] Priest-ley was also a personal friend of many others of the British electrical experimenters such as William Henley and Tiberius Cavallo. Priest-ley is generally known today only as a chemist, for his discovery of seven new gases (including oxygen) and for his important new techniques in pneumatic chemistry. But he made equally significant, if less revolutionary, contributions to electricity. He discovered the inverse square law of electrical force ("Coulomb's law" *),[2] the conducting power of charcoal,[3] and of hot glass,† the "Priestley rings,"[5] the musical tones accompanying the discharge of different

---

* For the prehistory of Coulomb's law, see pages 546-547 below.

† Although, as Franklin reported in 1762 (see page 325 above), Wilson, Kinnersley, Canton, and Cavendish had reported signs of conductivity in heated glass, Priestley found that "electricians were not perfectly agreed about the conducting power of *hot glass*, and that the methods which had been used to prove it were liable to objec-tion."[4] He therefore devised new experiments to this end.

Leyden jars,[6] and made important studies of resistivity.‡ Thus, as author of the history of electricity, he was a master of the subject as well as a gifted historian.§ For us his book has the particular merit of expressing the point of view and the foci of interest of the third quarter of the eighteenth century. Hence we may lay great stress on Priestley's analysis of the differences and similarities between Franklin's electric fluid and Newton's æther:

> The electric fluid is supposed to be, like ether, extremely subtile and elastic, that is, repulsive of itself; but instead of being, like the ether, repelled by all other matter, it is strongly attracted by it; so that, far from being, like the ether, rarer in the small than in the large pores of bodies, rarer within the bodies than at their surfaces, and rarer at their surfaces than at any distance from them; it must be denser in small than in large pores, denser within the substance of bodies than at their surfaces, and denser at their surfaces than at a distance from them. But no other property can account for the extraordinary quantity of this fluid contained within the substance of electrics *per se*, or for the common atmospheres of all excited and electrified bodies. . . .[8]

The very fact that Priestley, so often in his history, compared Franklin and Newton is an instance of the place in science attributed to Franklin by his peers. That Priestley and others found differences between Franklin's concepts and Newton's is not in itself surprising, but it does afford the student of eighteenth-century science occasion for gauging the degree of originality in Franklin's thought.

Enough has been said in the preceding chapters to enable each reader to see how Franklin's concepts arose from the matrix of speculative Newtonian experimental science. In what follows, therefore, I have not at every point indicated the congruity of Franklin's ideas and points of view with those of his age. It would be equally supererogatory to draw attention to every instance of Franklin's departure from the conventional conceptual framework. Yet I hope that each reader—as he explores with me the growth and reception of Franklin's concepts, hypotheses, and theories—will make for him-

‡ According to Priestley, this subject had arisen in a conversation he had had with Franklin, Canton, and Price. Priestley had asked "whether it was probable that there was any difference in the conducting power of different metals; and if there was, whether it was possible to ascertain that difference?" The experiments performed by Priestley consisted of "transmitting the same explosion of the battery [of condensers] through two wires at the same time, of different metals, and of the same thickness . . . [&] exactly the same length."[7] This was a "scheme proposed by Dr. Franklin."

§ It should be pointed out, however, that Priestley's history of optics is a poorer book than his history of electricity. The reason, I believe, is two-fold. Priestley himself was not a master of this subject and made no contribution to it. Furthermore, in the eighteenth century there was not the same progress in knowledge of optics as in electricity. These facts may serve to explain why there was only one English edition of the history of optics, but five of the history of electricity.

self the necessary comparisons between the Franklinian statements and those of his predecessors and contemporaries, not only in relation to the subject of electricity but also to the general system of ideas in physical science.

We cannot help but observe that whereas Newton hoped that the hypothesis of one universal æther would explain a variety of phenomena—including light, radiant heat, gravitation, molecular and atomic forces, electricity, magnetism, nervous impulses—the men of the second half of the eighteenth century postulated a single subtle matter, in some cases a pair of such matters, for each set of phenomena. In part this trend resulted from the specialization that arose from the intense concentration on a single subject. To imagine two or more types of phenomenon to be similar, or to be produced from the same cause, is always easier when little is known about them than when a great deal is known. But there can be little doubt that one of the reasons why the scientists of the twentieth and the late nineteenth century have scorned the concepts of subtle fluids is not so much the inadequacy of these concepts to explain all phenomena, as the fact that the invention of a special kind of matter to account for each type of phenomenon has seemed to later generations an unnecessary multiplication of physical causative agents.

Franklin's Introduction to Electricity

In the mid-1740's electricity was a topic of polite conversation and news of the new phenomena produced by rubbing globes and tubes reached Franklin in a number of different ways. In 1745 he might have read the long article published in that year in *The American Magazine and Historical Chronicle* (printed and sold in Boston by Rogers & Fowle), entitled "An historical account of the wonderful discoveries made in Germany, &c. concerning electricity." Perhaps he saw the issue of the London *Gentleman's Magazine*, from which the Boston version was reprinted. In it there is a reasonably good summary of all the work done in the eighteenth century on electricity. The research of Hauksbee and Gray is presented, and then the discoveries of Du Fay. According to the anonymous author, Du Fay had shown that what "proceeds from the electrised body is really the production of fire, for electricity produces flame as well as light, in both respects resembling lightening." After Du Fay, "and excited by his example, the German naturalists took the subject under examination. And from the year 1743 they discovered phenomena so surprising as to awaken the indolent curiosity of the public, the ladies and people of quality, who never regard natural philosophy but when it works miracles. Electricity became all the subject in vogue, princes were willing to see this new fire which a man produced from himself, which did not descend from heaven." The remainder of the article describes the new electrical machines and the experiments performed by such men as Bose, Hausen, Gralath, Ludolf, and Winkler. In America in the mid-1740's, scientists and non-scientists could readily learn about the new subject of electricity.

Another source available to Franklin in 1744 was Desaguliers's *Course of Natural Philosophy*. The first volume, published in that year, and used by Franklin in his pamphlet on " fireplaces," contains a summary of what had been done by Gray and mentions the work of Du Fay. Appearing in the final appendix of Desaguliers's book, this brief introduction of the facts of electricity perhaps would not have escaped Franklin's attention.*

Franklin encountered discussions of electricity in other books which he was reading in the 1740's.† A little more than twenty years later [9] he wrote that " the first notice I had of that curious subject, which I afterwards prosecuted with some diligence," was in 1745 when Peter Collinson sent to the directors of the Library Company of Philadelphia " an account of the new German experiments in electricity, together with a glass tube, and some directions for using it, so as to repeat those experiments." ‡ Peter Collinson, F. R. S., was a London Quaker merchant who had many contacts with the New World. He made no scientific contributions of note, and he is known today to students of the history of science mainly for his extensive scientific correspondence. Of an independent mind, he was willing to argue against his friend Linnæus' view that swallows hibernate under water. But his fame derives from his patronage of the American naturalist, John Bartram, and of Benjamin Franklin. Collinson kept Franklin informed of European progress in electricity and he introduced into the meetings of the Royal Society of London Franklin's papers reporting his new discoveries. He forwarded to Franklin news about the comments on those papers, notably by Watson, and he eventually arranged for the papers to be issued in book form and got Dr. John Fothergill to write the preface. Collinson also corresponded about scientific matters with Franklin's friend, Cadwallader Colden, Lieutenant-Governor of New York, author of

---

* See Chapter Seven.

† We have seen that Franklin encountered discussions of electrical phenomena specifically in the books of 'sGravesande and Hales, and in Newton's *Opticks*.

‡ Franklin also saw some electrical experiments in Boston in the spring of 1743, " imperfectly performed " by Dr. Adam Spencer, who " was not very expert." Since these experiments were " on a subject quite new to me, they equally surprised and pleased me." Dr. Spencer came to Philadelphia in 1744 and Franklin purchased his apparatus.[10]

a book explaining the *vis inertiæ* in matter, according to what he thought was an improvement over the Newtonian basis of mechanics.

We have no way of knowing exactly what Franklin meant when he wrote about an "account of the new German experiments" which Collinson had sent to Philadelphia, supposedly in 1745. The records of the Library Company provide no information on this subject. I believe there can be little doubt that Collinson had described in his own words the experiments of igniting combustible substances by the electric spark, which had been largely prosecuted by the Germans and had been repeated and improved by Watson. (In 1745 Watson had been demonstrating such ignition at the Royal Society, of which Collinson was a Fellow.§) That this is likely to have been the case may be seen in a letter which Collinson wrote in the spring of 1745 to Cadwallader Colden in New York,[11] in which he remarked, "As this may I think very justly be stiled an age of wonders, it may not perhaps be disagreeable to just hint them to you. The surpriseing phenomena of the polypus entertained the curious for a year or two past but now the vertuosi of Europe are taken up in electrical experiments. . . ." Collinson was, in other words, so taken by the new electrical phenomena that he felt he must write about them to his American correspondents. These new wonders of electricity were described by Collinson, in his letter to Colden, as follows:

. . . and what can be more astonishing than that the base rub[b]ing of a glass tube should investigate [invest ?] a person with electric fire [!] He is not touched by the tube but the subtile effluvia that flies from it pervades every pore and renders him what wee call electrified [;] for then lett him touch spirits of wine & the spark . . . from his finger on the touch will sett the spirits in flame [.] This is a common experiment, but I have seen oyle of Sevil-oriangs [Seville oranges]—& camphire [camphor] sett on fire & gun powder mixt with oyl of lemmons will take fire—but what would you say to see fire come out of a piece of thick ice * & sett the spirits in flame [;] or electrical fire drawn through water & performe the same [?]—these are some few of a great number of surprising things that are formed [performed ?] by the electrical power which you will find difficult to comprehend but are all facts [.]

According to Franklin, Collinson sent to the members of the Library Company of Philadelphia a glass tube and directions for rubbing it, and news of the German experiments, in 1745. Since Collinson's letter to Colden, written in 1745, described these very experiments,

§ In the last chapter it was shown that Watson specifically referred to this kind of experiment as a development of the Germans.

* This particular experiment, using ice, appears to have originated with Watson.

we may reasonably suppose that Collinson's letter to the Library Company had been written along similar lines.

One year later Collinson told Colden that "the surpriseing phenomenon of electricity engages the vertuosi in all Europe." He was sending Colden news of "what has been done in France & with us; I have marked those experiments that I have felt & can vouch for the facts." [12] Most likely Collinson had sent the pamphlets of Watson, about Le Monnier's experiments and his own, which were published in 1746, and perhaps he sent Martin's little book too. In 1746, Collinson obtained these publications of Watson—and also those of Martin and Wilson—for the Philadelphia group. Franklin read these works at once to find out whether the Europeans might possibly have anticipated the experiments and conclusions of the Philadelphia experimenters: Benjamin Franklin, Ebenezer Kinnersley, Philip Syng, and Thomas Hopkinson.† Franklin wrote to Collinson on 28 March 1747 that "several of us" had been using the tube which had been sent to Philadelphia. "Some particular phænomena that we look upon to be new" had been observed; Franklin would communicate them in a subsequent letter.‡ This letter makes it plain that Franklin had found the proper subject for his talents: "I never was before engaged in any study that so totally engrossed my attention

† Philip Syng (1703-1789) was a silversmith who was born in Ireland and came to America in 1714. He was a member of the Junto and the American Philosophical Society, one of the original guarantors of the Library Company, and one of the organizers of the Academy and College of Philadelphia. His sole contribution to electricity seems to have been the invention of a simple electrical machine, for which see page 440 below.

Thomas Hopkinson (1709-1751) was born in London and came to Philadelphia in 1731, where he took up the practice of law and held many provincial offices, among them Judge of the Vice-Admiralty for the Province of Philadelphia. Like Syng, he was associated with Franklin in the American Philosophical Society, the Library Company, and the Academy and College. His chief contribution to electricity was the discovery that pointed conductors can "draw off the electric fire," for which see pages 437, 472 below.

Ebenezer Kinnersley (1711-1778) was the "principal" member of Franklin's group of co-experimenters. He was born in England and came to America with his father in 1714. He was a Baptist minister who became Professor of the English Tongue and of Oratory at the College in Philadelphia. Kinnersley was famous for his public lectures on electricity, which he gave in Philadelphia, Boston, Newport, New York, and Antigua. Some of his discoveries have already been presented in Chapter Eight. He found that the Leyden jar could be charged through the outer coating as well as through the hook, and he improved on Priestley's investigations of the conducting power of charcoal by exploring the effect of different sorts of wood. Beccaria, Æpinus, Cavendish, and many others who wrote about the Franklinian system of electricity mentioned Kinnersley's discoveries, and Priestley said, "If Kinnersley continues his electrical enquiries, his name after that of his friend, will be second to few in the history of science."

‡ By July, 1747, the members of the Library Company had also received "a compleat electrical apparatus" from Thomas Penn, Proprietor of the Pennsylvania Colony.[13]

and my time as this has lately done; for what with making experiments when I can be alone, and repeating them to my friends . . . , I have, during some months past, had little leisure for any thing else." [14]

Dr. N. H. de V. Heathcote has, I believe, solved the problem of the conflicting statements made by Franklin concerning his first knowledge of electricity. I shall present his conclusions here with one or two modifications. The experiments performed by Dr. Adam Spencer in Boston in 1743 and in Philadelphia in 1744 included an electrical experiment performed with a glass tube and some leaf-brass, and the impressive demonstration that sparks can be drawn from a suspended (insulated) boy if the rubbed tube is held near him. These experiments must have interested Franklin, but apparently they meant very little to him; at least they did not excite him sufficiently to induce him to perform experiments. Perhaps Franklin did not even know at the time that the demonstrations he saw were electrical. Two witnesses to Dr. Spencer's experiments described them as illustrating the principle that " fire is diffused through all space, and may be produced from all bodies," the proof being in the " sparks & fire emitted from the face and hands of a boy." Dr. Heathcote calls attention to the absence of the word " electricity " in the reports of the witnesses of these experiments. But by the time Collinson's gift had arrived in 1745 (or perhaps 1746) , Franklin had been reading on the subject, and perhaps for the first time recognized that the experiments performed by Dr. Spencer had been electrical experiments. Spencer thus may have " introduced Franklin to an experiment with a glass tube and leaf-brass," but " Collinson introduced him to electricity." [15]

Collinson's presentation of the new and astonishing subject of electricity was not confined to a bare relation of the facts of experiment and a description of the instruments. Electricity, as he observed to Colden, seems to furnish " an inexhaustable fund for enquiry." So " various " and so " wonderful " are the phenomena of electricity that they must arise from " very general and extensive causes," of " great moment " to " the system of the universe." No doubt, he said, investigations in electricity will enable us to reach " higher truths, in particular to discover the nature of that subtile elastic and etherial medium, which Sir Isaac Newton queries on, at the end of his *Opticks*." Thus Collinson not only saw a possible connection between the *Opticks* and electricity, but envisaged a Newtonian mind to clarify the subject. Had these new discoveries been made, he wrote, " in that great man's time, his illuminated mind would have applied them to wonderful purposes." [16]

Franklin's First Thoughts on Electricity

The first scientific communication sent by Franklin to Collinson was dated May or June, 1747.§ It [19] begins with a description of the way in which pointed bodies " draw off " and " throw off " the " electrical fire." An insulated cork ball, " about the bigness of a marble," was suspended by a fine silk thread alongside an electrified " iron shot of three or four inches diameter " that was insulated by having been placed on the mouth of a clean, dry, glass bottle. A long slender bodkin was held in the experimenter's hand so that the point was six or eight inches from the shot; the result was that the shot lost its electrification as indicated by the cessation of repulsion between it and the ball. While a pointed object was found to " *draw off* " the electrical fire at six or seven inches from the shot, a blunt object had to be brought up to within an inch (where it would draw a spark) in order to destroy the electrification of the shot. If the blade of the bodkin was insulated from the man by taking the blade out of its wooden handle and fixing it in a stick of sealing wax, no such effect was observable; but by sliding a finger along the sealing-wax handle until it touched the blade, the effect could be produced as before. If performed in the dark, the above effect was accompanied by a luminous discharge.

§ In the first three printed editions of Franklin's book on electricity, this letter bears the date, 1 September 1747. It had been transposed with a later letter.

In the fourth English edition, of 1769, the first to be edited by Franklin himself, Franklin reversed the order of the first two letters and changed dates. The date in the later editions is given as 11 July 1747, which agrees with the manuscript notation in Franklin's own copy of the first edition of his book, which is in the Mason-Franklin Collection in the Yale University Library. In the " Bowdoin MS," a manuscript copy of these letters which Franklin made for James Bowdoin in 1751 and which is at present in the library of the American Academy of Arts and Sciences,[17] this letter bears the date of 25 May 1747. We shall see in a moment that, in his comments on this letter, Watson used the date of 1 June 1747.

Franklin very likely sent out this letter, as others, in more than one copy, and under different dates. For example, his second scientific communication to Peter Collinson is dated 28 July 1747 in the " Bowdoin MS," whereas the approved printed version bears the date 1 September 1747. Franklin introduced this letter as follows: " The inclosed is a copy of my last, which went by the Governor's vessel. . . ." Then he said: " The necessary trouble of copying long letters, which, perhaps, when they come to your hands may contain nothing new, or worth your reading, (so quick is the progress made with you in electricity) half discourages me from writing any more on that subject." Undoubtedly, the reason for sending more than one copy of the same letter was the fear of loss at sea owing to the international situation. Thus, on 30 May 1746, Colden wrote a letter to the Dutch naturalist, Gronovius, in which he enclosed " a copy of what I sent to you in the beginning of last winter directed to the care of Mr. Collinson," and observed that the ship which carried the communication had been " taken betwixt Portsmouth & the Douns & carried into Dieppe," so that he presumed that the original papers were lost. Such misfortunes are to be expected, Colden wrote, and so he included " an outside direction on the packet in French, desiring the captors in such case to send them to the gentlemen of the Royal Garden at Paris." [18]

A companion discovery to Franklin's was the power of points to " *throw off* " electrical fire, discovered by Thomas Hopkinson, one of Franklin's co-experimenters. A long sharp needle was laid on top of the shot, which then could not be electrified sufficiently to repel the cork. If in Hopkinson's experiment, the needle was fixed to one end of a suspended gun-barrel or iron rod, the application of the rubbed tube to the other end could not electrify it sufficiently to enable it to give a spark, since the electrical fire would be " continually running out silently at the point." The effect discovered by Hopkinson * had been partially anticipated by Watson in his *Sequel*, in the experiment in which a wire was attached to a charged gun-barrel, and had also been the subject of investigation by the Germans. But the ability of points to draw off the fire from a charged insulated conductor seems not to have been generally known prior to Franklin's investigations.†

Watson had been concerned largely with the conditions under which bodies can be charged and discharged, but in his first letter on electricity Franklin approached the problem of the various mechanisms by means of which a discharge could be produced. He noted that the repellency between the cork ball and shot could be destroyed (i. e., the shot could be discharged) by sifting fine sand on the shot, by breathing on it, by enveloping it with wood smoke, and by candle flame. The mechanism supposed in order to account for the loss of electrification was simple and straightforward. The shot, charged ‡ by contact with a rubbed glass tube, has a super-abundant quantity of " electrical fire." Particles of sand, moisture, and smoke are attracted to the shot, become charged, and are then repelled; charging, in the case of these particles, means obtaining a small portion of the electric fluid from the shot which they then carry away. This electrical fire remains in those particles until they, in turn, communicate it to another body. Electrical fire is never destroyed, nor is it created; it merely moves from one body to another. The situation is analogous to common fire; when water is thrown on burning material, that " element " is not destroyed or annihilated, but is merely dispersed—" each particle of water carrying off in vapour its portion of the fire, which it had attracted and attached to

* " Mr. Hopkinson's experiment [was] made with an expectation of drawing a more sharp and powerful spark from the point, as from a kind of focus, and he was surprised to find little or none."

† See Appendix Two.

‡ Franklin used the words " electrified " and " electrised " in his earlier writings. In describing his experiments and his explanations, I have used the more conventional term " charged," which actually achieved its modern sense in electrical discourse in terms of Franklin's theory, and which was later used by Franklin himself.

itself." Franklin had already assumed the material theory of " fire "
as expounded by Boerhaave.

Franklin noted that a burning candle held at a foot's distance from
the shot will discharge it suddenly; but to discharge the shot with
" the light of a red-hot iron " or " the light of a bright coal from a
wood fire," they must be brought much closer. By contrast, sunlight reflected by a mirror to either the cork ball or the shot did
" not impair the repellency in the least." Franklin and his friends
found this " difference between fire-light and sun-light " to be something new and extraordinary.§

The Philadelphia experimenters " had for some time been of
opinion, that the electrical fire was not created by friction, but collected, being really an element diffused among, and attracted by
other matter, particularly by water and metals." A number of experiments had been performed, including one that indicated the
impossibility of electrifying oneself by rubbing a tube while standing
on wax. When " Mr. Watson's ingenious *Sequel* came to hand,"
Franklin and his friends had found that these experiments had been
anticipated by Watson and, therefore, " some of the new things "
Franklin had intended to communicate to Collinson would not
prove to be new to English readers. Yet there were " some particulars not hinted in that piece [of Watson's] " which Franklin then
described " with our reasonings thereupon: though perhaps the
latter might well enough be spared."

In one of Franklin's experiments, two men stood on wax insulators; one rubbed the glass tube and the other drew the fire from
the tube. A third experimenter, standing on the floor, was then able
to draw a spark from either of the first two experimenters; i. e.,
they both appeared electrified to him. Yet if the two experimenters,
standing on wax, allowed their hands to touch each other while the
tube was being rubbed, then neither one would appear electrified
to the third experimenter on the floor. If, under the first conditions,
the two standing on wax (" after exciting the tube and drawing the
fire as aforesaid ") touched each other, the spark between them was
much stronger than between either of them and the man on the
floor; after such strong sparking, neither one of the experimenters
standing on wax appeared to be charged.

The explanation of these phenomena embodied the first form of
the Franklinian theory of electricity, based upon this simple premise:
" We suppose, as aforesaid, that electrical fire is a common element,
of which every one of the three persons above-mentioned has his

§ The significance of these observations for Franklin's theory of light has been
discussed in Chapter Nine.

equal share, before any operation is begun with the tube." *A*, who rubs the tube while standing on wax, transfers electrical fire from himself onto the tube; he is insulated from the floor (ground) by the wax, i. e., " his communication with the common stock [of electrical fire is] . . . cut off by the wax," so that the deficiency of electrical fire in his body cannot be restored. *B*, also on wax, draws the electrical fire from the glass by " passing his knuckle along near the tube," and retains this extra fire in his body because he too is cut off from the common stock, or insulated from the floor. If, now, *A* is approached by the third experimenter *C*, who stands on the floor, there is a spark as the deficiency of fire in *A* is made up by fire from *C*; likewise, if *B* is approached by *C*, there is a spark as the extra fluid on *B* passes over to *C*. But if *A* and *B* approach each other, there is a greater spark than if either were to be approached by *C*, " because the difference between them is greater "; but between *A* and *B* there will be no further spark, nor between them and *C*, since " the electrical fire in all is reduced to the original equality." Furthermore, if *A* and *B* touch " while electrising, the equality [between them] is never destroyed, the fire only circulating." To simplify discussion, some new terms had to be introduced into the language of electrical discourse. Bodies such as *B* were said to be electrified *positively* or *plus* and those such as *A* *negatively* or *minus*.

To electrise *plus* or *minus*, no more needs to be known than this, that the parts of the tube or sphere that are rubbed, do, in the instant of the friction, attract the electrical fire, and therefore take it from the thing rubbing: the same parts immediately, as the friction upon them ceases, are disposed to give the fire they have received, to any body that has less. Thus you may circulate it, as Mr. Watson has shewn; you may also accumulate or subtract it, upon, or from any body, as you connect that body with the rubber or with the receiver, the communication with the common stock being cut off.

The Philadelphia electricians, continued Franklin, believed Watson to have been " deceived " when he wrote of the electrical fire coming down the wire from the ceiling to the gun-barrel and from the gun-barrel to the sphere and thence to the machine and operator.* They supposed that since the machine and man were electrified minus while the globes and gun-barrel were electrified plus, the electrical fire must have been " *driven off*, and not brought on through that wire."

The remainder of this letter is devoted to brief accounts of new experiments and variations on old ones, written in a " telegraphic "

* See Chapter Eight, page 405.

style. " We fire spirits with the wire of the phial," " We electrise a person twenty or more times running, with a touch of the finger on the wire, thus: He stands on wax. Give him the electrised bottle in his hand. Touch the wire with your finger, and then touch his hand or face; there are sparks every time."

In closing, Franklin described how in Philadelphia the glass tubes were rubbed with buckskin, the same side always applied to the tube, which was handled with care to prevent sullying from handling. The tubes were kept in " tight pasteboard cases, lined with flannel, and fitting close to the tube "—details introduced by Franklin because " the *European* papers on Electricity frequently speak of rubbing the tube as a fatiguing exercise." † A simple electrical machine had been devised by Philip Syng, a sphere of glass mounted on an axle with a small handle so that the sphere turned like a grindstone. It was true, as Franklin said, that the sphere did not turn as swiftly as one attached to a great wheel, but he sagely noted that swiftness mattered very little since a few turns would charge a Leyden jar sufficiently in any event. Franklin concluded the letter by acknowledging receipt of Watson's first two pamphlets and B. Martin's book on electricity.

This letter contained a number of new discoveries and a major refinement of the concept of electrical fluid. Summarized for Collinson's benefit were the contents of Franklin's " Electrical Journal," which he sent to Colden in New York on 5 June 1747 with the following comment, " It is now discovered and demonstrated, both here and in Europe, that the electrical fire is a real elem[e]nt, or species of matter, not *created* by the friction, but *collected* only." Franklin willingly admitted, after having read Watson's pamphlets, that in " this discovery, they were beforehand with us in England; but we had hit on it before we heard it from them." However, as to what " relates to the wonderful effect of *points*, the difference between *candle light* & *sun light*, and several other things in these papers, the philosophers at home [i. e., in England], are still, as far as we know, ignorant. . . ." [21]

We may note, furthermore, that the behavior of the electric fire was, in Franklin's view, simpler. It was easier to comprehend than Watson's. The physical sense was made graphic by the new electrical terms, plus or positive and minus or negative, which implied a conservation of charge since electrification was said to be a

---

† Franklin was evidently referring to the 1746 report of Turbervill Needham on the development of electrical machines on the Continent, in which he informed the Royal Society: " I believe the use of the tube has been more improved in England than in any other place, but it is a downright slavery, and in its effects many degrees inferior to this machine." [20]

transfer of electric matter from one body to another. Watson's conception involved an electrical fluid (æther) that sometimes moved in one direction, at other times in the contrary direction, and at still other times in both directions at once, but he never gave a hint as to the nature of the physical situation determining which of these possible courses it would follow. Franklin agreed with Watson that electrical effects depend on the motion of an elementary matter, but Franklin insisted that this elementary matter must obey simple physical laws. He agreed with Watson that the globe is a collector of electrical fire, but if glass collects electrical fire from the machine and ultimately from the floor on which the machine stands during rubbing (gaining extra fire and becoming charged plus), it cannot also by rubbing give back that fire to the machine and floor as Watson had supposed. Franklin was clearly ahead of his British contemporary; for if the latter's ideas possibly could obtain, it was difficult to see how the globe could become charged in the first place. Franklin also avoided any mention of the word æther and he was careful not to identify electric fire with common fire (the matter of heat), light, or a subtle matter that might fill all of space.

Watson's Reaction to Franklin's Letter

While the Philadelphia experimenters were following their own path and reading Watson's two books of 1746, Watson was going ahead with new problems. He had been studying the long-distance transmission of electric shocks from the Leyden jar and had attempted to determine the relative velocities of sound and electricity. An ingenious series of experiments, made in the summer of 1747 while Franklin's letter to Collinson was crossing the Atlantic, involved discharging Leyden jars through circuits containing two or more persons, a length of wire, and a body of water.‡ In the first of

‡ These results were read at the Royal Society in 1747 and in 1748, and a supplement was read on 27 October 1748; both were printed in the *Philosophical Transactions*. Another communication, "Some further inquiries into the nature and properties of electricity," was read at the Royal Society on 21 January 1747/8 and also published in the *Philosophical Transactions*. These three articles, all that Watson published on electricity in the *Philosophical Transactions* "for the year 1748," were collected in book form and published by C. Davis in 1748 under the title, *An account of the experiments made by some gentlemen of the Royal Society . . . to which are added, some further inquiries into the nature and properties of electricity*. In this book, the supplement read on 27 October 1748 was printed at the end of the paper read in 1747 and in 1748 without separate title, with this explanatory footnote: "These experiments to measure the absolute velocity of electricity were made whilst this paper was at the press, but as they had so near a relation to the experiments made the preceding year, it was thought proper to insert them here."

In volume 45 of the *Philosophical Transactions* (for the year 1748), the above-mentioned supplement was printed twice. In its first printing (*Trans.* no. 485, pp. 85-

these a wire was carried over the Thames on the bridge at Westminster and the circuit was completed by the river itself. In later experiments, greater distances of transmission through water were used. Finally, it was found that a shock could be transmitted through the ground as well as through water, and in one experiment the circuit was composed of two miles of wire from the jar and a "return" of two miles through the ground.[22]

Then, on 21 January 1747/8 (i. e., 1748 New Style), Watson read a continuation and amplification of his *Sequel.*[23] In this new paper, Watson took a surprising stand. He inserted a long quotation from Franklin's first communication on electricity, addressed to Peter Collinson, in which Franklin had stated the major premises of his theory in relation to a fundamental experiment. Watson introduced the remarks of Franklin in these words:

At this time I am the more particular concerning the solution of this singular appearance, as Mr. Collinson, a worthy member of this Society, has received a paper concerning electricity from an ingenious gentleman, Mr. Franklin, a friend of his in Pennsylvania. This paper, dated June 1, 1747, I very lately perused, by favour of our most worthy president. Among other curious remarks there is a like solution of this fact; for though this gentleman's experiment was made with a tube instead of a globe, the difference is no-ways material. As this experiment was made, and the solution thereof given upon the other side of the Atlantic Ocean before this gentleman could possibly be acquainted with our having observed the same fact here, and as he seems very conversant in this part of natural philosophy, I take the liberty of laying before you his own words.[24]

Then, after three printed pages of quotation from Franklin's observations and conclusions, we find:

The solution of the gentleman, in relation to this phænomenon, so exactly corresponds to that which I offered early last spring, that I could not help communicating it.

Thus according to Watson, Franklin had invented concepts identical to his in devising an explanation of a very puzzling phenomenon. Since Franklin's letter bore the date of late May or early June, 1747, and Watson had offered his own explanation "early last spring," i. e., spring 1747—Franklin's creation was evidently independent.

I have been reflecting on Watson's statement for over a decade and have encountered the greatest difficulty in satisfying myself about

91) it appeared as in the book, with the same footnote. In its second printing (*Trans.* no. 489, pp. 491-496) it bore a separate title, "An account of the experiments . . . to measure the absolute velocity of electricity."

its exact meaning. The phrase "early last spring" was certainly intended to convey the impression of Watson's priority, since he drew particular attention to the date of Franklin's letter, 1 June 1747. But I have been unable to find any published statement by Watson dated in the spring of 1747 which in any way can be interpreted as being the equivalent of Franklin's. Certainly, no concepts similar to Franklin's are to be found in Watson's descriptions of the experiments in which "electricity" was transmitted over long distances and in which attempts were made to measure the speed of transmission. Nor do Franklin's concepts appear in the *Sequel*, which had been published in 1746. Franklin's theory is certainly not implicit in the statement in Watson's *Sequel* that "the glass tubes and globes had not the electrical power in themselves, but only served as the first movers and determiners of that power," nor in the discussions about the "current" of "electrical æther" or "electrical power." § In any event, the whole of Watson's *Sequel* had been read at the weekly meeting of the Royal Society on 30 October 1746, a time of year which is hardly "early last spring" in the Northern Hemisphere. The lines in Franklin's letter, immediately preceding the portion quoted by Watson, describe certain things which had ". . . occurred to us some months before Mr. Watson's ingenious *Sequel* came to hand, and these were some of the new things I intended to have communicated to you. But now I need only mention some particulars not hinted in that piece, with our reasonings thereupon: though perhaps the latter might well enough be spared." Franklin, in other words, knew that his novel ideas were "not hinted" in Watson's *Sequel*, and so did Watson when he read that letter.

Between the writing of the *Sequel* and the article in which he quoted from Franklin, Watson appears to have read but one paper at the Royal Society, on 29 October 1747,* which again is not "early last spring."

Watson said in January 1748 [1747/8] that in his *Sequel* he had described an experiment of Professor Bose in which the electrical machine and the man rubbing the globe were both insulated. In this case the man would give no sign of electrification if touched by "an unexcited non-electric." [25] Watson did not specify whether the latter were insulated or grounded. If, however, "another person, standing upon the floor," touched the moving globe with his finger or any conductor, the person rubbing the globe would become elec-

§ See Chapter Nine.
* It is the one that dealt with the transmission of the discharge of a Leyden jar over long distances and is notable for the absence of theory.

trified. This experiment had convinced Watson that the " power " of electricity is not " in the glass," and that the electrical machine is a kind of pump supplying " æther " from the floor (ultimately the ground, or body of the earth) . But Watson could now report that, one year ago, Dr. Bevis had introduced an important variation into the experiment; he had placed the second man (or " non-electric ") who touched the whirling globe, " upon originally-electrics." The new experiment, then, had an insulated man holding his hand against the whirling globe of an insulated electrical machine, while a second insulated man " held his finger near the equator " of the globe. Then, said Watson, if a third man, who stood on the floor, touched either one of the insulated men, " a snapping from either of them, I say, was perceptible upon that touch."

Watson said that he had asserted in his *Sequel*, and had described in that book many experiments to evince, that " contrary to the received opinion, the electricity was not derived from glass, the air, or other electrics *per se*." Therefore, " I was desired to consider " whether Bevis's experiment did not prove the " reverse of that assertion." Since both the man who rubbed the globe and the man who touched it with his finger were insulated, and could " receive " no " supply " of electricity " from the floor," how could each one " snap " when touched by a third man standing on the floor, and not insulated? Since " many experiments had proved that the electricity was not derived from the glass," Watson wrote, Bevis (and " several others to whom this gentleman shewed the experiment ") concluded that in this experiment " the electricity " was " communicated to the person rubbing from the air " through the " means " of the man who touched the globe. Watson was not satisfied with this conclusion. It was " directly contrary to numberless facts." He wrote that he " considered " the experiment carefully, compared its " effects " with those of other experiments, and " from surveying all the properties of electricity we are hitherto acquainted with, I gave . . . my opinion." †

Before describing that " opinion," stated by Watson under ten

† We may note that the experiment in its new form is all but identical to the one that Franklin had described, as Watson himself pointed out. In the Bevis experiment, an insulated man rubs a glass globe that is in contact with his hand, but insulated from the floor, while a second insulated man holds a finger near the globe; in Franklin's experiment, an insulated man rubs a glass tube that is in contact with his hand, but insulated from the floor, while a second insulated man draws fire from the tube. Like Franklin, Watson found that a man standing on the floor could draw a spark from either of the insulated men; Franklin drew a spark in this fashion when the rubbing had ceased, whereas Watson did so while the globe was turning. But Franklin had the better of Watson in one important respect; he showed that if the two insulated men touched each other, a spark passed between them, in fact a greater one than between either of them and the man on the floor.

propositions occupying three pages of print, let us ask the conditions under which he might have given it to a general or even a limited public. Not before the Royal Society, we may be sure! If he had, would he have ventured now to repeat that opinion in such detail? Furthermore, no evidence exists to show that the Royal Society was aware of it; it appears neither in the *Transactions* nor in the manuscript records of the meetings.‡ We can only suppose that Watson gave the opinion in private to one of those groups of gentlemen " of the Royal Society " with whom, or before whom he was in the habit of performing his experiments.

Watson's " opinion " is as follows.[26] [1] What is called electricity is the effect of " a very subtil and elastic fluid diffused throughout all bodies in contact with the terraqueous globe," and " every-where, in its natural state of the same degree of density." Probably, Watson says, an exception must be made for those substances " hitherto termed electrics *per se*." [2] The only occasions on which this fluid " manifests itself " occur when bodies " capable of receiving more thereof than their natural quantity are properly disposed for that purpose "; the " effects," by certain known operations, show themselves by the attraction and repulsion of light substances, by a snapping noise, and by sparks of fire, and so on, which are " directed towards other bodies, having only their natural quantity, or, at least, a quantity less than those bodies from which these snappings, etc., proceed." [3] If two bodies " in which the electricity is of the same density " are brought near each other, no snapping will be observed; snapping only occurs " in those bodies in which the density of the fluid is unequal." [4] The snapping is greater or less " in proportion to the different densities of the electricities in bodies brought near each other." [5] Glass and other bodies which are called electrics *per se* have " the property of taking the fluid from one body, and conveying it to another." [6] In the Bose-Bevis experiment, no snapping is observed when a person on the floor touches an insulated man who rubs the globe of an insulated electrical machine, unless simultaneously some other non-electric (conductor) is in contact with the globe. The reason is that the globe in motion takes away part of the " natural quantity of electricity " of the insulated man who rubs the globe. But this quantity is " restored to him again by the globe in its revolutions," so long as there is no " other non-electric near enough to communicate the electricity too." Thus, in this situation there is no diminution in the density of the electricity of the insulated man who rubs the globe, but the

‡ Information kindly provided by Mr. H. W. Robinson, former Librarian of the Royal Society of London.

situation is quite different [7] if a man who is on an insulator is placed near the globe in motion, or a gun-barrel is suspended in silk lines near the globe. In this case, " whatever part of the electricity of the person rubbing is taken from him " is now communicated to either the man or the gun barrel, since these are " the first non-electrics to which the electricity taken from the person rubbing can be communicated." In these circumstances [8], " as much electricity as is taken from the person rubbing, is given to the other "; so that the electricity of the man who is rubbing the globe becomes " more rare than it naturally was, and that of the last more dense." The result is that [9] " the electricity in either of these persons is in a very different state of density from what it naturally was," or from the density of a person standing " upon the earth," who is in a state of density intermediate between that of the other two men; in other words, his electricity is neither " so rare as the man rubbing the globe, nor so dense as that of him supported by electrics *per se*, and touching the equator of the globe." [10] Snapping may be observed if the man on the floor touches either of the other two, although the causes are different in the two cases. In one case the snapping " restores to him what he had lost," but in the case of the man " whose electricity is more dense, it takes of his surcharge, by which means their original quantity is restored to each."

Watson's Proposition 10 sounds remarkably like Franklin's position. By a suitable alteration of other propositions, and the elimination of yet others, the two conceptual schemes might be made to appear identical. It is not particularly remarkable that two men, independently of one another, should have simultaneously arrived at similar conceptions on opposite sides of the ocean, because independent simultaneous discoveries are very frequent in the history of science, and most often occur when there is intense activity in a given field. Franklin's ideas were developed by reflecting on the very same kind of experiment which Watson had been performing. Both experimenters were influenced by the same Newtonian " climate of opinion " with regard to the phenomena of attraction and repulsion and the principles of subtle fluids and the constitution of matter.

On the other hand we must observe that the differences between Watson's ideas and Franklin's are of more significance than their similarities. For example, in Proposition 1, Watson indicated that a subtle elastic fluid is diffused through every kind of body that is in contact with the earth with the probable exception of electrics *per se*. In the case of amber, an electric *per se*, which becomes negatively charged on being rubbed with wool or fur, the negative electrification implies—in Franklin's theory—that it has lost some of its electric fluid. Watson's theory would be unable to account for this simple fact in this way, because a body which does not contain any of the subtle fluid certainly cannot lose any of its natural quantity. Furthermore, this first proposition implies that in every body the subtle elastic fluid has the " same degree of density." A confusion is thereby established between the possibility of electrical effects occurring in a body by a net gain or loss of electric fluid and by a process in which the electric fluid becomes redistributed without any net alteration of the total quantity. In other words, Watson's theory does not directly imply—as Franklin's does—the principle that charging by rubbing arises from a transfer of electric matter. Proposition 2 assumes that the electric fluid manifests itself only in operations involving bodies " capable of receiving more thereof than their natural quantity," whereas in Franklin's theory the possibility is left open for snapping or a spark discharge between a neutral body (one with its normal quantity of electric fluid) and a negatively charged body (one which has lost some of its natural quantity). Proposition 5 implies that a material such as glass may remove electric fluid from a body with which it is in contact, but it does not make provision for the fact that there are electrics *per se* which do not " have the property of taking this fluid from one body," as Watson assumed, but rather have the property of giving up this fluid to other bodies; this includes the whole class of bodies which on rubbing become resinously electrified.

Wholly apart from the fact that Watson seems to have been unaware that when glass removes the fluid from a body, the latter body must suffer a loss of fluid, there is a fundamental difficulty about density. For example, if two bodies of very different sizes, or of very different masses, may be presumed to have the same density of electric fluid, then the quantity of electric fluid in each of the two bodies must be different. If by some process, such as rubbing, a small amount of electric fluid is taken from one of these bodies and given to another, the increase in density—in Watson's terms—in the one body is not comparable to the decrease in density of the other. But in Franklin's theory, the increase in electric fluid in the one body is quantitatively equal to the decrease in electric fluid in the other body: this is the law of conservation of charge.

In Franklin's theory, if two bodies of wholly different sizes and wholly different masses each gain the same amount of electric fluid, they will have the same net positive charge, and so can be presumed to exert the same force or effect on a third body. But in Watson's theory, even though these two bodies have gained the same net amount of electric fluid, the increase in density may be markedly different, and so the two bodies will be expected to behave quite differently. For example, if each of these two bodies should then be brought in contact with another body which has lost an amount of electric fluid exactly equal to the quantity that the two of them taken together have gained, Franklin's theory would predict that the contact could neutralize both of them. But in Watson's theory, an equalization of density would not imply that each of these two positively charged bodies would become electrically neutral on contact with each of a pair of negatively charged bodies, even though the negative charges were exactly equal to the positive charges. Thus the implications of Proposition 10 would seem to indicate a contradiction of the previous statements. Watson said in Proposition 10 that a discharge occurs when either of the two men is touched by a third man standing on the ground. But he failed to explore the difference between such a discharge and the discharge which would occur if these two men, while remaining electrified and insulated, were to touch each other. Unlike Franklin, Watson failed to compare (i) the intensity of the discharge between the insulated men and the man on the ground and (ii) the intensity of the discharge when the two insulated men touched each other. This comparison was the crucial step in the formulation of Franklin's concept of the electric fluid as a kind of matter transferred when bodies are electrified by friction and when they are discharged.

There is certainly no reason to suppose that Watson was anything but an honest and honorable man, and that he had actually expounded his views in private before Franklin had sent his similar views to England. Why he did not at once write up his results for presentation to the Royal Society, and publish his account forthwith, we will probably never know. He was pleased enough with what he had done to say that his " solution of this phænomenon . . . was satisfactory, not only to the gentleman [i. e., Watson himself] who proposed it, but to [many] members of the Royal Society, excellent judges of this matter, to whom I shewed the experiment." [27]

And yet, for all that, I do not really see how Watson can be given full credit for being an independent inventor of *Franklin's theory of electrical action*. In the first place, the basic postulate of Franklin's theory is the law of conservation of charge. Although in his eighth proposition Watson stated that only as much electricity would be taken from the person doing the rubbing as was given to the other, he never made a single experiment in support of it. That this postulate was a radical departure from the previous statements about electrical action is plain, and it could hardly be accepted unless there were provided a considerable evidence from experiment. Furthermore, as we shall see presently, the introduction by Watson of the concept of " density " of electricity was entirely misleading, as Watson might very well have found had he pursued his electrical investigations further. But the facts of the matter are that Watson never again published a contribution to electrical science, although he lived for forty years more, and maintained a lively interest in the subject. Franklin, on the other hand, made refinements in the original conceptual scheme and discovered a host of new phenomena which supported it. He advanced the state of knowledge of electricity until one decade later the whole subject was hardly recognizable as that to which Watson had devoted his energies. I believe that this is the reason why those nineteenth- and twentieth-century historians of electricity who give Watson credit for having independently invented *Franklin's theory of electrical action* do not quote Watson, but rather give Franklin's statements as illustrating the ideas held by both men. Such statements are not usually taken from Franklin's first letter, but are apt to be the more refined versions which appear in his later papers.

The only communications on electricity which Watson brought to the attention of the Royal Society after this time, and which were printed in the *Philosophical Transactions*, were two minor articles, a review of Franklin's book on electricity, a review of Nollet's book attacking Franklin, and a report on the experiments to test Franklin's hypothesis of the electrification of clouds and the electrical nature of the lightning discharge.[28] Perhaps Watson had reached the end of his ingenuity, or perhaps he knew that the subject of electricity which he had so notably advanced was now in good hands, perhaps better hands than his own, and for this reason stopped doing research on electricity. Yet it must be confessed that in other cases in the history of science, when one man discovers that another is working along to the very same lines, he is apt to be so stimulated by the rivalry that his productivity increases rather than ceases altogether.

Furthermore, although Watson reviewed Franklin's book favorably, while taking exception to a number of points which we shall discuss in a later chapter, he also wrote a favorable review of Nollet's book attacking Franklin's theory, thereby adopting a kind of neutral position between the Nollet theory which he had at first espoused and the Franklin theory to which he laid some claim of independent invention. What I have always found to be especially puzzling about Watson's conduct was not his claim, made in 1748 and repeated on one other occasion, to the early form of Franklin's theory, but the fact that once having made the claim, he disowned it by supporting Nollet. Nollet himself, in a long paper published in the memoirs of the French Academy of Sciences, was equally puzzled, and pointed out, with reference to line and page, that Watson's position was very much like his own, and the opposite of Franklin's.[29]

Franklin's theory was based on the assumption that all charges or states of electrification must be caused by a motion of electric matter. The Leyden jar is discharged whenever a conducting circuit is made between the inner and outer conductors of the jar; if there is a small gap in this conductor there will be a spark discharge. Hence the two conductors of the jar must have different charges. For instance, one might be plus and the other minus, or one might be plus and the other neutral, or one might be minus and the other neutral. But in each such possible case, Franklin's theory implied a flow of electric matter from the more positively charged conductor to the less positively charged conductor. There could be no ambiguity on this point. That Watson's ideas were certainly not identical to Franklin's can be seen in an important example. In the same pamphlet in which he said that he and Franklin held basically similar ideas, Watson raised the question of the direction in which the " electricity " would move in the discharge of a Leyden jar.[30] He wanted to know " whether the electricity, in compleating the circuit from the matter contained in the glass [of a Leyden jar], passed, either by the wire in the mouth to the coating on the glass, or the contrary way by the coating to the wire in the mouth, or otherwise directed itself both ways at once." If Watson had truly believed in a single-fluid of electricity, as Franklin did, the third possibility would have been ruled out at once as a contradiction of the basic concept; it is the old " afflux " and " efflux " of Nollet.§

When, on 5 June 1747, shortly after sending Collinson his first letter on electricity, Franklin wrote to Colden that the Europeans had also discovered that " the electrical fire is a real element, or species of matter, not *created* by the friction, but *collected* only," Franklin evidently meant that in Watson's writings and elsewhere he had encountered many forms of the general idea that electrical effects arise from a form of motion or a change of some kind of subtle substance or fluid that may be ordinarily within bodies. This was

§ In his first letter on electricity to Collinson, Franklin described " little light wind-mill wheels made of stiff paper vanes, fixed obliquely and turning freely on fine wire axes " and similar ones " formed like water-wheels." They had been devised by " my worthy and ingenious friend " Philip Syng and they had been used to discover and demonstrate the electric fire's " afflux to the electrical sphere, as well as its efflux." Franklin had been reading uncritically and had used language which he soon realized had no place in his conceptual scheme for electricity. " We afterwards discovered," he wrote in a footnote, " that the motion of those wheels was not owing to any afflux or efflux of the electric fluid, but to various circumstances of attraction and repulsion. 1750."

the sense in which Watson had ingeniously compared the electrical machine to a pump. Yet the question that was unresolved until Franklin and his Philadelphia friends attacked the problem was whether electrification is to be considered due to an increase in the activity of the subtle substance, or a rearrangement of the substance within the body, or even a variation in the density but not necessarily the total quantity of the substance in or around a body, or possibly a transfer of the substance from one body to another. Nor was it known whether that subtle substance was the matter of fire or of light, or the Newtonian æther, or even a wholly different kind of matter *sui generis*. At this point Franklin suggested a fluid or matter of electricity that exists in all bodies and is transferred from one body to another by friction. Such a clear statement had not been made by his European colleagues and Franklin backed it up with one experiment after the other. Watson and others had supplied the primitive notions and Franklin the refinements that proved to be the distinguishing aspects of a new conceptual scheme that had surprising implications. Certainly no one suspected, before Franklin's research, that a charged Leyden jar has equal negative and positive charges on the two conductors, so that there is no more electric fluid in a charged jar than in an uncharged one.

Watson stated his claim to the Franklin theory for the sake of the record, but was gracious to his American rival. We may, on this occasion, particularly admire Watson's character. It must have been a great shock for him to have come upon Franklin's statement and to have seen in it what seemed the major points of his own conceptual scheme which he had circulated among members of the Royal Society in private. Had he been a different sort of man, he might have rushed into print so as to stake a claim for his priority before the provincial. Instead, he chose to make a joint publication of a sort, printing together his own views and those of Franklin— in a manner that reminds us of Charles Darwin's conduct when he received Alfred Russell Wallace's paper on the origin of species before he had ever published his own concepts. And we may imagine the feeling of encouragement that Franklin must have felt to see his first scientific contribution published with approval by the leading electrician of the time. Having been the first to recognize Franklin's scientific ability, Watson never wavered in his support of Franklin, even when it became clear that Franklin's theory and experiments were upsetting some of his most cherished opinions, particularly as to the action of the Leyden jar. Watson, of course, made public his disagreement with some of Franklin's conclusions, but he supported Franklin's nomination for Fellowship in the Royal Society and the recommendation that Franklin be awarded the Society's Copley Medal. How gracious a tribute it is to these men that in an age often characterized by acrimonious dispute, Franklin and Watson found each other's measure and let their scientific opinions be judged by subsequent tests of experiment and not by skill in polemic or debate. I would guess that Watson too hastily concluded that Franklin's theory was like his own, that his honest deception may well have been caused by the fact that the superficial resemblances tended to mask some of the profound differences which became apparent only later when Franklin developed the initial concept to a higher degree.

Watson was willing to be corrected whenever he was shown to have been in error. In his *Sequel* * Watson had conceived that at times a current of electrical æther might run down a wire from the wainscoting to the prime conductor and then be delivered to the operator of the machine by the rubbing of the globe. In the letter quoted by Watson, Franklin gave a better interpretation, thus avoiding the inconsistency of Watson's position.† Watson accepted Franklin's correction and found supporting evidence in experiments. But he did not specifically acknowledge Franklin as the source of the correction. He said, only, that his conclusion about the "inversion of usual course of the electricity" had arisen from his "not having considered this experiment in a statical view, and from not then imagining the velocity of electricity so great as we have since found it." [31]

Franklin's Early Experiments with Leyden Jars

Franklin's second electrical letter to Collinson was written some time before 28 July 1747 ‡ and dealt largely with the phenomena of the Leyden jar, or "M. Muschenbroek's wonderful bottle," classified under five propositions.[32] [1] When a non-electric (conductor) is electrified, the electric fire accumulates on the surface and forms an electrical atmosphere around it (as Watson had already indicated); but in the Leyden jar, the glass confines the electric fire save for the upper surface of the non-electric (water, lead shot, etc.) and so the electric fire must be "crowded *into the substance* of the" non-electric. This is a pure conjecture and was not supported by experiments. Franklin himself proved it to be incorrect within a year.

* See Chapter Nine, page 405.

† See page 439 above.

‡ In the "Bowdoin MS," this is the letter dated 28 July 1747, "a copy of my last, which went by the Governour's vessel. . . ." For easy reference to the original, I have included within square brackets, the numbers assigned to the sections of the letter by Franklin.

[2] The wire going down into the water of the bottle is electrified plus (through contact with the gun-barrel which, in turn, is in contact with the positively charged globe §), and at the same time the outer coating of the jar, grounded during charging, becomes electrified minus—and to the same extent, i. e., "whatever quantity of electrical fire is thrown in at the top [or inside of the jar], an equal quantity goes out of the bottom [or outside coating]." This proposition, the first specific application of the principle of conservation of charge, was demonstrated by a series of ingenious experiments. An electrified jar was placed on wax and a small cork-ball hanging on a dry silk thread was brought near the wire; the ball was found to be attracted by the wire and then repelled. The ball was next brought near the outer coating and was instantly attracted until it lost its electrical fire. Had the coating a plus charge (or "a *positive* electrical atmosphere") like the wire, argued Franklin, the electrified cork would be repelled from the coating as well as from the wire. We must note here that Franklin did not try the reverse experiment, i. e., to see whether an uncharged cork would be initially attracted by the outer coating and then repelled and, in the subsequent negatively charged state, be attracted by the positively charged wire. The reason lies in a fundamental weakness in Franklin's theory which did not take cognizance of the repulsion between two negatively charged bodies—a subject which did not arouse his interest at this time. We will return to this problem presently.

A second experiment (see Fig. 9) made use of a bent wire sticking into a table, from which a small linen thread depended about half an inch away from a charged Leyden jar. When Franklin touched the wire of the jar, the thread was attracted by the outside (coating) of the bottle. This experiment was obviously suggested by Watson's experiment of holding a wire near the electrical machine. Franklin concluded that as "soon as you draw any fire out from the upper part [or inside of the bottle], by touching the wire, the lower part [or outside] of the bottle draws an equal quantity in by the thread." The conclusion concerning the "equal quantity" is a result of the theory as a whole * and could not be properly inferred from the

§ In the previous letter, Franklin had referred to his homemade electrical machine, but in an introductory paragraph to this letter, he acknowledged "the Proprietor's handsome present of a complete electrical apparatus, etc., [which] is also come to hand in good order, & put up in the library." This paragraph, which is to be found in the "Bowdoin MS," does not appear in the printed version. From it we learn that the experiments which Franklin was describing had been performed with his own machine and not this one, because he says of the Proprietor's gift, ". . . little use has been done with it yet, the weather having been excessively hot and moist ever since it arrived." [38]

* This experiment could be interpreted in a different way, by assuming that the

experimental data just presented, although such data were provided by a wholly different experiment. This was a demonstration of " electrical convection," and was given an important place in the discussion of electric current by Clerk Maxwell [34] a century or so later.† A Leyden jar with an outer coating of lead foil (fig. 10) has a wire with a " ring-end " affixed to the lead, so that the " ring-end " is level with the top or " ring-end " of the wire going down into the inside of the bottle. The Leyden jar is charged and placed on wax. A cork is then suspended by a silk (insulating) thread between the two wires. Under these circumstances, the cork " will play incessantly from one to the other, 'till the bottle is no longer electrised; that is, it fetches and carries fire from the top to the bottom [from the inside to the outside ⟨B. F.'s correction⟩] of the bottle, 'till the equilibrium is restored." This experiment provided conclusive proof that the positive electrification of the inside of the jar was quantitatively equal to the negative electrification of the outside although the charges were of opposite sign: that, to use the terminology of Franklin's theory, the inside had gained as much (and no more!) electrical fire as the outside had lost. Park Benjamin, in his history of electricity, remarked that this was the first occasion when the electric fluid had been made to show itself in any kind of discharge other than an instantaneous spark, shock, or explosion. By " breaking up the explosion, so to speak, into a great many successive little explosions," there began " the evolution of the electric current: the forging of the link between the Leyden jar and the voltaic cell." [35]

[3] Franklin's next proposition is that in a charged jar, the equilibrium cannot normally be restored by inward communication through the glass, but only by an external communication between the outer conductor and the inner (or the wire) —by means of a non-electric touching or approaching both simultaneously (in which case the equilibrium is restored instantly), or by touching each alternately (in which case the equilibrium is restored by degrees). An experiment may demonstrate this proposition. A charged jar (fig. 11) stands on a wax block. The electric fire does not circulate through the glass of the bottle; hence the jar remains charged and

negatively charged outside of the jar attracted the linen thread. It was well known that resinously electrified bodies (negative, in Franklin's theory) would attract neutral bodies, a somewhat different problem from that of the mutual repulsion of two negatively charged bodies.

† The term convection was suggested by analogy. In discussions of heat, there is transmission by radiation, and also by conduction and convection. The movement of electric charge in a wire is conduction, similar to the conduction of heat in a wire. Franklin's experiment invoked a process of the transfer of charge midway between radiation and conduction, and so was given the name convection.

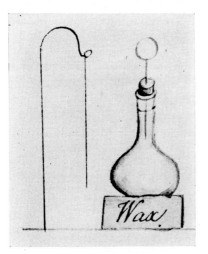

FIG. 9. One of Franklin's experiments on the Leyden jar. *Courtesy of the American Academy of Arts and Sciences.*

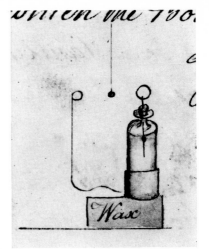

FIG. 10. Franklin's "electrical convection" experiment. *Courtesy of the American Academy of Arts and Sciences.*

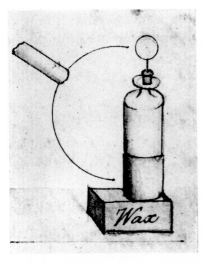

FIG. 11. Leyden jar on insulated stand. *Courtesy of the American Academy of Arts and Sciences.*

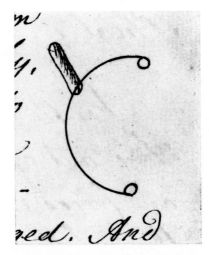

FIG. 12. Wire set in an insulated handle, used to discharge a charged Leyden jar. *Courtesy of the American Academy of Arts and Sciences.*

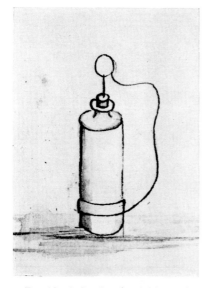

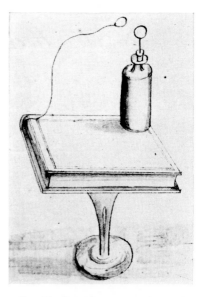

FIG. 13. A Leyden jar with a wire connecting the inner and outer conductors. *Courtesy of the American Academy of Arts and Sciences.*

FIG. 14. Experiment to show the passage of electric fire when a Leyden jar is discharged. *Courtesy of the American Academy of Arts and Sciences.*

FIG. 15. Franklin's "battery" of Leyden jars, presented to the Society by Joseph Hopkinson, April 1, 1836, in accordance with the request stated in Franklin's Will. The box measures 13 x 18 inches and the jars stand 15 inches high.

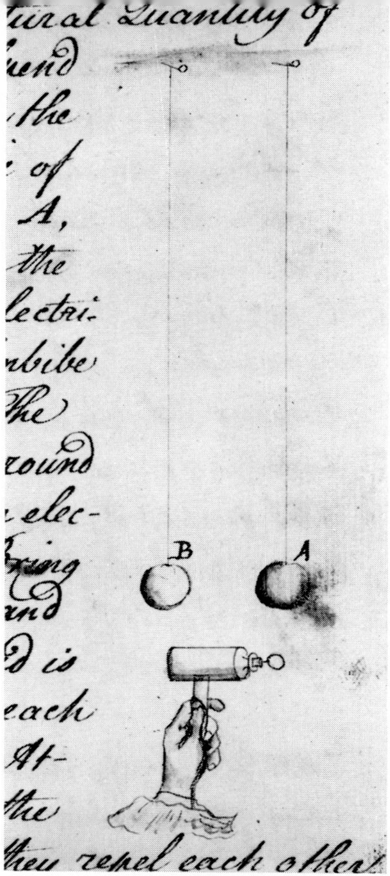

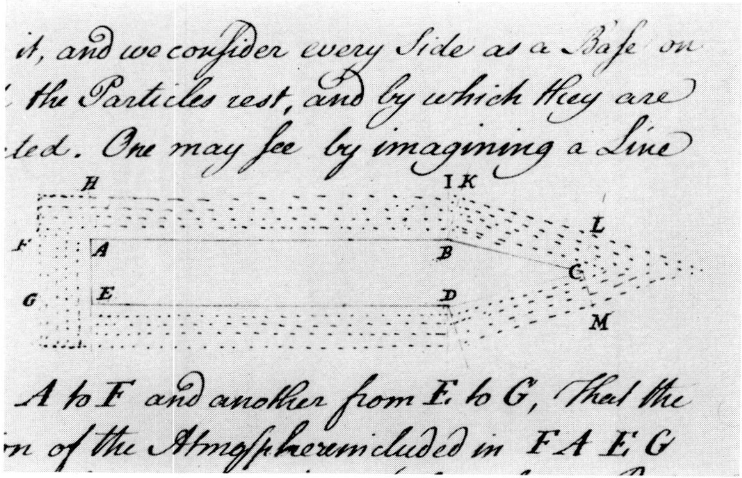

Fig. 17. An attempted explanation of the effects observed in charged pointed conductors. *Courtesy of the American Academy of Arts and Sciences.*

Fig. 16. An experiment to show that the two conductors of a Leyden jar have equal and opposite charges. *Courtesy of the American Academy of Arts and Sciences.*

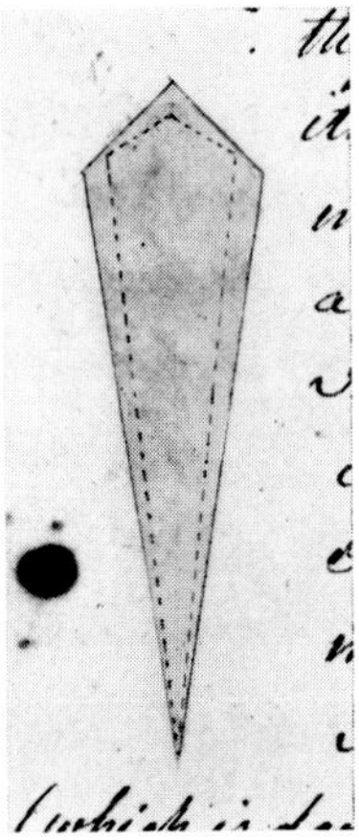

FIG. 18. An experiment on the properties of pointed conductors. *Courtesy of the American Academy of Arts and Sciences.*

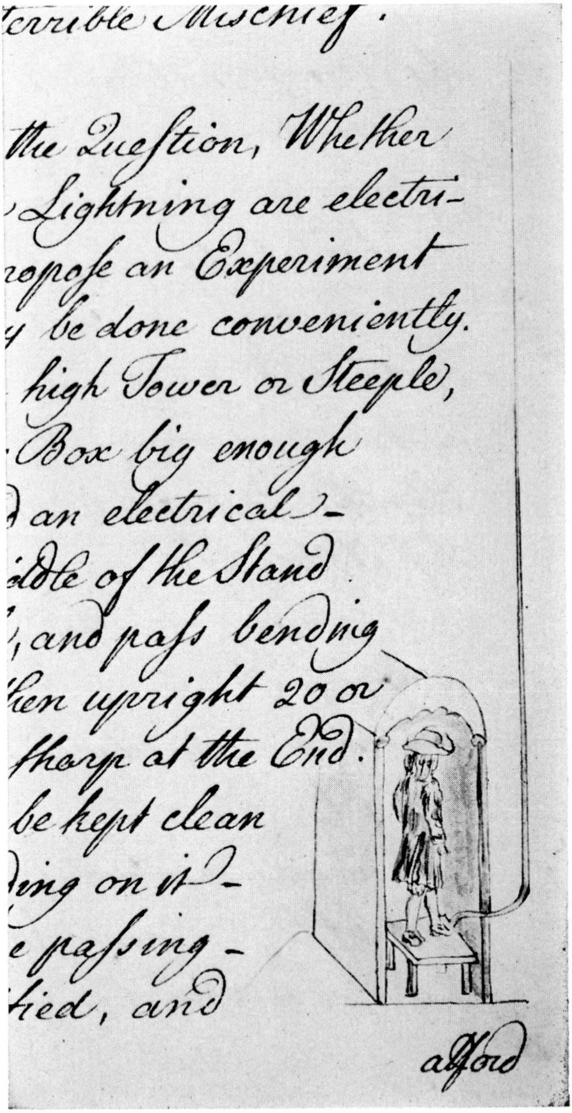

FIG. 19. Franklin's sentry-box experiment, designed to test the electrification of clouds. *Courtesy of the American Academy of Arts and Sciences.*

does not discharge internally. But bring up a bent wire in a sealing-wax handle (fig. 12) and touch one end of the bent wire to the wire of the jar, then gradually bring the other end to the outside of the jar—several sparks can be obtained before the equilibrium is restored. (The bent wire can be made first to touch the outside of the jar and then be gradually brought to the wire of the jar, and the same phenomenon will occur.) If the bent wire is made to touch the outside of the jar and the jar-wire simultaneously, the jar will be discharged at one stroke.

[4] When all the electric fire normally contained in the outside coating has been driven out, no more can then be added to the inner coating. This is a theoretical speculation, since Franklin never claimed to have produced a situation in which all of the fire had actually been removed from a non-electric. But this was the extreme of a working principle, namely, if fire cannot be forced out of the outer coating, then none (or only a very little) can be got inside. Thus, if the glass is too thick, or if the outer coating is insulated as in standing the jar on wax, practically no fire can be got into the wire or the water within the jar. Similarly, very little fire can be got out of the wire or water of a charged jar if there is no way for fire to get to the outside at the same time. One cannot get the fire out of the inside of a charged jar resting on wax, although this is possible if the jar rests on a non-electric. If a jar (see fig. 13) has a wire connecting the outer coating of the jar with the jar-wire, and is then placed on wax, it can never be charged; owing to the external communication, whatever is driven out of the external coating is immediately supplied through the wire. Thus we may see why a moist jar (" if such moisture continue up to the cork or wire ") can never be charged.‡

[5] The shock or convulsion of the nerves when a jar is discharged through a man or an animal is a result of the sudden passage of the

---

‡ Franklin had attempted a quantification of this process, but the numbers he used were merely to serve as illustration of an idea, rather than to represent any degrees of actual quantity. He supposed that before a jar was charged that there was a " common quantity of electricity in each part of the bottle . . . equal to 20." At every stroke of the tube, he supposed that " a quantity equal to 1 is thrown in." Thus after the first stroke, the wire and the inner conductor of the jar will contain a quantity equal to 21, and the outer coating 19. Proceeding in this way, step by step, a moment will be reached (after 20 strokes) in which the wire and inner conductor will have " a quantity of electrical fire equal to 40, the lower part none." Does this correspond to some real physical state? Franklin could not, of course, be sure about this, but he did know that there was a situation in which the jar would be fully charged, and in which no more electrical fire " can be thrown into the upper part, when no more can be driven out of the lower part." If you attempt to add still more electrical fire to a fully electrified jar, that electric fire " is spued back through the wire, or flies out in loud cracks through the sides of the bottle."

electrical fire through the body. " Other circumstances being equal," the " fire takes the shortest course, as Mr. Watson justly observes." Yet experiment does *not* prove that a communication with the floor is necessary, since one may hold the charged jar in one hand and be shocked as much on touching the wire with the other, " though his shoes be dry, or even standing on wax, as otherwise." Furthermore, " on the touch of the wire, (or of the gun-barrel, which is the same thing) the fire does not proceed from the touching finger to the wire, as is supposed, but from the wire to the finger, and passes through the body to the other hand, and so into the bottom of the bottle." §

A concluding experiment was designed to make visible the passage of the electrical fire in an external circuit when a Leyden jar is discharged. A book (fig. 14) is chosen " whose covering is filletted with gold " (i. e., with gold embossed lines on the cover) and a bent wire is arranged in place so that it is in contact with the gold lines and terminates in a ring. A charged Leyden jar is placed on the lines of the cover of the book at the opposite end. The bent wire is pressed upon by a stick of wax until its ring is close to the ring at the end of the jar-wire. A spark jumps between the two wires " and the whole line of gold, which completes the communication, between the top and bottom of the bottle [i. e., the inside and outside], will appear a vivid flame, like the sharpest lightning." In the figure, the book rests on a wine glass. This condition, Franklin said, is not necessary for the success of the experiment, but " is only to show that the visible Electricity is not brought up from the common stock in the earth." Franklin claimed that in this experiment, the " passing of the electrical fire from the upper to the lower part of the bottle [i. e., from the outside to the inside], to restore the equilibrium, is rendered strongly visible." What is rendered visible, however, is only the passage of electricity through the external circuit to discharge the jar. The experiment by itself provides no warrant for a motion in one direction or the other, and the direction results only from the arbitrary choice of positive charge in the case of rubbed glass.

Although we know by his own testimony that Watson had read Franklin's first letter, our knowledge that he had also read the second letter is only circumstantial. Watson read the continuation or amplification of his *Sequel* to the Royal Society on 21 January 1748 (new style) and there was ample time for him to have seen Franklin's letter of 28 July 1747. Since Watson had read Franklin's first letter and had found it sufficiently worth while to be discussed and quoted at length, he would not likely have ignored the next one.

§ This, again, is a conclusion from theory, which demands that the direction of motion of the electric fire be from plus to minus.

In the paper read by Watson at the Royal Society in January 1748, immediately following the extract from Franklin, there is a paragraph revising his earlier statement concerning electrical fire going from the wainscoting through the globe to the operator. The next paragraph corrects another error in the *Sequel*, the statement that when the Leyden jar was discharged through a man's body or any other non-electric, " as much electricity as was taken from his body, was immediately replaced by the floor of the room upon which he stood." Franklin's experiments, described in his second electrical letter, had plainly shown this conclusion to be wrong. The discharge of the jar did not involve electrical fire coming from the floor to the jar, but rather the excess of fluid in the inside being taken externally to the outside to make up the deficiency of fluid there. Franklin had demonstrated by the " electrical convection " experiment that no fluid needed to be brought up from the ground to discharge the jar. A second experiment confirmed this fact, that of the bent wire held in a sealing-wax handle which is brought up to a jar standing on wax so that one end touches the wire of the jar and the other end the outer coating. Watson did not acknowledge Franklin as the source of the correction, but the experiment he described is so much like Franklin's that it seems impossible that it was not devised as a result of his having read Franklin's letter. Franklin had discharged the jar by bringing an insulated wire into contact with the jar-wire and coating; Watson merely bent the jar wire until it came near the outer coating of the jar, whereupon the jar was discharged—even though no other non-electric was nearby " from which such quantity could be supplied." The reader could not have told whether this correction, like the preceding one, had been due to further work by Watson himself or by some other person, although Watson did state that the study of electricity was in its infancy ". . . and therefore it behoves us, as often as we can be justified therein by experiment, to correct any conclusions we may have drawn, if others yet more probable present themselves." [36]

Collinson must have been pleased that his Philadelphia protégés had made such progress, and wrote to Franklin concerning Watson's remarks. Franklin replied on 18 October 1748 that he was pleased to learn that his electrical experiments " were acceptable to the Society " and that he looked forward to reading " the ingenious Mr. Watson's new Piece " when published.[37] Little experimenting had been done in Philadelphia, but there was a prospect of " the approaching peace " restoring that " ease in our minds " conducive to scientific research; " possibly we may resume those enquiries this coming winter." [38]

Additional Experiments on Leyden Jars

Franklin did resume his research and the results achieved in 1748 were embodied in his third electrical communication to Collinson, dated 29 April 1749, containing an article entitled "Further Experiments and Observations in Electricity . . . , 1748." [39] This communication adopted the style used by Watson, that is, each paragraph was numbered, a style used also in later articles of Franklin's, and in the writings of Faraday and Clerk Maxwell. A notable stylistic difference exists between the preceding letters and this one (and the one following it). The former had been informal, but these were not. Franklin had, of course, learned that his communications were being transmitted to the Royal Society and he wrote them accordingly, omitting discussion of personal or business matters, and getting right down to the job at hand.

The article entitled "Further Experiments and Observations" begins with a description of a new way of charging the Leyden jar; the hook is held in the hand and the coating brought to the gun-barrel or the globe or tube. In this case, the "phial" will be electrified just as strongly as when the coating is held in the hand and the hook brought to the globe or tube—"a discovery of the very ingenious Mr. Kinnersley, and by him communicated to me." Since in this experiment the direction in which the fire moves during charging is different from that followed in the normal way of charging, the direction must also be different in discharging, "for the fire must come out the same way it went in." According to Franklin, a bottle charged through the hook gains an excess of fire (positive charge) on the hook and is discharged by a loss of that fire from the hook; in the new way of charging, an excess of fire is given to the outer coating and discharge is accomplished by causing the outer coating to lose that excess fire. An experiment to prove this concept to be in accordance with the facts made use of two Leyden jars, one held in each hand, charged equally in the normal way by bringing their hooks to the globe, tube, or prime conductor. Bringing the two hooks together, after the jars have been charged, produces no spark "because each hook is disposed to give fire, and neither to receive it." [40] But if one jar is placed on glass and then picked up by the hook, and it is then moved so that its coating is near the hook of the jar which is held in the other hand, both will be discharged.* In a variation of the experiment reported by Franklin, one jar is charged through the hook while the coating is held in

* In this situation the discharge through the experimenter results from the two Leyden jars or condensers being joined in series.

one hand, and a second jar is charged through the coating while held by the hook. Bringing the hook of the first jar to the coating of the second then produces no discharge. But if the first jar is set down on glass and then grasped by the coating, bringing the two hooks together will discharge both, or restore " the equilibrium within them." This result follows naturally enough from theory, since the negative charge on one hook equals in magnitude the positive charge on the other. As Franklin explained the matter, " The *abounding* of fire in one of the hooks (or rather in the internal surface of one bottle) being exactly equal to the *wanting* of the other: and, therefore, as each bottle has in itself the *abounding* as well as the *wanting* [on opposite surfaces of the glass], the wanting and abounding must be equal in each bottle." [41] When a man holds a Leyden jar in each hand, one fully charged and the other not charged at all, and brings their hooks together, both bottles become equally [half] electrified—" the one being half discharged, and the other half charged." †

Franklin's discovery that the two conductors on opposite sides of the glass in the Leyden jar have equal but opposite charges implied that the use of the terms " charging " and " discharging " with respect to Leyden jars was misleading since " there is really no more electrical fire in the phial after what is called its *charging*, than before, nor less after its discharging." [43] Suppose, argued Franklin, that this were not so. Then, it might possibly be the case that, on discharge, electric fluid would leave the hook but none would enter through the coating. In this event, if a man standing on wax held a charged Leyden jar by the coating in one hand and discharged it by touching the hook with the other, the man would gain electric fluid from the hook without losing any to the coating and he would end up by being charged. This is, however, contrary to experience; the experimenter does not end up by being charged. Therefore, he must lose to the coating as much as he gains from the hook, so that the total quantity of electric fluid in the discharged jar remains exactly what it was when the jar was charged. This beautiful example of reasoning provides an illustration of the vast simplicity and

† A nice experiment of Franklin's employed two equally charged Leyden jars placed on a table about five or six inches apart. A cork ball, suspended by a silk thread, hung between the two jars. Franklin observed that, if both of the jars had been charged through their hooks, the cork would be first attracted and then repelled by one hook, but it would not next be attracted by the other hook, which would repel it. On the other hand, if one of the jars were charged through the hook, the other through the coating, then, when the cork ball is repelled from one hook, it will be strongly attracted by the other one, and " play vigorously between them, fetching the electric fluid from the one, and delivering it to the other, till both phials are nearly discharged." [42]

superiority of Franklin's form of the theory to Watson's concept of " densities."

The requirement that the total quantity of electric fire ‡ or fluid in the jar remain constant explains why the jar cannot be charged through the hook unless the coating be grounded, and *vice versa*, since electric fluid cannot be added to one part unless an equal quantity can leave from the other. Two or more jars may be hung from the prime conductor, " one hanging on the tail of the other " (i. e., hook to coating), with a wire from the coating of the last one going to the floor, and they will all be charged simultaneously by a few turns of the globe—what " is driven out at the tail of the first, serving to charge the second; what is driven out of the second charging the third; and so on." [44]

The fact that a jar cannot be discharged unless at the very same time some fire can leave one part and enter another, was likened by Franklin to the condition of a bent spring which, to restore itself to straightness, must " contract that side which in the bending was extended, and extend that which was contracted." [45] One cannot occur if the other be prevented. Yet we do not say a bent spring is " charged " with elasticity, Franklin said, nor do we say it is " discharged " when unbent.§ According to Franklin, then, a piece of glass in a Leyden jar has within it a constant quantity of electric fire which it " strongly and obstinately retains." No alteration is ever made in that quantity although the disposition of it may be altered, i. e., some may be removed from one side and added to the other. In this case, Franklin explained, " it will not be at rest or in its natural state " until restored to its original disposition, and such restitution can be made only by a non-electric communication from one surface to the other, never through the glass itself. " Thus, the

‡ In this communication Franklin wrote of electric " fire " but later he wrote of electric " fluid " and electric " matter."

§ Franklin's observation that the deformation in a bent body is a combination of contraction on one side and expansion on the other indicates to us his knowledge of general physics, such as he might have learned by reading the *Course* of Desaguliers. The analogy, of course, " does not agree in every particular," as Franklin observed. Franklin lived long before the introduction of the concept of potentials, and great care must always be exercised to ensure that history is not being read backwards. Yet I cannot help but note the felicity of Franklin's comparison of the charging of a Leyden jar with the bending of a spring. Both require work and, hence, both represent a condition of stored potential energy. Euler, in 1744, had written of the *vis potentialis* of an elastic body when bent, although potential energy was not generally applied to such situations prior to the nineteenth century. Franklin, like Watson, was not able to distinguish effects of potential difference or voltage from effects of charge. Yet in the fumbling insecure way that was the only possible way at the time, Franklin chose a felicitous analogy that may reveal what we call—for want of understanding, perhaps—his physical intuition.

whole force of the bottle, and power of giving a shock, is in the GLASS ITSELF; the non-electrics in contact with the two surfaces, serving only to *give* and *receive* to and from the several parts of the glass; that is, to give on one side, and take away from the other." [46]

This startling conclusion had been reached by a series of ingenious experiments which were intended " to analyse the electrified bottle, in order to find wherein its strength lay." Known as Franklin's experiments on " the dissectible condenser," they are still performed in almost every introductory course in physics. A Leyden jar, with a cork fitting loosely, was charged in the usual way and placed on a glass insulator. The wire, and the loosely fitting cork in which it was fixed, was carefully removed, and the jar was then held in one hand while a finger of the other hand was brought to the mouth of the jar. Then, Franklin found, " the shock was as violent as if the wire had remained in it, which shewed that the force did not lie in the wire." Next a test was made of an earlier opinion: that the force " resided in the water, being crouded into and condensed in it, as confined by the glass." A jar was charged as before, set on glass, and the cork and wire once again carefully removed. The water was carefully decanted into an empty uncharged Leyden jar also on glass, but that jar did not now give any evidence whatever of a charge. Hence, Franklin argued, the force or charge must either have been lost during the decanting operation or it must have remained behind in the first bottle. The latter was shown to be the case by refilling the first bottle with unelectrified water, whereupon it gave the shock in the normal way.[47]

Franklin knew, from his previous discoveries concerning the action of pointed conductors, that the electrical properties of bodies depend on their shape. Hence, the next question to be studied was " whether glass had this property merely as glass, or whether the form contributed anything to it." Franklin took a flat " pane of sash-glass," laying it horizontally on one hand and placing a flat plate of lead on top it. The lead plate was brought to the prime conductor and was then touched by a finger of the other hand, whereupon the same spark and shock ensued as when a Leyden jar was charged and discharged. Next a parallel plate condenser was made of two identical lead plates, of the same rectangular shape as the glass but two inches shorter and narrower, separated by the glass. The bottom plate was grounded and the upper plate electrified (e. g., it could be brought to the prime conductor), so that the parallel-plate condenser was charged. The lead plates were then separated from the pane of glass " in doing which, what little fire might be in the lead was taken out, and the glass being touched in the electrified parts with a finger, afforded only very small pricking sparks," although " a great number of them might be taken from different places." But when the uncharged (or discharged) lead plates were again placed one on each side of the pane of glass, a conducting circuit between the two plates afforded as powerful a shock as before. Thus it was demonstrated that the power of giving a spark or shock in the condenser " resides " in glass as glass, and that the non-electrics (conductors) in contact with the glass serve only " to unite the force of the several parts, and bring them at once to any point desired: it being the property of a non-electric, that the whole body instantly receives or gives what electrical fire is given to or taken away from any one of its parts."

Franklin's next step was to join together a number of such parallel-plate condensers to make " what we call an *electrical-battery* " consisting of 11 panes " of large sash-glass " each " armed " with lead plates pasted on both sides. They were hooked together in series by wire and chain " from the giving side of one pane, to the receiving side of the other," as had been done with the Leyden jars in a previous experiment. To discharge the " battery," a special contrivance was used to connect together all the " receivers " (positively charged plates) of lead while a separate connection linked together all the " giving sides," so that by two long wires the " battery " could " give the force of all the plates at once through the body of any animal forming the circle with them." Franklin noted [48] that according to " the ingenious Mr. Watson's last book, lately received," Dr. Bevis had used " panes of glass to give a shock " before this had been done in Philadelphia, so that such a device could be no novelty to English readers.* Even so, he said, " We tried the experiment differently . . . and, as far as we hitherto know, have carried it farther." Of even more importance, we " drew different consequences from it. . . ." †
Franklin knew that he was now far ahead of Watson because, as he

* In a footnote, Franklin later said, " I have since heard that Mr. Smeaton was the first to make use of panes of glass for that purpose."

† Kinnersley designed a " magical picture," in which a picture of the King was put on one side of a plate of glass which was gilded to form a parallel-plate condenser. The " magical picture " form of the condenser was charged, and a small metal crown was placed on the monarch's head. If someone were in contact with the back plate and attempted to remove the crown, he would receive " a terrible blow, and fail in the attempt." If the picture were held in a place where no contact would be made with the back plate, the crown could be removed easily " without danger, which he pretends is a test of his loyalty." This provided an amusing game called " Treason," but a ring of persons could take the shock together, in which case the experiment would be called " The Conspirators." At the end of the eighteenth century, manufacturers of apparatus for electrical demonstrations included the " magical picture," with the result that the " Franklin panes " or " Franklin squares " were also called " magic squares." For example, Galvani, who used such a device in his experiments on the irritability of frogs, referred to the device under these names.

pointed out, " Mr. Watson still seems to think the fire [is] *accumulated on the non-electric* that is in contact with the glass." [49] But Franklin had just shown that there is no electric fire accumulated on the inner conductor of the Leyden jar, since the act of pouring the water from a charged Leyden jar into an empty uncharged jar does not carry a charge over to the second jar.

A final observation of Franklin's concerning the Leyden jar arose from the experiment of making one of a " thin glass bubble, about an inch in diameter, weighing only six grains, . . . half filled with water, [&] partly gilt on the outside." [50] This tiny condenser had a mighty action and gave " as great a shock as a man can well bear." Not much curiosity was aroused by this experiment; none of the Philadelphia group was interested enough in it to inquire into why this small Leyden jar was so powerful. The facts were at hand to indicate that the smallness of the surface area might be compensated by the thinness of the glass, a feature of Leyden jars that had already been observed by Watson and Wilson. Yet it is, of course, much easier to be aware of such a conclusion from today's vantage point (when we know the factors governing the capacitance of Leyden jars) than it was then. What seemed of greater interest to Franklin was the relation of the action of this tiny Leyden jar to the general theorem that the total quantity of electrical fire in a charged jar is the same as that in the jar before charging. For, if this be so, he concluded, " how great must be the quantity in this small portion of glass." ‡

A final experiment [51] revealed a very puzzling phenomenon, namely, that two negatively charged bodies will repel each other just as two positively charged bodies do. I have referred several times to the want of such experiments, and the significance of this problem will be discussed in a moment.

Franklin and Watson disagree on the Leyden Jar

On the same date, 29, April 1749, on which Franklin sent his " Further Experiments and Observations in Electricity made in

---

‡ Franklin wrote, " It is amazing to observe in how small a portion of glass a great electrical force may lie." It would seem, therefore, as if the electric fire were of the very "substance and essence " of glass. Perhaps, Franklin wrote, " if that due quantity of electrical fire so obstinately retained by glass, could be separated from it, it would no longer be glass; it might lose its transparency, or its brittleness, or its elasticity. . . . Experiments may possibly be invented hereafter, to discover this." The results of this experiment were certainly curious, since one might more readily expect that the larger the piece of glass, the more electric fire might be " crowded " into it. In Franklin's day, when there was no understanding of capacitance, all such phenomena remained unexplained mysteries.

Philadelphia 1748 " to Collinson, he sent a communication dealing with the electrification of clouds and the nature of the lightning discharge to his old friend, Dr. John Mitchel, F. R. S., who had removed from America to London. Since this communication opened a wholly new field of inquiry,§ I will postpone a discussion of it so that the thread of the Franklin-Watson development may not be lost.

The reception of Franklin's third electrical letter, " Further Experiments and Observations . . . 1748," sent under the date 29 April 1759, is recorded in the Journal Book of the Royal Society as follows * (14 December 1749) : " An Account of some Electrical Experiments made by Mr Franklin of Philadelphia in Pennsylvania was presented to the Society from the Author, and the same was refer'd to Mr Watson to give an Account of." The choice of Watson was proper enough, since he was the foremost electrician in England, and had previously discussed an earlier paper of Franklin's. Although his own theory was, in large measure, being corrected and revised by Franklin's findings, Watson, as before, was generous to his American colleague even though he did not agree with his conclusions. The Journal Book tells us that a week after Watson was given Franklin's communication (21 December 1749) :

Mr Watson, to whom Mr Franklin of Philadelphia's paper on electricity was referred at the last meeting, reported that he thought the paper worthy of being read at the Society.

And the said paper which is directed to Mr Peter Collinson, London, dated Philadelphia April 29, 1749 and intitled further Experiments and observations in Electricity made in Philadelphia 1748, was read.

Mr Watson made some observations on some things contained in this paper, which he promised to communicate in writing.

Thanks were ordered to Mr Watson for the trouble he has taken.

Watson's comments reveal the natural reluctance of a scientist to discard his own ideas. The Journal Book of the Royal Society records (11 January 1749/50, i. e., 1750 New Style) :

Mr Watson communicated in writing the observations which he made at the last meeting upon the reading of Mr Franklin's paper concerning electricity, which observations were read.

The first thing which Mr Watson observes is that when Mr Franklin in his paper mentions that the electricity is in the glass, he always means

---

§ The communication to Mitchel contained Franklin's " Observations and suppositions, towards forming a new hypothesis, for explaining the several phænomena of thunder-gusts. See Chapter Eleven.

* This extract, and the following ones, are printed here for the first time from the manuscript, through the courtesy of the Royal Society of London. I am indebted to Mr. H. W. Robinson for copies of these extracts.

the accumulated electricity. As he in his former papers, which Mr Watson has seen, is of opinion constantly that the electrical power is originally furnished by what have been hitherto called the non-electric substances applied to the glasses in rubbing them, and not from the glasses themselves.

Secondly the author of the paper imagines, contrary to what Mr Watson has laid before the Society, that in all the improvements of the experiment of Leyden the violence of the shock is not owing to any accumulation of the electric matter in the water or other non-electrics made use of in that experiment, but that the shock is owing to the glass that contains this water and such like.

Mr Watson says he has yet seen no reason to alter or retract his former sentiments, and that he has frequently made an experiment which appears to him very conclusive in determining this point. Which is, that if one person causes to be fully electrified a vial two thirds full of water, or other proper non-electric matter, by means of a wire connected with the prime conductor, so as easily to be drawn out. If this person pours the water contained in this vial into a bason held in one hand of a second person supported by wax, who the instant of the pouring presents the finger of his other hand near some warm spirit of wine in the hand of a third person, there will ensue a snap and the spirit will frequently be fired. This testifies the accumulation of the electricity in the second person, which he can receive by no other means than by the pouring the water from the vial into the bason held in his hand. Now as the water only, and not the vial, touched the bason, the electricity it must be presumed came from the water.

Thanks were ordered to Mr Watson for this communication.

Watson's first comment is well taken and refers to the apparent contradiction between Franklin's present insistence that the glass in the charged jar has no more electrical fire when the jar is charged than it had before charging and his earlier statement that glass becomes positively charged when rubbed, deriving that charge from the electrical fire " accumulated " from the rubber.† Watson did not refer specifically to Franklin's actual discoveries; there was no need to do so since Franklin's paper had been read to the Society in its

† Franklin could have avoided this criticism had he written with more precision. For instance, in the paper discussed by Watson, Proposition 13 reads as follows: " Glass, in like manner, has, within its substance, always the same quantity of electrical fire, and that a very great quantity in proportion to the mass of glass, as shall be shewn hereafter." Franklin was, of course, referring to the fact that the glass in the Leyden jar, which he had shown to be the component of the jar in which the charge " resides," has an equal positive charge on one side and negative charge on the other. Yet a piece of glass that has been rubbed was said by Franklin to have a positive charge because it has an excess of electric fluid. Franklin did not actually make it clear as to whether a positively charged glass rod has " within its substance " no more electric fluid than when uncharged; i. e., he did not specify whether the excess electric fluid simply accumulated around its exterior to form an " electric atmosphere."

entirety—*res ipsa loquitur.* But Watson was unable to abandon his own idea that the Leyden jar worked through an accumulation of electrical fire in the water or other non-electric (conductor) in contact with the glass, and he was evidently annoyed to find that in Philadelphia this idea—hitherto held as strongly as in London—had been discarded and had been replaced by a totally different one, viz. that "the shock is owing to the glass." We do not know whether Watson repeated Franklin's experiments as described; at any rate, he did not state that these experiments were not reproducible. Instead, he offered a variant which appeared to him to be "fully conclusive," and to support his own ideas in contradiction to Franklin's. A jar was charged (and the cork and wire removed) and was then held in the hand of a man who poured the water into a "bason" held in the hand of a second man standing on wax. The aim of the experiment was to prove that this second man—standing on wax and, therefore, unable to receive electrical fire from any source save the water—would become charged. So it would be proved, supposedly, that there must have been an accumulation of electricity in the water of the Leyden jar. That the second man did become charged was "proved" by having a third man hold some warm spirit of wine near a finger of the man holding the "bason," and at the instant of pouring a snap was observed and the spirit ignited.

These comments were forwarded to Franklin by Collinson and were duly copied by Franklin into his own record.‡ He replied in a letter to Collinson dated 27 July 1750, in which he dismissed the first comment by referring Watson to the Philadelphia experiment of the "dissectible condenser." § As to the new experiment introduced by Watson to show that the electricity accumulates in the water of the jar, Franklin said simply that Watson was mistaken in his interpretation "and I persuade myself he will change his opinion

‡ The "Bowdoin MS"—the collection of all of Franklin's communications to London, which Franklin gave to James Bowdoin in 1752—contains an "extract from the Minutes of the Royal Society: containing some remarks of Mr. W. Watson, F. R. S. concerning the foregoing letters, and a request that Mr. P. Collinson, F. R. S. write to his correspondent in Philadelphia, concerning the electrocution of a turkey." This extract, evidently sent to Franklin by Collinson, has been printed in the 1941 edition of Franklin's book on electricity. Watson presented his objections in substantially the same way in both documents, although the one forwarded to Franklin contains the statement that "Mr. Watson is not quite master of part of this gentleman's reasoning." Furthermore, after describing Watson's experiment which was intended to confute Franklin's, the communication sent to Franklin contained the statement, "Mr. Watson would further recommend to our worthy brother Mr. Collinson, writing to his correspondent Mr. Franklin to desire to know his success in attempting to kill a turkey by the electrical strokes." [52]

§ Franklin's letter began by observing that Watson had evidently written out "his observations on my last paper in haste, without having first well considered the experiments related."

of it." [53] If two experimenters stand on the floor, one holding a charged jar by the coating and the other bringing a spoon of warm spirits to the wire or hook of the jar, the spirits will be fired and the jar discharged—as everyone knows—but such an experiment, Franklin wrote, will not determine whether the accumulation of electrical fire was in the glass of the jar or the water. Franklin then said that at the instant of pouring, in Watson's experiment, a conducting circuit was made from the water to the basin and to the body of the experimenter standing on wax. During the time of pouring, together they formed a circuit acting like a single " long wire, reaching from the internal surface of the phial to the spirits." I do not see how anyone can fail to accept Franklin's analysis of this experiment. In Watson's experiment, there can be no question but what the stream of water being poured must be considered as a conductor, similar to a continuous wire.

The remainder of this letter dealt with other topics: lightning, the reversal of the polarity of magnetic needles by an electric discharge, and the melting of the heads and points of needles, and the like.

The Full Statement of the Franklin Theory

Franklin was now ready for a complete statement of his theory of electrical action, and it was embodied in a paper entitled " Opinions and Conjectures concerning the Properties and Effects of the Electrical Matter, arising from Experiments and Observations made at Philadelphia, 1749." This was a formal article, as was the previous communication to Collinson. There can be no question of its having been written in full knowledge that it would be presented to the scientists in England. It contained numbers preceding each paragraph (in the style learned from Watson) which facilitated reference and cross-reference. Franklin sent it enclosed with a note to Collinson dated 29 July 1750.[54]

This paper began with the proposition [1] * that the electric matter consists of " extremely subtile " particles since it can easily permeate all common matter, even metals, without " any perceptible resistance." Here Franklin used the term " electrical matter " for the first time. Although he indicated a cause for belief in its " subtility," he took its atomicity or particulate composition for granted.†
Watson had contrived a number of experiments to prove that elec-

---

* As before, I have included within square brackets the numbers assigned by Franklin to the separate sections of his paper.

† This was Newton's procedure, to show that the axioms of a physical system are derived from experience, but never to question the general atomism underlying physical thought.

tricity passes through conductors and not just along their surfaces, but Franklin was content to say that [2] if any one should have doubts on this point, a good shock taken through his body from a Leyden jar would convince him. [3] The difference between electric matter and "common matter" lies in the mutual attraction of the particles of the latter and the mutual repulsion of the particles of the former (which causes "the appearing divergency in a stream of electrified effluvia"). In eighteenth-century terms, electrical matter exists in the form of a particulate, subtle, elastic fluid. [4] The particles of electric matter, though mutually repellent, are attracted strongly by "all other matter." ‡ [5] Therefore, if a quantity of electric matter be applied to a mass of common matter, it will be "immediately and equally diffused through the whole." In other words [6], common matter is "a kind of spunge" to the electric fluid. A sponge absorbes water more slowly than common matter absorbs electric matter since the "parts of the spunge" are impeded in their attraction of the "parts of the water" owing to the mutual attraction of the "parts of the water" which the sponge must overcome. Generally [7], in common matter there is as much electric matter as it can contain; therefore, if more be added, it can not enter the body but collects on its surface to form an "electrical atmosphere," in which case the body "is said to be electrified." § All bodies, however [8], do not "attract and retain" electrical matter "with equal strength and force," a phenomenon presently to be explained, and those called electrics *per se* "attract and retain it strongest, and contain the greatest quantity." [9] That common matter always contains electrical fluid is demonstrated by the fact of experience that a rubbed glove or tube enables us to pump some out.*

The electrical atmospheres surrounding charged bodies are a means for explaining the observed repulsion between them, but we

‡ Here we may observe the influence on Franklin's thought of his reading during the 1740's. He had adopted the notion of two kinds of matter, each composed of particles. The interaction between these two particulate forms of matter serves as the basis for all explanations. The particles of common matter attract one another, but the electric matter forms an elastic fluid (in the sense that we have seen in earlier chapters), because of the mutual repulsion of the particles. Franklin's theory, in other words, drew heavily on the general preconceptions of his age. But the specific development of concepts of two kinds of particulate matter, one composed of repellent particles and the other of attractive particles, the particles of one kind having an attraction for the particles of the other kind, represents a distinct departure from the generally accepted ideas of his day. Such a view was not to be found in Winkler, Bose, Watson, Martin, or Wilson.

§ In this way, Franklin was able to avoid the ambiguity which Watson had seized upon in his criticism.

* This statement is a direct contradiction of Watson's Proposition 10; see page 446 above.

must note again that this explanation takes cognizance only of the repulsion between positively charged bodies (i. e., those which have gained an excess of fluid over their normal quantity). It offers no aid whatever in understanding the repulsion between negatively charged bodies—a phenomenon that had been observed by Franklin and reported by him in an earlier paper.

The concept of electrical atmospheres was not wholly novel with Franklin; we have seen the growth of this concept in the writings of Desaguliers, Watson, and others. Franklin's original contribution lay in the particular use he gave to this concept in his theory of electrical action, and the way in which he developed it. For example, Franklin stated that [15] it takes the "form . . . of the body it surrounds." A sphere will thus gain a spherical atmosphere and a cylinder a cylindrical one. Desaguliers had supposed that both would have a sphere of effluvia, and Watson had never pursued the question of shape at all.†

Franklin was able to apply his theory of the production of electrical atmospheres in a beautiful way as follows. [14] Two uncharged apples or balls of wood are suspended from the ceiling by silk threads. One of them A is charged by contact with the positively charged wire or hook of a Leyden jar. The fluid gained cannot be "imbibed," since this body has its normal quantity, and therefore the fluid will flow around it to form an atmosphere. Bring A into contact with the second apple or ball B, and half of the excess fluid

† Franklin supposed [11] that if one had a piece of common matter "entirely free from electrical matter," and a single particle of electric matter were brought near, it would be attracted, and would enter the body. Inside the body, it would move until it rested at the very center, or "where the attraction is every way equal." At this point, of course, Franklin was getting a little bit over his depth. He had no knowledge of what the law of attraction might be, or of its effects. For instance, one might ask what would have happened, had one presented to Franklin the question of the fate of a particle of electric matter brought near a spherical shell "entirely free from electrical matter"; could he have found the answer? The problem of hollow bodies was one which Franklin later studied experimentally.

Suppose one particle of electric matter had entered a piece of common matter, and then more particles were allowed to enter. According to Franklin they would assume places where "the balance is equal between the attraction of the common matter and their own mutual repulsion." It may be supposed that they will form triangles, and that the sides of these triangles will become shorter as the number of electric particles increases, until at last "the common matter has drawn in so many, that its whole power of compressing those triangles by attraction, is equal to their whole power of expanding themselves by repulsion; and then will such piece of matter receive no more." When a body becomes negatively charged, and loses electric fluid, the triangles which are formed by the remaining particles may be supposed to be enlarged as a result of their mutual repulsion, "until they occupy the whole piece." If the quantity of electric fluid which has been removed can be restored again, these triangles which had expanded on the loss of electric fluid will become compressed again "till there is room for the whole."

on A will be communicated to B, so that both will have atmospheres and they will repel each other as observed.

In a second experiment, a stick of sealing wax is attached to a Leyden jar (see fig 16), which is charged and then brought up to the two uncharged balls A and B, suspended as before, so that the coating touches B and the hook or wire touches A. According to Franklin's theory, the ball A receives just as much fluid as B can lose; the fluid received by A forms an atmosphere around it. If now the balls are brought into contact, the atmosphere of A will not be divided into two as before, but "B will drink up the whole atmosphere of A, and both will be found again in their natural [i. e., uncharged] state."

To render visible the spherical atmosphere surrounding a sphere [15], a little rosin may be dropped into a hot spoon held underneath a charged sphere. An entertaining speculation will result from imagining the possible consequences to Franklin's elegant theory of atmospheres, had he tried this experiment with a negatively charged sphere as well as a positively charged one! In the case of a sphere [16], the atmosphere has no greater disposition to leave any one part than any other, being "equally attracted by every part." But in cubes, the atmosphere may be drawn more easily from the vertices than the faces, and in general most easily from the most acute angles.

Let us suppose, Franklin wrote, that we have a charged body (as in fig 17) of the form of a pentagon $ABCDE$. Franklin thought that the atmosphere would take a shape indicated by drawing five lines parallel to the edges of the pentagon, all of them at a common distance from the edges parallel to which they were drawn. From the figure it appears that the electrical atmosphere has everywhere within it the same "fluid density." A series of lines are next drawn through the atmosphere perpendicular to each of the edges of the pentagon and erected at both extremities of each edge; these are the lines AF, AH, BI, BK, CL, CM, etc. If we now "consider every side [of the pentagon] as a base on which the particles [of the atmosphere] rest," Franklin said, we can explain why the atmosphere can most easily be drawn off from its pointed extremities or vertices. That part of the atmosphere included in the parallelogram $AFGE$ has the side AE "for its basis," that part included in $ABIH$ has the side AB "for its basis," and that included in $BCLK$ has BC "to rest on," and so forth. Hence, if a blunt smooth body is used to draw off the atmosphere midway between A and B, it must come very near before its attraction exceeds the "force or power with which this side holds its atmosphere." By contrast, that portion of the atmosphere included in BIK has less surface to rest on and be attracted by; this circumstance coupled with the mutual repulsion of the particles of the atmosphere explains why the blunt body will attract away the atmosphere at B " with more ease, or at a greater distance " than at a point midway between A and B. The vertex at A is more acute (or more " pointed ") than that at B. Hence, at A there is a greater quantity of atmosphere (AFH) with relatively less surface to rest on or attract it than at A. But at vertex C, there is a quantity bounded by LCM relatively largest and with " surface to attract it and keep it back the least." It follows that fluid may be drawn off most easily at C, then at A, then B. From the nature of fluidity and the mutual repulsion of the particles of electrical fluid, we can see that if some of the atmosphere is removed at one point, the remainder will redistribute itself, and eventually it may be all removed at one point. Furthermore, the extremity of the atmosphere opposite the most acute vertex C is further from the body than the similar extremity opposite A, which in turn is further than that opposite B, which finally is further than the edge of the atmosphere from any point on a side that is not an extremity, as the midpoint between A and B. Hence the attraction between the body and particles of the fluid located at the vertices of the atmosphere is less than at other points in the outer boundary of the atmosphere. Thus air particles can more easily remove particles of the electrical atmosphere from a vertex than an edge. This process of removal is aided by the mutual repellency of the atmosphere particles. Thus Franklin explained why electrified bodies will discharge into the air if they have points.

Apart from the continual restriction we must impose (that all explanations apply only to positively charged bodies), this explanation is quite impressive. Although the geometrical construction of the atmosphere and the means of dividing it into rectangular segments (at least in cross-section) show a certain naïveté in geometry, the conception as a whole indicates that power of physical intuition which always characterizes great investigators. Crude though the diagram was, the major idea—that a greater quantity of fluid collected in the nieghborhood of vertices than at edges, and the greatest amount of all at the sharpest or most acute vertices—was completely sound. We no longer, of course, believe in electrical atmospheres or clouds of charged particles surrounding charged bodies. In terms of our modern concept of surface charge-density, however, we still explain charge distributions by assuming a greater concentration of charge at points; in general, the charge density is least at regions of greatest curvature, i. e., where the radius of curvature, as in a pear-shaped conductor, is greatest. We demonstrate this fact for our students in our physics courses by using a proof-plane to " wipe off " a little charge, from first one area and then another, and then test the relative quantity of charge removed from each by bringing the proof plane to an electroscope or electrometer.

Franklin's explanation of how a pointed object will draw off the electrical fluid from a charged object was of poorer quality. In its essence, it stated that [17] a blunt body cannot easily draw off " a number of particles at once," but a pointed body can (" with no greater force ") remove the particles of the electrical atmosphere one by one—just as " a degree of strength not sufficient to pull away a handful [of hairs from a horse's tail] at once, could yet easily strip it hair by hair." ‡

When these explanations had first occurred to Franklin, they seemed to be perfectly satisfactory, but after he had written them down, Franklin found that he had doubts about both. Since, however, [18], " I have at present nothing better to offer in their stead, I do not cross them out: for even a bad solution read, and its faults discovered, has often given rise to a good one, in the mind of an ingenious reader." Franklin readily admitted that this explanation was inadequate; we need not, therefore, charge him with it.

The law [26] " that points as they are more or less acute, draw on and throw off the electrical fluid with more or less power, and at greater or less distances, and in larger or smaller quantities at the same time," was invoked by Franklin in order to explain the experiment Watson had described, in which a leaf of metal was suspended between two parallel plates. Franklin had learned that the suspended-leaf experiment had been explained by Watson in terms of a simultaneous " efflux " and " afflux," implying a movement of electricity in two contrary directions at once. That such an explanation was exactly the opposite of the theory of electrical action proposed by Franklin is plain. Franklin had previously corrected Watson's notion that the electrical fire might equally go from the operator (rubbing the globe) to the ground through the globe, and also from the ground through the globe to the operator. Now he had to explain in his own terms how the leaf might remain suspended between the two plates or, like Watson, actually surrender the whole theory and acknowledge the superiority of the concepts made popular by the Abbé Nollet.

‡ In Franklin's discussion of pulling the hair out of a horse's tail, we may discern the " homespun philosopher " in the realm of science. We are reminded of the statement at the very beginning of this paper of Franklin's as to the doubt that anyone may have concerning the passage of the electric matter through the substance of bodies or only over their surfaces. Said Franklin, " a shock from an electrified large glass jar, taken through his own body, will probably convince him."

Franklin's eighteenth-century readers, of course, recognized the source of the fable of the horse's tail in Plutarch's life of Sertorius.

In this experiment, two flat metal plates are placed horizontally, one above the other, the upper one continually electrified (plus) — for example by being in contact with the prime conductor of an electrical machine in operation—and the lower one being grounded by being held in the hand of a man standing on the ground. The leaf is attracted by the uppermost plate and would fly to it, Franklin said, [26] save that it is pointed and therefore draws off a quantity of electric fluid (forming an atmosphere) and is then repelled. It is not, by repulsion, driven all the way to the lower plate since the bottom of the leaf is also pointed and therefore throws off the electric fluid as fast as the upper point draws it. The electric fluid thrown off from the leaf to the lower plate is conducted to the ground and dissipated. If the upper and lower points were cut so as to be of the same angle, the leaf would remain midway between the plates. But if (see fig. 18) the points are unequal, the most acute point (drawing or throwing off the electrical fluid more efficiently than a more obtuse one) will naturally be further from the plate nearer to it than the opposite point will be from the other one. By making the leaf extremely blunt above and acute below, it will discharge quickly enough into the air to enable the experimenter to dispense with the lower grounded plate altogether. *Exeunt* " afflux " *et* " efflux "!

Franklin had stated [8] that all the different kinds of common matter do not equally attract the electric fluid, and that those attracting and retaining it most strongly are the group called electrics *per se,* such as glass. In his explanation, Franklin emphasized (by underlining the sentence in his manuscript) that no means had yet been discovered to force the electrical fluid through glass.§ This position was in direct contradiction to that of Watson's, which was apparently supported by experiment. Franklin knew that [28] a feather suspended by a thread in an hermetically sealed glass bottle will move when a rubbed tube is brought near the outside of the bottle, and that this phenomenon was alleged to prove that the electrical fluid passed through the glass of the botle. But if the fluid could go through glass, Franklin said, then how could the Leyden jar be charged? The fluid transferred to the wire from the prime conductor would simply travel down into the water, cross the glass walls, and escape into the floor. If instead of glass, a bottle of conducting material (a metal, for instance) were employed, the bottle would not be charged while held in the hand of a man standing on the floor—for this very reason. A very fine crack anywhere in the glass would also prevent the jar from becoming charged under the

§ Later he learned that hot glass was a kind of conductor.

above circumstances, even though less subtle fluids than electricity (e. g., water) would not go through such a crack.

A " slight observer " might be fooled by an experiment that gives the appearance of electrical fluid passing through glass. An uncharged jar is placed on an insulating stand, a bullet is hung from the prime conductor by a chain so that it is a quarter of an inch from the wire or hook of the jar, and a man standing on the floor then places a knuckle a quarter of an inch from the coating of the jar. The globe of the electrical machine is then turned and a spark leaps from the bullet to the wire and simultaneously from the coating of the jar to the grounded man's knuckle. Does it not appear, Franklin asked, as if the electrical fire, passing from the prime conductor to the bullet, goes right through the glass to be discharged from the outer coating? Referring to his previous experiments, Franklin explained that " the fire that thus leaves the bottle, though the same in quantity, cannot be the very same fire that entered at the wire "; if it were, the jar would not become charged during the course of the operation, whereas it manifestly is charged.* If [30] the fire leaving the coating is not the same as entered through the wire, it must have been in the bottle (actually in the glass) before charging and [31] there must be a great quantity of electrical fire in glass.

That [32] glass exerts a strong attraction on the electric fluid is proved by the fact that a whole piece of glass cannot be electrified minus, as can be done in the case of metals. A piece of glass holds on to its electric fluid strongly and has as much as it can hold. (Positive electrification results from adding an atmosphere of electrical fluid around the glass, not forcing more fluid in between the pores.) The only way known to achieve negative electrification in glass † is

---

* In order to see this line of reasoning more clearly, we may suppose that a certain charge Q had been transferred from the bullet to the wire, had travelled down the wire into the water, had passed through the glass into the outer coating, and had then jumped through the air to the grounded knuckle of the experimenter. This charge Q would have completely traversed the Leyden jar as if it had been an ordinary conductor, and there would be no remaining charge. On the basis of Franklin's theory, this charge Q would have been transferred from the bullet to the wire in a spark discharge, and then would have traveled down the wire into the water and given the inner surface of the glass a charge of $+ Q$. At the same time the outer surface of the glass would have received a charge of $— Q$, because an equal charge Q would have left it and been transferred to the outer metal coating, and then would have jumped from the outer coating to the grounded knuckle of the experimenter. In both explanations, a quantity of electric fluid Q would have entered the wire of the jar and have left the outer coating. But in one case the jar would not become charged in the process, whereas in the other the jar would have received a charge of $+ Q$ on the inside and of $— Q$ on the outside.

† Franklin's friend, John Canton, later found the charge on a rubbed object depends on the surface conditions and the kind of material used in rubbing. See Chapter Eleven.

to cover each surface with a non-electric and then " throwing an additional quantity of this fluid on one surface, which spreading on the non-electric [conductor], and being bound to it by that surface, acts by its repelling force on the particles of the electric fluid contained in the other surface, and drives them out of the glass into the non-electric [conductor] on that side from whence they are discharged, and then those [that have been] added [to the non-electric] on the charged side can enter [the glass]," leaving the glass as a whole with no more electrical fluid than prior to charging. The above quotation is one of the most remarkable passages to be found in Franklin's scientific writings. In it we can see clearly that Franklin was able to distinguish—as others were not—between " the repelling force " going through a sheet of glass while the electrical fluid does not. Franklin also appreciated a role of the non-electrics in contact with the glass, since as conductors the charge placed on them would spread out and move; this would not happen on a dry glass surface, which is non-conducting. Furthermore, Franklin saw clearly—for what was, so far as I know, the first time—the mechanism of induced charges that produces a negative charge on a grounded conductor when a nearby conductor receives a positive charge.

We need not be overly concerned with the theory adduced by Franklin to explain the nature of glass in relation to its electrical properties because he later appreciated that he had been in error. He had believed that [33] in the furnace (" in its first principles ") glass has no more electric fluid than " other common matter." He next supposed that whenever heated glass begins to get cool, the "vacuum " left by the departure of the " common fire " or heat is filled with electric fluid attracted by the glass particles (as water in a porous stone). This electric fluid is not " fixed " in a chemical sense but is held in place as a fluid whose particles are attracted by the particles of glass. In cooling further, the texture of glass becomes most closely knit in the middle, so that fluid cannot penetrate and so go from one side of a piece of glass to the other. Franklin pointed out once again that even though the particles of electric fluid cannot traverse the central portion of a glass sheet, " their repellency can." Although the particles of electric fluid are held together in glass by the particles of glass, they still maintain their mutual repulsion. But if fluid is acquired by a conductor on one side of a piece of glass, then the total fluid on that side of the impermeable central section is increased over what it is normally. There is then exerted a much greater repelling force than usual on the electric fluid on the other side. Even so, electric fluid will not be driven out of that side unless a non-electric (conductor) is placed there to receive it. The earlier experiments and conclusions concerning the action of the Leyden jar were of a sort "favouring (if I may not say confirming) this hypothesis"—Franklin freely admitted it was one ‡—which could also explain other "appearances."

Glass is elastic (and perhaps is so because of the elastic fluid of electricity it contains) and [34] when rubbed must undergo a stretching of the rubbed surface. This stretching is nothing more than an increase in separation of the particles of glass and a concomitant enlargement of the "vacancy" between the particles in which the electric fluid subsists. Thus, there is room for more electric fluid, which enters the glass from the hand doing the rubbing and is replaced to the hand from "the common stock" or ground. But at the instant that a part of the glass has "passed the friction," when the motion of the globe or tube has brought the rubbing to a new area, the glass particles return to their former state. Then the additional electric fluid is forced out at the surface, where it must remain (since glass is a non-conductor) until that part of the glass comes to the rubber again, unless some non-electric (the prime conductor, for instance) is in a position to remove it. Although Franklin did not make the point explicitly, a reason appears for the possibility of a vastly greater positive charge being given to one side of a Leyden jar than that obtainable by rubbing.

In the Leyden jar, Franklin insisted, the application of a charge to one side of the glass will not cause the other side to discharge electric fluid unless a grounded conductor be placed in contact with it. Electric fluid will then leave the surface of the glass and move along the grounded conductor away from the jar. Franklin offered a variety of evidence to show that air is the cause of resistance to the electric fluid leaving bodies. It keeps confined in an atmosphere the fluid which would otherwise tend to be dissipated owing to the mutual repulsion of the particles and which would actually dissipate *in vacuo*. Take the case of a feather in the "glass vessel hermetically sealed" (presumably, from the context, *in vacuo*). [34] When a rubbed tube approaches the glass, its atmosphere repels and drives out some fluid from the inside surface of the glass vessel which affects the feather, and the feather is again affected when the rubbed tube is removed and the fluid in this atmosphere returns to the inside

‡Franklin later said that this "hypothesis . . . was certainly wrong." He ground away five-sixths of a thickness of glass from the side of one of his Leyden jars, so that the removal of the supposed impermeable and denser central portion would allow the electric fluid to "come through the remainder of the glass, which I imagined more open." (See pages 350-351 above.) He was mistaken; the jar behaved just as if it had not been altered. Franklin confessed that he was "now, as much as ever, at a loss to know how or where the quantity of electric fluid, on the positive side of the glass is disposed of." Actually, all such phenomena are extremely complex.

surface of the glass. This explanation is not on a par with the explanation of the charging of a condenser, yet we may note again Franklin's insistence that the particles of the fluid do not pass through the glass. Much is explained by the hypothesis, but per-haps—Franklin said—it is " not a true one, and I shall be obliged to him that affords me a better."

There are [35] two chief distinctions between non-electrics or conductors and glass, an electric *per se*: (1) the quantity of electric fluid in a non-electric may easily be changed and, above all, it can be lessened so that the non-electric may be charged minus; but to charge glass minus, and at that on but one surface, the other surface must be charged plus. (2) The electric fluid moves freely " from place to place, in and through the substance of a non-electric, but not so through the substance of glass." Since glass, in distinction to non-electrics such as the metals, is not a conductor [36], experiments were useless to try to get the electric fluid and effluvia of cinnamon (or other odoriferous substances) simultaneously to pass from within a globe to the prime conductor, since the " electric fluid itself cannot come through " the glass.§

A supplementary experiment was related to the conclusion that Franklin repeated again and again and demonstrated over and over in a variety of ways; it was designed to prove " that the Leyden bottle has no more electrical fire in it when charged, than before; nor less when discharged: That, in discharging, the fire does not issue from the wire and the coating at the same time, as some have thought, but that the coating always receives what is discharged by the wire, or an equal quantity; the outer surface being always in a negative state of electricity, when the inner surface is in a positive state." Since the experiment adds nothing new to the Franklin theory, there is no need of describing it.[57]

§ The reference here is to the reports, chiefly from Italy and Germany, by Pivati, Verati, Bianchi, and Winckler, that " if odorous substances were confined in glass vessels, and the vessels excited, the odours and other medicinal virtues would transpire through the glass, infect the atmosphere of the conductor, and communicate the virtue to all persons in contact with it." These supposed experiments, according to Priestley, are instances of the " want of persons attending to all the essential circumstances of facts." Priestley, therefore, had nothing but praise for the Abbé Nollet, " who was deeply interested in every thing that related to his favourite study, and who set no bounds to his labour or expences, in the pursuit of truth," and who went to Italy to see these " experiments." He found that in no instance had " odours been found to transpire through the pores of excited glass." When Winckler sent a report of such experiments to the Royal Society, the Secretary wrote to him for exact details and " some globes and tubes, filled up by himself, for that purpose," Watson and others, Priestley reported, " were not able to verify Mr. Winckler's experiments even in one single instance." [55] Franklin wrote that " Abbé Nolet has our thanks for the pains he took to discover the truth relating to those pretended Italian experiments." [56] Unfor-tunately, this sentiment was expressed in part of a letter that was not published until 1941, and Nollet never knew of Franklin's applause for this task.

The account of this experiment, together with Franklin's preceding papers and letters, was assembled by Collinson in a 90-page book which was issued by E. Cave of London in 1751,* with a preface (unsigned) written by Dr. John Fothergill. It appeared in a French translation in the following year and this publication on both sides of the Channel made available to electricians everywhere the Franklinian theory of electrical action. Save for a number of revisions and extensions to new phenomena, all the main elements of Franklin's theory were contained in this book.

---

* In this chapter, there has been presented an analysis of all the contents of Franklin's book on electricity as it appeared in the original issue of 1751, with the exception of the paper sent to Dr. John Mitchel in 1749, dealing with the formation of clouds, and lightning. This communication will be presented in Chapter Eleven, where the subject to which it is devoted will be treated.

SOURCES

This chapter is based primarily on a study of Franklin's own works in published and manuscript writings, the reactions to them by his correspondents in their publications and manuscript letters, and the contemporary published literature on electricity. Priestley (1775) has been especially valuable as a guide and so has Sigaud de la Fond (1781). Valuable accounts of Franklin's work in electricity are to be found in Hoppe (1884), Benjamin (1898), Rosenberger (1898), and Wolf (1952). For bibliographical information concerning Franklin's book on electricity, see Franklin (1941: intro., pt. 4).

Brett-James (1926) is an imperfect biography of Collinson. Many Collinson letters exist in manuscript in the Library of the American Philosophical Society and in English repositories. Published letters may be found in Darlington (1849), Colden (1919-1920), Linnæus (1821), and Franklin (1941), intro.

There is no adequate study of Kinnersley. One of his lectures is published in Franklin (1941), appendix, where there is also a brief biographical sketch and a guide to the literature concerning him, which should be supplemented by Bell (1955b). For Syng, see the brief article in the *D. A. B.*, and for Hopkinson see the article in the *D. A. B.* on his son, Francis. Keys (1906) is an inadequate biography of Colden, especially weak on the scientific interests. Colden (1919-1920) contains a mine of information about Colden and his contemporaries; for a guide to the literature, see Bell (1955b). For Fothergill, see Fox (1919) and also Abraham (1933).

REFERENCES

1. See Walker (1934).
2. Priestley, 1775: **2**: 374, pt. VIII, sec. XVI, expt. xv.
3. *Ibid.*, 192, sec. III.
4. *Ibid.*, 202, sec. IV.
5. *Ibid.*, 329, sec. XIII.
6. *Ibid.*, 355, sec. XVI, expt. iv.
7. *Ibid.*, 369, sec. XVI, expt. xiv.
8. Priestley, 1775: **2**: 32-33.
9. Franklin to Michael Collinson, Franklin, 1907: **5**: 185-186.
10. " Autobiography "; see Cohen, 1943b; Heathcote, 1955.
11. P. Collinson to C. Colden, 30 March 1745, Colden, 1919-1920: **3**: 110.
12. P. Collinson to C. Colden, 3 Aug. 1746, *ibid.*, 237.
13. See Franklin, 1941: intro., pp. 58-59.
14. Franklin, 1941: 169; 1769: 1.
15. Heathcote, 1955.
16. P. Collinson to C. Colden, 30 March 1745, Colden, 1919-1920: **3**: 110.
17. See Franklin, 1941; intro., p. 152.
18. Colden, 1919-1920: **3**: 209-210.
19. Franklin, 1941: Letter II; 1769: Letter II.
20. Needham, 1746.
21. Colden, 1919-1920: **3**: 397.

22. Watson, 1748*b*: 49.
23. *Ibid.*, 57.
24. *Ibid.*, 63, § VI.
25. *Ibid.*, 57-58, § II.
26. *Ibid.*, 59-62, § IV.
27. *Ibid.*, 62, § V.
28. Watson, 1751-1752*b*; 1751-1752*c*.
29. Nollet, 1753*b*, 477.
30. Watson, 1748*b*: 51.
31. *Ibid.*, 66-67, § VII.
32. Franklin, 1941: Letter III; 1769: Letter III.
33. Franklin, 1941: 179n.
34. Maxwell, 1881: ch. 9, § 113.
35. Benjamin, 1898: 546.
36. Watson, 1748*b*: 68-69, §§ VIII, IX.
37. Franklin, 1907: 2: 364-365.
38. *Idem.*
39. Franklin, 1941: Letter IV; 1769: Letter IV.
40. *Idem*, § 5.
41. *Idem*, § 6.
42. *Idem*, § 7.
43. *Idem*, § 8.
44. *Idem*, § 10.
45. *Idem*, § 12.
46. *Idem*, § 16.
47. *Idem*, § 17.
48. *Idem*, §§ 18, 19.
49. *Idem*, § 19.
50. *Idem*, § 26.
51. *Idem*, § 28.
52. Franklin; 1941: 239-240.
53. Franklin, 1941: Letter VI; 1769: Letter VI.
54. Franklin, 1941: 213 ff.; 1769: 54 ff.
55. Priestley, 1775: 1: 179, 185, 187.
56. Franklin, 1941: 242n.
57. Franklin 1941: 237-238; 1769: 86-89.

CHAPTER ELEVEN

THE RECEPTION OF THE FRANKLIN THEORY: ATMOSPHERIC ELECTRICITY AND LIGHTNING RODS

> Ich habe kein Werk des vorigen Jahrhunderts gelesen, was
> so leicht und klar verständlich geschrieben ist, wie jene Briefe,
> die Franklin nach London sandte, wodurch er in wenigen
> Monaten weltbekannt wurde.
>
> EDM. HOPPE (1884)

IN the preceding chapter, the development of the Franklinian theory of electrical action was traced in terms of the clarification of pre-existing concepts, particularly an electric matter or fluid, and the attendant introduction of allied new concepts such as the plus or minus state. Attention was paid primarily to Franklin's contribution to electrical theory and the analysis of the phenomena of the Leyden jar. Franklin's reputation among scientists was founded on these advances in pure science, and also on one application of his theory that was of special importance because it was concerned with phenomena on a large scale, rather than those produced in the laboratory. His study of the electrification of clouds produced a " new hypothesis for explaining the several phænomena of thunder-gusts," as Franklin entitled the communication on this subject which he sent to Dr. John Mitchel, F. R. S., from Philadelphia under the date 29 April 1749.* Franklin's ideas on the electrification of clouds were developed by him in the following steps.†

Non-electric (conducting) bodies that are charged positively [1] will keep the excess electric fluid or fire until they approach another non-electric that has " less," on which occasion the excess will be divided between the two. Electric fire [2] is strongly attracted by water and will adhere to water particles. Dry air, an electric *per se*, will not [3] " conduct " the electric fire, and will not sensibly " re-

---

* This is the paper that was described by Franklin, in his " Autobiography," as one " which I wrote for Mr. Kinnersley, on the sameness of lightning with electricity, [which] I sent to Dr. Mitchel, an acquaintance of mine, and one of the members also of that society [i. e., the Royal Society], who wrote me word that it had been read, but was laughed at by the connoisseurs." That this letter was addressed to Mitchel, rather than Collinson, is apparent from the version in the " Bowdoin MS," [1] and from Watson's comment on it, printed below.

† The numbers in square brackets refer to the paragraph numbers in Franklin's article.[2]

ceive it, nor give it to other bodies "; if it did, no body in air could ever become charged plus or minus. If water becomes electrified plus [4], the vapor arising will also be electrified plus and will form charged clouds which will retain their excess electric fire until they meet clouds or other bodies less positively electrified, whereupon the excess electric fire will be divided between them to the accompaniment of a snap, as in laboratory experiments.

Since particles with the same kind of charge repel one another [5], positively electrified water will, by this repulsion, tend to vaporize more rapidly than usual, just as heating by " common fire " will produce more rapid vaporization. The reason is that [6] the normal attraction of cohesion of the water particles is weakened or overcome by the repulsion " introduced with the electrical fire."

A number of laboratory experiments ‡ provided evidence [8] that the production of electric fire by friction between a non-electric and an electric *per se* is not the result of " *creating*, but *collecting* " the electrical fire " diffused in our walls, floors, earth, and the whole mass of common matter." Since the ocean is [9] a " compound of water, a non-electric, and salt, an electric *per se*," friction [10] among the parts near its surface will collect the electric fire from the sub-surface ocean, and the positively charged water particles will rise to form vapors. They will attach themselves [11] to particles of air which [12] " are said to be hard, round, separate and distant from each other; every particle strongly repelling every other particle, whereby they recede from each other, as far as common gravity will permit." Common fire [15] increases the repulsion between air particles, or rarefies the air, making the air " specifically lighter " so that it will rise.§ Both common fire and electric fire [16] assist in forming vapors by giving " repulsion to the particles of water " and overcoming their normal attraction of cohesion. If particles of water, which [17] normally " mutually attract each other," were to attach themselves

‡ " Thus the whirling glass globe, during its friction against the cushion, draws fire from the cushion, the cushion is supplied from the frame of the machine, that from the floor on which it stands. Cut off the communication by thick glass or wax, placed under the cushion, and no fire can be *produced*, because it cannot be collected."

§ In these sentiments, we see Franklin accepting as axioms the Newtonian principles about the particles of ordinary air forming an elastic fluid because of a repulsive force between them; heat or " common fire " increases the repulsive force. These particles (between which there is a repulsive force) were said by Franklin to be located at the corners of triangles, since " an equilateral triangle " is always the orientation of " any three particles equally repelling each other." This doctrine of triangles, which we encountered in the last chapter, in a letter written to Peter Collinson during the same year as the letter on cloud formation and lightning, was used by Franklin to explain the compression and rarefaction of air. " In air compressed, these triangles are smaller; in rarefied air they are larger. Common fire joined with air, increases the repulsion, enlarges the triangles, and thereby makes the air specifically lighter."

to air particles, their mutual attraction would tend to overcome the " air's repulsion "; the moist air would become denser and sink to the ground, rather than rise to form clouds. But if every particle of water that attaches itself to an air particle were to bring with it [18] " a particle of common fire," or [19] some electric fire, then the normal repulsion of the air particles would be increased, as he had just shown. Such air becomes " rarer and specifically lighter "; it rises, " carrying up with it the water." This process would be greatly increased if the particles of water brought with them [20] " portions of *both sorts* of fire," common and electric, rather than only one or the other.

If this air and its water, in the form of clouds, [23] should be compressed by winds or should lose some of the " fire that assisted it in expanding," the air and its water might descend " as a dew." Or " the water surrounding one particle of air " might come in contact with the water surrounding another air particle and, the two coalescing, form a drop and so produce rain. The vapor arising from water has always [24] some common fire which the " sun supplies (or seems to supply) ," but clouds " raised from the land," i. e., from [26] " fresh waters within land, from growing vegetables, moist earth, etc." have little electric fire compared with clouds raised from the ocean. Hence, when clouds raised from the land ascend into the cold regions above the earth [25] where the cold diminishes the common fire, rain will fall back on the land. But, when clouds raised up from the ocean ascend, " the cold will not diminish the electrical fire, [even] if it doth the common." In this way we may see, Franklin said, how [27] the clouds formed by vapors rising from the ocean can travel far before depositing their water. The winds may move the clouds to " the middle of the broadest continent from the middle of the widest ocean," thus bringing water from the oceans to [28] " the land where it is wanted." But [26] " the greatest part of the water raised from the land, is let fall on the land again; and winds blowing from the land to the sea are dry; there being little use for rain on the sea, and to rob the land of its moisture, in order to rain on the sea, would not appear reasonable." The world had been devised economically to keep waste at a minimum.

So Franklin returned again to the question asked so often during the preceding two decades: What is the role of electricity in the Creation? What " useful " function does the electrical fluid, so widely dispersed in natural and artificial bodies, have in the œconomy of Nature? In Franklin's " Opinions and Conjectures," written later in the year, Franklin pointed out that no one yet knew " the beneficial uses of this electric fluid in the creation," even though

" doubtless such there are, and those very considerable." It is to be noted that the uses are said to be beneficial. In the difference postulated by Franklin between land clouds and sea clouds, the electric fluid was said to act in such a way as to permit the operations of nature to be reasonable. Here is no concept of nature " red in tooth and claw," presenting an eternal struggle between man and nature, but rather the reasonable and harmonious world machine of Boyle and Newton, in which the divine plan had included natural causes to ensure the smooth functioning of the universe. The Creator had plainly provided that in the world there should be just the right quantity of electric fluid and no more. Franklin noted some " pernicious consequences that would attend a much greater proportion of it." For instance, we might suppose that the earth were charged positively to the same extent as a globe of iron or wood in laboratory experiments. Then, said Franklin, particles of dust and other light matter would become positively charged and be repelled by the earth and by one another. As a result, the air would become continually more and more clogged with foreign matter until it was no longer fit for respiration. This was the occasion of that outburst of sentiment which, we observed, seemed to echo that of Stephen Hales, Franklin concluding that electricity provides yet " another occasion of adoring that wisdom which has made all things by weight and measure."

In his explanation of the formation of clouds and the production of dew and rain, Franklin introduced two possible mechanisms whereby sea clouds might discharge their water over the land. Thus [29], being charged, they might be attracted by mountains which would draw off the electric fire and (being cold) also the common fire. Then the air and water particles would come closer together and produce dew or rain, depending on the degree to which the air was " loaded " with water.

But even if a country is plain, without mountains to intercept the clouds, rain might be produced by the meeting of a land cloud (with little or no charge) and a sea cloud (with its greater quantity of electric fire) . [32] One will " flash its fire " into the other, and " thereby both clouds shall be made suddenly to deposit water." If [35] the two types of clouds are too far apart " for the flash," they could be drawn together by electrical attraction until within flashing distance: in agreement with the observation that the " sphere of electrical attraction is far beyond the distance of flashing."

There is no point in entering here into too extended a discussion of Franklin's meteorological conjectures in terms of their present value or correctness; our aim is not to make a critical display of every scientific idea Franklin expressed. All that is important in the present context is to note that as early as April, 1749, Franklin had already assumed that the lightning discharge is an electrical phenomenon and had devised a mechanism to account for the electrification of clouds. It was not a completely happy device and five years later Franklin freely admitted that he was " still at a loss about the manner in which they [the clouds] become charged with electricity; no hypothesis I have yet formed perfectly satisfying me." [3] Yet electrified they must be, and he was convinced that lightning must consist in the sudden discharge of electric fluid.

On 7 November 1749, about six months after writing his letter to Mitchel, Franklin drew up a list of twelve observable similarities between the lightning discharge and the ordinary electrical discharge produced in the laboratory. He concluded: " The electric fluid is attracted by points.—We do not know whether this property is in lightning.—But since they agree in all the particulars wherein we can already compare them, is it not probable they agree likewise in this? Let the experiment be made." [4] Even before the experiment was made, however, Franklin assumed that the results would be favorable. Thus in his letter to Mitchel, he noted [43] that high hills and trees, towers, spires, masts of ships, chimneys, and the like, act " as so many prominencies and points, draw the electrical fire, and the whole cloud discharges there," assuming—without any proof by experiment—that clouds are electrified and that lighting is simply an electrical discharge from a cloud to the earth or from one cloud to another.*

Watson was again responsible for Franklin's work being brought to the attention of the Royal Society, and the Journal Book records that on 9 November 1749, " Part of a paper containing a new theory of thunder-gusts by Mr Franklin, communicated by Mr Watson, was read. But the same being long the residue was defer'd 'till next meeting." A week later, on 16 November 1749, " The remainder of a paper entitled Observations and suppositions towards forming a new hypothesis for explaining the several phenomena of thunder gusts, by Mr Franklin of Philadelphia in Pennsylvania and transmitted by him to Dr Mitchel, F. R. S. part of which had been read

---

* Franklin therefore advised his readers that it was dangerous " to take shelter under a tree, during a thunder-gust. It has been fatal to many, both men and beasts. It is safer to be in the open field for another reason. When the cloaths are wet, if a flash in its way to the ground should strike your head, it may run in the water over the surface of your body; whereas, if your cloaths were dry, it would go through the body, because the blood and other humours, containing so much water, are more ready conductors." This conclusion was illustrated by an experimental fact: ". . . a wet rat cannot be killed by the exploding electrical bottle, when a dry rat may."

at the last meeting, was now read. Thanks were ordered to Dr Mitchel and to Mr Franklin for this communication." †

Lightning Rods for Exploring the Electrification of Clouds and for Protecting Man

In the paper entitled " Opinions and Conjectures," which Franklin sent to Collinson in July, 1750, and which contains the full statement of his theory of electrical action,‡ there is some discussion of the electrification of clouds and the lightning discharge. This subject was introduced immediately following Franklin's discussion of the property of pointed bodies to " draw on " and " throw off " the electric fluid at great distances. Although the latter phenomena had been plainly marked in Franklin's experiments, he was not fully satisfied with his discussion of why pointed bodies should draw off the electric atmosphere of [positively] charged bodies, and he noted the doubt he had concerning his explanations, apologizing for not having anything " better to offer in their stead." In any event, a good solution might be had if " an ingenious reader " discovered the faults in a bad one, so he did not " cross out " the explanations.[5] It was at this point that Franklin, echoing Newton's phrases in the General Scholium to Book Three of the *Principia*, commented: " Nor is it of much importance to us, to know the manner in which nature executes her laws; it is enough if we know the laws themselves." We have seen, in an earlier chapter, that these remarks of Franklin have on occasion been cited to show his supposed practical turn of mind in scientific matters, or a tendency to applied rather than pure science. Yet he was only showing himself to be a good Newtonian in this as in other matters. And no one would describe Newton as a pursuer of applied rather than pure science, or attribute his point of view to a particularly American attitude in regard to science.

In " the present case," Franklin insisted, " to know this power of points may possibly be of some use to mankind, though we should never be able to explain it." A number of experiments had shown clearly that a needle placed on the floor with its point upright could discharge a prime conductor and prevent a stroke from the conductor to a nearby metal punch. Franklin asked: might not the same principle " be of use to mankind " in teaching how to protect houses, churches, ships, and other structures, from the damage oc-

---

† These two extracts are printed from the manuscript records through the courtesy of the Royal Society of London.

‡ See the previous chapter.

casioned by lightning? If men would " fix on the highest parts of those edifices, upright rods of iron made sharp as a needle, and gilt to prevent rusting," and from those rods run a wire down the outside of the building into the grounds, or down " around one of the shrouds of a ship " and then down the side into the water, would " not these pointed rods probably draw the electrical fire silently out of a cloud before it came nigh enough to strike, and thereby secure us from that most sudden and terrible mischief? "

This suggestion of the lightning rod depends, of course, on the lightning being an electrical discharge. Franklin therefore had to ascertain whether " clouds that contain lightning are electrified or not." If so, they must obey the laws of electrified bodies and so the electrical character of the lightning discharge could be satisfactorily demonstrated. The question should, therefore, be put to the test of an " experiment to be tried where it may be done conveniently," as follows. On a high tower or steeple, a sentry-box was to be erected large enough to contain a man and " an electrical [insulating] stand." A large iron rod was to be affixed to the middle of the stand and rise out, through the door of the sentry-box, and then 20 or 30 feet up in the air, where it would terminate in a point. (See fig. 19.) The electrical stand was to be kept clean and dry so as to maintain its insulating properties and then a man standing on it, " when such clouds are passing low, might be electrified and afford sparks, the rod drawing fire to him from a cloud." Franklin thought there would be little danger. Yet, if any " should be apprehended," the man standing on the floor might hold in his hand a wax handle affixed to a " loop of a wire " that has been attached to the ground; he could bring this loop to the rod—" so the sparks, if the rod is electrified, will strike from the rod to the wire, and not affect him." [6]

In this experiment the iron rod was not to be grounded since its function was to serve as a kind of test rod: not as a lightning rod preventing the stroke but as a charge accumulator. The experiment depends on the properties of pointed conductors which had been discovered by Franklin. It was to be a test of whether the lightning might be silently " drawn off " charged clouds by pointed conductors in the way that Franklin had observed in electrified bodies in the laboratory. Although Franklin modestly said that this experiment was not " an out-of-the-way one," but " might have occurred to any electrician," we must bear in mind that it depends on Franklin's own discoveries and *no one else did think of it*. Franklin's " sentry-box experiment " was first performed at Marly in France in May, 1752, with results agreeing exactly with Franklin's suppositions.

After Franklin's electrical papers had been printed in book form by Cave in 1751, the work was brought to the attention of Buffon who arranged to have it translated into French. The French translation, made by the naturalist, D'Alibard, appeared in 1752 and attracted considerable attention. The Philadelphia experiments were performed to the applause of Louis XV by M. De Lor, " Master of Experimental Philosophy." " These applauses of his Majesty " inspired Buffon, D'Alibard, and De Lor with " a desire of verifying the conjectures of Mr. Franklin, upon the analogy of thunder and electricity," according to the experiment described by Franklin. On 13 May 1752 D'Alibard reported to the Paris Academy of Sciences, " In following the path that Mr. Franklin has traced for us, I have obtained a complete satisfaction." § De Lor, soon afterwards, successfully performed this experiment. The French experiments were repeated by others in France, in Germany, and in England [9] and Franklin soon had the satisfaction of having achieved an immediate and wide-spread international reputation.*

Many others, prior to Franklin, had supposed or suspected electricity to be the active agent in the lightning discharge. But no one had previously been able to envisage any possible sort of experimental test which would give such a supposition the full measure of a physical hypothesis. This is, without doubt, the main reason why the scientists of the eighteenth century, such as Watson, although conversant with pre-Franklin speculations, referred to the verification " of Mr. *Franklin's* hypothesis."

§ The account of the successful performance of Franklin's experiment, read at the Académie Royale des Sciences, was printed in the second French edition of Franklin's book on electricity and was reprinted by Franklin in the later English editions.[7] Actually, this event occurred during the absence of D'Alibard himself; he had arranged for a former dragoon, Coiffier, and the village priest, Raulet, to attend the apparatus while he was away. A letter addressed by the Abbé Mazéas to Stephen Hales, describing the presentation of the Philadelphia experiments to the King of France, and the lightning experiments, was published in the *Philosophical Transactions* and later reprinted in Franklin's book.[8]

* Franklin later devised a second experiment to test the electrification of clouds, the famous experiment of the lightning kite. Franklin reported this experiment to Peter Collinson in a letter of 1 October 1752, written after Franklin had read " in the publick papers from Europe, of the success of the *Philadelphia-Experiment* for drawing the electrick fire from clouds by means of pointed rods of iron erected on high buildings. . . ." Franklin appears to have flown his electrical kite in June, 1752, prior to his having learned of D'Alibard's experiments of the preceding May. The kite letter, as published in the *Philosophical Transactions*, mentioned the erection of lightning rods on two public buildings in Philadelphia.[10]

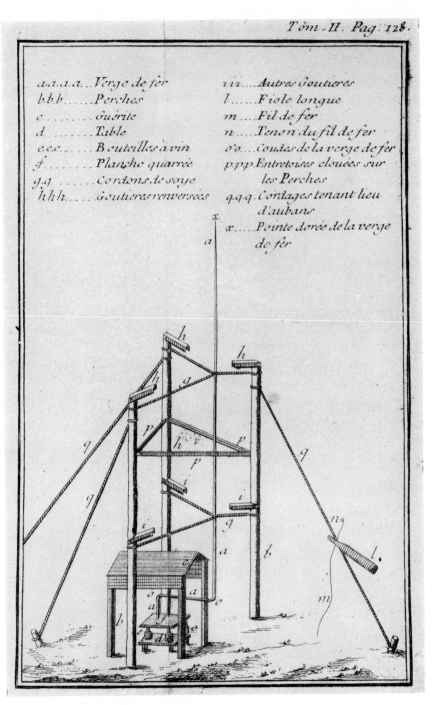

FIG. 20. D'Alibard's version of Franklin's sentry-box experiment.

Duc de Chaulnes's Improvement of Dr. Franklin's Electrical Kite.

Presented to Dr Franklin June 20, 1788.

Fig. 21. "Duc de Chaulnes's Improvement of Dr. Franklin's Electrical Kite." Print presented to the Society by Dr. Franklin, June 20, 1788.

The Scale of Electrical Phenomena: In Nature and in
the Laboratory

Save for its meteorological aspects (e. g., how clouds are formed, how they become electrified, and under what circumstances rain and dew descend), Franklin's inquiries concerning lightning added nothing specifically new to his general theory of electrical action except the bald fact that thunder clouds are apparently electrified and that, therefore, lightning is an electrical discharge and must follow the laws of the electric fluid in the laboratory. Yet one cannot consider the subsequent history of Franklin's ideas and their reception without giving the lightning experiment its due weight. The reasons are many. In the first place, the publicity given to this important demonstration was enormous. Franklin's name became known in every country of Europe, both among the public at large and in scientific circles. There is no exaggeration in the statement that it constituted the first major achievement of the little more than a century old, new subject of electricity. This is the reason why Priestley, in his *History of Electricity*, called it a " capital " discovery †— " the greatest, perhaps, since the time of Sir Isaac Newton."

Prior to the time of the Marly experiment, electrical investigations had consisted of small-scale laboratory experiments in which rods or globes of glass had been rubbed and, to the accompaniment of sparks, other bodies had had the electric virtue of the rod transferred to or through them. The German electrical machines had, to be sure, made the sparks bigger and the Leyden jar had made the effects somewhat greater still, so that a shock might actually hurt a human being, or be given to a large number of individuals simultaneously, or even kill a bird. But the subject remained in the area of " toy physics " and was treated as such. Watson, like Franklin and Kinnersley, invented games to make electrical amusements more popular and entertaining; one was called " the electrical mine," a device partially concealed in the floor to shock an unsuspecting person walking over it. Buffon had sponsored the translation of Franklin's book into French because of his appreciation of its genuine scientific worth, but the experiments described in the book were probably performed before the French Court at St. Germain because of their entertainment value.

Within a year of the publication of Franklin's book, however, the situation had been markedly altered. Every electrician knew thenceforth that the experiments performed with his little laboratory toys

---

† Franklin used the same adjective when he described this experiment in his " Autobiography."

might reveal new aspects of one of the most dramatic of nature's catastrophic forces. Electrical studies took on a new importance and the belief that the operations of the electric fluid might hold the key to important natural processes was partially vindicated. " The discoveries made in the summer of the year 1752 will make it memorable in the history of electricity," Watson wrote in 1753. " These have opened a new field to philosophers, and have given them room to hope, that what they have learned before in their museums, they may apply, with more propriety than they hitherto could have done, in illustrating the nature and effects of thunder; a phænomenon hitherto almost inaccessible to their inquiries." [11]

Franklin not only showed that the artillery of nature was only the electric discharge of the laboratory on a vaster scale; he also devised an instrument to circumvent its destructive effects—the lightning rod. In Franklin's day, the bells on churches still bore a legend including the words, *fulgura frango*; bells continued to be rung during lightnig storms despite the high mortality amongst bell-ringers. In Franklin's invention men of the eighteenth century could find a vindication of Bacon's belief that a knowledge of how nature operates leads to a better control of nature. The lightning rod was, in the eighteenth century, an outstanding example of a practical innovation issuing as a fruit of pure disinterested scientific research.

Franklin tamed the lightning in a double sense. To use Turgot's phrase, Franklin snatched it from the heavens and showed it to be electric fluid in motion; but he also tamed lightning by inventing a device to protect homes, churches, barns, ships, and arsenals from its destructive stroke. Franklin achieved a degree of scientific eminence never before attained as a result of research in electricity alone, which marked the coming of age of electrical science and the full acceptance of a new field of specialization. In his speech at a meeting of the Royal Society on 30 November 1753, on the occasion of awarding Franklin the Society's Sir Godfrey Copley gold medal " for his discoveries in electricity," the Earl of Macclesfield emphasized this very point. Electricity is a neglected subject, he said, which " not many years since was thought to be of little importance, and was at that time only applied to illustrate the nature of attraction and repulsion; nor was any thing worth much notice expected to ensue from it." But now, thanks to the labors of Franklin, it " appears to have a most surprising share of power in nature." [12]

Franklin's book was widely read and reprinted in English and in French, and a few years after the experiments on lightning a translation into German appeared. As a product of the foremost electrician of the time, the whole body of Franklin's thought on electricity began to influence others engaged in research. Both his major premises and his minor interpretations became subjects of violent approbation or acrimonious debate. Franklin's place in science was so assured that everything he later wrote on science was guaranteed a wide audience of supporters and critics. It is, therefore, of no surprise that the future progress of electrical theory was for half a century either an extension of his doctrine or a critical revision of certain points of it. But before examining how those steps were taken, let us first trace the additions Franklin made to the theory of electrical action contained in his first book and analyzed in the preceding pages.

Resinous Electrification: The Problems associated with Negatively charged Bodies

Franklin continued to produce interesting new experiments. Some were described in a letter of 29 June 1751 to Peter Collinson in London and summarized in a letter of the same year to Cadwallader Colden in New York. By an electric spark he was able to melt brass pins and steel needles, to invert the poles of a magnetic needle, to magnetize unmagnetized needles, and fire dry gunpowder. Other experiments showed that points " throw off or attract the electrical matter more freely, and at greater distances " *in vacuo* than in air. Of much greater importance, however, was a series of experiments dealing with negatively charged bodies.

I have already indicated the nature and extent of Watson's influence on Franklin. Watson, like others in his day, performed his experiments by rubbing a glass rod or globe and giving it—in Franklin's terminology—a positive charge. He did not experiment with rubbed sulphur or amber. His papers, therefore, exhibit little or no concern with Du Fay's resinous electricity, only with the vitreous. Franklin followed in Watson's steps and initially confined his attention to effects produced by rubbing glass. Rubbed glass, in his conception, gains electric fluid so as to become charged plus or acquire an electric atmosphere. A negatively charged body is one that has lost electric fluid. Negatively charged bodies, therefore, would not be expected to have electric atmospheres which, in positively charged bodies, come from the excess fluid. In his earliest papers, Franklin never thought much about the interaction between two negatively charged bodies. He recorded the observation that " bodies having less than the common quantity of electricity, repel each other, as well as those that have more," but his only comment was that this phenomenon " surprises us, and is not hitherto satisfactorily accounted for." [13]

Negative electrification was brought to Franklin's notice by Kinnersley, who wrote from Boston on 3 February 1752 about a number of experiments.[14] Chief among them was one in which a cork ball, suspended on a silk string, was brought up to a piece of rubbed amber. The ball became charged and was then repelled. In this state of electrification, the ball was also repelled by rubbed sealing wax and sulphur. Yet this electrified ball was attracted by rubbed glass and china until on contact " it became electrified again." In this new state it was repelled by the rubbed glass and china but attracted by the rubbed amber, sealing wax, and sulphur. This experiment, originally due to Du Fay,‡ is still performed in elementary physics courses to demonstrate that like charges repel one another, whereas unlike charges attract one another. These phenomena, Kinnersley admitted, " surprized " him very much and induced him " to infer " several " paradoxes." The latter all depend on the supposition that two globes, one of sulphur and the other of glass, will (" both being equally in good order, and in equal motion ") produce equal and opposite electrifications. Hence, Kinnersley argued, if both are in contact with the same prime conductor, the latter will not become charged since one globe will draw off as much electric fluid from the prime conductor as the other will lose to it " but which [one] I cannot say." Kinnersley asked Franklin to get the sulphur globe from his house and try the experiment, to attempt to confirm his supposition that the sulphur and glass globes would charge the prime conductor differently. He concluded with the hope that Franklin would " be able to discover some method of determining which it is that charges positively."

Franklin replied to Kinnersley on 2 March 1752 that the " brimstone globe " needed repairs. He suspected that the phenomena observed by Kinnersley in Boston resulted from " the greater or smaller quantities of the [electric] fire you obtained from different bodies " and not from its " being of a different *kind,* or having a different *direction.*" He was wrong, as he found when he had put the sulphur globe into operation. On 16 March 1752 he reported to Kinnersley that he had been " agreeably surprised." He had mounted the glass globe at one end of the conductor and the sulphur globe at the other end, to discover that while both were in motion no spark could be obtained from the prime conductor.

" I imagine," wrote Franklin, " it is the glass globe that charges positively, and the sulphur negatively." [15] A number of observations supported this opinion,§ and they reveal the way in which experi-

‡ See page 372 above.
§ This choice agreed with the earliest statement of the theory (see page 439 above)

mental evidence and theory mutually acted upon each other in Franklin's mind to produce immediate and reasonable answers to difficult questions. We may note, furthermore, how well Franklin's general conceptual scheme accommodated itself to new discoveries as they arose.

Franklin's first bit of evidence for the positive electrification of the glass globe and the negative electrification of the sulphur one was [1] that when the prime conductor was charged by the sulphur globe alone, the spark between his knuckle and the conductor was never " so large and distant " as when the glass globe was used. The reason adduced to explain this phenomenon was that in negative electrification, at first some electric fluid is drawn from the surface and any additional fluid taken away must be drawn from the inside of the body where it is strongly attracted on all sides. Negative electrification is more difficult than positive electrification because in the latter case the additional fluid merely accumulates around the gun-barrel in the form of an electric atmosphere. In addition, [2], the " stream or brush of fire " appearing at the end of a wire attached to the prime conductor appeared long, large, and diverging, and made a snapping or rattling noise when the glass globe was used. But with the sulphur one the " brush " was short and small, and made a hissing noise. The reverse happened when the wire was held in the hand and brought near the prime conductor. In this case the brush was large, long, diverging, and sounded snapping or rattling when the sulphur globe was in operation (as if the prime conductor were " throwing the fire out " to the sulphur globe). But the brush was short and small and made a hissing noise when the glass globe was used (as if the prime conductor were " drinking in " the electrical fire from the glass globe). When Franklin [3] held his knuckle near the rotating sulphur globe " the stream of fire . . . seems to spread on its surface, as if it flowed from the finger; on the glass globe it is otherwise." To this day we use Franklin's names of " plus " and " minus " for the " vitreous " and " resinous " electrifications, respectively, in accordance with his statement of his findings to Kinnersley.

In 1753 Cave issued a supplemental pamphlet to Franklin's book, which had been published originally in 1751. It contained Kinnersley's letter to Franklin and Franklin's two letters to Kinnersley, a letter to Collinson discussing the experiment alleged by Watson to disprove Franklin's explanation of the action of the Leyden jar, another letter to Collinson describing the magnetic effects of an

in which Franklin had assumed that rubbing a glass tube gives that tube an excess of electric fluid.

electric discharge, a letter to Colden on the difference between electrics *per se* and non-electrics and on the effects of air in electrical
experiments, the report of the French and British executions of the
sentry-box experiment, and Franklin's letter describing the lightning-
kite experiment. While the account of the lightning experiments
was the most startling part of the book, the identification of vitreous
electrification (rubbed glass or china) as positive, and resinous
(rubbed amber, sealing wax, sulfur) as negative, was theoretically
the most interesting.

When Franklin proposed to Kinnersley on 16 March 1752 that
the rubbed glass globe was positively charged while the sulphur one
was negatively charged, he added that "these are hasty thoughts."
In a letter to Collinson written eighteen months later, in September
1753, he begged "leave to recommend it to the curious in this
branch of natural philosophy, to repeat with care and accurate observation" the experiments he had reported concerning "*positive*
and *negative* electricity" and to perform such others as may occur
to them so "that it may be certainly known whether the electricity
communicated by a glass globe be *really positive*." [16]

Are Clouds Electrified Plus or Minus?

The problem of positive and negative electrification had become
extremely important for Franklin owing to a startling discovery in
relation to atmospheric electricity. Franklin had discovered that
apparently lightning does not always consist of "thunderbolts from
Heaven," but more often of thunderbolts sent from the earth up
into the sky. This discovery, described in Franklin's letter to Collinson written in September, 1753, was made with an iron rod which
Franklin had erected in September, 1752, "to draw the lightning
down into my house, in order to make some experiments on it."
Two Leyden jars were used. One was to be charged by "lightning
from the iron rod" and the other was to be given an equal charge
by "the electric glass globe." Then the two were to be placed within
a few inches of each other on a table, and a small cork ball on a
fine silk thread was to be suspended between their wires. If both
wires were electrified plus, the ball would be first attracted by one of
the wires and then repelled by it and by the other wire. But if one
wire were electrified plus and the other minus, "then the ball
would be attracted and repelled alternately by each, and continue
to play between them as long as any considerable charge remained."
The experiment was not performed until 12 April 1753,* and

* The delay, according to Franklin, arose from the circumstances of his having
"happened to be abroad during two of the greatest thunder-storms we had early

Franklin observed " with great surprize " (although also with " pleasure ") that the cork ball moved briskly back and forth between the wires of the two Leyden jars, convincing him that " one bottle was electrised *negatively*." [17] Franklin performed the experiment with similar results " several times during the gust, and in eight succeeding gusts." If his arguments for the positive electrification of the glass globe ("for reasons I formerly gave in my letter to Mr. Kinnersley, since printed in London " †) were valid, Franklin concluded, then the " clouds are *always* electrised *negatively*, or have always in them less than their natural quantity of the electric fluid."

We may note in passing how careful Franklin was in writing scientific reports. He recorded the observed fact that the ball moved back and forth between the wires of the two jars. Since one was charged positively by contact with the glass globe, and since his theory interpreted the experiment as indicating that the wires of the two jars had charges of different sign, he " was convinced that one bottle was electrised *negatively*." Many experiments, repeated during nine storms, showed him that the phenomenon was general and that, therefore, clouds may be electrified negatively or have less electric fluid than their normal quantity—provided, of course, that rubbed glass actually has an excess of electric fluid. We do not know enough of the conditions of the experiment to be certain about what occurred, but it is most likely the case that the jar was charged by induction. The lower surface of the cloud would then have been negatively charged, inducing a positive charge at the pointed tip of the rod while the lower end would become negatively charged, thereby giving the wire of the Leyden jar a negative charge on contact.

Notwithstanding the number of experiments, Franklin " concluded too soon," for on 6 June he found in a " gust " (that lasted from five to seven in the afternoon) a positive cloud among the negative ones. This positive cloud was discovered by a " concurring experiment, which I often repeated, to prove the negative state of the clouds." Franklin had arranged two rods, one going up to the roof and one to the ground, each terminating near the other in a large bell (see fig. 2). Between them there hung a " pendulous brass ball." Thus the bells would ring whenever the rod became charged.‡

in the spring, and though I had given orders to my family, that if the bells rang when I was from home, they should catch some of the lightning for me in electrical phials, and they did so, yet it was mostly dissipated before my return. . . ."

† This particular letter, from Franklin to Collinson in September, 1753, was one of the five items making up the second supplement to Franklin's book on electricity, which was printed in 1754.

‡ Soon after erecting a rod on his house, in September, 1752, " With two bells to give notice when the rod should be electrified," he had discovered that " the bells rang sometimes when there was no lightning or thunder, but only a dark cloud over

Franklin reasoned that, if the clouds were electrified plus, the rod ("which received its electricity from them") must also be electrified plus.§ Hence, he argued, bringing the positively charged wire of the Leyden jar to the upright rod would make the rod more positive still, so that the bells would ring more quickly. But if the clouds and rod were both electrified minus, with the electric fluid of the rod exhausted, then bringing up the plus wire of the Leyden jar would lessen the negative state of the rod by supplying the rod at once with the fluid it lacked and "which it was obliged otherwise to draw from the earth by means of the pendulous brass ball playing between the two bells," and the ringing would "cease till the bottle was discharged." The latter phenomenon usually occurred, so that he concluded that the common electrification of the clouds is minus. Franklin noted that the bells stopped ringing while the jar was discharged, and also that the wire gave up so much fluid to the negatively charged rod that the charge on the wire went from plus to minus (the outer coating of the jar being all the while grounded by being held in the hand). But during the above-mentioned storm (on 6 June), the rod—having first shown itself to be charged minus—reversed itself as another cloud passed by, and the bells stopped ringing and then started again. This time there was no spark, as before, between the positively charged wire of the Leyden jar and the rod although "the bells continued ringing vigorously." Franklin concluded that his first statement had been too general and should be reduced to this: "*That the clouds of a thunder-gust are most commonly in a negative state of electricity, but sometimes in a positive*

the rod; that sometimes after a flash of lightning they would suddenly stop; and at other times, when they had not rang before, they would, after a flash, suddenly begin to ring; that the electricity was sometimes very faint, so that when a small spark was obtained, another could not be got for some time after; at other times the sparks would follow extremely quick, and once I had a continual stream from bell to bell, the size of a crow-quill: Even during the same gust there were considerable variations."

Franklin described this electrical bell as "a contrivance obvious to every electrician." Six years earlier Watson had written of "a German who travelled with a small electrifying machine; who . . . made two small bells ring. One of the bells was suspended to an electrified wire, which was conducted without touching along the sides of the room; at about an inch distance, detached from this wire, a little clapper was hung by a silk line; at an equal distance from this last was hung another little bell, which communicated with the sides of the room. As soon as the machine was in motion, the electrified bell attracted the clapper, which immediately by the repulsive blast was blown off to the unexcited bell. By the time the second bell was struck, the former attracted again; and this jingling of the two bells continued not only during the motion of the machine, but several seconds after it was stopped. This was occasioned by the small volume of the clapper, being able to convey away only a small quantity of the electrical æther at each stroke; by which it was some time, before the æquilibrium was restored." [18]

§ It would have been more accurate to have written "lower surface of the clouds" and "bottom end of the rod."

state.'' This statement, which I have presented—as Franklin did—in italics, led him to the following conclusion: " So that, for the most part, in thunder-strokes, *it is the earth that strikes into the clouds, and not the clouds that strike into the earth.''* [19]

This extraordinary conclusion forced Franklin to ask what revisions must be made in regard to his concepts of the action of lightning and its effects. He found that " the light gained from these experiments makes no alteration in the practice, [although] it makes a considerable one in the theory." For, whether lightning usually proceeds from clouds to the earth or from the earth to clouds, i. e., whether the clouds usually are charged plus or charged minus, " the effects and appearances must be nearly the same in either case,'' as those " versed in electrical experiments " will readily see. There will be the same explosion, the same flash from one cloud to another or from a cloud to a mountain or church steeple. The electric fluid will rend trees and walls and produce the same shock to animal bodies, no matter which direction it pursues. Since points both draw off and throw off the electric fire with " equal power," and " rods will conduct up as well as down,'' pointed rods on buildings or masts of ships (ending, respectively, in the earth or the sea) " must be of the same service in restoring the equilibrium silently between the earth and clouds, or in conducting a flash or stroke, if one should be, so as to save harmless the house or vessel." * But how can we explain the negative electrification of clouds?

Franklin's hypothesis to explain how clouds may become negatively charged need not detain us. He admitted the weakness of his hypothesis before introducing it, as well as at its conclusion.† Yet the building of the hypothesis introduced one novel fact of signal importance. We have seen, earlier, that both Franklin and Watson had been led to investigate the relation of electrical behavior to the masses and densities of bodies, always with negative results. Franklin, pursuing this topic in relation to his hypothesis of negative electrification in clouds, came to the conclusion that the natural

---

* In this statement, as in many others, Franklin insisted that the lightning rods performed two separate functions. One is to prevent a stroke, and the other is to conduct it to the ground if there should be one. Many of Franklin's critics confined their attention to the first use, without paying much attention to the second.

† " I cannot forbear venturing some few conjectures on this occasion. They are what occur to me at present, and though future discoveries should prove them not wholly right, yet they may in the mean time be of some use, by stirring up the curious to make more experiments, and occasion more exact disquisitions." Then, after having presented his hypothesis, he observed: " One seemingly material objection arises to the new hypothesis." After explaining the nature of this objection, he concluded: " To this difficulty I own I cannot at present give a solution satisfactory to myself: I thought, however, that I ought to state it in its full force, as I have done, and submit the whole to examination."

quantity of electric fluid that bodies may contain is neither " the same in all kinds of common matter under the same dimensions, nor in the same kind of matter under all circumstances." A cubic foot of one kind of common matter, for example, may contain more electric fluid than a cubic foot of another kind; just as a pound of the same kind of matter may contain more electric fluid when " in a rarer state " than when " in a denser state." [20]

Franklin formulated this principle in general terms as follows: Any " increase of surface makes a body capable of receiving a greater electric atmosphere." In modern terms we would say that the amount of charge that can be received by (or, the capacitance of) a given mass of conducting material depends on its surface area (other factors being equal). Franklin had, as usual, a pretty demonstration to support his principle, to " show that a body in different circumstances of dilation and contraction is capable of receiving or retaining more or less of the electric fluid on its surface."

A small silver can was placed on an insulating clean wine glass. Three yards of brass chain were placed in the can, one end attached to a long silk thread that went over a pulley in the ceiling so that the chain might easily be drawn part way or completely out of the can. A bit of cotton was suspended by a silk thread so that it touched the side of the can. The wire of a charged Leyden jar was then made to touch the can, while the whole chain was inside and lying on the bottom. A spark ensued and the cotton was repelled to a distance of about ten inches. Further contact between the wire of the jar and the can produced no spark nor any alteration in the situation of the cotton. But as the chain was slowly drawn out, Franklin reported, the electric atmosphere of the can itself (we would say, the charge) was diminished since some of it flowed away from the can to surround the exposed chain, as evidenced by the lock of cotton drawing nearer and nearer to the side of the can. But a lowering of the chain into the can caused the repulsion to increase again. When the chain was only partly withdrawn, the observed diminution in the repulsion of the cotton by the can wall was supposed by Franklin to be due to a decrease in the can's electric atmosphere, since part of that atmosphere now surrounded the exposed chain. If this reasoning was correct, then the chain and can in the new circumstances should reasonably be able to support a greater total electric atmosphere (we would say, charge) than had been possible originally when the chain was inside the can. Franklin found this to be the case when he once again brought up to the can the positively charged wire of the Leyden jar. As before, there was a spark accompanied by the cotton jumping away from the can to the same ten inches from the wall as at first.‡

These experiments on the can and chain indicate the superiority of Franklin's concepts over Watson's. The electric atmosphere, or excess electric fluid, received by the can and chain was constant during the first set of experiments. But as the chain was withdrawn, this same quantity of charge became distributed over the whole conducting system, composed of a chain and a can, in a wholly different manner from formerly. A variation in the density of electric fluid occurred without any change in the total charge or quantity of electric fluid. Whereas Watson's discussion was confined entirely to density, Franklin's made allowance for the fact that a distinction can be made between the total charge and the density or distribution of that charge.

Franklin's discovery of the negative electrification of clouds was an important topic in his correspondence at this time. In addition to the discussion of it in the letters which were printed in his book on electricity, and which have been discussed earlier, this phenomenon is mentioned in two further letters written by Franklin to Peter Collinson in 1754. These two letters, which have not been published previously, are at present in the Library of the American Philosophical Society. The first, a manuscript copy, is dated 28 May 1754. In it Franklin wrote:

By Capt. Cuzzine I sent you a Paper containing my new Experiments and Observations on Lightning, and on the positive and negative Electricity of the Clouds: But I fear the notion that Thunder Strokes are sometimes upwards from the Earth to the Clouds will appear so extravagantly whimsical, that none of your Electricians will give themselves the trouble of repeating and verifying the Experiments and the Society will be half asham'd of the Honour they have done me. I am not certain whether a Postscript to that Paper, dated April 18th, 1754, was sent with it, and therefore now send a Copy enclosed.

In this letter, Franklin mentioned that " Mr. Smith is since arrived, and has brought me your favour of March 7th with the Medal your Society has honoured me with." Certain periodicals had come, and " the 3 Barometers, two of which cam safe, but the Ball of the third was broke to Pieces and the Mercury gone. This Loss added to the former, leaves me but 2 out of nine." Franklin said that the breakage seemed to be the result of a fault in manufacture, which he then

‡ These experiments led naturally to Franklin's discovery that there is no charge on the inner surface of a charged insulated metal cylinder, from which observation Priestley inferred the inverse-square law of electric force.

explained at some length. Franklin said he looked forward to seeing
M. Le Cat's Letters " on my Experiments." §

The difficulties of making electrical experiments at this time become clear in the last two paragraphs, wherein Franklin said:

> I am asham'd to say anything more of the great Philosophical Pacquet,
> I so often threatened you with: It's enormous Bulk, and the little time I
> can spare to transcribe things, together with the Fits of Diffidence that
> sometimes seize me, have hitherto occasioned its Delay. But I believe you
> will get it at last.
>
> I am just about setting out for the Treaty at Albany and do not
> expect to be at home again for some Months, as Mr Hunter and myself
> are to make a progress thro' all the Colonies after the Treaty, in order
> to regulate the Post Offices, and must Travel at least 3000 Miles before
> we sit down at home again.

The Second unpublished letter of 1754 to Collinson, in the Library of the American Philosophical Society, begins: " I am just
return'd from Albany, where were Commissioners from seven Prov-
inces to treat with the Indians of the Six Nations." Following a
description of the doings at Albany, Franklin turned to scientific
matters:

> Yesterday I receiv'd yours of May 2 per Capt. Joyce, with the Box and
> Books in good Order. I have just had time to run thro' Father Beccaria's
> Piece *Dell'Elettricismo artificiale e naturale*, which pleases me very much;
> and the more, as I find his Experiments & Observations on Lightning
> have led him to the same strange Opinion with me, *that Thunder-*
> Strokes are sometimes UPWARDS *from the Earth to the Cloud*; so that I
> hope the Paper I sent you last Spring on that Subject, will now be kept
> a little in Countenance, till your Philosophers have Opportunity of veri-
> fying the Experiments therein related.

A postscript reads as follows:

> As Mr. Dalibard has promised to send me that Italian Book, and I have
> no Letter from Mr. Delor, I imagine what you say the latter sent me,
> was only his Translation of Pere Beccaria's Letter,* so have acknowledg'd

§ Claude-Nicolas Le Cat, F.R.S., published some remarks on Franklin's book in the
Journal Œconomique for November, 1752, in the form of letters to Dr. Phineas Bond,
described as having been " un des pensionnaires de M. le Cat." According to Le Cat,
". . . at Rouen, as everywhere else in France, people applauded Franklin." Le Cat's
article is of interest chiefly in showing the extent to which Franklin's book had
attracted attention throughout France. Le Cat summarized many of Franklin's experiments and described how he himself had repeated others. He found fault with some
explanations, and concluded that, if Franklin's lightning rods would work in the way
their inventor had suggested, they alone would be sufficient to make Franklin's work
" immortal." In Volume 47 of the *Philosophical Transactions* there are two articles
by Le Cat dealing with surgico-anatomical subjects.

* De Lor's translation of Beccaria's letter attacking Nollet and defending Franklin
is discussed below on page 508.

only the Receipt of that from him, and the Italian Book from M. Dalibard. Be pleased to forward my Letters to them per first convenient Opportunity.

There follows an extract in the hand of Peter Collinson, which reads:

I am much pleased with Mr. Beccaria's Book on Electricity for his curious experiments, Clear Expression, & excellent Methods. I beg the favour of you to present Him my sincere Thanks for the Countenance he has afforded my opinions & the handsome defence he has made of some of them, against the attacks of Mr Nollet. Our Different experiments & observations on Lightening have led us both to the Same Strange opinion, viz: That Thunder-Strokes are frequently from the Earth to the Clouds—which Opinion I imagine will be found true by such as example it with the requisite attention.†

Further Scientific Relations between Franklin and Watson

In 1752 Watson published in the *Philosophical Transactions* " An Account of Mr. Benjamin Franklin's Treatise, lately published, intituled, *Experiments and Observations on Electricity, made at Philadelphia in America.*" Read at the Royal Society on 6 June 1751, this review was devoted largely to " the latter part of this treatise," since the first four letters " have either in the whole or in part been before communicated to the Royal Society." Watson pointed out that " this ingenious author, from a great variety of curious and well-adapted experiments," believed that the electric matter consists of extremely subtle particles which can permeate matter, that it differs from common matter in that the parts of common matter mutually attract one another while the particles of the electric matter mutually repel one another. Watson, in other words, gave an admirable summary or paraphrase of Franklin's views, saying that " from various experiments recited in our author's treatise, to which the curious may have recourse, the preceding observations are deduced." Then Watson made a claim anew for his independent invention of the theory: " You will observe how much " Franklin's conclusions " coincide with and support those which I some time since communicated to the Society upon this same subject." Watson concluded:

Mr. Franklin appears in the work before us to be a very able and ingenious man; that he has a head to conceive, and a hand to carry into execu-

---

† The fourth English edition of Franklin's book contains an "Extract of a letter concerning electricity, from Mr. B. Franklin to Mons. D'Alibard at Paris, inclosed in a letter to Mr. Peter Collinson, F. R. S.," read at the Royal Society on 18 December 1755. It begins: "You desire my opinion of Père Beccaria's Italian book. I have read it with much pleasure, and think it one of the best pieces on the subject that I have seen in any language." [21]

tion, whatever he thinks may conduce to enlighten the subject-matter, of which he is treating: And altho' there are in this work some few opinions, in which I cannot perfectly agree with him, I think scarce any body is better acquainted with the subject of electricity than himself.[22]

In a letter from Franklin to Peter Collinson, dated 4 February 1750/1, there is a postscript: " My Respects to Dr Fothergill, and to Dr Watson to whom I purpose to write per next Ship." ‡ Franklin did not communicate at once with Watson. After he had read Watson's generally flattering review of his book, he could no longer postpone writing and sent the following letter, here published for the first time.§

Philad[elphi]a   19th April 1754

Sir

I have lately perused the 47th Vol. of the Transactions, wherein I find your very candid and favourable Account of my Electrical papers, for which be pleased to accept my grateful Acknowledgments.

My Friend Mr. Collinson once gave me reason to hope for the pleasure and advantage of a Correspondence with you, by telling me you intended me a Letter. I never received it, and would have wrote to you, but that I heard you were much engaged in business, and I fear'd to incommode you; but the good Opinion of me you are pleased to express in that account, encourages me to think a few lines whose chief aim is the Improvement of knowledge, will not be disagreeable.

I was exceedingly pleased with your curious account of the Phaenomena of Electricity in Vacuo, which I had long expected but never before seen.

There is but one particular of that account in which I am not yet perfectly satisfy'd. It is in Page 367. where you seem to think from observing the Electricity to pass in Vacuo in one continued stream of the same Dimension, etc., " that the cause of that very powerful Repulsion of the Particles of Electrical Fire one to the Other, which we see in Open Air, is more owing to the Resistance of the Air, than to any natural Tendency of the Electricity it self," etc.

At first View this appears likely; But may not the cause of the Stream's not diverging in Vacuo possibly be this, that the inner sides of the Receiver, being first electrify'd, and having themselves an electric Atmosphere, the same repels every way and operates equally on every side of the Stream so as to confine it, and prevent it's Expansion? this being the Case even when the Receiver is not exhausted: For let a [. . . .] *

4. That the holes made thro Pasteboard by the Electric Strokes afford

‡ The original letter, in the possession of the Royal Society, has not been published in full.[23]

§ A photostat of a copy of this letter is in the Library of the American Philosophical Society. This photostat consists of two pages; a third page—presumably the second page of the letter—is missing.

* At this point, the first page ends. See the previous note.

very equivocal Signs of the Direction (as I have shown more largely in a Paper to Mr. Collinson) the Appearances varying according to the Circumstances.

In the same 47th Vol: of the Transactions, there is I think a small mistake, page 552. in relating the Experiment with a pair of Scales; when it is said, that an Electrified Scale[?] was attracted by a Needle, and repelled by an obtuse Body. Which I take to be a reverse of the Fact, and to have led the Gentleman who wrote that Letter, into an Error in the Consequence he draws from the supposed State of the Experiment.†

The Paper abovementioned to Mr. Collinson, contains a Doctrine so seemingly Paradoxical, Viz. That Clouds are most commonly Electrified Negatively, and the Strokes of Lightning therefore most frequently *upwards* from the Earth to the Cloud That I fear it will be thought whimsical, and that many of your Electricians will scarce think it worth while to repeat the Experiments. I hope however that you will not suffer it to be condemned too hastily; but procure it a fair and thorough Examination.

I am with the greatest Esteem and Respect

Sir your most humble serv[an]t

B. Franklin

P. S. I have repeated all the Experiments proposed by M. Nollet (in his Letters to me) in opposition to my Opinions, and intend him a private letter on the Subject thro' your hands. Much Business has prevented my finishing it so as to send it per this ship.

The paper by Watson to which Franklin referred was published in the same volume of the *Philosophical Transactions* as Watson's review of Franklin's book. It is entitled " An Account of the Phæ-nomena of Electricity in vacuo, with some observations thereupon," and was read at the Royal Society on 20 February 1752; it is Watson's last contribution to the subject. In a footnote to this article, Watson said that between the time of communication of his paper to the Royal Society and the time of publication there had been " a dis-covery made in France, in consequence of Mr. Franklin's hypothesis, of being able, by a proper apparatus, to collect the electricity from the atmosphere during a thunder-storm, and to apply it to the usual

---

† The reference here is to a letter from Abbé Mazéas to Stephen Hales, dated Paris, 21 August 1752, and read at the Royal Society on 23 November 1752. Mazéas wrote of an " experiment I was informed of, without knowing the author of it. The dishes of a pair of scales were suspended to the balance by silken cords; the two dishes were electrified, and a very sharp needle was presented to one of them. The scales im-mediately lost their equilibrium; and that dish, under which the needle was held, was attracted. The direct contrary happened, when an obtuse or round body, such as a leaden bullet, was put upon the point of the needle, for then the dish was re-pelled." In a footnote, Mazéas added this comment: " Since I wrote to Dr. Hales, I found this experiment among those of Mr. Franklin." [24]

experiments, which demonstrates that the matter of thunder and lightning and that of electricity are one and the same." [25] In this footnote, Watson said that he still held to his previous ideas that although electric matter may be taken from the earth's atmosphere during a storm of thunder, or even when there is no storm—if there are thunder clouds in the air ("when the atmosphere is replete with heterogeneous phlogistic matter"). Yet he did not believe that electric matter could ever come from pure dry air which in its natural state has scarcely any of it but is only the agent "by which we are enabled to communicate electricity to other bodies." As a result of the Franklinian experiments on lightning, "the truth of" Watson's own doctrine is put out of all doubt: ". . . to wit, not only that the electricity is furnished by those bodies, hitherto called non-electrics, and not by the electrics *per se*; but also, that we are able to add to, or take from, that quantity of electricity, naturally adherent to bodies." This statement is written in the language of Franklin's theory, not Watson's, and does not contain expressions such as "electrical æther" or "density." Yet Watson's views still differ from Franklin's in that Watson failed to explain how the rubbing together of two electrics *per se* (say glass and dry cloth) can give one some electric matter from the other.

Watson presented what he called a summary of his earlier views, but it also bears the mark of Franklin. For instance, he now said that the electric fluid is in all bodies, whereas he had previously said that electric matter is only in non-electrics and not in electrics *per se*. Watson's statement also combines the Franklinian concept of the plus and minus state with his own concept of rarity and density of the electric matter within bodies. "I have shewn," Watson said, "in my communications on this subject," that "electricity is the result of a very subtil and elastic fluid, occupying all bodies in contact wtih the terraqueous globe; and that every-where, in its natural state, it is of the same degree of density." Franklin wrote that all bodies have a natural quantity of electric fluid and made no additional hypothesis about the density of this fluid in different types of bodies. Watson also claimed to have shown "that glass and other bodies, which we denominate electrics *per se*, have the power, by certain known operations, of taking this fluid from one body, and conveying it to another, in a quantity sufficient to be obvious to all our senses: and that, under certain circumstances, it was possible to render the electricity in some bodies more rare than it naturally is, and, by communicating this to other bodies, to give them an additional quantity, and make their electricity more dense." Such bodies were said to continue in this extraordinary state of density "until their natural quantity is restored to each." These were matters which Watson had " copiously treated of in . . . former communications upon this subject." But, he added, he thought " this short recapitulation " was " necessary, for the more easy illustrating what I propose to subjoin." [26]

Yet Watson's concept of a " very subtil and elastic fluid " is not necessarily the same as Franklin's. He concluded what is practically his last report on original research in electricity by raising a number of questions on the possible identity of the elastic fluid causing electrical effects and other known elastic fluids. He did mention the æther, and he did not even suggest that the electric fluid might be a kind of subtle matter *sui generis*, as Franklin had supposed. He merely asked:

By what denomination shall we call this extraordinary power? From its effects in these operations, shall we call it electricity? From its being a principle neither generated nor destroyed; from its being every-where and always present, and in readiness to shew itself in its effects though latent and unobserved, till by some process it is produced into action and rendered visible; from its penetrating the densest and hardest bodies, and its uniting itself to them; and from its immense velocity; shall we, with Theophrastus, Boerhaave, Niewentyt, s'Gravesande, and other philosophers call it elementary fire? ‡

" Or," he said, " shall we, from its containing the substance of light and fire, and from the extreme smallness of its parts, as passing through most bodies we are acquainted with, denominate it with Homberg and the chemists, the chemical sulphureous principle . . . ? " [27] These comments are particularly significant, because Franklin was always very careful to record the differences as well as the similarities between light and electricity, fire and electricity, and the like. Franklin concluded that electrical effects arise from a special kind of matter endowed with particular properties and he indicated the experiments that made each aspect of this hypothesis seem reasonable. Watson merely put his speculations in the form of questions, and offered no supporting data from experience.

Franklin and the Abbé Nollet

The missing page in Franklin's letter to Watson appears to have consisted in large measure of comments addressed to an article of the Abbé Nollet. Nollet, we may be sure, was terribly annoyed by the events of 1752. Suddenly there had appeared a book written by a " M. Franklin " who lived in " Philadelphie "—in the wilds of

‡ See similar views expressed earlier by Watson in his *Sequel*, discussed on pages 411-412 above.

America, the last place in the world from which one could reasonably have expected a major contribution to electricity. This book,
furthermore, contained a theory that apparently disregarded the
experiments and ideas of the Abbé Nollet and presented a wholly
different kind of theory based on new concepts. We may well
imagine Nollet's consternation and see him—as described by Franklin in his " Autobiography "—conceiving the whole book to be nothing but a fabrication by his enemies. Surely this could be the only
reason why D'Alibard had minimized the place of Nollet in the
history of electricity he had written as a kind of foreword to the
book. Then, too, the publication had been sponsored by Buffon,
who evidently did not like Nollet.§ The King and Court had been
treated to a new kind of display of electrical entertainment, the
Philadelphia experiments performed by De Lor which were " greatly
applauded " by His Majesty Louis XV. This was poaching on Nollet's private preserve; up till then he had always performed the
experiments for the entertainment of the Court. Finally, as if his
enemies had not done enough to him, Messieurs de Buffon, D'Alibard, and De Lor had performed the greatest electrical experiment
in history, the fame of which would certainly be everlasting: Franklin's sentry-box experiment, which drew the lightning down from the
skies and proved that the discharge is a simple electrical phenomenon on a large scale.

The lightning experiments had been performed in May, 1752,
and, on the following 6 June, Nollet wrote a letter to Watson, of
which a long extract was read at the Royal Society and published in
the *Philosophical Transactions* for that year.[29] Nollet said that he
was " more interested than any body to come at the facts, which
prove a true analogy between lightning and electricity; since these
experiments establish incontestably a truth, which he had conceived,
and which he ventured to lay before the public more than four years
ago." There followed a quotation from his *Leçons de Physique*, but
in that quotation there is not even a hint that such an experiment
might be possible, only a hope of proof " from a well-connected
comparison of phænomena." Immediately following this statement,
Nollet described a curious experiment, said to " demonstrate that
glass is not absolutely impermeable to the electric fluid," thus to
prove the error in one of Franklin's basic propositions. Next, there
is an experiment to " prove that, in the experiment of Leyden, the
electrical virtue, or power of giving a shock, does not reside *only* in

§ Buffon described this situation in a number of letters and even claimed that he
had been the person responsible for the performance of the lightning experiment
devised by Franklin.[28]

the glass." This turns out to be a variation of the old experiment performed by Watson, in which an uncharged Leyden jar was made to discharge *while* the water was being poured from a charged jar.*
Watson, in a footnote to Nollet's letter remarked on the similarity of the two experiments, and described his own, with this comment: " I then considered this experiment, as a proof of the electricity being accumulated in the water." [30] From the word " then," we may conclude that he no longer held to his previous opinion and had graciously accepted Franklin's correction. Certainly Kinnersley's experiment, in which a Leyden jar was charged by bringing the coating to an electrical machine while the water or inner conductor was grounded, had killed forever the idea that a Leyden jar is charged by an accumulation of electricity in the water.

Nollet's final point, corresponding to comment no. 4 in Franklin's letter to Watson, dealt with the character of the hole made in a piece of cardboard by an electric discharge. The hole in the cardboard was much larger on one side than on the other, from which fact Nollet concluded that the discharge followed a certain direction contrary to Franklin's supposition that glass is positively charged. The shape of such holes was later an important subject in discussions of whether there is one electric fluid or two. In his letter to Watson, Franklin properly observed only that caution must be exercised in interpreting this kind of evidence. Franklin referred Watson to his earlier discussion of this problem. In a letter to Collinson, written in September, 1753, Franklin had expressed the hope that others would attempt to verify the experiments he had interpreted as indicating that rubbed glass is positively charged. He also requested that all people who might have an opportunity to observe the " recent effects " of lightning on buildings and trees would " consider them particularly with a view to discover the direction." Franklin believed that in the explosion or rending of wood, brick, or stone, the splinters always " fly off on that side where there is the least resistance." [31] This effect is similar, he said, to the production of a hole in cardboard by a discharge from a Leyden jar. If both surfaces of the cardboard are " not confined or compressed," a burr will be raised on both sides, " but if one side be confined, so that the bur cannot be raised on that side, it will be raised on the other, which way soever the fluid was directed." The burr is not, therefore, only " an effect of the direction." †

Within a year Franklin's ideas received additional support from

* A description of this experiment and Franklin's comment on it may be found on pages 464-467 above.

† The fourth (1769) edition of Franklin's book on electricity contains a number of analyses of the course and direction of the lightning discharge.

Italy. The Abbé Beccaria of Turin published a large treatise on " artificial and natural electricity "[32] which was described as a " work . . . written conformable to Mr Franklin's theory." It contained " a letter to the Abbé Nollet, in defense of Mr Franklin's system."[33] Beccaria, one of the major Italian scientists of the mid-eighteenth century, had made many new experiments which he interpreted in Franklinian terms with some additional concepts and minor alterations. Beccaria was one of the first Italians to attempt the introduction of lightning rods[34] and he repeated Franklin's experiment of the lightning kite.[35] Franklin must have been especially pleased by the appearance of as good a man as Beccaria on his side.

In his letter to Watson Franklin had said that he was preparing a reply to Nollet's book of " letters " attacking the Franklinian theory in general and Franklin's description or interpretation of a number of important experiments. But he never entered this debate, owing to an innate dislike of scientific polemics.‡ But he surely must have been delighted by Beccaria's letter, answering the major points of criticism of Nollet. This letter was translated into French by De Lor, who had demonstrated Franklin's experiments at the French Court, and who had performed the experiment of the sentry box. The translation was published in 1754[36] and Nollet replied to Beccaria in a supplementary volume of " letters." Beccaria answered the objections raised by Nollet in the best way possible. He repeated some of the major experiments made by Nollet to show the inadequacy of Franklin's theory and found that Nollet had been careless. In other cases Beccaria proved that Nollet had not quite grasped the point of Franklin's explanations.

The controversy between the two theories divided the Royal Academy of Sciences in Paris. In the volume of the Academy for the year 1753, considerable attention is devoted to the subject of electricity. In the general review (or " histoire ") at the beginning of that volume, under " Physique générale," it is said that up until the present time physicists have been in agreement about electricity. The doctrine of the Abbé Nollet, first proposed in 1745, had not hitherto produced many contradictors in Europe, but now America has just furnished one.§ Franklin, one of the adversaries of Nollet, produced a book which divided the physicists of Europe, some having taken the side of Franklin and the others remaining loyal to the ideas of Nollet.

‡ See Chapter Three.

§ ". . . si cependant on peut nommer contradicteur un Philosophe, qui travaillant à l'autre extrémité du globe, sans avoir probablement aucune connoissance de ce qui avoit été fait ici, est parvenu à tirer de ses expériences des conclusions peu conformes à celles que M. l'abbé Nollet a tirées des siennes."

The section of "mémoires," making up the bulk of the volume of 1753, contains an article by Nollet devoted entirely to the defense of his own theory against Franklin. In rebuttal there is an article by Jean B. Le Roy, defending the doctrine of Franklin and offering many experiments in support of the Franklinian theory. This is followed in turn by another article of the Abbé Nollet,[37] which is particularly significant in that in it Nollet used the writings of Watson to support his own position against that of Franklin. Nollet said that Watson was one of the first physicists "who had discovered and proved the simultaneous effluences and affluences," and that Watson had always considered the electric matter as a fluid which could become condensed, and rarefied or extended. It did not seem to Nollet that Watson had ever "formally retracted his first opinion, I mean that of simultaneous effluences and affluences, with respect to which this new idea is superfluous and even incompatible." Interestingly enough, Nollet insisted that Franklin was the first to introduce the distinction "of electricities in plus and in minus," [38] and he ignored any claim made by Watson to have been an independent discoverer of this concept.

Watson's reaction to Nollet's attacks upon Franklin is contained in a kind of book review which he read at the Royal Society on 17 May 1753, and which was published in the *Philosophical Transactions* as "an account of a treatise presented to the Royal Society . . . extracted and translated from the French, by Mr. William Watson, F.R.S." Watson neither defended Nollet nor did he reply to any of his arguments. He described the book as "the production of a great master upon the subject of electricity," who for several years "has done me the honour of being my correspondent. . . . I have communicated several valuable papers from him to the Royal Society." Watson then pointed out that the year 1752 will always be memorable in the history of electricity because of the great experiments on lightning. He was anxious to prevent extravagant interpretations; if we wish to make "the most certain advantage of these new discoveries," he said, "we should confine ourselves to facts." And if we do draw any consequences from facts, they "should be immediate and necessary ones; for, whenever our discoveries seem to promise to be useful and important, we are apt to hope and expect great success from them: we must therefore be careful to restrain our imagination, or we shall fall into error." [39] I do not see how such a statement, a paraphrase of Nollet, can be interpreted in any other way except as an indication of Watson's approval of Nollet's position that despite the Marly experiments, and others made on the electrification of clouds, man has no warrant whatever to erect lightning rods in the vain hope of protecting himself from the destructive effects of lightning. Watson, in fact, said that Nollet had examined this subject very carefully and " thinks, he sees clearly, that the considering the electrification of pointed bodies as a proof of lessening the matter of thunder, is abusing a real discovery to flatter ourselves with a vain hope." This position may explain why Watson, like other English electricians, did not begin to introduce lightning rods into England immediately following the verification of Franklin's ideas about the lightning discharge.*

Watson's " review " consists primarily of quotations from Nollet, and paraphrases and summaries of his statements. While this may seem to be a neutral position, it is certainly plain that Watson was not willing to go along with the full development of the theory to which he had claimed to be an independent inventor, and to reject the older theory of the Abbé Nollet which he had previously espoused. On the other hand, Watson did not explicitly approve the statements of Nollet. He said that Nollet's experiments were " intended to demonstrate the validity of the conclusions exhibited therein. These merit the particular attention of those conversant in these matters. . . ." He concluded by observing that the treatise is " a very valuable one, as it gives us the still riper thoughts of an able writer upon a difficult, and, till very lately, an almost unknown, subject; of one, who, besides his inquiries into this part of philosophy, has a great compass in the knowledge of nature, and is therefore well qualified to investigate her phænomena."

Franklin's Reputation Established

By 1754 Franklin had been awarded the Copley Medal of the Royal Society and could boast of the three parts of his book on electricity in print in English in a second edition. In 1756 the second edition of the French version was published and two years later there was a German translation made by Johan Carl Wilcke, Professor of Experimental Physics at Stockholm, later Secretary of the Swedish Academy of Sciences. This translation must have given Franklin great joy because the translator, who added a valuable

---

* Writing from London on 20 February 1762, Franklin complained to Kinnersley that the lightning rod was not so highly regarded in England as in America: " You seem to think highly of the importance of this discovery, as do many others on our side of the water. Here it is very little regarded; so little, that though it is now seven or eight years since it was made publick, I have not heard of a single house as yet attempted to be secured by it. It is true the mischiefs done by lightning are not so frequent here as with us, and those who calculate chances may perhaps find that not one death, (or the destruction of one house) in a hundred thousand happens from that cause, and that therefore it is scarce worth while to be at any expence to guard against it." [40]

commentary of his own, was already distinguished for his contributions to electricity, notably the production of electric charges in heated tourmaline crystals. Franklin was elected a Fellow of the Royal Society on 29 April 1756, being supported in his candidacy by the Earl of Macclesfield, President, and, amongst others, his good friend, Peter Collinson, and William Watson and John Canton. He "deserved so highly of the Society" that his name was ordered to be "inserted in the Lists before his admission and without any fee, or other payments to the Society." The Certificate in his favour" as a candidate for election into the Society described him as "a gentleman who has very eminently distinguished himself by various discoveries in natural philosophy" and it particularly noted that he had "first, suggested the experiments to prove the analogy between lightning and electricity." [41]

The great controversy with Nollet had actually increased Franklin's fame because Nollet's attacks had brought Franklin's name before the scientific public in Europe in a more dramatic way than Franklin's writings would have done on their own. There were other great debates ahead. The erection of lightning rods was opposed by some men—Nollet among them—on pseudo-scientific grounds. In Switzerland, France, and Italy popular prejudice against the new device resulted in the tearing down of lightning rods. In Bologna, Pope Benedict XIV tried to help overcome the superstitious fears of simple men about the possible harm that might come from lightning rods, but to no avail. [42] At the same time the Reverend Thomas Prince in Boston warned that rods would make the lightning accumulate in the bowels of the earth and cause earthquakes; there was no way for man to escape the hand of an angry God. In 1780-1784 a lawsuit about lightning rods gave M. de St. Omer the right to have a lightning rod on his house despite the objections of his neighbors, and this victory established the fame of the lawyer in the case, young Robespierre. In England a great quarrel arose as to whether the rods should terminate in points, as Franklin advocated, or in knobs. Finally, a major subject of debate was whether electrification is caused by a single electric matter in excess or defect or by two distinct electric matters, one vitreous and the other resinous.

Franklin could not escape the controversy about the shape of lightning rods because the Royal Society appointed him a member of a committee to explore this subject. For the rest, he was willing to let experiments speak for themselves and to defend theories or working hypotheses only by new experiments, not by verbal polemics. He just could not see how the progress of science could ever be forwarded by endless discussions of old ideas and well-known experiments. He advised men to revise and improve existing ideas and to conceive new ones, to devise wholly new types of experiments. In politics and diplomacy he was a master of argument and he knew when to be serious, when to joke, and when to be bitingly satirical. But there is no possibility of cajoling nature, and he gladly recognized that all the wit of Benjamin Franklin could not alter a single brute fact of experiment or observation.

SOURCES

This chapter derives from a study of the publications of **Franklin**, Watson, Nollet, Beccaria, and others in the early 1750's, for which see the General Bibliography, and the publications for this period of the Royal Society and the Académie Royale des Sciences. Wheeler Gift (1909) is a particularly useful guide to the literature because the titles are listed chronologically rather than by author; it may be supplemented by Mottelay (1922).

In Schonland (1950), there is an exemplary discussion of the present state of knowledge on lightning and lightning rods and of Franklin's contributions. Of particular value is the section on pages 17-19, in which Schonland shows that although in Franklin's kite and the sentry-box experiment, the rod "does not draw electricity from the cloud," there is "the same effect as if it had done so." Schonland's views are summarized on pages 348-349 of Cohen (1952b), which contains a survey of all that is known about the dates of the performance of the kite and sentry-box experiments, and the erection of the first lightning rods. The May, 1952, issue of the *Journal of the Franklin Institute* (**253** (5): 393-440) contains four articles on Franklin and lightning rods. Some information about the prejudices against the introduction of lightning rods may be found in Cohen (1952a).

The various editions of Franklin's book on electricity are described in Franklin (1941: intro., pp. 139-148). As in previous chapters, I have distinguished Franklin's public letters from his private letters by reference to the 1769 (fourth English) edition of his book and the 1941 edition. I have not, in every case, indicated the date on which each paper was either read at the Royal Society or printed in the *Philosophical Transactions*.

REFERENCES

1. See Franklin, 1941: intro., pp. 77-78, 201 n.
2. Franklin, 1941: 201-211; 1769: 39-52. The numbers in square brackets correspond to Franklin's paragraph numbers.
3. Letter to Dr. Lining, 18 March 1755, Franklin, 1941: 334; 1769: 323.
4. *Idem*.
5. Franklin, 1941: 219, § 18; 1769: 62, § 18.
6. *Ibid.*, § 21.
7. Franklin, 1756: 2: 67-133; 1941: 257-262; not in Franklin, 1769, but an extract in Franklin, 1774: 108-113.
8. Mazéas, 1752; Franklin, 1941: 256-257; 1769: 106-107.
9. Watson, 1751-1752d; Franklin, 1941: 262-264; 1769: 108-110.
10. An account of these experiments, and the reactions to them, may be found in Schonland, 1950, 1952, Brunet, 1947, and 1948. All the available evidence is summarized in Cohen, 1942b.
11. Watson, 1753: 201-202.
12. Franklin, 1840: 5: 501.

13. Franklin to Collinson, 29 April 1749, "Farther Experiments and Observations, 1748," Franklin, 1941: 199, § 28; 1769: 36-37, § 28.

14. Franklin, 1941: 250; 1769: 99.

15. Franklin, 1941: 252-254; 1769: 102-104.

16. Franklin, 1941: 276; 1769: 123.

17. Franklin, 1941: 269; 1769: 114.

18. Watson, 1746b: 56-57, § LVII.

19. Franklin, 1941: 271; 1769: 116.

20. Franklin to Collinson, Sept. 1753, Franklin, 1941: 272; 1769: 118.

21. Franklin, 1941: 307; 1769: 161.

22. Watson, 1751-1752a: 210-211.

23. Printed in Church, 1908: 12-13, and reprinted in Van Doren, 1945.

24. Mazéas, 1752: 552.

25. Watson, 1751-1752c: 374n.

26. *Ibid.*, 371-372.

27. *Ibid.*, 375.

28. Buffon, 1860: 1: 56.

29. Nollet, 1751-1752.

30. *Ibid.*, 555n.

31. Franklin, 1941: 276; 1769: 123-124.

32. Beccaria, 1753; partial English translation, Beccaria, 1776.

33. Note of " J. B." [John Bevis?], Franklin, 1941: 307n; 1769:161n.

34. See Cohen, 1952a.

35. See Cohen, 1952b.

36. Beccaria 1754.

37. Nollet, 1753a, Le Roy, 1753, Nollet, 1753b.

38. Nollet, 1753b: 477.

39. Watson, 1753.

40. Franklin, 1941: 374-375; 1769: 416-417.

41. Quoted in Stearns, 1946.

42. See Cohen, 1952a.

CHAPTER TWELVE

FURTHER APPLICATIONS AND DEVELOPMENT OF THE FRANKLIN THEORY: THE ULTIMATE NEED FOR THE REVISION OF SOME CONCEPTS

La Nature est un Trésor inépuisable de faits merveilleux. À chaque pas que nous faisons dans leurs recherches, de nouvelles vuës se découvrent à nos regards. Toutes les fois qu'on s'imagine être au bout de quelque discussion, un examen plus attentif fait voir que le but auquel on s'étoit proposé d'atteindre est encore infiniment éloigné, & que ce qui nous a fait croire que le chemin étoit si court, c'est que nos yeux sont trop foibles pour en appercevoir le bout.

—ÆPINUS (1756)

Benjamin FRANKLIN had begun to learn about electricity in the mid-1740's and his last major contribution to the subject was made in 1755. During the remainder of his long life he never lost interest in science and he was particularly solicitous about helping others in their scientific careers. He made occasional experiments, often in concert with others, speculated about light and heat and other subjects of physical science, and wrote a number of papers on the effects of lightning and on lightning rods. In the great debate that arose concerning the foundations of his electrical theory—whether there might be two electric fluids and not just one—he took no part. Although he remained on the sidelines, he never capitulated and he rejoiced at any evidence that seemed to favor his own theory.

The whole subject of electricity was vigorously studied throughout the eighteenth century and important alterations were made in the Franklinian one-fluid theory of electricity, notably by Æpinus and Cavendish. By about the time of Franklin's death the uncovering of many phenomena had introduced into electrical theory some new considerations and a deep range of complexity. Most of the problems which had been of concern in the 1740's and 1750's were then relegated to the background. Men simply took for granted many of the basic principles of Franklin's theory of electricity—and to such an extent that even the opponents of the single-fluid theory of electrical action were apt to write in Franklinian terms.

515

Canton's Studies of Electrostatic Induction

Franklin's last paper to contain any electrical novelty of fundamental importance was stimulated by a remarkable series of investigations reported to the Royal Society on 6 December 1753 by John Canton, F. R. S., one of that group in Britain who had performed the lightning experiment in 1752. Canton sought to discover the sign of electrification of clouds, and his report on this topic was published in the *Philosophical Transactions* under the title, " Electrical experiments, with an attempt to account for their several phænomena. Together with some observations on thunder-clouds." It was immediately printed also in the second supplement (1754) to Franklin's book on electricity, together with Franklin's long letter to Collinson (September, 1753) about negatively electrified clouds, and David Colden's remarks on the Abbé Nollet's book of letters attempting to discredit Franklin's theory of electricity and Franklin's experiments.* When Canton's paper was published in Franklin's book, a subtitle was added to make the whole investigation appear to be ". . . In further confirmation of Mr. Franklin's observations on the positive and negative electrical state of the clouds." [1]

Canton's paper contains nine experiments. Experiment VIII deals with the production of light in a Torricellian vacuum by bringing an excited glass tube near it, " a kind of ocular demonstration of the truth of Mr. Franklin's hypothesis; that when the electrical fluid is condensed on one side of thin glass, it will be repelled from the other, if it meets with no resistance." In Experiment IX, Canton described how he had " observed, by a great number of experiments," that clouds are " some in a positive, and others in a negative state of electricity." † The major part of Canton's paper is devoted

---

* The three parts making up the first edition of Franklin's book on electricity were thus a Franklinian miscellany, containing not only letters and articles written by Franklin, but also two letters by Kinnersley, an article by David Colden, and another by John Canton. In this form, the book went through three editions in England. The second French edition, produced by D'Alibard in 1756, included all three parts as well as an account of the experiments in verification of Franklin's hypothesis on the electrical nature of the lightning discharge. The three parts were included in the German edition prepared by Wilcke and printed in Leipzig in 1758.

† The subtitle introduced into Canton's paper established Franklin's priority in the discovery that clouds sometimes show signs of positive electrification and at other times of negative electrification. Although Franklin's discovery of this pheomenon antedated Canton's observations, Canton apparently did not know about Franklin's experiments on this topic when he first reported his own work to the Royal Society. Priestley said, " This observation of Mr. Canton, on the different electricity of the clouds was made, and the account of it published in England, before it was known that Dr. Franklin had made the same discovery in America." [2] Franklin thought this discovery was so strange that he doubted whether it would be believed (see the preceding chapter, pages 499-503) and the confirmation of it by Canton and also by Beccaria, whether independently or not, was gratifying.

to a series of experiments dealing with the general topic of induced charges, the phenomenon of electrostatic induction or charging by influence. Canton's experiments on charging by induction are often considered to mark the foundation of this subject; they excited Franklin to produce further experiments and to improve Canton's explanations. Franklin's " Electrical experiments made in pursuance of those made by Mr. Canton, dated December 6, 1753; with explanations " was written on 14 March 1755 and read at the Royal Society on 18 December 1755. Printed in the *Philosophical Transactions*, it was also included in the fourth (1769) English edition of Franklin's book on electricity, and later editions, immediately following Canton's paper. A comparison of what the two men said on this same topic affords a nice measure of the clarity of Franklin's thought and expression in scientific matters. The modern reader is apt to be puzzled more than once in his first perusal of Canton's report, but Franklin's may be read without a single instance of doubt as to what happened during each experiment. Franklin's lucid explanations of the phenomena could be reprinted almost *verbatim et literatim* in any textbook today and would probably put to shame the remainder of the text.

In Canton's first experiment,[3] two tiny balls of cork or brass were suspended from the ceiling by conducting strings of linen or fine silver wire so that they were in contact with each other. He found that bringing a charged glass tube or piece of sealing wax a few feet below the balls caused them to separate a little. Bringing the charged body closer caused them to separate further. Finally, on removing the charged body altogether, the balls come together again. In Experiment II, the two balls were suspended by insulating threads of silk. Canton found that in this case the excited glass tube had to be brought within eighteen inches of the balls before they repelled each other. Furthermore, the repulsion continued " for some time " after the tube had been taken away. Canton said that " according to Mr. Franklin, excited glass *emits* the electric fluid, but excited wax *receives* it." Therefore, he reasoned, when an excited stick of wax is brought near a pair of non-insulated balls, as in the first experiment, the electric fluid " is supposed to come through the threads into the balls, and be condensed there," since it is attracted by the negatively charged wax which wants electric fluid. In other words, while the negatively charged piece of wax is near the balls, they become charged positively (i. e., gain electric atmospheres) and repel each other. When the wax is withdrawn, the balls, being grounded, return to their natural (i. e., neutral) state. But when a glass rod is brought near the non-insulated balls, " they cannot properly be said to be electrified," because they "are not insulated." Canton thought that when they are within "the atmosphere of the excited tube, they may attract and condense the electrical fluid round them, and be separated by the repulsion of its particles." He also conjectured that "the balls at this time contain less than their common share of the electrical fluid, on account of the repelling power of that which surrounds them; though some, perhaps, is continually entering and passing through the threads."

Canton had concluded correctly that when the negatively charged wax stick is brought near grounded conductors (i. e., the balls dangling at the end of wires), they exhibit a charge of the opposite sign. In this conclusion he was applying the results of Franklin's experiments and reasoning on the action of the Leyden jar. To use modern terminology, Franklin had shown that a negative charge on one of the conductors will always induce a positive charge on the other conductor if it is grounded. Franklin had also shown the reverse to be true; i. e., when one of the conductors is charged positively, the grounded one will by repulsion lose some electric fluid and become negatively charged. We might therefore, have expected Canton to have said that the presence of a positively charged rod would repel electric fluid out of the balls and the wire into the ceiling and leave the balls charged negatively, in analogy to the Leyden jar. My conjecture is that Canton was not willing to accept this "obvious" explanation since it implies that two negatively charged bodies must repel one another just as two positively charged bodies do. In terms of Franklin's theory, there is no reason why two negatively charged bodies should repel one another, although we have seen that Franklin reluctantly came to admit that such a phenomenon always occurs. Canton's way out of the impasse was ingenious. He assumed that the balls attract some of the electric atmosphere from the glass rod. This atmosphere produces repulsion between the balls and also drives some of the normal quantity of electrical fluid out of the balls and up the wire so that they "contain less than their common share." Canton's result is consistent with Franklin's principle that an electrified body always induces a charge of the opposite sign when brought near a grounded conductor and it also provides for an electric atmosphere to account for the observed repulsion. A negatively charged ball (deprived of some of its fluid and therefore hungry to have it replaced) could presumably attract particles of electric fluid from the surrounding atmosphere to make up its deficiency. Canton supposed that part of the atmosphere of the charging rod "is continually entering and passing through the threads."

Franklin, in a somewhat embarrassed manner, merely accepted the incontestable fact that negatively charged bodies repel one another, which relieved him of the necessity of Canton's complex, albeit clever, solution. Yet it seems clear that during Canton's experiments some of the electric atmosphere of the glass rod did actually pass to the balls, or, to use modern terminology, some of the charge was apt to leak off the glass rod onto the balls. How else can we explain Canton's observation that once the rubbed glass rod had been brought near the insulated balls, they continued to repel one another after the rod had been withdrawn?

Canton's next two experiments are of a sort familiar to all physics teachers and all who as students ever took a course in elementary physics. An insulated tin tube, four or five feet long and two inches in diameter, had two cork balls suspended from one end by conducting linen threads. In Experiment III the tube was electrified " by bringing the excited glass tube near the other end, so as that the balls may stand an inch and an half or two inches apart." Since the repulsion between the balls apparently continued after the glass tube had been removed, I presume that the tube gained positive charge through leakage from the rod, in agreement with the interpretation given to the previous experiments. " Then," to continue with Canton's description, " at the approach of the excited [glass] tube, they [i. e., the two cork balls] will, by degrees, lose their repelling power, and come into contact; and as the [glass] tube is brought still nearer, they will separate again to as great a distance as before." Next the excited glass tube is slowly withdrawn, and the balls will come together and then " repel as at first." ‡ When the tin tube was " electrified by wax, or the wire of a charged phial," the balls were observed to behave " in the same manner at the approach of excited wax, or the wire of the phial." In Experiment IV the cork balls were electrified by glass as in the previous experiment, and then an " excited stick of wax " was brought near the balls. The repulsion between the balls was increased. The same effect was observed when an excited glass tube was brought near the balls after they had been electrified by wax.§

The above account may seem puzzling to the reader today—because we usually do this experiment with a gold-leaf electroscope. If such an instrument is positively charged, the approach of a *positively charged* rod, a glass rod rubbed with silk, will make the leaves

‡ It would seem from the nature of the experimental results that after the electrification of the tube, the charged rod was made to approach the balls and not the " other " end of the tin tube as during electrification.

§ Once again, these results would follow only if the charged glass or wax had been brought near the balls; the opposite effect would follow from bringing the charged glass or wax near the " other " end of the tin tube.

more positive and produce a greater separation; the approach of a *negatively charged* rod, a wax stick or a rod of hard rubber or vulcanite rubbed with fur or wool, will make the leaves less positive until they collapse and a still nearer approach will cause them to separate again. The difference between Canton's experiment and ours is that we bring our rod near the *knob* of the charged electroscope rather than near the leaves. But Canton brought his rod or stick near the balls rather than the charged tube. A positively charged rod brought near the knob of a positively charged electroscope will make the *knob less positive* and the *leaves more positive*, and produce a greater separation. In Canton's experiment a positively charged glass tube brought near the balls of his positively charged instrument made the *balls less positive* and the *tin tube more positive* so that the separation decreased.

Canton's explanation of the phenomena he observed is not quite the same as ours. Apparently he took a little too literally Franklin's doctrine of " electric atmospheres " and leaned too heavily on the concept of " density of electrical fluid " which had been used by Watson but carefully avoided by Franklin. Canton said that " bringing the excited glass to the end, or edge of the tin-tube, in the . . . experiment, is supposed to electrify it positively," in agreement with Franklin's theory. Since electric fluid was added to a conductor, it must distribute itself and some will run " off through the balls, and they will repel each other. But at the approach of excited glass, which likewise *emits* the electrical fluid, the discharge of it from the balls will be diminished; or part will be driven back, by a force acting in a contrary direction; and they will come nearer together." Apparently, Canton supposed that the emission of fluid from the balls produces an electrical atmosphere around them and thereby causes repulsion. The glass, which has also an atmosphere of electric fluid, will cause that of the balls to re-enter them, thus reducing the repulsion. The fluid in the atmosphere of the glass, I suppose, could not enter the substance of the glass since glass is a non-conductor and supposedly impermeable to electric fluid. But the electric fluid in the atmosphere of the balls could enter the balls and travel up the thread to the tube, since these are conducting bodies. According to Canton,

If the tube be held at such a distance from the balls, that the excess of the density of the fluid round about them, above the common quantity in air, be equal to the excess of the density of that within them, above the common quantity contained in cork; their repulsion will be quite destroyed. But if the tube be brought nearer; the fluid without, being more dense than that within the balls, it will be attracted by them, and they will recede from each other again.

One obvious difficulty in the above explanation is that when the positively charged tube is brought more closely to the balls (brought together by its original approach) to produce a new repulsion, fluid is attracted to the balls from that tube; thus the system of tin tube, threads, and balls has to have more electric fluid than in their state of positive charge before the glass rod is brought near. This need not be manifested by an increased repulsion when the glass tube is completely withdrawn, since electric fluid could return to the glass during the process of withdrawal. This postulated motion of electrical fluid was unnecessary and cumbersome and we shall see in a moment that Franklin was able to dispense with it.

"When the apparatus has lost part of its natural share of this fluid . . . or is electrified negatively," continued Canton, "the electrical fire is attracted and imbibed by the balls to supply the deficiency; and that more plentifully at the approach of excited glass; or a body positively electrified, than before; whence the distance between the balls will be increased, as the fluid surrounding them is augmented." I must confess that the above passage is completely baffling, even after many readings. If the apparatus has lost fluid, what is the source from which "the electrical fire is attracted and imbibed by the balls to supply the deficiency"? One such possible source is the positively charged glass rod, and this "more plentifully," so that the separation of the balls is "increased, as the fluid surrounding them is augmented." But augmentation presupposes the existence of a quantity of "fluid surrounding them" which is increased, and yet how can there be a quantity of "fluid surrounding them" or forming an atmosphere if the balls are part of a system that is negatively charged, that has a deficiency of fluid rather than excess? The phrase "more plentifully" agrees with the observed fact that a positively charged rod brought near negatively charged balls will make "the distance between them . . . be increased." But if this increased separation results from a transfer of fluid from the glass rod to the balls, the subsequent removal of the glass rod should not be accompained by a return of the fluid to the glass as before.

Canton accepted the Franklinian postulates that all bodies contain a "normal" quantity of the electric fluid, that the particles of the electric fluid repel one another, and that the electric fluid moves freely along conductors. With these postulates as guides, he essayed an explanation of an elegant variation of the preceding experiments. In Experiment V he brought a positively charged glass tube near the midpoint of the insulated tin tube, so as to be "nearly at right-angles with it." The balls thereupon repelled one another and separated, and the repulsion was further increased by bringing the excited glass tube still nearer. As the glass tube was withdrawn, the repulsion between the balls diminished until they touched each other. But as the glass tube was completely removed, the balls began to separate once again. The residual electrification of the balls was tested: this repulsion was ". . . increased by the approach of excited glass, but diminished by excited wax; just as if the apparatus had been electrified by wax, after the manner described in the third experiment." In Canton's explanation, " the common stock of electrical matter in the tin-tube is supposed to be attenuated about the middle, and to be condensed at the ends, by the repelling power of the atmosphere of the excited glass tube," held near it. Hence, a satisfactory explanation could be had for the observation that when an excited glass tube is brought near the middle of the insulated tin tube, " the balls at the end will repel each other; and the more so, as the excited tube is brought nearer."

Although the preceding paragraph might make it appear that Canton had a simple modern view of electrostatic induction, the fact that he did not will be plain in the next statement, viz.: the tin tube to which the charged glass tube has been brought may lose some of its " natural quantity " of electric fluid from " the ends and edge of it," so that the whole apparatus becomes negatively charged. The fluid will more readily " run off from the ends and edge " than " enter at the middle." This explanation was necessitated by the observed fact of a net charge on the tin tube, indicated by a separation of the balls when the glass tube had been completely removed. A test indicated that the resulting charge is negative, implying a loss of electric fluid. In this test, Canton brought an excited glass rod under the balls and noted an increased repulsion between them; an excited wax stick underneath the balls decreased their repulsion. This test does show that the electrification of the balls was negative, as Canton said. Perhaps this negative charge arose from the discharge at the edges of the tin tube, but such a charge would also have been produced by a momentary grounding of the tin tube while the excited glass rod was near it. Canton said that during the process of charging the tin tube in this way, he found that as he withdrew the glass rod, the balls came together for an instant before separating finally. The later phenomenon—we know today—would have resulted whether the tin tube and balls received a negative charge by a leaking or discharge at the end and edges or by having been grounded. Canton never reported the experiments performed by Franklin in which, first, the balls were made to separate without an increase in the net charge on the tin tube, and then the tin tube was obviously and purposely grounded while an excited glass tube was held nearby. In these experiments Franklin separated some of the effects which appear to have been combined in the observations reported by Canton.

In the last of Canton's electrostatic-induction experiments [Experiment VI], two insulated tin tubes, A and B, were placed in a line, end to end, with half an inch between them, and with a pair of cork balls suspended from the " remote " end of each. A positively charged glass tube was brought near the middle of tube A, and both pairs of cork balls separated. When the glass tube was removed, it was found that the " balls of A will come together, and then repel each other again; but those of B will hardly be affected." When the glass tube was next brought " under the balls of A," their repulsion was increased; but when it was brought " towards the balls of B," their repulsion was diminished. Canton explained that in this experiment, " part of the fluid driven out of one tin-tube enters the other; which is found to be electrified positively, by the decreasing of the repulsion of its balls, at the approach of excited glass." This time Canton interpreted the test for the sign of the charge correctly. It is a pity that he did not explore the question of whether the only source of final charge on the tubes was the driving out of electric fluid from one tube to the other. He might have caused the two tin tubes to touch each other, so as to discover whether all signs of charge would then disappear. This step would seem to have been necessary in the light of Experiment V, in which the mere approach of a charged glass tube was said to have given an insulated tin tube a residual negative charge. Furthermore, Canton did not give any information as to whether, during the process by which the two tubes became charged, there was a discharge between them, nor did he say whether or not they came together for an instant.

Canton's paper brought to light a number of new phenomena * and he vastly extended the range of application of the concept of induced charges. Franklin had introduced this concept in order to explain the induction of charges through glass in a Leyden jar. Canton saw that induced charges might also be produced and detected in single insulated conductors, and that this class of phenomenon was not limited to grounded conductors, as Franklin's studies of condensers might have seemed to imply. Franklin's later experiments have a degree of refinement over Canton's, largely in that Franklin was more careful to differentiate charges produced by electrostatic

---

* Experiment VII introduces a wholly new subject. A tin tube with a pair of conducting balls was electrified " to a considerable degree " in a room in which the air was " rendered very dry by means of a fire." If an experimenter touched the tube " with a finger, or any other conductor," the repulsion between the balls continued though it was considerably diminished.

induction from those that might arise either by contact or by a spark discharge or leakage. Franklin also revised a number of Canton's explanations and was able to strip the problem of each non-essential or ambiguous point. The ease with which Franklin improved on Canton's discussion is a reflection of course of a high order of genius in scientific inquiry, but we must not forget that it is always easier to revise or criticize the pioneering work of others than to inaugurate a new type of investigation. Thus from the vantage point of two centuries later, the historian can easily see where a scientist of the past went astray, but he has two hundred years of research to sharpen his critical senses; his analysis would probably have been less acute had it been made then.

Franklin's Analysis of Electrostatic Induction

Franklin opened his paper on "Electrical experiments made in pursuance of those made by Mr. Canton . . ." with a statement of three principles.[4] Electric atmospheres [I] around two or more charged non-electric bodies will not mix to form a single atmosphere, but will remain distinct and repel each other: ". . . plainly seen in suspended cork balls, and other bodies electrified." † Not only will an electric atmosphere repel another electric atmosphere, but [II] since the particles of the electric fluid always repel one another, the electric atmosphere around a (positively) charged body will also repel the electric matter making up the normal quantity of electric fluid in a conductor. Thus a positively charged body may approach "and, without joining or mixing with . . . [the electric fluid in an uncharged conductor], force it to other parts of the body. . . ." This second principle, an acceptance for all practical purposes of action-at-a-distance, was shown to be valid by the series of experiments, described below. Lastly, [III] "bodies electrified negatively, or deprived of their natural quantity of electricity, repel each other, (or at least appear to do so, by a mutual receding) as well as those electrified positively, or which have electric atmospheres." This last principle could be demonstrated by a number of experiments, such as bringing the negatively charged wire of a Leyden jar into contact with two cork balls hanging by silk threads.

In the experiments that illustrate the foregoing principles, Franklin used a " prime conductor " made of tin, five feet long and four inches in diameter, suspended by insulating silk lines. At one end he attached a tassel of fifteen or twenty threads, three inches long.

† This statement refers only to positively electrified bodies. According to Franklin's theory, there is no reason for negatively electrified bodies to have electric atmospheres.

To make sure that the threads conducted as well as possible, he dampened them, but cautioned those who might repeat the experiments against getting the threads soaking wet. With this " preparation " he made three sets of experiments.

In Experiment I he brought an excited glass tube near the end of the prime conductor opposite to the tassel. Sparks were produced and the threads diverged. There could be no question in Franklin's mind that the prime conductor and tassel had become positively charged. Franklin said that the whole prime conductor and each thread acquired a positive charge, or an electric atmosphere. Since each thread had an atmosphere of its own, and since atmospheres always repel one another, the threads diverged. Their several atmospheres do not mix, he added, so there was no possibility that all the threads might " hang in the middle of one atmosphere, common to them all." Today, we would replace the phrase " acquiring an electric atmosphere " by " acquiring a charge," but our explanation is substantially the same.‡ Franklin then gave a fresh positive charge to the glass tube and brought it near the same end of the electrified prime conductor as before, but " crossways " and " not nigh enough to give sparks "; the threads then diverged a little more. The atmosphere of the positively charged rod, he explained, drove the atmosphere of the positively charged tube toward the end of the prime conductor where the threads hung. The threads thereby acquired more fluid or a greater atmosphere and the force of repulsion between them was thus increased. Next, the glass tube was withdrawn and the threads came closer together until their divergence was just the same as it had been before the glass tube had been brought near for the second time. This result was only to be expected, Franklin said, since the atmosphere of the glass tube did not mix with that of the prime conductor. Hence this operation neither increased nor diminished the total quantity of electric fluid on the prime conductor. When Franklin brought the electrified glass tube directly under the threads (but not close enough for a spark), the threads closed; but when the glass tube was removed, they diverged as much as before. The closing of the threads was, according to Franklin, owing to the electric atmosphere of the threads being repelled by that of the rod, and being forced up into the prime conductor, leaving the threads momentarily neutral or with lesser atmospheres, or smaller positive charges. Their final diverging to the previous extent, when the glass tube was withdrawn, came from the fact that the total charge or quantity of electric fluid in the system of prime

‡ This substitution is agreeable to Franklin's theory, since the " atmosphere " contains the excess electric fluid, or the positive charge.

conductor and threads was unaltered. The " portion of atmosphere " which the threads had temporarily " lost, returns to them again." Save for the expression " atmosphere," one might again be reading an electrical treatise of our own day. By bringing the rubbed glass tube near the threads and also near the other end of the electrified tube, all the time taking care that no sparks were produced, Franklin firmly established two confirmatory tests of the sign of the charge he had purposely and definitely given to the tin tube and threads.

In the next series of observations, Experiment II, the threads on the prime conductor were made to diverge without giving the prime conductor a permanent charge, as had been the case in Experiment I. Franklin brought a rubbed glass tube near the end of the prime conductor opposite to that on which the threads were attached. He was extremely careful to prevent the prime conductor from gaining any electric fluid or atmosphere from the glass tube: a condition which would become apparent in the " closing of the threads " on the removal of the glass tube. The threads diverged in this experiment, Franklin said, because they " received electric atmospheres from the electric matter before contained in the substance of the prime-conductor; but which is now repelled and driven away, by the atmosphere of the glass tube, from the parts of the prime-conductor opposite and nearest to that atmosphere, and forced out upon the surface of the prime-conductor at its other end, and upon the threads hanging thereto." Franklin then corrected an idea of Canton's by pointing out that no electric fluid or atmosphere passed from rod to threads during this experiment:

Were it any part of the atmosphere of the glass tube that flowed over and along the prime-conductor to the threads, and gave them atmospheres, (as is the case when a spark is given to the prime-conductor from the glass tube) such part of the tube's atmosphere would have remained, and the threads continue to diverge; but they close on withdrawing the tube, because the tube takes with it *all its own atmosphere*, and the electric matter, which had been driven out of the substance of the prime-conductor, and formed atmospheres round the threads, is thereby permitted to return to its place.

It is clear from the three principles invoked by Franklin at the beginning of his article, and especially from the explanation quoted just above, that the concept of " electric atmospheres " had begun to lose whatever physical reality it might have had earlier. All that Franklin was now saying is that a positively charged body will repel electric fluid from one part of a conductor to another. Even when bodies are close enough so that such action ensues, electric fluid need not actually be transferred, despite the fact that one body is " within " the atmosphere of the other. By " electric atmosphere " Franklin now only meant an accumulation of electric fluid, or positive charge, and no more. He was apparently tacitly accepting the bare fact that charges and charged bodies attract and repel one another, according to their sign, at a distance from one another. The concept of electric atmospheres had been an outgrowth of the old doctrine of effluvia surrounding charged bodies and was in conformity with accepted electrical notions in the 1740's. By means of this concept, it had been possible to explain such phenomena as the electrical repulsion between bodies with the same kind of electrification without invoking either action-at-a-distance or an æther that pervades all of space. Franklin had now reached a new position and he was willing to assume that the repulsion between particles of electric fluid, whatever the cause, might be sufficient to explain phenomena. There are a number of reasons for Franklin's attitude as expressed in the article under consideration. The concept of electric atmospheres had produced a satisfactory explanation of the repulsion of two positively charged bodies by a kind of extended contact reaching across space, but it was of no help whatever in explaining the similar repulsion between two negatively charged bodies. The undeniable facts of repulsion in the latter case—or, at least, a " mutual receding " —which Franklin explored in the second part of his book, rendered the whole doctrine of electric atmospheres less general than it had seemed at first. If this concept could not be applied universally, it was not very satisfactory.

The doctrine of electric atmospheres, essentially a device for showing how bodies might act at a place where they were not, had the virtue of distinguishing force (we would say " field ") from charge. In the most important example, the Leyden jar, Franklin had shown how a positive charge on one conductor may induce a negative charge on a second grounded conductor through the glass of the bottle. In this case, the excess electric fluid added to one conductor was supposed to repel fluid away from the other, even though no fluid permeated the glass. But if no fluid whatever permeated the glass §—and this was a point on which Franklin and his followers always insisted—then the atmosphere could certainly not permeate the glass to produce the repulsion, since the atmosphere was by definition merely electric fluid in a rarefied condition in the neighborhood of a positively charged body. Finally, in the experiments just described the atmosphere of the excited glass tube must have extended out far enough to envelope part of the prime conductor. If the atmosphere was electric fluid in an attenuated state, some of it

§ Unless the glass had a crack in it or had been rendered conductive by heat—and then the jar could not be charged at all.

would attach itself to the prime conductor and leave it positively charged as Canton had assumed. But this did not happen in Franklin's experiments and he no longer insisted on the literal sense which he had formerly given to electric atmospheres.

One of Franklin's experiments was to ground the prime conductor and give it a residual charge by induction. He caused the threads to diverge as before by bringing the charged glass tube near the other end of the prime conductor. Then, while the threads were diverged, he touched the prime conductor momentarily with his finger, drawing a spark. The threads then closed. When he removed his finger and withdrew the glass tube, the threads diverged once again and remained in this state, indicating that the prime conductor had become charged. The glass tube brought near the prime conductor, according to Franklin's previous explanation, had caused some of the normal quantity of electric matter in the tube to be repelled and to collect at the threads. Grounding the prime conductor robbed it of some of its normal quantity of electricity, removing from the threads " their atmospheres, composed of the electric matter driven out of the substance of the prime conductor, as aforesaid." When the finger was removed and the glass tube withdrawn, the tube and threads were in a state of negative charge. Some of the tube's " natural quantity " of electric matter had been lost in the spark. None had been " supplied by the glass tube, for when that is afterwards withdrawn, it takes with it its whole atmosphere, and leaves the prime-conductor electrised negatively." Franklin proved that the threads were negatively charged by bringing the glass tube under them, whereupon they diverged further. Franklin said that the threads became more negative in this case " because more of their natural quantity is driven from them into the prime-conductor, and thereby their negative electricity increased." But if the excited glass tube were brought near the other end of the prime conductor, the end away from the tassel, the threads collapsed. The reason, as Franklin said, is that the repulsion of the glass tube causes some electric fluid from the prime conductor to move into the threads, overcoming their negative state or restoring to them their natural quantity of electric fluid. This explanation has stood the test of time and is as basic today in the explanation of this class of phenomena as it was when it was invented two centuries ago.

Franklin's explanation of the phenomena of charging by induction may not by itself seem very remarkable to those who will simply recognize in it what is virtually the accepted teaching today—except that at present the " fluid " is considered to be made up of negative particles, so that the negative (and not the positive) state of electrification represents a sort of " overplus of fluid." But we can measure the importance of Franklin's contribution to this subject by comparing his crystal-clear statements to Canton's somewhat imperfect discussion—keeping in mind that Canton was a leading electrician of the time, the discoverer of the very important phenomenon that by using different rubbing materials a given substance (e. g., glass) can be charged either negatively or positively. The smooth working of Franklin's theory to account for electrostatic induction is another example of the easy way in which his concepts could be accommodated to one new kind of observation after another. Franklin's final contribution to electrical science displays, once again, his ability to think through the data of experiment to find a satisfactory clarification that would not violate basic physical principles.

In reading Franklin's paper, we may particularly admire the way in which he carefully kept distinct the effects of producing electrification according to three separate processes. The first is to give an insulated conductor the same kind of charge as an electrified body by bringing the two so close together that a spark passes between them. There is no essential difference between this manner of charging a conductor and an actual " physical " contact between the conductor and an electrified body; in both cases the conductor gains a charge of the same sign as the electrified body. In the second, there is no spark, and the effect of bringing an electrified body near an insulated conductor is only to effect a temporary unequal charge distribution on the conductor—lasting only so long as the electrified body is in the immediate neighborhood. In the third, the situation is like the previous one, save that the conductor is momentarily grounded and ends up with a charge of opposite sign to that of the electrified body producing the effect. Franklin clearly distinguished the charges produced by induction from those produced by contact (or a spark) and he studied separately the effects produced by a charged body on a conductor that is insulated and one that is grounded. When the word "atmosphere" was eliminated, these phenomena were presented in a way that has not required much alteration ever since, save to become subject to the refinements of computation.

The presentation of Canton's and Franklin's work on electrostatic induction has been based on the assumption that Franklin's explanations represent a considerable improvement on Canton's. The basis of this opinion is that I have found it possible to reproduce Franklin's experiments exactly as he described them. To obtain the results presented by Canton, however, has proved to be more difficult—and it has been necessary to assume that some accidental grounding or a leakage of charge occurred. Canton's explanations were unnecessarily complicated because his experiments did not always distinguish the effects of each parameter with sufficient clarity. I must admit, however, to an obvious bias in favor of Franklin's ideas: reinforced by the fact that, in the physics courses I took as a student and in the course I now teach, these experiments have been and are presented just as Franklin described them and the explanation is very similar to Franklin's. Yet the fact that almost every textbook on the subject today follows Franklin—wittingly or unwittingly—does not necessarily imply that two hundred years ago there would have been a concurrence with our judgment. As always, we must exercise the greatest caution whenever our historical evaluations may be conditioned by the present state of physical explanation.

To clarify this point, we may turn to Joseph Priestley's superb account of the rise of electricity. Priestley said that the subject of induced charges (the behavior of " bodies immersed in electric atmospheres ") presents to the reader " the finest series of experiments that the whole history of electricity can exhibit." [5] He had found that this set of investigations " displayed the genius and address of four of the most eminent electricians in this whole period; *viz.* Mr. Canton and Mr. Franklin, Englishmen; and Messrs. Wilcke and Æpinus, foreigners." According to Priestley, Canton made " all the essential experiments," and Franklin merely " diversified the experiments, and made some improvement in the method of accounting for them." Doctor Franklin, he wrote, " professedly " pursued these experiments, but—and Priestley underlined these words " *all his strength he put not forth* on this occasion." What bothered Priestley, apparently, was the fact that Franklin held " the common opinion of electric atmospheres," and yet did not make use of the supposed physical properties of these atmospheres at all. Priestley did not like Franklin's " supposition " that if two bodies with electric atmospheres were brought near to each other, the atmospheres would not mix, but would remain distinct and repel each other. He was puzzled by Franklin's notion that an electric atmosphere might repel the electric fluid normally in an uncharged conductor and, " without joining or mixing with it, force it into the other parts of the body that contained it." Priestley found it " difficult to assign a reason " why the force of repulsion exerted by the particles of one atmosphere on those of another atmosphere, or on the particles of fluid in another body, should be stronger than the force of repulsion among the particles of electric fluid composing an electric atmosphere or the repulsion between such particles and the particles of electric fluid within the very body to which the atmosphere pertains. If only one could accept Franklin's " idea of the mutual repulsion of electric atmospheres," said Priestley, then one could " certainly and clearly account for all the facts " by means of a " theory [that] pleases on account of its simplicity." [6] Priestley suggested a possible hypothesis of his own invention, followed by a description of the experiments of Wilcke and Æpinus, which led them to a rejection of the whole doctrine of electric atmospheres. The work of Æpinus, in particular, was based on a fundamental additional postulate to the Franklin system,* the first major revision of the one-fluid theory of electricity, which enabled Franklinians to explain the repulsive action between both negatively and positively charged bodies.†

The Repulsion between Negatively Charged Bodies

The third " principle " stated by Franklin in his paper on electrostatic induction is that negatively charged bodies repel one another just like positively charged bodies. There was no way to avoid the data of experiment and at least two courses were, therefore, possible. One was to assume that the repulsion between positively charged bodies is due to their electric atmospheres, but a different cause must be assigned to the repulsion between negatively charged bodies. Another was to suppose that a different type of explanation altogether might explain the repulsion between any two bodies with the same kind of electrification. Franklin did not appear to make a choice between such alternatives. He did not use the physical properties of electric atmospheres, and so might have appeared to have sanctioned a belief that a new explanation should be found for both kinds of electrification: perhaps such repulsions were merely to become part of the axioms of the theory. On the other hand, Franklin's statements could also be interpreted to mean that the two types of repulsion were different since he had said that negatively charged bodies only " appear " to repel each other " by a mutual receding." This question could not be avoided in discussions of the cause of electrical phenomena and it became a focal point for evaluating the merits of the whole Franklinian theory.

In the 1769 edition of Franklin's book on electricity, there was a letter from Kinnersley who had begun to doubt the " doctrine of repulsion in electrised bodies." [8] Perhaps " all the phænomena on which it is founded, may be well enough accounted for without it." Since cork balls separate equally far when negatively or positively

---

* See, below, pages 537-543.

† Priestley's statement about Franklin's contribution to the subject of electrostatic induction shows that he failed to grasp the connection between Franklin's original explanation of this phenomenon in the Leyden jar and the later variations invented by Canton and Franklin himself. Priestley's book has influenced every later account of electricity in the eighteenth century. Perhaps this explains the contrary-to-fact descriptions of Canton's and Franklin's experiments in many books and articles. [7]

electrified, Kinnersley suggested a new principle to account for both: " the mutual attraction of the natural quantity [of electricity] in the air, and that which is denser or rarer in the cork-balls." This principle was in harmony, he said with " one of the established laws of this fluid, that quantities of different densities shall mutually attract each other, in order to restore the equilibrium." Franklin's reply, printed immediately after Kinnersley's letter in the 1769 edition of Franklin's book,‡ is dated 20 February 1762. Franklin too had " always looked upon and mentioned the equal repulsion in cases of positive and negative electricity, as a phænomenon difficult to be explained." [9] From time to time, Franklin said, he had also been inclined " to resolve all into attraction." Yet, he said, " attraction seems in itself as unintelligible as repulsion." Furthermore, there are " some appearances of repulsion " that he could not " so easily explain by attraction." Chief among these was the set of experimental results he had reported as a complement to Canton's studies on induced charges:

. . . When the pair of cork balls are suspended by flaxen threads, from the end of the prime conductor, if you bring a rubbed glass tube near the conductor, but without touching it, you see the balls separate, as being electrified positively; and yet you have communicated no electricity to the conductor, for, if you had, it would have remained there, after withdrawing the tube; but the closing of the balls immediately thereupon, shews that the conductor has no more left in it than its natural quantity. Then again approaching the conductor with the rubbed tube, if, while the balls are separated, you touch with a finger that end of the conductor to which they hang, they will come together again, as being, with that part of the conductor, brought to the same state with your finger, i. e. the natural state. But the other end of the conductor, near which the tube is held, is not in that state, but in the negative state, as appears on removing the tube; for then part of the natural quantity left at the end near the balls, leaving that end to supply what is wanting at the other, the whole conductor is found to be equally in the negative state.

Franklin's conclusion from these " appearances " was as follows:

Does not this indicate that the electricity of the rubbed tube had repelled the electric fluid, which was diffused in the conductor while in its natural state, and forced it to quit the end to which the tube was brought near, accumulating itself on the end to which the balls were suspended? I own I find it difficult to account for its quitting that end, on the approach of the rubbed tube, but on the supposition of repulsion; for, while the conductor was in the same state with the air, i. e. the natural state, it does

‡ These two letters, although read at the Royal Society, were published for the first time in the 1769 edition of Franklin's book on electricity.

not seem to me easy to suppose, that an attraction should suddenly take place between the air and the natural quantity of the electric fluid in the conductor, so as to draw it to, and accumulate it on the end opposite to that approached by the tube; since bodies, possessing only their natural quantity of that fluid, are not usually seen to attract each other, or to affect mutually the quantities of electricity each contains.

In further support of his point of view Franklin then listed some " appearances of repulsion in other parts of nature." The particles of water, when sufficiently heated, separate from one another with a " violent force "; so do the particles of gunpowder " when touched with the smallest spark of fire." Then there is " the seeming repulsion " between the similar poles of magnets which Franklin assumed to contain " a subtle moveable fluid, in many respects analogous to the electric fluid." If, then, he concluded, " repulsion exists in nature, and in magnetism, why may it not exist in electricity? "

Having established his own position, he next showed that what Kinnersley had assumed to be " an established law of the electric fluid " was not " well founded " or " not well expressed." It was certainly not consistent with the data of experiment to say, as Kinnersley had done, " that quantities of different densities mutually attract each other, in order to restore the equilibrium." Franklin suggested an experiment which would convince his friend that he had been wrong. Two balls, let us say A and B, suspended on insulating silk strings, were " well and equally electrified," so as to separate to a " great distance." Then a contact was made between one of these balls, say A, and an identical but electrically neutral ball C, also hanging on an insulating string. This contact should, according to theory, divide the charge on that ball A between it and the neutral ball C brought into contact with it. Hence, if balls A and B each had, at the start of the experiment, a charge Q, A would now have a charge $\frac{1}{2}Q$, B a charge Q, and C a charge $\frac{1}{2}Q$. The ball C was then removed; the force of repulsion between balls A and B was reduced from what it had been at first, so that ball B now hung " at a less distance from the other." In this situation, Franklin said, one ball has twice the charge of the other, so that the density of fluid must be different in the two; yet " the full and the half quantities will not appear to attract each other, that is, the balls will not come together."

As a matter of fact, Franklin knew of no proof that one quantity of electric fluid will ever be " attracted by another quantity of that fluid, whatever difference there may be in their densities." It would be a curious law of attraction, Franklin said, if the attractive force between two " parcels of any kind of matter " would be great when the two " parcels " were unequal and cease altogether " when more matter of the same kind " was added to the smaller " parcel " to make it equal to the larger one. In the case of matter, Franklin added, the attraction was always stronger when " in proportion to the increase of the masses, and never in proportion to the difference of the masses." Hence, the law should be, " That the electric fluid is attracted strongly by all other matter that we know of, while the parts of that fluid mutually repel each other." It can be argued, of course, that Franklin answered Kinnersley but skipped the main issue. Could he not have given Kinnersley's statement a more favorable interpretation by saying that if two bodies both undergo an increase, or both undergo a decrease, in the density of their electric fluid, there will be repulsion? And that if one undergoes an increase, and the other a decrease, in the density of their electric fluid, there will be attraction? Had he done so, however, he would merely have been restating the fundamental proposition that bodies with the same kind of charge repel, while those with opposite signs of charge attract one another. In this way there would have been nothing new or helpful added to what had already been said.

Without question, there was a need for admitting that two electrified bodies with the same sort of charge will always repel each other. But Franklin had no contribution to make to the problem of why two negatively charged bodies repel each other.

Why Bodies Become Positively or Negatively Charged

When Franklin had originally formulated the theory of electricity that bears his name, he had little to say on the subject of why some bodies gain electric fluid on being rubbed, while others lose fluid. Then Kinnersley suggested that a rubbed sulphur globe probably loses electric fluid in a manner similar to the gain of electric fluid by a rubbed glass globe, which appeared to have been confirmed by Franklin's experiments. Thus it seemed likely that the nature of the rubbed substance might determine whether it loses or gains electric fluid. In a paper read at the Royal Society on 14 November 1754, John Canton tackled this subject in a strikingly original way. Glass, he said, had been supposed to gain electric fluid on rubbing because of its expansion by the frictional heat; it could then receive " more of the electric fluid than its natural share." This explanation has obvious faults, Canton noted, chief amongst them the fact that identical considerations do not apply to rubbed sealing wax or sulphur which part with some of their normal electric fluid. Canton was a brilliant member of that school of experimental philosophers who did not believe that speculation can solve fundamental problems in science, so he turned to experiment and discovered that the kind of charge given to a body by rubbing does not depend alone on the material of which it is made.[10]

Canton altered the surface of the traditional glass tube by rubbing it with " a piece of thin sheet-lead and flower of emery mixt with water " until it was no longer transparent. After the tube had been carefully washed and dried, it was rubbed with new flannel and was then found to act " in all respects like excited sulphur or sealing-wax." In other words, the altered (" rough or unpolished ") piece of glass seemed to gain a negative charge, the opposite of the positive charge that glass usually acquires when rubbed with flannel. This altered glass tube could also be given the customary charge (made to " act like a glass tube with its natural polish ") if it was rubbed with " a piece of dry oiled silk (especially when rubbed over with a little chalk or whiting) ." Canton also found that if the rough tube were " greased all over with tallow from a candle " and then rubbed with oiled silk (so it " will receive a kind of polish "), the same effect followed as when the tube had been " excited at first by flannel," i. e., there was a negative charge on the tube. But if the silk was covered with chalk or whiting, then the " greased rough tube " acted just like a normally polished one. Furthermore, if only one half of the glass tube was roughened in the above manner, both types of charge were produced simultaneously on the tube by a single stroke of flannel, a positive charge at one end and a negative charge at the other. Thus, Canton concluded, " the positive and negative powers of electricity may be produced at pleasure, by altering the surfaces of the tube and rubber." [11]

Franklin had asked other investigators to pay special attention to the experimental evidence he had used in deciding which is the positive and which the negative state of electrification. Canton was an ardent Franklinian and in these experiments he identified the positively and negatively charged states of a glass rod on the criteria that Franklin had suggested. He characterized the positive and negative states by the difference in the appearance of the discharge produced in air by a given electrified body. After the rough glass tube had been rubbed with flannel, Canton brought a knuckle or finger close to it and the " electric fire " seemed " to issue from the knuckle, or end of the finger " and to " spread itself on the surface of the tube " in a " beautiful manner." A number of handsome illustrations accompanied Canton's articles, to show the several types of discharge observed during the course of his experiments. In the positive state, the discharge appeared as " a great number of diverging pencils of electric fire." These " pencils " issued from " a polished glass tube, when excited by smooth oiled silk, if the hand be kept at least three inches from the top of the rubber," but Canton never observed this phenomenon when he rubbed pieces of sulphur, seal-ing-wax, and other resinous substances under the same conditions.

Canton and Franklin, and many of their contemporaries, assumed that in any electrical discharge there is a visible flow of electric fluid. Hence spark, or brush, coronal or glow discharges were taken as signs of the direction in which electric fluid moves away from bodies with an excess of fluid or toward bodies with a deficiency of fluid. They were, of course mistaken, but the error was not fully apparent until a century and a half later, when physical science had advanced to such a state that the production of light in association with the movement or production of ions in the air could be comprehended. But even though Canton had not found any new criteria for deciding whether vitreous electrification corresponds to a gain in electric fluid, he had shown beyond any doubt that the kind of electrification a body receives depends on the nature of its surface in relation to the surface of the rubbing material.

This notion was quickly picked up by other Franklinists. Wilcke, in his German translation of Franklin's book (1758), inserted an *Anmerkung* [12] in which he made a list of materials, which if rubbed together would gain contrary electrifications.* Wilcke's findings may be tabulated in part as follows: [14]

Experiment	Substance obtaining posi-tive charge	Substance obtaining nega-tive charge
Sulphur rubbed against glass	glass	sulphur
Sulphur rubbed against sealing wax	sealing wax	sulphur
Wood rubbed with cloth	[cloth]	wood
Wood rubbed against smooth glass	[smooth glass]	wood
Wood rubbed against rough glass	wood	[rough glass]
Sulphur rubbed against lead	lead	sulphur
Sulphur rubbed against other metals	sulphur	[metals]

---

* Wilcke's findings were also published in his *Disputatio physica experimentalis de electricitatibus contrariis* (Rostock, 1757). Of this work Priestley said, in the bibli-ography to his history of electricity: "This admirable treatise consists of four parts, but, to my great regret, the copy which I had contained only the three first of them. It was that which the author sent to Dr. Franklin, before the remainder was printed." [13]

As a result of such experiments, Wilcke made a list of common substances used in electrical experiments, in which the electro-positive and electro-negative properties appear in sequence. The place of each substance in this sequence indicates its disposition to acquire a positive or a negative charge, since any member of the list exhibits a positive charge if rubbed with a substance lower down on the list and a negative charge if rubbed with a substance above it in the list:

> Smooth glass,
> Woolen cloth,
> Quills,
> Wood,
> Paper,
> Sealing wax,
> White wax,
> Rough glass,
> Lead,
> Sulphur,
> Other metals.

A sequence such as Wilcke's is called today a " tribo-electric " series.

At the present time, our knowledge of phenomena arising from surface contacts is far from complete. " Explanations " are readily available about how one of the surfaces gains a negative charge because it has a greater " electron affinity " than the second surface which gains a positive charge. Yet, in the absence of direct experimental evidence on the effect of such contact, a description of all other chemical and physical properties of some new materials would not enable us to predict in every case which of two bodies would have the greater " electron affinity." Boyle warned that the mechanical philosophy has no place in it for such pre-mechanical qualities as " love " or " hate," but " affinity " has never been discarded— " chemical affinity " still clouds the literature of that subject. Two centuries after the work of Franklin, and of Canton and Wilcke, the problem of electrification by friction (or contact) is still partly shrouded in mystery.

Æpinus's Revision of the Franklinian Theory

The investigations begun by Canton led to knowledge that when contact is made between two surfaces, both may receive charges of opposite sign. This result agreed with the principle of conservation of change and did not violate the conclusions of the one-fluid theory of electricity. But these discoveries were related only to the conditions under which charges appear, and they did not help men to explain the repulsion between negatively charged bodies, or even to answer the question as to whether there was a fluid of electricity, as Franklin had postulated.

In the second half of the eighteenth century two explanations were suggested of the apparent repulsion of bodies supposedly deprived of some of their electric fluid. There was the theory that was based on a rejection of Franklin's concept that vitreous electrification is a negative state corresponding to a loss of electric matter. This theory introduced two electric fluids rather than the single fluid postulated by Franklin. The second way in which this puzzling phenomenon was explained was to revise the Franklinian theory in one important aspect. This alteration of Franklin's system was devised by Franz Ulrich Theodor Æpinus (or Œpinus, Epinus), the teacher and later collaborator of Wilcke. Æpinus was a leading member of the Berlin and St. Petersburg academies and was known in the early and mid-1750's for his research on the production of electric charges by the application of heat. In a treatise entitled *Tentamen Theoriæ Electricitatis et Magnetismi*, published in St. Petersburg in 1759, Æpinus introduced a new postulate into the Franklinian theory of electricity, one which made that theory more universal but destroyed in part its great simplicity. Thereafter, the "one-fluid theory" of electricity generally came to mean the Franklin theory as emended by Æpinus. Since this revision was accepted by most Franklinians, we must consider it carefully.

Æpinus began his treatise with a statement of five fundamental propositions to which the electrical theory of Franklin can be reduced—that theory "which agrees with phenomena in so fine and admirable a manner." [15] One cannot find fault with Æpinus's résumé of Franklin's theory and his resolution of it into the five axioms. Æpinus called attention to Franklin's insistence on the impermeability of glass to the electric fluid which he said "Franklin thinks is necessary to explain the phenomena of the Leyden jar." Æpinus wondered whether this "most perspicuous gentleman" did not perceive that this impermeability," or the power of resisting the passage of the electric fluid " is not only a property of glass but of all bodies called electrics *per se* (or "idio-electrics").§

As that most famous gentleman so correctly observed, bodies electric *per se* are those with pores through which electric matter cannot flow without difficulty. It is obvious at first glance that it is absolutely the

---

§ The following translations have been made freely from the original Latin of Æpinus. So far as I know, Æpinus's treatise was never reprinted nor has it ever been translated into any other language.

same thing whether a body is called electric *per se*, or impermeable with regard to electric fluid.*

Therefore I hold it entirely superfluous to add the mention of the impermeability of the glass when the general bases of electricity are to be established, because neither is impermeability a specific quality of glass, nor is it inherent in glass.[16]

Æpinus said that his aim was to deal with the causes of magnetic and electric phenomena, from which he would derive the positive principles of the Franklinian theory of electricity and his own theory of magnetism. Hence, before going more deeply into the subject of electricity, he would present the bases of the theory of magnetism:

. . . I suppose that all magnetic phenomena can be derived from the following few principles, extremely similar to those on which the Franklinian electrical theory is built.

(*a*) There exists a fluid which produces all the magnetic phenomena, on account of which it is called magnetic. It is very subtle and capable of passing through the pores of some bodies. Its parts, like those of the electric fluid, mutually repel one another.

(*β*) This fluid suffers no action on the part of many bodies which are met with in the world, and is neither attracted by them nor repelled.

(*γ*) There also exists a certain kind of body, the parts of which attract the magnetic mater and in turn are attracted by it. The body which holds the first rank in having this property is iron, and also all of the bodies called ferrous. The latter, which contain iron, as also various iron ores, include the well-known stone called magnet, a kind of black sand in Virginia also frequently found on the shores of the Baltic, and other bodies of this kind.

(*δ*) There is in iron and ferrous bodies a great similarity with bodies electric *per se*. Just as in the latter the electric fluid, so in the former the magnetic fluid, moves with difficulty. In fact, it seems the magnetic fluid encounters even greater difficulty in passing through the pores of iron than the electric fluid usually encounters in the pores of bodies electric *per se* until now known to us.

(*ε*) Until now, there is no body known which performs an action in magnetic matter that would be analogous to bodies not electric *per se*. There is, namely, no body whose parts attract magnetic matter and through the pores of which could be observed a free and unimpeded passage of the magnetic fluid. In iron itself it seems that there is a certain gradation in this respect.

The softer the iron is, namely, whether it be pure, or mixed with heterogeneous particles as is the case of ores, the more freely the magnetic fluid moves in it. The harder the iron is, however, the more difficult

* See a somewhat similar statement by Franklin in his discussion of " non-conductors " and " electrics *per se*," page 477, above.

is the motion of the magnetic fluid, so that soft iron comes nearer the analogy with bodies not electric *per se* than hardened iron [steel].[17]

In his comments on Æpinus's book, Franklin expressed admiration for this magnetic theory, constructed along lines so analogous to his own electrical theory. Thus, in the letter to Kinnersley defending the doctrine of repulsion, he wrote of a magnetic fluid in the terms introduced by Æpinus. We have no evidence that Franklin read very far in this book, and his general approbation of it might well have come from an examination of the first twenty or thirty pages and no more. In this case Franklin would have encountered a laudation of his perspicacity, a splendid account of his electrical theory, and a theory of magnetism constructed in harmony with his most cherished preconceptions. But Franklin never referred to the great revision of his theory introduced by Æpinus, though he said: " I think with him that impermeability to the electric fluid is the property of all electrics *per se*. . . ." [18]

The revolutionary idea of Æpinus was that in solids, liquids, and gases the particles of what Franklin called " common matter " repel one another just like the particles of the electric fluid in Franklin's theory. Æpinus's revision introduced a complete duality. The particles of common matter and of electric matter each have the property of repelling particles of their own kind while each kind of particle has the additional property of attracting particles of the other kind.

Æpinus recognized that the concept of the particles of matter having a mutually repulsive force would be repugnant to many physicists. He said that this concept occurred to him when he first began to reflect on Franklin's theory and that he was somewhat horrified by it. As time went on he saw that this concept was not really contrary to the general " analogy of the operations of nature," and he became used to it. The fact is, he explained, that " we observe innumerable cases in nature, where we find attracting and repelling forces inherent in bodies. Hence it is not proper for us to be afraid to speak about this new force detected in bodies among the number of primitive and fundamental forces of nature. What bothered me especially in the beginning was that this proposition seemed to be diametrically opposed to another universal law of nature, discovered by Newton, on the strength of which all bodies are said to attract each other in the direct ratio of their masses and the inverse ratio of the square of the distance." [19]

The natural repulsion among particles of matter is reduced to zero by the magnetic or the electric fluid, Æpinus explained, whenever bodies contain their natural quantity of these fluids. Hence this power of repulsion could actually " be considered as not existing at all, except in the cases where one has to consider phenomena arising from electricity or magnetism." Thus, " it can easily be seen that the universal gravitational attraction of Newton can remain unaffected, even though one admits that there may exist a repulsion of some kind." Yet Æpinus knew that " someone " might think

that there is a contradiction in my assuming that a bodily matter is endowed at the same time with two opposite forces, namely, the repelling and the attracting. I wish he would note that I do not consider either the repelling force here discussed, or the attracting force which is called universal gravity, as forces which are inherent in matter or implanted therein. It is therefore clear that I cannot be guilty of contradiction; indeed I do not assume that these opposite qualities are inherent in any subject; yet though I do not know what means nature uses in order to produce these forces, nevertheless I am also certain that each of these forces has some extrinsic cause. It is not a contradiction, either, to say that the same body at the same time and in the same moment is acted upon by two external and opposite forces." [20]

In its new form, the one-fluid theory of electricity bore a closer similarity to mid-eighteenth-century chemical ideas than it had in Franklin's original exposition: two kinds of matter composed of particles that repel their own kind, the two attracting each other to form a product giving no signs of repulsion.† Æpinus simply assumed, as a consequence of the postulates, that two bodies with positive charges repel each other because of the uncompensated force of repulsion between the excess electric matter on each, and that two bodies with negative charges repel each other because of the uncompensated force of repulsion between the particles of matter on each that have lost their normal complement of electric matter. Æpinus could also explain the unequal distribution of charge on an insulated conductor near a charged body on the basis of simple repulsion at-a-distance without even mentioning the words " electric atmosphere," and he concluded that the excess fluid on positively charged bodies is merely lodged in their surface.

The rejection of the doctrine of atmospheres was made necessary by the experiments devised earlier by Æpinus, together with Wilcke, on air-separated condensers. Although Wilson had created such a device, he had not recognized its similarity to a Leyden jar, nor had Franklin.‡ Æpinus and Wilcke [21] discovered that when a charge of one sign was placed on one of the plates, a charge of the opposite

---

†See Chapter Seven. It should be observed that the similarity was incomplete in so far as in Æpinus's theory, the particles of matter did not compose a fluid.

‡ See, above, pages 408, 474.

sign was induced on the other plate if grounded; just as Franklin had found to be the case in the Leyden jar.§ Furthermore, there were times when the " electricity " would be discharged spontaneously by a spark passing between the two plates, a phenomenon recognized as similar to the breaking of the glass in a jar when charged with too much electricity.[23]

Æpinus knew that his denial of the existence of atmospheres was a radical step, setting his ideas apart from everyone who had ever written about the one-fluid theory—including the " celebrated Franklin." He therefore reviewed some of the evidence usually considered to show that some sort of atmosphere or vortex or cloud of effluvia surrounds an electrified body.[24] From the time of Boyle and Hauksbee, if not earlier, the sulphureous smell and the tingling feeling on the skin when a person was close to an electrified body was considered to prove the existence of such effluvia, vortices, and atmospheres. Æpinus suggested that this sensation in the skin could very well arise from the action of the charged body on the electric fluid in the nostrils or hands of the person feeling the " electric wind " or other sensation. He made an experiment to test the effect of electric atmospheres by blowing a stream of dry air on a charged body and found, as Franklin before him, that the charge on the body was not diminished.* It might have been expected that the air would remove the particles of electric fluid loosely held together in a cloud around the body. Franklin had assumed that such experiments only indicated that the atmosphere of each charged body becomes an integral part of it, and so had come to consider an electric atmosphere in almost a figurative sense, although at first he had thought to make the atmosphere " visible " by dropping rosin on a hot piece of iron near a charged body. But Æpinus carried the matter through to its logical conclusion and said that by " electric atmos-

---

§ Priestley said of the parallel plate condenser with air separation: " This discovery, of the method of giving the electric shock by means of a plate of air, may be reckoned one of the greatest discoveries in the science of electricity since those of Dr. Franklin. It is beautiful to observe how this fine discovery took its rise from the experiments of Mr. Canton. Mr. Canton's experiments were pursued by Dr. Franklin, and those of Dr. Franklin, pursued by these gentlemen, produced the discovery. It is one and the same principle that, in different circumstances, accounts for this beautiful series of experiments.

" This experiment of charging a plate of air is likewise related by Mr. Æpinus, who says that he was led to the discovery, by reasoning from the consequences of Dr. Franklin's theory." [22]

* One of Franklin's experiments had been to charge a ball that was fastened to an end of an insulating string and then rapidly to whirl the ball around by the string. No diminution in charge was produced.

phere " he would intend only to denote the " sphere of action " of the electric charge on a body.†

By the last quarter of the eighteenth century, there was general agreement that there are no physical atmospheres ‡ or clouds of electric matter around positively charged bodies and that the word atmosphere should be given the general sense suggested by Æpinus.§ With the disappearance of this concept, all explanations of electrical phenomena seem to have been interpreted in the light of action-at-a-distance. Like Franklin and other Newtonians, Æpinus held that the property of attraction or repulsion was not innate in either particles of matter or of electric and magnetic fluid, and that these powers arose externally. But he did not find it necessary to explore any of these possible external circumstances, such as a subtle all-pervading medium, because the amended one-fluid theory of electricity worked perfectly in terms of its own postulates without any such considerations. It was not until the time of Faraday in the next century that some physical scientists recognized the importance of paying close attention to the space between charged and magnetic bodies, to the medium and not the bodies themselves.

Symmer's Dualistic Theory

The beautiful experiments of Canton and Wilcke should have prepared men's minds for the fact that contact between two different materials is apt to give them contrary electrifications, a phenomenon fully in harmony with the single-fluid theory of electricity which both Canton and Wilcke endorsed. The experiments of Gray and Du Fay had placed upon record the variation in electrical properties of materials treated with different dyes. It is, therefore, difficult for us to understand why so much interest was aroused by the experiments of Robert Symmer, reported in the *Philosophical Transactions* for 1759. Symmer had noticed that his stockings crackled and snapped and emitted sparks when he took them off in dry weather.

---

† Priestley said that Beccaria " was probably prior to Mr. Æpinus in supposing that electrified bodies have no other atmosphere than the electricity communicated to the neighbouring air." [25]

‡ The crucial failure of the doctrine of atmospheres occurs in such an experiment as Franklin's and Canton's: bringing a positively charged glass tube near an insulated tin tube. Surely, some of the mutually repellent particles of fluid supposed to surround the glass tube would be transferred to the tin tube and leave it charged positively—but this does not happen if the experiment is performed carefully. By the same reasoning, an air-separated condenser would have a negatively charged plate inside the atmosphere of the nearby positively charged plate; under such conditions both plates should lose their charges at once—but they do not.

§ A typical late eighteenth-century remark is: " The sphere of an excited electric's influence, or the distance to which it will extend its repellent or attractive effects. . . ." [26]

This phenomenon was especially marked when he wore black silk stockings over white worsted ones, and separated them upon their removal from his leg. Two white silk stockings produced no such effect. If he wore a black and white silk stocking on his leg, they showed strong signs of electrification when he took them off and separated them, and the same effect ensued when he wore black and white worsted stockings. After a number of experiments Symmer concluded that " the operations of electricity do not depend on one single positive power, . . . but on two distinct, positive, and acting powers; which by contrasting, and, as it were, counteracting each other, produce the various phenomena of electricity." In a positively charged body, he said, there is not " a larger share of electric matter than in a natural state," but only " a larger portion of one of those active powers." A negatively charged body does not, then, have a deficiency of electric matter, but only a larger portion of the "other" active power.[27]

Symmer produced an experiment to support his views. This experiment was described by Priestley as " a remarkable instance of the power of an hypothesis in drawing facts to itself, in making proofs out of facts which are very ambiguous, and in making a person overlook those circumstances in an experiment which are unfavourable to his views." [28] Symmer gave a Leyden jar a small charge and discharged it by bringing a finger of one hand to the coating and a finger of the other hand to the wire; the sensation he felt did not go beyond his fingers. When he repeated the experiment with a larger charge, the sensation was felt up to the wrists and no further; a still larger charge produced a sensation up to the elbows but a very large charge produced a shock which he felt in his chest. Hence, he argued, the positive and negative states in the two conductors must correspond to two powers, one lodged in each, which penetrate into the body to a degree determined by their relative strength.[29] Priestley pointed out that when twenty persons join hands, they may all be made to feel the shock in their wrists and elbows, " without having their breasts affected in the least. And can it be supposed, that the two currents of electric fire could come at all their wrists and elbows, without passing through their breasts? " *

A second type of experiment was based on Symmer's supposition that " if an electrical stroke should be made to pass through a solid

* Priestley said: "According to Mr. Symmer's hypothesis, it should seem, that, in a large circle, those persons only who stood near the phial, on either hand, should feel a small shock; that a few persons more, at each extremity of the circle, should feel one something stronger; and that it could only be a very strong shock, which could at all affect the person who stood in the middle; and that then he should be affected the least of any person in the company. But all these consequences are contrary to fact." [30]

body, with so much force as to pierce and tear the substance of it, such marks would be left, as might enable us, with certainty, to trace the course of the electrical power in its passage through the body." Symmer had no apparatus of his own capable of producing effects of this sort, so he appealed, as he said,

to a worthy member of this Society, Doctor Franklin, who was possessed of a very good one. I had communicated all my observations to this gentleman as they occurred, and, in return, met with an ingenuity and candour, that render him as estimable in private life, as the improvements he has introduced into electricity, and particularly his discovery in relation to thunder and lightning, will render his reputation lasting in the learned world. We differed in opinion with regard to the point in question; nevertheless I found him ready to give me all the assistance in his power, for bringing the matter to a fair decision.[31]

By examining the holes in the sheets of paper pierced by an electric discharge, Symmer convinced himself that two powers are active, one entering in one direction and the other in a contrary direction. In some of his experiments he used a quire of paper, or a book, with sheets of tin foil between some of the pages. Curiously enough, the outermost sheets of paper were ragged " about the orifice, and those ragged edges pointed mostly outwards from the body of the quire." Symmer did not include in his report any information about Franklin's reactions to these findings, although Franklin was present when some of the experiments were performed. Symmer's theory is not mentioned in any of Franklin's correspondence which I have seen and there is ample evidence that Franklin never gave up his theory. Franklin's words of caution about the interpretation to be given to empirical evidence relating to the direction of flow of electric matter has already been discussed; he surely could not have accepted Symmer's experiments as a proof of the failure of his own theory.† The contrary electrification produced in two stockings could be readily explained in terms of the one-fluid theory of electricity, and offered another instance of the conservation of charge. Thus, Franklin actually referred to this part of Symmer's work in the 1769 edition of his book on electricity.[32] Symmer did not relate his experiments on stockings to his new hypothesis, being content—as Priestley said— to do " little more than relate naked facts." But these experiments " were diversified, and pursued much further by Mr. Cigna, of Turin, who has also explained them upon the principles of Dr. Franklin's theory; though he was of opinion, that no experiments

† Franklin had always said that the appearance of burrs or ragged edges, when a spark was made to pass through wood or paper, did not give reliable evidence as to the direction of motion of the electric fluid. See page 507 above.

that had yet been made were decisive in favour of either of the two hypotheses." [33]

Symmer's lengthy account of his experiments concluded with a brief theoretical statement. Throughout, he had used the notion of "two distinct electrical powers, acting in contrary directions." Thus, he said, it might seem as if he merely held to the opinions of M. l'Abbé Nollet. But Nollet had written of only one kind of electricity, as if the two contrary currents (or simultaneous affluences and effluences) consisted of "but one and the same fluid." Symmer held a quite different view,

> that there are two electrical fluids (or emanations of two distinct electrical powers) essentially different from each other; that electricity does not consist in the efflux and afflux of those fluids, but in the accumulation of the one or the other in the body electrified; or, in other words, it consists in the possession of a larger portion of the one or of the other power, than is requisite to maintain an even ballance within the body; and, lastly, that according as the one or the other power prevails, the body is electrified in one or in another manner.[34]

The Law of Electrical Force

In presenting the subject of electrical theory up to this point, I have avoided any of the mathematical developments. Plainly, the great desideratum was to discover the law of electrical attraction and repulsion. Æpinus developed a singularly beautiful mathematical theory of electricity, based on considerations of the forces of repulsion between particles of matter and between particles of electric matter and the forces of attraction between particles of the two kinds—but he did not specify the quantity of force under different conditions.‡ He apparently assumed that these forces most likely vary inversely as the squares of the distances between particles, in analogy with the Newtonian gravitational force, but he had no basis whatever to support his guess and he did not insist on it.[35] By reflecting on Franklin's experiments, which showed that inside a charged cylinder there is no electrical force,[36] Priestley concluded that the electrical force follows an inverse-square law. His argument was Newtonian, based on Newton's proof that only in the case of an inverse-square law will there be no field of force within a spherical shell.[37] Although published in the many editions of Priestley's book on electricity (in English, French, and German) beginning with the *editio princeps* of 1767, Priestley's brilliant deduction went un-

---

‡ Perhaps this is the reason why Æpinus's mathematical theory of electricity has never gained the place it would have deserved if it had not been invented too early, before the exact law of electrical force was known.

noticed. Most likely, the argument was too sophisticated for the state of electrical science. Furthermore, Franklin's experiment was made with a cylinder and not a sphere. Cavendish contrived a variation of Franklin's experiment to prove that practically no charge exists on the inner surface of a charged sphere and inferred that the law of electrical repulsion and attraction cannot depart from the inverse square by more than one part in fifty. But Cavendish did not publish his result and it remained in his manuscript notes for a century until rediscovered and printed by Clerk Maxwell.§ Cavendish, who served with Franklin on the committee appointed by the Royal Society to study lightning rods, published only two papers on electricity in his lifetime: one on the torpedo and another an elegant improvement on the mathematical theory of Æpinus. In the latter paper, printed in the *Philosophical Transactions* for 1771, he said that since he " first wrote " it he had found that " this way of accounting for the phænomena of electricity is not new. Æpinus, in his *Tentamen Theoriæ Electricitatis et Magnetismi,* has made use of the same, or nearly the same hypothesis that I have; and the conclusions he draws from it agree nearly with mine, as far as he goes. However, as I have carried the theory much farther than he has done, and have considered the subject in a different, and, I flatter myself, in a more accurate manner, I hope the Society will not think this paper unworthy of their acceptance." [39] In this paper Cavendish began with the statement that the attractions and repulsions, respectively, between particles of electric fluid and particles of matter, and between similar particles, vary " according to the same power of the distances "—the force varies " inversely as some less power of the distance than the cube." Later in the paper he explored a repulsion which he " let . . . be inversely as some power of the distance between the square and the cube."

So it remained * for Coulomb, in 1785, to discover by experiment the inverse-square distance relation and later the law of the force in direct ratio to the charge, thus making possible the definition of a unit charge of electricity and the subsequent mathematical development of electrostatics inaugurated by Poisson. Coulomb favored the

§ Maxwell described Cavendish's apparatus as follows: " It consisted of a pair of somewhat rickety wooden frames, to which two hemispheres of pasteboard were fastened by means of sticks of glass. By pulling a string these frames were made to open like a book, showing within the hemispheres the memorable globe of 12.1 inches diameter, supported on a glass stick as an axis. By pulling the string still more, the hemispheres were drawn quite away from the globe, and a pith ball electrometer was drawn up to the globe to test its ' degree of electrification.' A machine so bulky, so brittle, and so inelegant was not likely to last long, even in a lumber room." [38]

* Apparently Daniel Bernoulli had suspected in 1760 that electrical attraction follows the law of the inverse square. [40]

two-fluid theory, and many writers were influenced by him, on the supposition that so great a discovery as the law of electrical force must imply a superior insight into the nature of electricity. Coulomb also rejected the one-fluid theory of magnetism developed by Æpinus and advocated a magnetic theory based on two magnetic fluids. Coulomb, however, was more cautious than many of his followers. He did not say in so many words that there actually are two electric fluids. "Whatever be the cause of electricity," he wrote, " we can explain all the phenomena by supposing that there are two electric fluids, the parts of the same fluid repelling each other according to the inverse square of the distance, and attracting the parts of the other fluid according to the same inverse square law." We may note that one of the reasons for his advocacy of this doctrine was the then current idea about gases, developed notably by Stephen Hales in the Newtonian tradition. Coulomb said:

The supposition of two fluids is moreover in accord with all those discoveries of modern chemists and physicists, which have made known to us various pairs of gases whose elasticity is destroyed by their admixture in certain proportions—an effect which could not take place without something equivalent to a repulsion between the parts of the same gas, which is the cause of its elasticity, and an attraction between the parts of different gases, which accounts for the loss of elasticity on combination.[41]

Two Fluids or One

The historical point of view that has been adopted throughout this monograph is that the true measure of any contribution to science—whether of Newton, Franklin, or anyone else—is the degree to which it can be proved to have exerted a beneficial influence on the progress of knowledge. Yet in any age the historical judgment is complemented by the degree to which the concepts and methods of any earlier theory may still be useful. Anyone who writes about Newtonian dynamics in the mid-twentieth century cannot help being aware that—despite the relativistic rejection of Newton's concepts of absolute space and time and invariant mass—our approach to most problems of the motion of gross bodies is essentially along the lines laid down by Newton in the *Principia*. Our appreciation of the revolutionary progress in science wrought by that book is based on our knowledge of the state of physics in the sixteenth, seventeenth, and eighteenth centuries, but an awareness of the degree of validity of Newtonian mechanics today is necessary for a full recognition of Newton's heroic work. So it is that we cannot help being aware that Franklin's theory of electricity, as emended by Æpinus, was based on a doctrine of matter that is remarkably similar to the one held by physical scientists in the twentieth century. The worth of that theory is, therefore, greatly enhanced in our judgment by the fact that we conceive matter and electricity very much like the Franklinians of two centuries ago.

In earlier chapters, some of the evidence concerning the immediate reaction to Franklin's experiments and ideas was presented. That progress in electricity was built upon the foundations laid by Franklin is amply demonstrated by the books and articles written during the last half of the eighteenth century and the first third or so of the nineteenth. Practically every general book on electricity or on physics written between 1775, say, and 1830 either shows the impress of Franklin's concepts, principles, and fundamental experiments or contains an explicit statement of their merit. Priestley, whose book on the history and present state of electricity appeared in a third English edition in 1775, may be considered a suspect witness because of his indebtedness to Franklin, but this is hardly true of the other authors. In his three-volume *Elements of Natural or Experimental Philosophy* published in London in 1803, Tiberius Cavallo, F. R. S.—friend and correspondent of Volta,† who had notably improved the electrometer—presented the Franklinian theory without even bothering to "mention any other of the numerous hypotheses that have been offered in explanation of the electrical phenomena, as they are too deficient to deserve any particular notice." [42] His often reprinted treatise on electricity was written from the same point of view.

Many scientists of the nineteenth century simply admitted their inability to decide between one theory and the other. In many cases, they adopted a very modern point of view—usually associated with the mid-twentieth century—that science is always limited only to statements which lead to descriptions or predictions of physical events and that the ultimate nature of physical reality is a meaningless phrase. We may even find the rather advanced notion that the truth or falsity of the basic physical hypothesis is irrelevant so long as they lead to mathematical statements that coordinate phenomena. Abbé René-Just Haüy, the founder of scientific crystallography, author of a splendid exposition of the theory of Æpinus (1787),[43] later wrote a textbook (1803) in which he advocated the two-fluid theory of Coulomb. But he was careful to say that "the existence of these two fluids is not founded upon . . . satisfactory reasons." Nevertheless, the adoption of the two-fluid concept "conduces . . . to a simple and plausible manner of representing the results of ex-

---

† Volta, like Galvani, advocated a one-fluid theory, although the Voltaic concepts contained a number of original aspects; see page 569 below.

perience. . . ." This point of view was repeated in a note of the translator, who actually favored the one-fluid hypothesis: " But it is of comparatively little importance, whether one fluid, or two component fluids really exist, or be merely hypothetical, provided the assumed hypothesis enables us faithfully and satisfactorily to exhibit and connect the results of experiment." [44] In this *Elementary Treatise on Natural Philosophy*, one of the textbooks written to fit the reorganized French educational system, a popular work which was several times reprinted in both the original French and the English translations, Haüy abandoned the Franklin-Æpinus theory and adopted the two-fluid theory of Coulomb. Even so, Haüy praised Franklin for his lightning experiments and lightning rod, but above all for " his doctrine of positive and negative electricity " and the " happy application [he made of it] to the experiment of the Leyden phial, the discharge of which he referred to a simple re-establishment of equilibrium." [45] The " philosopher of Philadelphia " drew partisans to his theory because of " this mechanical manner of conceiving and illustrating a fact which then held the first rank among the wonders of electricity." ‡

By the early years of the nineteenth century, even those who still advocated the original Franklinian theory, with the modifications introduced by Æpinus, were apt to express themselves on the subject without too much positiveness. Thus Thomas Young, presenting the Franklin-Æpinus theory, made it clear that no evidence was available to prove the existence of the electric fluid and that there was no way of telling truly which of two bodies is electrified plus and which minus. " It is in fact of little consequence to the theory whether the terms positive or negative be correctly applied," he said, " provided that their sense remain determined; and that, like positive and negative quantities in mathematics, they always be understood of states which neutralise each other." [47]

In 1822 there appeared a four-volume *System of Mechanical Philosophy* by John Robison, Professor of Natural Philosophy in the University of Edinburgh—a posthumous publication, edited with notes by David Brewster. Robison said he would " venture to assume the existence of this substance, which philosophers have called *the electric fluid*, as a proposition abundantly demonstrated; and to affirm, on the authority of all the above-mentioned facts, that

‡ Haüy, describing Franklin's explanation of the action of pointed conductors, said that Franklin " afterwards suspected the accuracy of his explication, and he avowed his suspicion with that freedom and candour which is, with regard to true philosophers, another means of acquiring honour, in addition to that resulting from their discoveries." [46] For the sake of a reader who might wish to compare the hypotheses of Franklin and Coulomb, Haüy presented both.

its mechanical character is such as is expressed in Mr. Æpinus's hypothesis." [48] Although Robison was well acquainted with the writings of Coulomb,§ he preferred to apply Coulomb's law to one fluid and not two, and to adopt the Æpinus version of Franklin's original theory. Robison usually referred to the revised Franklinian theory only in the name of Æpinus; yet he was careful to indicate at every point exactly what Franklin had contributed. Thus Robison referred to Franklin's great discovery, in relation to the Leyden jar, that glass is impermeable to " electric fluid " so that a dual process occurs: " The abstraction of it [i. e., electric fluid] from the one side [of the glass] while it was accumulated on the other." Franklin's great principle, " that all the phenomena of electricity arise from the redundancy or deficiency of electric fluid, and that a certain quantity of it resides naturally in all bodies . . . ," was for Franklin " the inlet to the whole science; and the greatest part of what has been since added is a more distinct explanation how the redundancy or deficiency of electric fluid produces the observed phenomena." * Robison said that " it was for these reasons, as much as for the important discovery of the sameness of electricity and thunder, that Dr. Franklin stands so high in the rank of philosophers, and is justly considered as the author of this department of natural science." [50]

Among the writers who espoused the two-fluid theory but also emphasized the achievement of Franklin was Thomas Thomson, known chiefly for his having published one of the first versions of Dalton's atomic theory. Thomson, a professor of chemistry at Glasgow, was a major supporter of the new atomic theory of Dalton. In 1830 he published *An Outline of the Sciences of Heat and Electricity*, in which most of the discoveries of Franklin were fairly presented—despite Thomson's advocacy of the rival theory. Thomson said of Franklin's book that " this publication forms a remarkable era in the history of electricity. It was translated into almost every European language, and the opinions which it contained were almost universally adopted." [51] Thomson's succinct presentation is accurate and all the more remarkably so in that Thomson found greater merit in the two-fluid theory. Although agreeing that Franklin's research on lightning was remarkable, Thomson believed that it was Franklin's theory which " was probably the cause of the immediate ce-

§ Robison indicated that he had anticipated Coulomb in discovering the inverse-square law of electrical force, but laid no claim to the discovery.[49]

* Robison, however, was wrong in his sequence of events when he said that " Dr. Franklin deduced this leading principle from observing, that as fast as one side of a glass plate was electrified positively, the other side appeared negative, and that, unless the electricity of that side was communicated to other bodies, the other side could be no farther electrified."

lebrity of Dr. Franklin "—the first theory to correlate all the known phenomena and to predict accurately the outcome of experiments. The science of electricity, according to Thomson, is indebted to Franklin for " three capital discoveries, upon which his reputation will finally rest ": the effects of points (which led to the lightning rod), the electrification of clouds (and the consequent electrical character of lightning discharge), and the analysis of the Leyden jar, which " contributed more than anything else, to establish his peculiar theory of electricity."

It is out of the range of this monograph to explore in any detail the kind of arguments used for and against these two theories during the nineteenth century. In a day of mathematical theories, it could be held, as Joseph Henry said, that the one-fluid and the two-fluid theory were mathematically equivalent, so that the problems of possible gain or loss of an electric matter were hardly of primary concern.† In this sense Franklin's day was past, because the positive results he sought so hard to establish were now merely taken for granted and—after mid-century at least—not even associated with his name as formerly had been the case.

Yet the presentations of the two-fluid theory of electricity actually bear Franklin's mark. The two electric fluids are Franklinian fluids in the sense that each one is made up of particles which repel one another, " elastic fluids " in the Newtonian sense. Furthermore, both

---

† The considerations of a mathematical theory of electricity are limited to the production of equations which represent physical situations and the derivation of some of these equations from the others. For example, in the mathematical theory of electrostatics, two of the fundamental equations are known respectively as Coulomb's law and Gauss's theorem: the first describes the forces between charged particles and the second relates the electric field from a closed surface to the total charge on the surface. One of these equations can readily be derived from the other in complete independence of any physical assumptions about one or two fluids. Yet, since all mathematical statements in a physical theory have overtones of physical conceptual schemes, these two equations may carry connotations of two distinct views of electrical phenomena. Coulomb's law states a force between charged particles or small charged bodies and may seem to imply a primary consideration of bodies acting on one another at-a-distance. Gauss's theorem indicates a property of the electric field around a charged body and thus focusses attention on the strains and stresses in the space outside of bodies rather than the forces emanating from one body to affect another. Traditionally, textbooks present the subject in historical order, with Gauss's theorem derived from Coulomb's law. But the implications of action-at-a-distance are still bothersome today. In a currently used introduction to the mathematical theory of electricity and magnetism (written in 1936 for candidates for Part I of the Mathematical Tripos at Cambridge University), Gauss's theorem is stated as a fundamental hypothesis—justified by the fact " that the theory which we are able to build up on this hypothesis accords with experiment." Coulomb's law is then deduced from Gauss's theorem, contrary to the common practice, because the author believed that " on the whole it is more satisfactory " to take Gauss's theorem rather than Coulomb's law " as our fundamental hypothesis and so avoid basing our theory on the idea of action at a distance." [52]

of these fluids are " subtle " in that they can insinuate themselves into, or are normally to be found in, the empty space within bodies. Finally, each of these two fluids was said to obey the kind of conservation principle applied by Franklin to his single fluid. In a typical presentation of the two-fluid theory, Thomas Thomson said: " Friction has the property of decomposing the combined electrical fluid, the positive electricity accumulating in one of the bodies rubbed while the negative electricity accumulates in the other. Hence the reason why when two bodies are rubbed against each other and separated, they are always in two opposite states of electricity." [53] In such accounts, the mutual attraction postulated by Franklin and Æpinus between particles of the electric fluid and particles of matter had been replaced by an attraction between the kinds of electric particles, and the law of attraction and repulsion was specified to be the inverse-square law of Coulomb.

The basic elements of Franklin's thoughts on electricity had thus influenced both the revised one-fluid theory of Æpinus and its rival two-fluid theory. The expositions of the two-fluid theory continued to use the terms " positive " and " negative " which had been introduced into electrical discourse by Franklin. The two fluids were called " positive " and " negative " in what had become a figurative sense. Thus Thomas Thomson did not " adopt the hypothesis of Franklin, that only one electric fluid exists. The phenomena do not seem explicable on any other supposition than the existence of two electric fluids. But the terms *positive* and *negative* applied to these two merely as proper names are more convenient and less objectionable than the terms *vitreous* and *resinous* applied to them by the French Electricians." [54]

It also became customary to write of " the electric fluid," of which each body has " a certain quantity . . . which depends upon the nature of the body, [and] remains as though enchained in its interior, so long as the two fluids are neutralised one by the other." This " electric fluid " is a compound fluid, " composed of the vitreous and resinous fluids," [55] or the positive and negative fluids, which during electrification " became disengaged, . . . lose their tendency to continue in the body, and only obey their natural repulsive force."

Many of the physicists of the nineteenth century, especially on the Continent, were more concerned to develop the mathematical basis of electrostatics, electromagnetism, and current electricity, than to wrestle with the apparently insoluble problem of " What is electricity? " Such men as Poisson, Helmholtz, Riemann, Webber, Gauss, Kirchhoff, and others tended to favor the two-fluid theory over the one-fluid theory, if they chose a fluid theory at all. From the success of their work we can see that the two-fluid theory had considerable merit, especially when viewed from considerations of symmetry and the attendant simplicity of equations. Furthermore, from the physical point of view the two-fluid theory seemed more natural in relation to the phenomena of electrolysis, which exerted a profound influence on the development of electrical concepts. Thus the concept of two electric fluids or two types of electricity was more in harmony with the development of chemical theory as a whole than the Franklin-Æpinus theory. The very notion of electrochemical dualism seemed to require two electric substances, and so the two-fluid theory was apparently implied by the chemical theories of Bergmann and Berzelius.[56]

Thus, in 1830, Thomas Thomson held that it was " chiefly in consequence of the galvanic discoveries " that the hypothesis of two fluids " is gradually superseding the Franklinian hypothesis, and will probably very speedily be universally adopted by electricians." ‡ Thomson explained that the two-fluid theory of Coulomb " involves no assumptions inconsistent with the phenomena of nature." Poisson had found the theory " to apply so accurately to all the different cases, that the probability of its accordance with truth is very great." Apparently at this point Thomson had gone a little too far; at least he added another sentence: " At any rate it enables us to reduce all the electrical facts into a simple and luminous system, and to foretell the result of any combination of electrical actions." It may be that the concept of two electric fluids is " a mere mathematical hypothesis," he concluded, but even so " its importance and utility to all who wish to understand this most important science, must be admitted to be very great." [57]

Faraday and Maxwell on the Electric Fluid or Fluids

Throughout the nineteenth century there were no experiments to indicate whether electric currents consisted of a kind of electric matter moving in a single direction or of two kinds of electric matter moving simultaneously in both directions. Maxwell agreed that the two-fluid theory had appealed to many scientists because it led to fewer mathematical complications, but he also pointed out that the two-fluid theory is " considerably more difficult to reconcile with the facts than the one-fluid theory." [58] Maxwell belonged to that group of scientists, including Sir William Thomson (Lord Kelvin) and Faraday, who thought that there might be some possibility of finding out whether there really is an electric fluid after all.

‡ See Helmholtz's remarks to the same effect on page 562 below.

Faraday, who was no mathematician, tended to think in terms of physical models that could be visualized and he scorned physics that was no more than a set of abstract equations. He sought for illumination on matters of electricity and magnetism in the medium around or between bodies and not in charged or conducting bodies as such. Yet in his early studies of electrolysis Faraday had to face the question of one electric fluid or two. " Some philosophers," he said, " with Franklin assume but one electric fluid; and such must agree together in the general uniformity and character of the electric current." But there are " singular differences " among the advocates of two fluids. These disagreements arose in considering whether the two electricities decompose separate portions of water, whether the two always flow into a solution in equal or differing amounts, and so on. Faraday " sought amongst the various experiments . . . for any which might be considered as sustaining the theory of two electricities rather than that of one." He had " not been able to perceive a single fact which could be brought forward for such a purpose." [59] Although he attacked the weaknesses in expositions of the two-fluid theory and not of the one-fluid theory, Faraday did not explicitly advocate the one-fluid theory.§ On this score, he wanted his readers to understand,

I am giving no opinion respecting the nature of the electric current . . . ; and that though I speak of the current as proceeding from the parts which are positive to those which are negative, it is merely in accordance with the conventional, though in some degree tacit, agreement entered into by scientific men, that they may have a constant, certain, and definite means of referring to the direction of the forces of that current.[60]

In his *Treatise on Electricity and Magnetism* (1873), the crowning glory of classical physics, Clerk Maxwell addressed himself to the nature of electricity and the rival theories. He established three fundamental propositions, which together state in a precise fashion the principle of conservation of charge discovered by Franklin.* On this basis he was able to state that the " electrification " of a body is " a physical quantity capable of measurement " and could apply to

§ In discussions of electrolysis, Faraday, like Maxwell, almost wrote as if electricity might be a substance—but only in relation to this problem. Discussions of all other electrical phenomena by Faraday and Maxwell were apt to have a different character, as we shall see below.

* " I. The total electrification of a body, or system of bodies, remains always the same, except in so far as it receives electrification from or gives electrification to other bodies. . . . II. When one body electrifies another by conduction, the total electrification of the two bodies remains the same, that is, the one loses as much positive or gains as much negative electrification as the other gains of positive or loses of negative electrification. . . . III. When electrification is produced by friction, or by any other known method, equal quantities of positive and negative electrification are produced." [61]

it the language of " quantity " as well as " quality." But he did not want his readers to assume too hastily that electricity " is, or is not, a substance . . . or that it belongs to any known category of physical quantities." [62] In most theories, he found, " Electricity is treated as a substance." But there are two kinds of electricity, vitreous and resinous, which may combine and annul each other, i. e., two insulated conductors with equal but opposite charges may be brought into contact, whereupon neither will show any electrification or charge. Maxwell argued that " we cannot conceive of two substances annulling each other "; hence a distinction is made " between Free Electricity and Combined Electricity." [63] Maxwell next presented the two-fluid theory, in which all neutral or unelectrified bodies are supposed to contain equal quantities of positive and negative electricity, and in such great amounts that " no process of electrification has ever yet deprived a body of all the electricity of either kind." According to this theory, two bodies A and B become charged when a quantity P of positive electricity is transferred from body A to body B, or a quantity N of negative electricity is transferred from body B to body A, or some combination of both occurs simultaneously. If there is a double transfer, body A will have a negative charge of amount $P + N$, or will have $P + N$ units of negative electricity plus an additional quantity of negative electricity combined with that positive electricity remaining in the body. The remaining negative electricity which is combined with positive electricity is called " Combined, Latent, or Fixed electricity," while the $P + N$ units represent the " Free electricity " or uncombined electricity. In such theories, Maxwell pointed out, the " Combined, Latent, or Fixed electricity " gives rise to no effects whereby its quantity may be estimated. Even in the case of an unelectrified body, there is no way of determining how much of the two electricities is present; in the electrified case referred to above, all we know is that there are $P + N$ units of " Free electricity " of the negative or resinous sort. Maxwell argued that this final state might result from " *any one* of three different processes." One has just been presented, the simultaneous transfer of P units of positive charge from body A to body B, and N units of negative charge from B to A. The other two are, respectively, a transfer of $P + N$ units of positive charge from A to B; $P + N$ units of negative charge transferred from B to A. (See fig. 22.)

In each of these three cases, we start out with two electrically neutral bodies A and B and end up with two bodies with equal charges of opposite sign. Thus three physically distinct processes result in the two bodies having the same final charges, the same quantities of

" free electricity." Yet the resulting quantities of " combined electricity " will be different in each case, as the following table shows, assuming that at the outset body A would have Y units of positive and Y units of negative electricity in combination, while body B would have Z units of positive electricity and Z units of negative electricity in combination. These three modes of giving body A a charge of $P + N$ negative units while body B simultaneously receives $P + N$ positive units are illustrated in the table. It will be

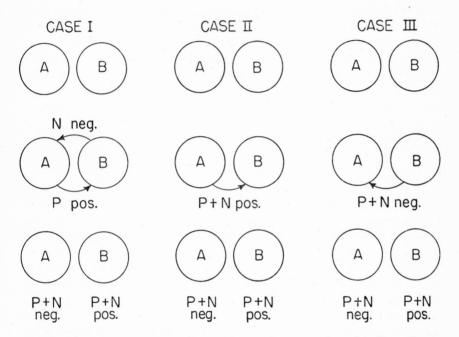

FIG. 22. Diagram to illustrate three possible ways for two uncharged bodies to become electrified with equal and opposite charges. The top row shows the two bodies in an unelectrified state; the second row shows the process of electrification; the bottom row shows the final electrified state.

seen that in all three cases the resulting " free electricity " on the two bodies is the same, but the quantity of " combined electricity " on body A is greater in Case I than in Case II and greater in Case III than in Case I.

Thus, Maxwell concluded, in the terms of the two-fluid theory, it is possible " to alter not only the amount of free electricity in a body, but the amount of combined electricity. But no phenomena have ever been observed in electrified bodies which can be traced to the varying amount of their combined electricities. Hence either the combined electricities have no observable properties, or the amount

THREE PROCESSES WHEREBY BODY A AND BODY B RECEIVE CHARGES, RESPECTIVELY, OF $P + N$ UNITS OF NEGATIVE ELECTRICITY AND $P + N$ UNITS OF POSITIVE ELECTRICITY

	CASE I		CASE II		CASE III	
	Body A	Body B	Body A	Body B	Body A	Body B
Combined electricity in unelectrified state	Υ units of negative electricity / Υ units of positive electricity	Z units of negative electricity / Z units of positive electricity	Υ units of negative electricity / Υ units of positive electricity	Z units of negative electricity / Z units of positive electricity	Υ units of negative electricity / Υ units of positive electricity	Z units of negative electricity / Z units of positive electricity
Process of electrification	N units of negative electricity gained / P units of positive electricity lost	N units of negative electricity lost / P units of positive electricity gained	$P + N$ units of positive electricity lost	$P + N$ units of positive electricity gained	$P + N$ units of negative electricity gained	$P + N$ units of negative electricity lost
Free electricity in electrified state	$P + N$ units of negative electricity	$P + N$ units of positive electricity	$P + N$ units of negative electricity	$P + N$ units of positive electricity	$P + N$ units of negative electricity	$P + N$ units of positive electricity
Total electricity in electrified state	$\Upsilon + N$ units of negative electricity / $\Upsilon - P$ units of positive electricity	$Z - N$ units of negative electricity / $Z + P$ units of positive electricity	Υ units of negative electricity / $\Upsilon - P - N$ units of positive electricity	Z units of negative electricity / $Z + P + N$ units of positive electricity	$\Upsilon + P + N$ units of negative electricity / Υ units of positive electricity	$Z - P - N$ units of negative electricity / Z units of positive electricity
Combined electricity in electrified state	$\Upsilon - P$ units of positive electricity / $\Upsilon - P$ units of negative electricity	$Z - N$ units of positive electricity / $Z - N$ units of negative electricity	$\Upsilon - P - N$ units of positive electricity / $\Upsilon - P - N$ units of negative electricity	Z units of positive electricity / Z units of negative electricity	Υ units of positive electricity / Υ units of negative electricity	$Z - P - N$ units positive electricity / $Z - P - N$ units of negative electricity

of the combined electricities is incapable of variation." The first of these alternatives " presents no difficulty to the mere mathematician, who attributes no properties to the fluids except those of attraction and repulsion," for he conceives the two fluids simply to annul one another, like $+e$ and $-e$, and " their combination to be a true mathematical zero." The fact that the two-fluid theory was almost universally adopted by the nineteenth-century mathematical " electricians " was considered by Maxwell to be significant enough to warrant further discussion. The main point, according to Maxwell, is that the mathematical results are " deduced entirely from data which can be proved by experiment " and, hence, these deductions are as true as those experimental data and are, therefore, independent of " whether we adopt the theory of two fluids or not. The experimental verification of the mathematical results therefore is no evidence for or against the peculiar doctrines of this theory."

Maxwell explained that the advocates of this theory use the word " fluid " in a special sense. The two electricities " are capable of being transferred from one body to another, and are, within conducting bodies, extremely mobile "; hence, they may legitimately be called " fluids " even though " those who have used the theory for merely mathematical purposes " do not attribute to these fluids the " other properties [of ordinary fluids] . . . , such as their inertia, weight, and elasticity." In the theory of two fluids, the very word " fluid " has " been apt to mislead the vulgar, including many men of science who are not natural philosophers." † One of the basic problems in the two-fluid theory, as Maxwell saw it, was the sense to be given this word " fluid ": to conceive " that the combination of the two fluids shall have no properties at all, so that the addition of more or less of the combination to a body shall not in any way affect it, either by increasing its mass or its weight, or altering some of its other properties." To avoid this difficulty, some physicists had made the supposition that in every electrification, equal quantities of both fluids are transferred in opposite directions. This new " law " insures the total quantity of both fluids in any body being a constant. For example, if a body A attains a negative charge of $N + P$, it must have lost $\frac{1}{2}(N + P)$ positive units and have gained $\frac{1}{2}(N + P)$ negative units; if, then, prior to electrification, the body had Y units of negative electricity and Y units of positive electricity, after electrification it would have $Y + \frac{1}{2}(N + P)$ units of negative electricity and $Y - \frac{1}{2}(N + P)$ units of positive electricity, or a total amount of $2Y$ units of electricity of both kinds, just as prior to electrification.

† For Maxwell's deprecation of the use of the word " fluid " in relation to electricity, see, below, page 561.

Maxwell dismissed this whole procedure in the language used by Milton to ridicule the Ptolemaic system: " By this new law," he said, " they ' contrive to save appearances,' forgetting that there would have been no need of the law except to reconcile the ' Two Fluids ' theory with facts, and to prevent it from predicting non-existent phenomena."

Maxwell then addressed himself to the theory of one fluid in Franklin's terms as modified by Æpinus.‡ This theory, Maxwell said, explains all the observed phenomena as well as the two-fluid theory. But it has the advantage that it " does not, like the Two Fluid theory, explain too much." [64] Maxwell indicated two problems in relation to this theory. It requires the supposition that the mass of the electric fluid be " so small that no attainable positive or negative electrification has yet perceptibly increased or diminished either the mass or the weight of a body." Furthermore, the theory " has not as yet been able to assign sufficient reasons why the vitreous rather than the resinous electrification should be supposed due to an *excess* of electricity." Maxwell defended the theory at some length against an objection, raised " by men who ought to have reasoned better," that if particles of matter repel one another, the theory must be in opposition to universal gravitation.§

Maxwell concluded the presentation of the two theories by the promise that throughout the treatise he would test them both " in the light of additional classes of phenomena." His own view was that " additional light on the nature of electricity " would come from " a study of what takes place in the space intervening between the electrified bodies. Such is the essential character of the mode of investigation pursued by Faraday. . . ." No one who read Maxwell's *Treatise* could help noticing the degree to which he favored the one-fluid theory over the two-fluid theory. Helmholtz, generally an admirer of Maxwell, even took him to task on this point.

---

‡ Maxwell described the theory as one that was much like the two-fluid theory, save that one of the fluids, " generally the negative one, has been endowed with the properties and name of Ordinary Matter, while the other retains the name of the Electric Fluid. The particles of the fluid are supposed to repel one another according to the law of the inverse square of the distance, and to attract those of matter according to the same law "—which is Franklin's statement of his theory, with the added quantification of the force (Coulomb's law). " Those [particles] of matter are supposed to repel each other and attract those of electricity "—the additional postulate of Æpinus.

§ See, below, page 564.

The Irreconcilability of the Concepts of Electric Fluid and Æther

In the 1820's and the 1830's there was no lack of appreciation of the solid worth of Franklin's contribution to electricity. So long as men believed in fluid theories of electricity, whether one fluid or two, they could not help admiring the creator of the first fluid theory, or of the very concept of electric fluid. By the 1870's a number of leading physicists had come to doubt the worth of any theories based on subtle fluids. To a large degree, it was believed that Franklin's single fluid and Coulomb's two fluids should be laid to rest alongside that other discarded fluid, caloric. Such men rejected the Franklinian way of explaining the phenomena, and for them, all that remained valid or useful out of Franklin's whole contribution to electricity was the principle of conservation of charge, the designations " positive " and " negative," and a number of major experimental results. Faraday and Maxwell had led physicists to think of electrical phenomena in terms of the stresses and strains in the medium surrounding bodies. The experimental production of electromagnetic waves " in " that medium (by Hertz in 1887) was generally conceived as a triumph of this point of view. Thus it seemed that Franklin's concept of electricity as a particulate substance, while important as one of those older concepts that had enabled men to reach their present advanced point of view, should be quietly discarded. In 1874 Maxwell wrote out the text of his lectures on electricity at the Cavendish Laboratory. He now introduced the " common phrase " *electric fluid* only " for the purpose of warning . . . against it." " As long as we do not know whether positive electricity, or negative, or both, should be called a substance or the absence of a substance," Maxwell said, " and as long as we do not know whether the velocity of an electric current is to be measured by hundreds of miles in a second or by an hundredth of an inch in an hour, or even whether the current flows from positive to negative, we must avoid speaking of the electric fluid." [65]

During the latter part of the nineteenth century, physicists generally had a dual view of electrical phenomena, one for electrostatics or currents in metallic conductors, and another for electrolysis. This situation has been described by Millikan as follows:

Between 1833 and 1900, . . . the physicist was in this peculiar position: when he was thinking of the passage of electricity through a solution, he for the most part, following Faraday, pictured to himself definite specks or atoms of electricity as traveling through the solution, each atom of matter carrying an exact multiple, which might be anywhere between one and eight, of a definite elementary electrical atom, while, when he was thinking of the passage of a current through a metallic conductor, he gave up altogether the atomic hypothesis, and attempted to picture the phenomenon to himself as a continuous " slip " or " breakdown of a strain " in the material of the wire.[66]

The perplexity of physicists in understanding " electricity " can be seen in the Faraday Lecture given by Hermann v. Helmholtz at the Royal Institution in 1881. Helmholtz was one of the greatest men of physical science in his day, and it was he who encouraged Heinrich Hertz to perform those experiments in 1887 that proved " that electrical forces are indeed transmitted in the form of electric waves, which travel through space with the speed of light exactly as the Faraday-Maxwell theory had predicted, the triumph of the ether-stress point of view. . . ." [67] Helmholtz said:

It is not at all necessary to accept any definite opinion about the ultimate nature of the agent which we call electricity. Faraday himself avoided as much as possible giving any affirmative assertion regarding this problem, although he did not conceal his disinclination to believe in the existence of two opposite electric fluids. For our own discussion of the electrochemical phenomena, to which we shall now turn, I beg permission to use the language of the old dualistic theory, which considers positive and negative electricity as two imponderable substances, because we shall have to speak principally on relations of quantity.[68]

Helmholtz was referring to the quantitative laws of electrolysis discovered by Faraday. In order to explain why, as a current passes through a solution, two different components are released respectively at the positive electrode (anode) and negative electrode (cathode), it was much easier to suppose that a substance was added to each component to transform it from a charged fragment (ion) to an ordinary atom or molecule. Even Faraday and Maxwell had inclined toward the concept of electrical substance when treating this subject.* The choice for Helmholtz seemed to be only between having one substance or two. He could assume that there is only one kind of electric substance and that different processes occur at the two electrodes: one type of ion giving up electricity and the other gaining electricity. But he could also assume that there are two electrical substances, in which case the identical process occurs at both electrodes; each type of ion either gaining or giving up the kind of electricity associated either with it or with the electrode. Helmholtz chose the latter:

---

* See below, page 564. As early as 1830, this phenomenon of electrolytic dissociation had conditioned men's minds favorably to the two-fluid theory of electricity.

I prefer the dualistic theory, because it expresses clearly the perfect symmetry between the positive and negative side of electric phenomena, and I keep the well known supposition that as much negative electricity enters where positive goes away, because we are not acquainted with any phenomena which could be interpreted as corresponding with an increase or a diminution of the total electricity contained in any body. The unitary theory, which assumes the existence of only one imponderable electrical substance, and ascribes the effects of opposite kind to ponderable matter itself, affords a far less convenient basis for an electrochemical theory.

Helmholtz was aware, of course, that the hypothesis of two imponderable fluids was, as he said, " rather complicated and artificial " and that " the mathematical language of Clerk Maxwell's theory expresses the laws of the phenomena very simply and very truly." Yet he saw no way " to explain without the use of mathematical formulæ " what Maxwell considered to be " a quantity of electricity," or why " such a quantity is constant, like that of a substance." For Helmholtz, mathematical formulæ were not, by and of themselves, sufficient to constitute a scientific explanation. He still felt the need for physical concepts that would underlie each of the several mathematical parameters. Since he believed that " the original old notion of substance " was applicable to electrical theory, he suggested its use while pointing out that this old notion is not necessarily identical to that of matter. His reason was the very reason that was used by Franklin to support the concept of an electric matter: conservation. Helmholtz believed the concept of substance to signify " that which behind the changing phenomena lasts as invariable, which can be neither generated nor destroyed, and in this oldest sense of the word we may really call the two electricities substances."

This problem of substance had arisen in Maxwell's *Electricity and Magnetism*. In Part Two, he said that of the classes of electrical phenomena, " electrolysis appears the most likely to furnish us with a real insight into the true nature of the electric current, because we find currents of ordinary matter and currents of electricity forming essential parts of the same phenomenon." But Maxwell soon found himself on " very difficult ground " because of the " tempting hypothesis " of Clausius in relation to Faraday's discovery of electrochemical equivalents; he admitted, for instance, that the " electrification of a molecule . . . , though easily spoken of, is not easily conceived." † Maxwell suggested that one way out of the difficulty was

---

† Maxwell said that the theory of electrolysis " explains the electric current, the nature of which we do not understand, by means of the currents of the material components of the electrolyte, the motion of which, though not visible to the eye, is easily demonstrated. It gives a clear explanation, as Faraday has shewn, why an electrolyte

simply to assert " the fact of the constant value of the molecular charge," and to call this " constant molecular charge, for convenience in description, *one molecule of electricity*." This phrase, he said, " will enable us at least to state clearly what is known about electrolysis, and to appreciate the outstanding difficulties." Yet Maxwell knew that this " phrase " was " gross " and he referred to it as " out of harmony with the rest of this treatise." [69] It implied the definite view of electricity as a substance, of electric charge as a collection of particles, and of an electric current as a movement of charges. Necessary though it might be for electrolysis, the concept of a " molecule of electricity " was contrary to the whole spirit of Faraday's and Maxwell's view of all other electrical phenomena—including currents—as electric stresses and strains in bodies or in æther outside of the affected bodies. Hence, Maxwell disparaged the conclusions he was led to adopt, calling them examples of the " exercising [of] our imagination." The theory of " molecular charges " he developed could " serve as a method by which we may remember a good many facts about electrolysis," he said; but it was so contrary to the general standpoint he had adopted in relation to electrical phenomena that he doubted if it would survive " in any form " after we " come to understand the true nature of electrolysis."

Thus we may see how one of the crises in nineteenth-century physics arose from the contrariety of the respective developments of eighteenth-century concepts. The concept of one or two electric matters or fluids, singly or together following a conservation principle, seemed at first to be a logical extension of the generally accepted canons of speculative Newtonian experimental science, and was so much in harmony with the experimental facts of electrolysis that it appeared a necessary doctrine of classical physics. Not only was there an empirical basis for assuming an atomicity of electricity, but by the century's end it was thought likely that perhaps mass itself was to be accounted for in terms of electromagnetism. At the same time, the development of the undulatory theory of light by Young and Fresnel reached its highest form in the electromagnetic theory of light of Maxwell. The proof by Hertz of the possibility

---

which conducts in the liquid state is a non-conductor when solidified, for unless the molecules can pass from one part to another no electrolytic conduction can take place, so that the substance must be in a liquid state, either by fusion or by solution, in order to be a conductor." In this theory " we must assume that in every electrolyte each molecule of the cation, as it is liberated at the cathode, communicates to the cathode a charge of positive electricity, the amount of which is the same for every molecule, not only of that cation but of all other cations. In the same way each molecule of the anion when liberated, communicates to the anode a charge of negative electricity, the numerical magnitude of which is the same as that of the positive charge due to a molecule of a cation, but with sign reversed."

of producing electromagnetic waves, which had been predicted by Maxwell, seemed to give the luminiferous æther a kind of " real " existence. Newton had conceived the æther as the responsible agent for a variety of physical manifestations, but Young and Fresnel saw the æther only as the medium for light waves. Maxwell's great achievement was thus to restore to the æther a greater role than the limited function assigned to it by Young and Fresnel. Yet he recognized, and admitted with candor, the utter irreconcilability of his whole doctrine of the æther in relation to the theory of electricity and magnetism, and the need for admitting the concept of " atoms " or " molecules " of electricity.

It is fascinating to observe that the Newtonian æther, in its nineteenth-century form, contained the seeds of its own destruction. We must not forget that the paper in which Einstein set forth the Special Theory of Relativity was entitled, " On the electrodynamics of moving bodies," implying how basic to the very considerations of space and time and mass—the foundations of classical Newtonian mechanics—were the results and point of view arising from Maxwell's theory. We are thus apt to see the later stage of the contrary qualities of the concepts of æther and the matter of electricity in the decline of the former and the rise—during the last fifty or sixty years —of the latter, beginning with the first of the charged " fundamental particles," the electron, and at present including so many that their very number challenges the very idea of " fundamental particle."

Particles of Electric Matter

Maxwell's concern about the irreconcilability of the concepts of particles of electric matter and æther current arose in the study of electrolysis, but the advances that helped resolve the problem came from other areas of research. Sir Arthur Schuster has recorded his doubts of the possibility that the phenomena of electrolysis by themselves would ever have led to the present view of electrical matter, or " electron theory." It might have been possible, he said, " to treat the quantitative relationship between electrolytic decomposition and current as a secondary phenomenon." The early followers of Maxwell had a rather " crude view " of the " æther current," and possibly they could conceive that such a current might equally well pass through liquids and solids and induce a " secondary action of electro-chemical effects " in conformity with the results obtained by Faraday. Schuster assumed " that several physicists were trying to develop some such idea; at any rate I did." Although Schuster explained those views at a meeting of the Physical Society (London), he refrained from publication and soon afterwards became convinced "that the 'molecule of electricity' could not be explained away." [70] Therefore, he turned to the study of the electric discharges in gases, the subject which led to J. J. Thomson's final discovery of the electron, to which Schuster, Varley, Crookes, Perrin, and others made important contributions.

In 1903 J. J. Thomson said that "the physicists and mathematicians who did most to develop the fluid theories confined their attention to questions which involved only the law of forces between electrified bodies and the simultaneous production of equal quantities of plus and minus electricity, and refined and idealized their conception of the fluids themselves until any reference to their physical properties was considered almost indelicate." [71] When Thomson made this remark, the situation in electricity had just undergone a radical alteration. Studies on cathode rays, the discharges which occur in gases at low pressure, had indicated that there are unit carriers of electric charge which are apparently identical. The experiments of Thomson and others proved that these particles have the same ratio of charge to mass no matter what gas is used and no matter what material the containing tube and electrodes are made of. The discovery that there is a fundamental unit of negative charge, an "electron," was completed in the second decade of the twentieth century by R. A. Millikan. Millikan devised a method of determining, with a very high degree of accuracy,‡ the charge on small droplets of oil which were in an electric field of which the direction and intensity were readily controlled. Millikan found that every such charge—whether produced on the drop by the friction in the atomizer, by x-rays, or by cathode rays—was without exception the product of an integer and some highest common multiple of all the charges observed; this highest common multiple was taken as the charge on the "electron."

As a result of such experiments, all theories of matter in the twentieth century have rested on the basic postulate that all atoms in the neutral state contain one or more charged negative particles which are identical and indistinguishable one from the other, and which repel one another according to Coulomb's inverse-square law. Since atoms are held to become charged ions by the gain or loss of one or more of these negative particles, and since gross bodies must gain or lose charge because of what happens to their component atoms, the doctrine of matter and charge universally accepted in the twentieth century is very much like Franklin's—as has been said

‡ There had been earlier experiments to measure charges on drops, but the technique had not been sufficiently fine to yield precise results. Both Thomson and Millikan were great admirers of Franklin.

earlier—save that the mobile " electric matter " (which causes bodies or atoms to become charged by being transferred from one to another body or atom, or which flows along conducting wires as an electric current), is the " resinous " or " negative " electricity rather than the " vitreous " as Franklin supposed. We too assume that the electric matter penetrates bodies, is particulate, and is always conserved. The major difference between our concepts and Franklin's is not, however, the sign of charge of the particles of the " electric matter " or the consequent direction of current flow, but the fact that our doctrine of matter contains an additional postulate very much like the one which Æpinus added to Franklin's original theory. The Rutherford model of the atom, with modifications by Bohr and others, is based on the idea that in addition to the electrons all atoms contain a small region in which practically all of the ponderable matter (or mass) is concentrated and which contains one or more units of positive charge to balance the units of negative charge in the electrons external to such a nucleus. Since the positively charged nucleus of an atom must exert a force of attraction on the negatively charged electrons, and since a positively charged nucleus must repel any other positively charged particle, the concept of the Rutherford atom recalls Æpinus's reluctant postulate that the particles of " common matter " not only attract the particles of " electric matter " but repel one another. We may pride ourselves that the Rutherford concept derives from careful experiments on α-particle scattering whereas Æpinus was driven to his position only by the iron necessity of reconciling Franklin's theory with stubborn observed facts. In this respect, Rutherford did not revive the Æpinus-Franklin theory any more than Einstein revived the old Newtonian theory of light when he invented the concept of photons in 1905.§ We know that Rutherford had heard of Æpinus at the time of the experiments on the scattering of α-particles,* but that fact is irrelevant. In 1905 Rutherford spoke about Franklin's one-fluid theory as being " in a modified form . . . the generally accepted explanation of the connection between positive and negative electricity." But he also warned against any consequent underestimation of " the fundamental importance and magnitude of the advances made in electricity since Franklin's time." [73] I have found no comment on Æpinus by Rutherford after 1905, and I cannot therefore tell whether the

§ See Chapter One.
* Rutherford may have heard of Æpinus by reading an article by Kelvin called " Æpinus atomized," which he referred to jokingly in 1905 as " Franklin and Æpinus Kelvinized." [72] At this time Rutherford had not yet found experimental evidence for a nuclear atom.

analogy between his own concepts and those of Æpinus ever passed through his mind.

It is certainly a moot question as to whether the twentieth-century emergence of a theory like Franklin's, together with a postulate like Æpinus's, is any proof of a special quality of vitality in those eighteenth-century concepts. The resemblance may be no more than a kind of historical accident, but the actual fact of a similarity which crosses a span of almost two hundred years is itself striking. In one of the great modern classical presentations of the theory of electricity Jeans said: " The modern explanation of electricity is found to bear a very close resemblance to the older explanation of the one-fluid theory—so much that it will be convenient to explain the modern view of electricity simply by making the appropriate modifications of the one-fluid theory." [74]

It would perhaps be most accurate to describe the present situation by saying that our theory of matter is based on a two-fluid theory of electricity with variations, in the sense that there are conceived to be charged fundamental particles of both signs, plus and minus, in every neutral atom. Yet in a large variety of phenomena, notably many of those of concern to Franklin, our explanations are based on the transfer or movement of only one of these types of " electric matter," and so we continue to use a modified form of the Franklinian one-fluid theory. Above all, the fundamental principle of conservation of charge remains one of the cornerstones of our edifice of electrical theory and theory of matter.

Franklin's Convictions about the Reality of His Own Concepts

In the eighteenth century, as ever since, and as was the case in earlier periods, one of the major problems in physical science was how to prove a theory true. Since all theories rest on primitive concepts, and since the success of theories always enables scientists to act as if the concepts were endowed with empirical reality, we can only with difficulty attempt to evaluate the degree of reality assigned to a given concept. For example, the men of the eighteenth century wrote as if the particles of gases repel one another with a force varying inversely as the distance between them, and we have seen them say that " this " had been " proved " by Newton. We have no way of telling, at any given stage in the development of his scientific thought, how deeply Newton believed in the æther he postulated, but we can say something of the depth of Franklin's belief in his single-fluid theory of electricity and the concept of an electric matter on which it was based.

A discussion of this point is necessary in any account of Franklin's

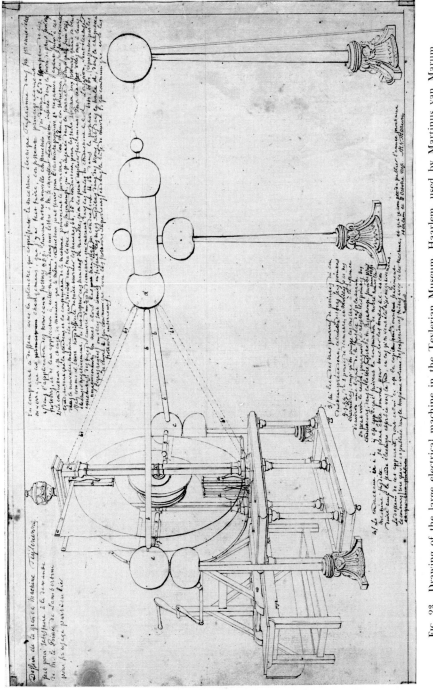

Fig. 23. Drawing of the large electrical machine in the Teylerian Museum, Haarlem, used by Martinus van Marum.
Courtesy of the Burndy Library.

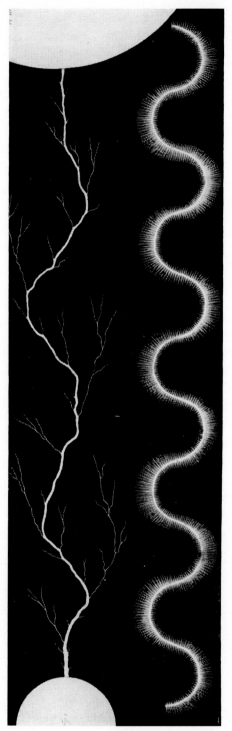

FIG. 24. Martinus van Marum's experiment, which seemed to offer a convincing ocular demonstration of the single-fluid theory of electricity; the discharge shown in the upper part of the plate appears to originate at the positively charged conductor at the left and to terminate at the negatively charged conductor at the right. *Courtesy of the Burndy Library.*

scientific thought because of his avowed willingness to surrender his theory to anyone who could produce a better one. I assume that Franklin made such statements in relation to a particular explanation, and that they referred only to some limited aspects of his conceptual scheme. There is certainly no evidence that he ever had a moment's doubt that there is an electric matter and that its properties were being uncovered by his own experiments and those of others. His convictions on this score were as secure as Newton's on the atomic constitution of matter.

Believing strongly in his own creation, Franklin appears to have been certain that he would never encounter a better theory—at least that his own concepts would not be totally rejected but only modified and improved. But, although he held firmly to a belief in the reality of an electric matter, he believed that there was but one kind of electric matter and not two. When, in the last decades of his life, he saw the growth of a theory based on two electric fluids, he hoped that, when all the evidence was in, his own theory would be victorious over its rival.

During his last days in Paris, after the American Revolution had been won, he learned of the experiments that had been made at the Teylerian Museum in Leyden by Martin Van Marum, who had at his disposal the most powerful electrical machine ever constructed until that time. Van Marum was a convinced Franklinian and he sought to demonstrate the truth of Franklin's theory by argument and experiment. A careful study of the spark discharges obtained from the electrical machine he had had constructed in 1784 seemed to him, he said, to furnish " an incontestable argument in favour of the system for which I had long been searching for a decisive proof." [75] The great Volta was convinced, and on 8 March 1786 wrote a letter of approval to Van Marum attacking the " sect " that has " latterly appeared . . . who pretend to resuscitate the two opposite electric fluids which meet together, and catch fire from the shock." Now these gentlemen could be confuted by experiment, and Volta congratulated Van Marum: " All orthodox electricians must be obliged to you for having thus overturned for ever the heresy of the dualists—the new partisans of the Du Fays, the Nollets, and the Symmers." [76]

In June, 1785, Van Marum was in Paris and distributed copies of his account of the experiments with the Teylerian electrical machine to the following members of the Académie Royale des Sciences: MM. Le Roy, Brisson, Lavoisier, Berthollet, Monge, and Van der Monde. Van Marum said that " they all agreed with me that, considering the visible direction of the sparks produced by the large machine, it was incontestibly proved that, in conformity with Franklin's theory, a single electric fluid proceeds from the positive conductor, and passes into the next conductor, which receives it; while, on the contrary, when the machine is made to act negatively, the electric fluid proceeds in a contrary direction from the adjoining conductor, and passes into that which is negatively electrified." [77] Van Marum was urged to present what he called " the first fruits of my electrical experiments with the large Teylerian machine " to Franklin himself who was living in Passy, and who was then " on the point of returning to America." Van Marum's account of this interview has not been known to Franklin's biographers and it presents a dramatic portrait of Franklin on the eve of his departure from the scene of his diplomatic triumphs:

M. Le Roy accompanied me to Passy, where we were the last of those who were introduced to Franklin previous to his return to America. On being first announced, we perceived that it was his intention, after having granted us a short interview, to excuse himself on account of his approaching departure. But perceiving that the experiments, of which I offered him the descriptions, were very important with regard to that branch of physics in which he himself had formerly made so many successful researches, this venerable old man, whose presence inspired me with a profound respect, made me sit down beside him, and begged me to communicate and point out to him whatever I judged most likely to throw a light upon this science. After attentively considering the figure of the spark, and the direction of its lateral branches, he inquired of me very seriously whether one might be satisfied that the drawing represented nothing but what had been actually observed? When I had given him assurances on this head that seemed to remove his doubts, he said, " This then proves my theory of a simple electric fluid, and it is now high time to reject the theory of two sorts of fluids."

There can be no doubt about the firmness of Franklin's conviction of the correctness of his theory.

In one of his most celebrated compositions, Franklin wrote an epitaph in which he compared " the body of B. Franklin printer " to the cover of an old book, " its contents torn out and stript of its lettering and gilding." " But the work shall not be lost," Franklin said, " for it will (as he believed) appear once more, in a new and more elegant edition, revised and corrected, *by the Author*." [78] How pleased Franklin would have been had he known that his electrical theory, having served to advance physical science and to create a recognized new discipline in the eighteenth century, was not afterwards buried in the records of historical scholarship, described only in learned monographs and old books lying on the library shelves, " food for worms," but that one hundred fifty years after its creation, his theory could " appear once more, in a new and more elegant edition."

SOURCES

The early part of this chapter is based on an analysis of Canton's and Franklin's papers. There is no adequate secondary material on Canton. Although Wilcke is the subject of a full-length biography in Swedish (Oseen, 1939), there is no comparable work on Æpinus. Priestley, in his history, did not show an appreciation of Æpinus's modification of the one-fluid theory, which he apparently did not understand; presumably this is the reason that some later historians, e. g., Mottelay (1922), also have omitted this major contribution of Æpinus. A valuable account of his work appears in Robison (1822:4).

The rise of the two-fluid theory of electricity at the end of the eighteenth century and in the early nineteenth century has never been fully studied. Most of the secondary literature does not distinguish between the concept of two electrical powers ("virtues") and two distinct fluids or forms of "matter." The roles of T. O. Bergmann and Berzelius badly need study. Hints as to the relation of this concept to the rise of electrochemistry are given in Thomson (1830). I have received much help in understanding this subject from a member of my seminar, Miss Constance Brewer.

The quality of the nineteenth-century thoughts about the nature of electricity can be found only by sampling the primary literature. Valuable clues may be found in Hoppe (1884) and Whittaker (1951); Bauer (1949), Millikan (1947), Rosenberger (1898), and Witz (1921) are also helpful. Windred (1932) is suggestive but all too brief. Faraday's main ideas can be found in his collected papers and his journal, Faraday (1838, 1844, 1855, and 1932-1936); the best secondary works on Faraday are Thompson (1898) and Tyndall (1870). Clerk Maxwell's masterpiece is still in print, Maxwell (1873); his shorter treatise, Maxwell (1888), and his collected papers, Maxwell (1890), are equally rewarding to the student of the history of scientific ideas. The chief secondary works are Campbell and Garnett (1882), Glazebrook (1900), and Maxwell (1931). Full-length critical studies of both Faraday and Maxwell are great desiderata. The role of electrochemistry in nineteenth-century physical thought is traced in Ostwald (1896).

For the development of the concept of the electron, see Romer (1942a and 1942b). Schuster (1911) is particularly useful as a contemporary witness; see also Chwolson (1925) and Poincaré (1929). The books of J. J. Thomson are valuable keys to the successive stages in the growth of this concept; see also his autobiography, Thomson (1936), and Rayleigh (1942). Millikan (1947) contains a glimpse of the historical record as a prelude to his own work and may be supplemented by his autobiography, Millikan (1950).

REFERENCES

1. Franklin, 1941: 293-299; 1769: 143-152.
2. Priestley, 1775: 1: 388.
3. Franklin, 1941: 293-299; 1769: 143-152.
4. Franklin, 1941: 302-306; 1769: 155-160.
5. Priestley, 1775: 1: 286.
6. *Ibid.*, 294.
7. E. g., Poggendorff, 1883: 533; Thompson, 1888.
8. E. Kinnersley to Franklin, 12 March 1761, Franklin, 1941: 349-351; 1769: 386 389.
9. Franklin, 1941: 365-368; 1769: 404-408.
10. Canton, 1754.
11. *Ibid.*, 782.
12. Franklin, 1758: Anmerkungen, § 41.
13. Priestley, 1775: 2: appendix, p. iii.
14. *Ibid.*, 1: 275.
15. Æpinus, 1759?: ch. 1, p. 9.
16. *Ibid.*, 10.
17. *Ibid.*, 11-12.
18. See Franklin, 1907: 3: 481; 4: 250; 6: 25, 25n.
19. Æpinus, 1759?: 39.
20. *Ibid.*, 40.
21. *Ibid.*, 72-82.
22. Priestley, 1775: 1: 302-303.
23. *Ibid.*, 303.
24. Æpinus, 1759?: 257-258.
25. Priestley, 1775: 1: 304.
26. Morgan, 1794: 1: 12.
27. Symmer, 1759.
28. Priestley, 1775: 1: 322.
29. Symmer, 1759.
30. Priestley, 1775: 1: 323.
31. Symmer, 1759.
32. Franklin, 1941: 255n; 1769: 106n.
33. Priestley, 1775: 1: 308-309.
34. Symmer, 1759.
35. Æpinus, 1759?: 38-39.
36. Franklin, 1941: 336; 1769: 325.
37. Priestley, 1775: 2: 374.
38. Cavendish, 1879: intro., p. xxxi; Cavendish's sketch of his apparatus is reproduced on p. 104 and described in § 217-234.
39. *Ibid.*, 3.
40. Whittaker, 1951: 53; a complete discussion may be found in Roller and Roller, 1954.
41. Coulomb, 1884: sixième mémoire (1788), trans. in Whittaker, 1951: 58.
42. Cavallo, 1803: 3: 349-350, 349n.
43. Haüy, 1787.
44. Haüy, 1807: 1: 347, 347n.
45. *Ibid.*, 342, art. 378.
46. *Ibid.*, 387, art. 416.
47. Young, 1807: Lecture LIV.
48. Robison, 1822: 4: 66-67.
49. *Ibid.*, 68.
50. *Ibid.*, 108.
51. Thomson, 1830: 347-348.
52. Ramsey, 1937: 20.

53. Thomson, 1830: 426.
54. *Ibid.*, 347n.
55. Haüy, 1807: 1: 364, art. 396; also p. 348, art. 387.
56. Berzelius, 1811.
57. Thomson, 1830: 425.
58. Cavendish, 1879: editor's notes, p. 367.
59. Faraday, 1838, 1844, 1855: 1: § 511, 516.
60. *Ibid.*, § 667.
61. Maxwell, 1873: pt. I, ch. 1, art. 34.
62. *Ibid.*, art 35.
63. *Ibid.*, art. 36.
64. *Ibid.*, art. 37.
65. Maxwell, 1888, art. 10.
66. Millikan, 1947: 18-19.
67. *Ibid.*, 17.
68. Helmholtz, 1881: 282-283.
69. Maxwell, 1873: pt. 2, ch. 4, art. 255-260.
70. Schuster, 1911: 51.
71. See Millikan, 1947: 14.
72. Rutherford, 1906: 154.
73. *Ibid.*, 124, 156.
74. Jeans, 1908: 20, art. 28.
75. Van Marum, 1820: 441.
76. *Ibid.*, 444. Volta's original letter is printed in Bosscha, 1905: 12.
77. Van Marum, 1820: 443.
78. Van Doren, 1945: 29.

NEWTON'S USE OF THE WORD *HYPOTHESIS*

In Chapter Five the Newtonian usages of the word "hypothesis" were enumerated. In the following pages, the way in which each such usage was applied explicitly or implied by Newton is presented; thus the reader may understand the sense in which Newton's contemporaries understood this word when they examined his writings. Emphasis has been placed primarily on examples from the *Principia*.

1. *A system of the world.* This was an accepted meaning of hypothesis in the seventeenth century, illustrated in such phrases as the "Copernican hypothesis."

2. *The "premise" of a mathematical theorem.* This was the standard usage in geometry in Newton's day. Thus in the popular edition of Euclid prepared by Newton's teacher, Barrow, we find "hypothesis" used throughout. The first appearance is in Proposition IV of the First Book: "If two triangles *BAC*, *EDF*, have two sides of the one *BA*, *AC* equal to two sides of the other *ED*, *DF*, each to its corresponding side [that is, *BA = ED*, and *AC = DF*] and have the angle *A* equal to the angle *D* . . . ," then the two triangles are congruent and the third corresponding sides are equal and also the other corresponding angles. As the proof proceeds, it is necessary to make use of the equality of *DE* and *AB*, and a postil indicates "*hyp.*" The postils, or marginal notes justify the steps in the proof and they invoke the postulates and axioms, previous theorems, constructions, and earlier parts of the proofs, as well as hypotheses. In this sense, whenever in the *Principia*, Newton wrote a problem in the form, "supposing that a body oscillating in a cycloid is resisted as the square of the velocity; to find the resistance in each place," the supposition of "a body oscillating in a cycloid . . . resisted as the square of the velocity" is a mathematical hypothesis.

3. *A general proposition in mathematics that is not proved.* Such an hypothesis is introduced in order to see what theorems may follow from it, and is similar to the preceding category although more general. Newton explained this usage in the *Principia* when he said, "In mathematics we are to investigate the quantities of forces with their properties consequent upon any conditions supposed."[1] Thus Newton explored the consequences of various laws of attraction, not only of bodies which have a mutual attraction

"inversely proportional to the squares" of the distance between them, but also an attraction which may "increase in a simple ratio of their distances from the centres,"[2] and so on. Now the major achievement of the *Principia* was to apply (in Book Three) the inverse square law of gravitation to falling bodies on the earth's surface, to the moon, and to the solar system. Yet, in the earlier parts of the treatise, Newton was developing mathematical consequences of various types of "assumptions" or hypotheses, without constant regard for physical application. This category of hypotheses differs from the previous one in that they apply to a whole set of theorems, rather than a single one.

Hypotheses of this type may have any of several degrees of generality. For instance, the types of attractive force just mentioned are used in scattered propositions in Book One of the *Principia*. In Book Two, however, each section is devoted to the elaboration of the mathematical consequences of a single mathematical hypothesis, a different one for each section. Section One is subtitled, "The motion of bodies that are resisted in the ratio of the velocity." It contains four propositions; in each one, there appears such a phrase as "if a body is resisted in the ratio of its velocity," or a minor variant of it. Newton observed specifically that this assumption is "more a mathematical hypothesis than a physical one" and indicated that in a medium "void of all tenacity" the resistance is proportional to the square of the velocity.[3] In Section Two, therefore, Newton investigated the mathematical consequences of the hypothesis that the resistance is proportional to the square of the velocity. This hypothesis is stated explicitly in many theorems in Section Two. Section Three explores an assumption or hypothesis of resistance of bodies "partly in the ratio of the velocities and partly as the square of the same ratio," but these words do not occur in every theorem, being at times replaced by such a phrase as "the same things being supposed." In a scholium Newton pointed out that the "resistance of spherical bodies in fluids arises partly from the tenacity, partly from the attrition, and partly from the density of the medium."[4] Here is a physical statement, to indicate how the mathematical results are to be combined when applied in nature. The statement of the laws of force owing to each of the three variables is a physical hypothesis, or—as Newton said—a "speculation."

The form of Section Nine differs a little from the preceding ones, in that it begins with a general hypothesis, stated as such: "HYPOTHESIS—The resistance arising from the want of lubricity in the parts of a fluid is, other things being equal, proportional to the velocity with which the parts of the fluid are separated from one another." There is, I believe, no special significance to the fact that this particular hypothesis is displayed, whereas the hypothesis in each of the preceding sections is not. Very likely Newton merely adopted this device so that the ensuing theorems would not be inordinately long by having to repeat it in each theorem, or even having to write it out in full in the first theorem (which is long enough as it stands).

4. *The premise in a philosophical (or physical) proposition.* Proposition XXIII (Theorem XVIII) of Book Two of the *Principia* states that if "a fluid be composed of particles fleeing from each other," Boyle's law implies a "centrifugal force" between the particles that is "inversely proportional to the distances of their centres." The converse is also stated: if particles "fleeing from each other" have such a mutual repulsive force, they "compose an elastic fluid, whose density is as the compression." [5] Now this is intended to be a mathematical theorem, and it is then generalized in the scholium immediately following. If the centrifugal forces are inversely as the square of the distances between the centers of the particles then "the cubes of the compressing forces will be as the fourth power of the densities," and so on. In this way Newton produced a general result: if the centrifugal force F is inversely proportional to D^n, where D is the distance between the centers of the particles,

$$F \propto \frac{1}{D^n} \, ,$$

then the compressing forces Φ (or pressure) will be proportional to $\sqrt[3]{E^{n+2}}$

$$\Phi \propto E^{(n+2)/3},$$

where E is the density of the compressed fluid. In the case of $n = 1$,

$$F \propto \frac{1}{D}$$

and $$\Phi \propto E,$$

or Boyle's law holds.

Newton insisted that he had done no more than to demonstrate "mathematically the property of fluids consisting of particles of this kind," which means that the assumption of any particular value of n (say $n = 1$) is only a mathematical hypothesis, of the kind explored above.

"But" said Newton, "whether elastic fluids do really consist of particles so repelling each other, is a physical question." Newton had introduced the mathematical demonstration, "that hence philosophers may take occasion to discuss that question." Newton avoided any discussion of the philosophical hypothesis that particles of an elastic fluid obey the law that $F \propto 1/D$, even though it led to the experimentally observed relation of Boyle's law. Since Newton had proved both the theorem and its converse, he knew that such a law was not only a sufficient condition but a necessary one. The element of hypothesis did not, therefore, rest on this particular law of force, but rather on the assumption that elastic fluids are made up of particles that repel one another. There was no evidence for the latter assumption in " phenomena." Hence, in the physical proposition that would have resulted if Newton had assumed that Proposition XXIII (Theorem XVIII) were more than merely mathematical, the hypothesis would be only that part which said: " if a fluid be composed of particles fleeing from one another."

Boyle's law presents an admirable occasion for the examination of physical hypotheses in relation to Boyle's own attitude and the later interpretations of Newton's discussion of this law by his contemporaries and by other scientists of the eighteenth century down to Dalton. The premise of Prop. XXIII (Th. XVIII) of Book Two of the *Principia* becomes a philosophical (physical) rather than a mathematical hypothesis if we take the proposition in a physical sense. As such, it becomes the basis of a system " laid down from one's own imagination " to be used to " account for some phæ- nomenon or appearance in nature," which—as we saw in Chapter Five—was John Harris's definition of hypothesis in his *Lexicon Technicum*. It is categorically similar to an hypothesis which Newton later condemned, that atoms cohere to form solid bodies because they have " hooks " which link them together.

When Boyle described the " spring of the air," he noted that this particular " phænomenon or appearance in nature " (if we may paraphrase the remarks of Boyle, quoted in Chapter Four, in the language of Harris) could be accounted for by one of two products of the " imagination ": the hypothesis of air particles being like feathers and the alternate hypothesis of air particles being like coiled springs. By refusing to declare for one or the other in his book on the " spring of the air," Boyle was saying (in effect) that in this place he will " frame no hypothesis." Boyle had adopted the Torricellian concept that the mercury in the barometric tube was supported by the pressure of the air which results from the weight of the atmosphere pushing down on the compressible air (an elastic fluid). This was a generalization of the deductions from the phenomena of experience, a general law of nature and not (in Newton's sense) an hypothesis. But one of those who objected to Boyle's writings on this subject invented an hypothesis of a " funiculus " or invisible thread which supported the mercury column by suspending it from the top of the glass tube. This was plainly an hypothesis, since no datum of experience shows us that such a thread exists. Boyle rejected it, but to make others reject it too, he undertook a program of experiments to show that this hypothesis was not consistent with phenomena. Boyle's procedure was like Newton's when Newton showed that Descartes' hypothesis of vortices must be rejected because it led to a contradiction of the best astronomical observations.

5. *Propositions which Newton was unable to prove.* In this category, we would place the proposition that, if the earth were replaced by a ring, the ring would precess just like the earth, whether the ring were fluid, or hard and rigid. In a sense, such a proposition is an extra axiom or postulate. But I should guess that Newton called it an hypothesis because he thought it might be proved eventually. He could not have envisioned such a proof for the other hypothesis that appeared in Book Three of the *Principia,* in the second and third editions, the proposition that " the center of the system of the world is immovable," which he said " is acknowledged by all." *

6. *Counter-to-fact conditions.* When Newton, in the " System of the World," proved the proposition that the " circumterrestrial force decreases inversely as the square of the distances from the earth," he did so first " on the hypothesis that the earth is at rest " and later " on the hypothesis that the earth moves." [6] Since both of these hypotheses cannot be true, one of them must be false. By showing that the proposition was universally true, Newton proved that it was independent of any particular hypothesis. Yet in this case, Newton may have been using the word in the sense of *category 1* above, as implying the Copernican (heliocentric) hypothesis in one case and either the Ptolemaic or Tychonian (geocentric) hypothesis in the other.

In general, it was the custom in Newton's work to introduce only such hypotheses as were possible or plausible. In the example just presented, although one of the above " hypotheses " had to be false, both were plausible, at least to the extent that history showed thinking men who had supported one as well as the other. Unlike our contemporary mathematicians and logicians, Newton was not willing to consider the logical or mathematical consequences of an absurd hypothesis, one that was not " possible," to use Harris's phrase. (Har-

* See the discussion of these two hypotheses in Chapter Five, pages 132-138, and pages 585-586 below.

ris had also indicated that an hypothesis should also " be probable.")
Newton was willing (as in the above examples) to find the consequences of a mathematical hypothesis that need not be physically
true, but he had no concern for utterly implausible ones.

We may obtain illumination on the problem of hypotheses in
physics and mathematics being " possible " by turning to the writings
of Isaac Barrow, Newton's teacher. In his *Mathematical Lectures*,
Barrow said that the hypotheses supposed by mathematicians, like
the postulates they admit, are only " such as are evidently possible,
and most easy to the imagination." [7] Thus when the hypothesis is
supposed of a straight line being drawn between two points, a body
being cut by a plane, or a semicircle being turned on its axis, such
suppositions are " evidently possible " because of experience: they
are " things which . . . [everybody] sees and experiences to be done
daily." But in physics there are often hypotheses and postulates
" which are altogether arbitrary, hard to be digested, and mon-
strously immodest: things which are not only difficult to be believed,
but oftentimes hard to be conceived." An example was that " certain
corporeal effluvia, or thin skins, peeled from the thing objected [an
object], more fine than thought itself, are every where carried in a
direct course towards whatsoever is placed in view." [8]

The possibility of mathematical hypotheses, according to Barrow,
is actually " deduced " from sensations. The falsehood of an hypothesis is, in the same manner, " nothing but the conception or
position of a thing as effected or existing, which cannot be effected
or exist "; examples are the supposition that a triangle may have
four angles, that a man may be " void of sense and reason," or that
a circle may have a circumference four times its diameter.[9]

Barrow indicated that Galileo " thinks that he invented a new
science concerning motion, *by supposing that heavy things are
naturally carried towards the center of the earth with a motion uniformly accelerated.*" Even if it should be false that this particular
kind of motion exists " in the present œconomy of nature," yet it
might " exist at the pleasure of God " because it implies nothing
" contrary to possibility." Hence the conclusions from such an hypothesis " ought to be accounted for lawful demonstrations," even
if not physically true in the world around us. It is, in other words,
possible for " demonstrations " resting on such hypotheses to be true
in the sense of being " true, not indeed of this world, but of the
other, which is supposed capable of being created by God." [10]

But how, among all possible or plausible hypotheses, do we find
one that applies to " this world " ? Barrow's reply is: by experiment.
In optics, for example, there is an hypothesis: " That a ray or lumi-

nous right line may be extended from any (at least a physical) point of a visible object to the eye wheresoever placed in a homogeneous medium." Such an hypothesis, said Barrow, is admitted because of experimental data, or phenomena. In this case, the evidence is that by experience we know that "an object is every where seen, except there be a body placed somewhere in a right line between it and the eye." [11]

These statements of Barrow's should make it plain that the procedure of the mathematicians and physicists of the seventeenth century was not that of the modern logician. Their hypotheses, even the limited usages we have seen in the categories up to this point, were—like their axioms and postulates—never arbitrary assumptions, but always possible assumptions, and supposed to be ultimately derived from experience.

7. *Mechanisms supposed in order to explain laws or phenomena.* Newton's law of universal gravitation, like the three laws of motion, was considered by Newton to be founded in experience. As in the example offered by Barrow of the rectilinear propagation of light, such "laws" are tested by experiment and observation: they are deduced from phenomena and rendered general by induction. But when Newton supposed an æther, composed of mutually repulsive particles, capable of penetrating all bodies, and differing in density by degrees, he was advancing an hypothesis, as he freely admitted in his communication to the Royal Society, and in his letter to Boyle. His suggestion that, in the æther, waves might be caused by the motion of light particles, and that these waves might overtake the particles and put them into successive fits of easy reflection and easy refraction, was said by Newton himself (in Book Two of the *Opticks*) to be an hypothesis. Hypotheses of this kind were advanced by Newton at all stages of his life and thought. We may observe that their purpose was to explain a theory, but that the theory was considered to be built on deductions from principles that were based on experiment or on concepts that arose from experiment. Newton tried to keep such hypotheses distinct from his theories, and in the main did it successfully. Such hypotheses were generally introduced by Newton *after the fact*; I have found few examples in which Newton used such an hypothesis to predict the outcome of an experiment.

An hypothesis of this sort comes under Newton's definition of not being "deduced from phenomena" and then rendered general by induction. Is the corpuscularity of light to be taken under theory or hypothesis? In Newton's sense, the supposition of light corpuscles is like the hypothesis of an æther. Newton actually tried to show that his "theory" of color would conform to either a corpuscular or an undulatory hypothesis. Yet he believed in the hypothesis of corpuscularity, although with undulatory overtones provided by the supplementary æther hypothesis, and held that neither one by itself could explain all the phenomena.

From the point of view of the experimental scientists of the eighteenth century, this type of hypothesis was very fruitful. The scientists in the age of Newton developed explanations which, although based on concepts of subtle fluids and particles that were not deduced from phenomena, nevertheless enabled them to correlate more and more aspects of nature and to predict accurately the outcome of experiments.

8. "*Philosophical Romance.*" The kind of hypothesis described in *category* 7 is to be taken in distinction to the Cartesian hypothesis of vortices, or any hypothesis that produced an arbitrary theory in the absence of experience. Newton's hypothesis of the æther was constructed to explain gravitation, what we would call today " interference " phenomena in optics, and other things, but Newton's theory of gravitation and his theory of optics was not necessarily dependent on the particular form that his hypothesis took. Newtonian hypotheses of this type explained a theory that was based on experience (phenomena), a theory that furthermore was tested by that same kind of experience. Hence, it was not conceived that such an hypothesis could ever contradict phenomena. In one case, the prediction of Newton's hypothesis of light as corpuscular was that the speed of light is greater in water than in air; whereas the prediction of the rival undulatory hypothesis of Huygens was that the speed is greater in air than in water. So, if one could measure such speeds, one of the two hypotheses could be rejected as false, while the other would remain as a possibly true explanation of Barrow's " this world." But such a test did not come within the possibility of experimental techniques until the nineteenth century. Newton would never have continued to suggest an hypothesis contrary to observed fact.

By contrast, the Cartesian hypothesis was shown by Newton to be contrary to results based on experience. Furthermore, it was not even created as an explanation of a sound theory based on sufficient experience. As a result, it actually inhibited the production of experiments and was designated by the Newtonians as a " philosophical romance." In this sense Newton never " framed " an " hypothesis," and he correctly said, during that early controversy on light, that his results were not the logical consequences of an hypothesis and that they would have been valueless if they had been so produced.

Thus it becomes clear how we must read the new " Rule " (IV) introduced by Newton into the third edition of the *Principia*. Propositions, he wrote, that " are inferred by general induction from phenomena " are to be considered " as accurately or very nearly true " until other phenomena are found " by which they may either be made more accurate, or liable to exceptions." And we are to consider such inductions to be " accurately or very nearly true " despite " any contrary hypotheses that may be imagined." Only in this way can we be sure " that the argument of induction may not be evaded by hypotheses." [12] Hypotheses might suggest experiments or explain the results of induction, but the acceptance of experimental laws or theories based on testable deductions from such laws should never be inhibited by products of the imagination in divorce from the solid conclusions of experiment.

9. *Axioms or postulates.* Barrow's writings tell us that in physical science a generally received hypothesis is founded on experience: experiment or observation. An hypothesis may be similar to an axiom, as Newton explained the matter. Hence, Newton on occasion used the term hypothesis to serve for axiom, in most cases (but not all!) making it clear that there was evidence in experience or phenomena to support it. In his first published paper on light and colors, Newton referred to Snel's law as an hypothesis; later on, in the *Opticks*, it became Axiom V: " The sine of incidence is either accurately or very nearly in a given ratio to the sine of refraction."

In *Isaaci Newtoni Propositiones de motu*, a " specimen " of the great work, sent to the Royal Society in 1685, there are three definitions followed by four " hypotheses " and two lemmas, after which come the theorems and their proofs, problems and scholia. " Hypothesis II," for example, relates to the motion of bodies: " Corpus omne sola vi insita uniformiter secundum lineam rectam in infinitum progredi, nisi aliquid extrinsecus impediat." [13] (This " hypothesis " is similar to " Lex I " in the *Principia*, considered by Newton to be the primary axiom of the system.) In a paper sent to John Locke and indorsed " Mr. Newton, March 1689," entitled " A Demonstration, That the Planets, by their Gravity towards the Sun, may move in Ellipses," Newton begins with three hypotheses, as follows:

Hypoth. 1.—Bodies move uniformly in straight lines, unless so far as they are retarded by the resistance of the medium, or disturbed by some other force.

Hypoth. 2.—The alteration of motion is proportional to the force by which it is altered.

Hypoth. 3.—Motions impressed by forces in different lines, if those lines be taken in proportion to the motions, and completed into a parallelogram, compose a motion whereby the diagonal of the parallelogram shall be described in the same time in which the sides thereof would have been described by the compounding motions apart.[14]

Here, again, the " laws of motion " are presented as " hypotheses."

" Mathematical Principles " and " Natural Philosophy "

Newton's *Principia* was devoted to two major aims, the establishment of mathematical principles and their application to natural philosophy. Over and over, throughout the book, Newton made it plain that the first two parts dealt with mathematics, general theorems which might or not apply to the phenomena of the real world. Book Three was conceived differently; it was to demonstrate the application of some of these theorems to the system of the world. Thus Book Three deals with physical science exclusively, with natural philosophy. Book Three is the part of the *Principia* which contains the fruit of the mathematical principles previously established. Hence Newton saw that Book Three must contain procedural rules for the transition from pure mathematics to applied, from laws which might apply to some conceivable universe to the laws which experience shows us to hold in " this world." In the first edition, Book Three, " De Mundi Systemate," opens with the same introductory paragraph to be found in later editions, followed immediately by the " HYPOTHESES." There are nine of them, which in later editions were partially revised and regrouped into three categories: REGULÆ PHILOSOPHANDI, PHÆNOMENA, and HYPOTHESES.

On 21 July 1706 Newton showed David Gregory an interleaved copy of the *Principia* " corrected for the press, . . . intirely finished as far as Sect. VII. Lib. II, page 317." Gregory noted, " In the beginning of Lib. III. he leaves out Hyp. III, and puts another in its place as in my copy. These three he now calls *Regulæ Philosophandi.* Hyp. V, etc., he calls by the title of *Phænomena.* Hyp. IV is the only one that he leaves that name to; & it comes after the *Phænomena.*" [15] Later, Newton moved this " hypothesis " to the place where it was first needed. This alteration of the original version of the *Principia*, we must observe, took place many years before Newton wrote out the final General Scholium to Book Three, with its statement of *Hypotheses non fingo.*

The first three of the original " hypotheses " deal with " causes " and procedures. They are hypotheses in that they are not " deduced from phenomena," and there was no inconsistency in calling them so. They could equally have been called " laws " or " axioms " or

" rules." Thus we can readily understand both their having originally been called " hypotheses " and the later, more precise name of
" regulæ philosophandi." Hypotheses I-III, which became Rules I-
III, are as follows:

[*First edition*] Hypothesis I: *Causas rerum naturalium non plures
admitti debere, quàm quæ & vera sint & earum Phænomenis explicandis
sufficiunt.* ("We are to admit no more natural things than such as are
both true and sufficient to explain their appearances." [16]) In the first
edition the discussion contained but a single sentence, *Natura enim sim-
plex est & rerum causis superfluis non luxuriat.* ("Nature is pleased
with simplicity and affects not the pomp of superfluous causes." [17] In
this rendition Andrew Motte added some adornment to the austere
original.) In the second edition, this Hypothesis I became Regula I
and Newton added an additional sentence in the discussion of it: *Dicunt
utique philosophi: Natura nihil agit frustra, & frustra fit per plura quod
fieri potest per pauciora.* ("To this purpose the philosophers say that
Nature does nothing in vain, and more is in vain when less will serve." [18])
In the second edition, the misprint *vera* was corrected.

[First edition] Hypothesis II: *Ideoque effectuum naturalium ejusdem
generis eædem sunt causæ.* ("Therefore, to the same natural effects we
must, as far as possible, assign the same cause." [19]) This Hypothesis II
became Regula II in the second edition; the discussion of it by Newton
was unaltered.

[First edition] Hypothesis III: *Corpus omne in alterius cujuscunque
generis corpus transformari posse, & qualitatum gradus omnes intermedios
successivè induere.* (This may be translated as follows: "Every body
can be transformed into a body of any other kind, and assumes successively all the intermediate degrees of qualities.") In the second edition
of the *Principia*, this hypothesis was considerably altered to become
Regula III: *Qualitates corporum quæ intendi & remitti nequent, quæque
corporibus omnibus competunt in quibus experimenta instituere licet,
pro qualitatibus corporum universorum habendæ sunt.* ("The qualities
of bodies, which admit neither intensification nor remission of degrees,
and which are found to belong to all bodies within the reach of our
experiments, are to be esteemed the universal qualities of all bodies
whatsoever." [20] A fourth "Rule," added in the third edition, states: " In
experimental philosophy we are to look upon propositions inferred by
general induction from phænomena as accurately or very nearly true,
notwithstanding any contrary hypotheses that may be imagined, till such
time as other phænomena occur, by which they may either be made more
accurate, or liable to exceptions." [21] These "Hypotheses" I-III or
" Regulæ " I-IV are general procedural precepts for science, or natural
philosophy. They do not refer particularly to the *Principia*.

" Hypotheses IV " in the first edition contains the statement that:
Centrum systematis mundani quiescere (" The center of the system

of the world is at rest "). There is a comment that this is admitted by everyone, although some claim that it is the sun, and others the earth, that is at rest at the center. In the second edition, this theorem remains an hypothesis. It no longer stands at the beginning of Book Three, however, but is removed to the place where it is first needed, following Proposition X (Th. X). In the second edition, as in the third, this proposition is called " Hypothesis I." In the second and third edition there is also an " Hypothesis II." (The statement which has recently been made—about the second edition having, in Book Three, an " Hypothesis I " but *not* an " Hypothesis II "—is incorrect.) Hypothesis II appears just before Proposition XXXIX (Problem XX), and contains the statement about the precession of a rotating ring being similar to that of the earth. In the first edition, this " hypothesis " had been Lemma III to Proposition XXVIII (Prob. XVII), stated without proof. Curiously enough, the description of alterations made by Newton in his own interleaved copy of the *Principia* would indicate that the new order of statements at the beginning of Book Three was the " Regulæ Philosophandi " (the old " Hypothesis I," " Hypothesis II," and the new " regula " to replace the original " Hypothesis III "), then the " Phænomena " (the old ' Hypothesis V," etc.), and then the " hypothesis " about the center of the system of the world being at rest (originally " Hypothesis IV "), the only hypothesis that Newton " leaves that name to." Evidently, Newton had thought he would be able to prove this proposition and only gave up at the time of publication of the second edition of the *Principia*; a century later Laplace did find a proof.

Of greater interest is the alteration of " hypotheses "—supposedly neither phenomena nor deductions from phenomena—to the category of " phenomena." The five final " hypotheses " in the first edition, later the six " Phænomena," † all deal with the Copernican system.

---

† These " Phenomena " are as follows: I, " That the circumjovial planets, by radii drawn to Jupiter's centre, describe areas proportional to the times of description; and that their periodic times, the fixed stars being at rest, are as the $\frac{3}{2}$th power of their distances from its centre." II, " That the circumsaturnal planets, by radii drawn to Saturn's centre, describe areas proportional to the times of description; and that their periodic times, the fixed stars being at rest, are as the $\frac{3}{2}$th power of their distances from its centre." III, " That the five primary planets, Mercury, Venus, Mars, Jupiter, and Saturn, with their several orbits, encompass the sun." IV, " That the fixed stars being at rest, the periodic times of the five primary planets, and (whether of the sun about the earth, or of the earth about the sun) are as the $\frac{3}{2}$th power of their mean distances from the sun." V, " Then the primary planets, by radii drawn to the sun, describe areas in no wise proportional to the times; but the areas which they describe by radii drawn to the sun are proportional to the times of description." VI, " That the moon, by a radius drawn to the earth's centre, describes an area proportional to the time of description." 22

Phenomenon I was Hypothesis V in the first edition. Phenomenon II was not one of the original set of hypotheses. Phenomena III, IV, V, and VI were respectively Hypotheses VI, VII, VIII, and IX in the first edition.

In all three editions of the *Principia*, Newton referred to this system as the " Copernican hypothesis," a fact which may furnish us with the key. In " Phænomenon V," for example, Newton indicated that in the Copernican system (" hypothesis ") a radius vector drawn from the sun to a " primary " planet will sweep out, for each such planet, an area proportional to the time, but that in the geocentric system, no such law may be observed. Thus, this proposition merely states that a mathematical relation may be derived from observations in one of two alternative systems (or " hypotheses "), but not in the other; it seems likely, therefore, that in the original writing of the *Principia*, Newton may have thought of this proposition as an expression of the characteristics of one of two rival " hypotheses " and so was itself an hypothesis. In the same way, the statement in " Phænomenon III," (originally " Hypothesis VI "), that the five planets—Mercury, Venus, Mars, Jupiter, and Saturn—revolve about the sun, might have been considered by Newton as a descriptive statement about either the Tychonic or the Copernican system (or " hypothesis "), but not about the Ptolemaic system (or " hypothesis "), and as such was also to be considered under the rubric of hypothesis. " Phænomenon IV " (formerly " Hypothesis VII ") states the harmonic law of Kepler in a form that would likewise apply to either the Copernican or the Tychonian system (or " hypothesis ") but not the Ptolemaic, so it too might be properly considered an hypothesis. " Phaenomenon VI " (formerly " Hypothesis IX ") may be thought to be different from the ones just mentioned —in that it provides a statement of Kepler's second law with respect to the moon in its orbit around the earth—because the moon was considered to revolve around the earth in all the major systems of the world, i. e., the Ptolemaic, the Tychonian, and the Copernican. Yet if these three systems were considered as " hypotheses," then plainly this statement too, as a derivation from an hypothesis (even if a derivation from *all* hypotheses hitherto stated), could be placed in the same category as the others. The first of the " Phænomena," being merely a statement of Kepler's second and third laws for the Jovian satellites, is in a similar category to the application of Kepler's second law to the earth's moon.

When Newton originally wrote down the " phænomena " as " hypotheses," he indicated the evidence for their validity. Thus, when he stated (Hyp. V; later Phæn. I) that the moons of Jupiter obey the second and third laws of Kepler, he pointed out that this was " known " from astronomical observation (" Constat ex observationibus astronomicis ") and presented supporting data. And in his statement about the five primary planets encircling the sun (Hyp. VI; later Phæn. III), he indicated the evidence from the observed phases of Mercury, Venus, and so on. This procedure was in accord with the doctrine that hypotheses must be possible and should be probable. Since the data were presumably reliable, any statement about Kepler's laws might be presumed to be as true a statement about the planets and their satellites as the Copernican system was a true description of the universe in general. And to the extent that all systems of the universe were hypotheses, in the sense that they could not be proved by phænomena to be such true descriptions, then any statement about the planets and their satellites (no matter what system was invoked) was by definition an hypothesis.

In any event, the distinction between " phænomena " and " hypotheses "—so important in the second edition—was not of great importance in the first edition, or at the time when he first composed the *Principia*. Then his concern was only to show by phenomena that, to use Harris' phrase, the hypotheses he presented were " possible " and very " probable," or that the evidence from phenomena was so great that they were to all practical intents and purposes " non-hypothetical " in the modern sense and, in fact, true. The presentation, in the first edition, of the phenomena of observation on which he based the " hypotheses " at the beginning of Book Three, indicates to us that these particular " hypotheses " were to some degree based upon phenomena and, in this sense, in some way similar to the axioms in Book One, which were called the " laws " of motion.

I cannot believe that Newton was ever careless in his choice of words, and so I am convinced that there was a reason for the difference between the use of " laws " for the axioms in Book One and " hypotheses " in Book Three. It would seem likely that Newton had used " laws " for the general axioms that were applied throughout the whole treatise, and " hypotheses " for the general propositions that applied only to Book Three and which were guides to " natural philosophy " or statements about the solar system, or parts of the solar system. Hence, in every edition of the *Principia* they were given a different classification from the postulates of all dynamics, being called " hypotheses " (or " Regulæ Philosophandi," " Phænomena," " Hypotheses "), rather than " Axiomata " or " Leges."

It is not surprising that in the first edition Newton called the later " Phænomena " hypotheses. But it is certainly puzzling that he should have later given the name " Phænomena " to statements which, at best, were generalizations based on observations, or perhaps derivations from phenomena, i. e., statements of the conditions under which Kepler's harmonic law and law of areas hold—to the satellites of Jupiter and Saturn, to the five primary planets in relation to the sun (and not in relation to the earth).

SOURCES

The subject of Newton's use of " hypotheses " is a neglected topic in the history of science. Undoubtedly, one of the reasons why no one has ever explored this aspect of Newton's thought is the lack of a critical edition of Newton's scientific works. A brave beginning was made by Jourdain, in a series of articles in *The Monist,* to understand the development of Newton's hypotheses, but the lead he gave was not pursued by others. In an article that appeared as this monograph was going to press, Koyré has given a brilliant analysis of some of the changes in the editions of the *Principia*; see Koyré (1955). Koyré's findings parallel mine, but he confines his attention to the alteration from " Hypotheses " to " Regulæ Philosophandi," without paying too much attention to the " Phæ-nomena." His discussion of the use of the term "hypothesis" in the scientific writings on astronomy of the sixteenth and seventeenth centuries is most valuable.

REFERENCES

1. *Principia*, bk. I, scholium following prop. LXIX (th. XXIX) ; Newton, 1934: 192.
2. E. g., *Principia*, bk. I, prop. LXIII (prob. XXXIX) , prop. LXIV (prob. XL) ; Newton, 1934: 169.
3. *Principia*, bk. II, scholium following prop. IV (prob. II) ; Newton, 1934: 244.
4. *Principia*, bk. II, scholium following prop. XIV (th. XI) ; Newton, 1934: 280-281.
5. Newton, 1934: 300-301.
6. *Ibid.*, 559-561.
7. Barrow, 1734: 57.
8. *Ibid.*, 58.
9. *Ibid.*, 75, 109.
10. *Ibid.*, 110-111.
11. *Ibid.*, 133.
12. Newton, 1934: 400.
13. Rigaud, 1838: 25 ff.; appendix, p. 1.
14. King, 1830: 1: 388.
15. Hiscock, 1937: 36.
16. Newton, 1934: 398.
17. *Idem.*
18. *Idem.*
19. *Idem.*
20. *Idem.*
21. *Ibid.*, 400.
22. *Ibid.*, 401-405.

ORIGINALITY IN SCIENTIFIC DISCOVERY, WITH SPECIAL REFERENCE TO FRANKLIN'S EX-PERIMENTS AND HIS CONCEPT OF THE ELECTRIC FLUID

Here and there throughout this book, reference has been made to the problem of evaluating the degree of originality in scientific work. In some cases, the job of the historian is simple, as when a chemist produces in his laboratory a synthetic substance that never had existed up until that time, or a naturally occurring substance that had not previously been obtained in a pure state. We may easily date the first occurrence of such man-made substances as the trans-uranium elements and compounds like 2-4-dichlorphenoxyacetic acid and trinitrotoluene. Generally, there is no question of the date of the first preparation or isolation of oxygen, carbon dioxide, nitrogen, chlorine, uranium, sodium or potassium.

Yet once the historian leaves the relatively simple topic of the preparation or isolation of pure substances, and explores the discovery of effects or phenomena, great questions arise at once—of a kind which have been all too little explored. Franklin complained that the creator in the realm of science always faces the possibility of attack by those who seek to discredit him by digging up a reference to each new discovery in some obscure work of the past. Hence, even if it is not possible to deny the discovery, at least it can often be shown that the research itself was not very original after all and not therefore the great creation claimed by the author. An instance: Lavoisier was confronted by the work done a century earlier by Jean Rey on the calcination of tin, which would have remained forgotten had it not been rediscovered by the opponents of Lavoisier.[1] Again, when Volta discovered the electrical effects that arise when two different metals are linked by acid or salt—a discovery which seemed to confute Galvani's concept of an animal electric fluid—Aldini, the nephew of Galvani, dug up a reference to this type of phenomenon in an older book by Sulzer. Sulzer's book dealt with the theory of sensations and contained a reference to the curious feeling that arises when two coins of different metals are placed respectively below and above the tongue and then brought together until they touch. Sulzer did not, of course, recognize that the effect was in any sense related to electricity nor did it enter the literature of electrical science until after Volta had made his discovery.[2] Neither the work of Volta nor that of Lavoisier had been influenced by the writings of the " precursor " dug up by their opponents; plainly, so far as the positive advance of knowledge is concerned, the writings of Rey and Sulzer were not of the major importance that might seem to be attributed to them in an uncritical chronological record of the appearance in print of relevant information on the subjects of chemistry and electricity.

The two last examples indicate that a distinction must be made between the publication of a new fact or idea and its effective incorporation into the living stream of scientific knowledge. Without venturing far into the reasons why a major or minor discovery may not become at once a part of scientific knowledge, we may say that some discoveries achieve their significance only when they become part of a growing body of theory or when the subject to which they belong has advanced sufficiently for the discovery to be related to other information. The histories of electricity generally give much credit to Otto von Guericke, in whose book of 1672—it is often said —there are many major discoveries, including " the discovery of electrical conduction, of electrical polarity, of the transmission of electrification over an elongated conductor, of electric light, of sound produced by electricity, of the discharging capacity of points, of the dissipation of charge by hot air, and of the vibration of a freely-movable body due to its charge and discharge; the first recognition of electrical repulsion as such, a direct suggestion of the identity of electrical attraction and gravity, and the construction and successful use of the first machine for the production of electricity." [3] But we have recently been reminded that Guericke did not conceive his investigations to be related to the nascent science of electricity, that those who wrote on electricity for the next half century showed no awareness of Guericke's work, and that Guericke's writings were not recognized as being of importance to electricity until they were mentioned by Du Fay in the 1730's.[4] Du Fay wrote as if he were the discoverer of Guericke's contribution to electricity and said that much of what had been found out in this subject since Guericke's day was to be found in Guericke's book.

The previous examples may serve to illustrate the general proposition that the historian's judgment on the importance or originality of a scientific discovery should not be distorted by the mere finding of the statement of some precursor. This proposition may even apply to cases in which the precursor's statement was widely read, but in which the discovery was not complete, either in some detail or degree of generality, or perhaps in the manner of proof. It would not then be fair to the final discoverer to say only that his demonstration made the discovery more generally acceptable, or that he had not done something of considerable originality. A case in point, to which reference has been made in Chapter Twelve, is the fact that the inverse-square law of electrical force had been printed in five English editions of Priestley's book on electricity, as well as in the French and German versions, before the law was " discovered " by Coulomb. Yet Priestley's " discovery " was incomplete. It was based on an inference from Franklin's experimental demonstration that the inner walls of an electrified hollow cylinder show no sign of charge; but what Priestley needed, in order to make his inference sound, was a demonstration that there is no charge on the inner surface of an electrified hollow sphere. Coulomb effectively discovered the law by direct experiment with a torsion balance, uncovering both the variation of the force in relation to the distance between two small charged objects and also—something of which Priestley was not apparently aware—the effect of the magnitude of the two charges. The many readers of Priestley's book were not convinced by his brilliant inference; we may say, therefore, that prior to Coulomb's work no one knew what the law of electrical force is, even in respect to the effect of the distance between two charged bodies that act upon each other.

A somewhat similar situation holds in the case of the discovery of the properties of blunt and pointed conductors in electric discharges. A number of investigators before Franklin had observed some differences between the action of the blunt and pointed ends of the same conductor. We may ignore Guericke's statements on this subject since they were not generally known, but we cannot in the same fashion dismiss what Stephen Gray had to say in his widely read papers, nor what others said on this topic. Hauksbee had seen a glow discharge at his finger-tips, and many of the German investigators in the 1740's had shown " fire hissing from the ends of iron rods " in the engravings accompanying their publications; [5] so had Nollet and Watson. Gray and Du Fay had electrified pointed conductors and Gray had even found that a pointed rod held near an electrified object causes it to discharge slowly and silently while a blunt rod produces a discharge consisting of a single snap.[6] How then could Franklin have claimed, in his first letter on electricity,[7] that among the " particular phænomena, which we looked upon to be new," was the fact that an electrified shot would lose its power of repelling a cork ball on a silk thread rapidly when a pointed object was held nearby? The answer lies in the fact that although this observation had been made, it had remained a curious isolated

phenomenon that had not been fully explored. Franklin presented
it as part of a general study of the different ways in which an electrified object may become discharged. Furthermore, he showed that a
grounded sharp object will produce such a discharge readily but
that an insulated one (the " blade of a bodkin " fixed " in a sealing
wax ") will produce no such effect. Sliding one's finger along the
wax to the blade (i. e., grounding it) produces the effect anew.
Franklin thus completed the discovery in the sense of showing the
necessity of grounding, and he showed the relevance of it to the
subject at large by relating it to the whole range of modes of discharge. Then he brought this interesting phenomenon into the prov-
enance of theory by indicating that the electrified object (charged
plus) which has a surplus of " electrical fire " can have its surplus
fire " drawn off " by the pointed conductor so long as it can go from
the pointed conductor to the ground, but if the pointed conductor
is insulated, it can accumulate on itself only a limited quantity of
" electrical fire " and thus not completely discharge the electrified
object. Finally, Franklin applied this new and complete knowledge
to the experiment of testing the electrification of clouds and to the
invention of a device for protecting man's structures from the ravages
of the lightning discharge. Hence we can understand why Franklin's
contemporaries generally attributed to Franklin the " discovery " of
the difference in effect of presenting blunt and pointed conductors
to an electrified body.[8]

When we turn from the subject of effects or phenomena to
theories, originality requires an even more precise definition. The
basic reason is that in this realm every man is the creature of his
environment. He not only thinks and expresses himself in terms of
the symbols, concepts, and language of his day, but takes as his
point of departure the theories and laws of his contemporaries and
immediate predecessors. Scholarly research may thus make it appear
that any given new conceptual scheme is so related to its environment that it can never be wholly original. It is apparently the rule
in the development of scientific thought that no theory or conceptual
scheme of scientific explanation ever appears, of which some of the
major features cannot be found in earlier writings. Prior to Galileo's
time, many of the principles and laws of motion associated with his
name had been discovered and were even well known. Yet it is
demonstrable that prior to Galileo these principles and laws had
not been systematized into the new kinematics we ascribe to Galileo;
since no one else saw, as Galileo did, how the new kinematics was
to be formulated and applied, we may consider the uniqueness of
his achievement as a measure of his genius. Such an example shows

why the historian must always be careful in defining the terms of originality in scientific thought; otherwise, the uncovering of isolated examples of anticipations may lead him to deny the great revolutions that have occurred in science and to produce a parody of history.[9] After all, even Newtonian dynamics did not spring from Newton's mind as a wholly new creation, in the sense that none of its primary concepts or postulates had ever existed before, like the synthesis of a completely unknown type of chemical compound. Of the three laws of motion, even Newton said that the first two came from Galileo. That there was a force of gravitation varying according to the inverse square of the distance had been suspected by a number of people in Newton's day; yet it would be contrary to the very spirit of science viewed in its historical development to deny to Newton in his dynamics the highest degree of creative originality and genius.

This type of question was raised and discussed in an admirable way by Johann Karl Wilcke, the eighteenth-century physicist who translated Franklin's book on electricity into German. Wilcke was exceptionally qualified to write on the subject of originality in scientific concept because he was one of the foremost investigators in electricity in the age of Franklin; some of his contributions have been described earlier in Chapters Eight and Twelve. Wilcke evidently thought well of Franklin's book, else he would not have made a translation of it. He was well acquainted with the existing literature—in German, English, French, Latin, and Italian. In the preface to his translation [10] he pointed out that there existed a vast literature on electricity, but that most of it was not " profound "—" Nature's caprice is at fault," he said, " she will permit only her few favorites to penetrate her secrets "—chief among them, Franklin. He did not wish to praise Franklin's book since " His work may speak for itself. The general admiration and marked attention with which the book has been received, not only in England but also universally among the connoisseurs of electrical experiments, praises it more emphatically than the often uncertain eulogy of a translator." Proud of his nation's contributions to the subject, Wilcke nevertheless believed, " This American supplies us with a work which will be instructive even in the homeland of electricity." He had been induced to translate the book into German because of its " scarcity in our country, its value, and the great advantage I was able to derive from it."

Wilcke wished that Franklin's book might " affect its opponents just as it did myself." He described his own experience:

I drew many conclusions and corollaries from Mr. Franklin's system on which I constructed a scheme of still further experiments, the success of which either confirmed or annihilated those theorems. The more experiments that I attempted, the further new reasons and proofs I discovered in justification of Mr. Franklin's system and explanations. I repeated his own experiments frequently and with such success that I may state with confidence that they are correct and without fault. No person will fail to attain the success Mr. Franklin promises, if only he endeavours to form a clear and general concept of the entire system and those particular cases which now and then may carry weight.

Wilcke could not understand the basis of Nollet's opposition and accused the French scientist of making an inadequate study of Franklin's experiments, " analyzing them only partly, denying the conclusions drawn from them, in place of which he cites his own. He denies that many of the experiments were as successful as Mr. Franklin asserts." But Wilcke found that Franklin's experiments succeeded with him, and the experiments used by Nollet to attack Franklin seemed to Wilcke to be susceptible of interpretations that " may be taken as arguments for rather than against Mr. Franklin's theory."

Wilcke was a man of independent mind and he did not wish to display what might seem an " unfair partiality " in " yielding to Mr. Franklin on every point." As a matter of fact, he pointed out,

There are certainly many points in his letters against which any natural scientist might justly raise doubts precisely as Mr. Nollet has opposed them. But those points, as a rule, do not concern the essential part of the system, and may be regarded as superfluous. They were subsequently corrected in part by Mr. Franklin himself.

The theory of the structure of glass and the forming of electricity in the clouds from the sea, may serve as an example. The other objections are not of a nature to induce anyone to change from a Franklinist to a partisan of Nollet. Let us confront these two theories and one will easily recognize which of the two has the more characteristics of the natural, the simple, or of hypothesis.

Wilcke said that he had placed his own experiments in an appendix of *Anmerkungen*, and he hoped that they would be considered a contribution to knowledge, not merely an attack on Nollet.

On the score of originality, here is what Wilcke said:

The *elaboration of the theory of electricity* is the chief part of this work. I emphasize the *elaboration* of this theory. The system proper and its principles which I desire to sketch in brief are not the invention of Mr. Franklin. Because all this may already be discovered in other works written earlier and with which, we may say justly according to Mr. Franklin's own statement, he was familiar. Messrs. Watson and Ellicot had already used them for treatises which these competent men published in the English *Transactions* No. 485. There one may already find these principles applied to the phenomena of attraction and repulsion; the power of pointed bodies and the fire appearing thereon; the flowing of water through capillary tubes, etc. Mr. Waiz's well known and excellent treatise on electricity and its cause, for which he was awarded a prize in Berlin, contains in part the fundamentals of precisely those theories which can be found in any good treatise on electricity.

No. 485 of the *Philosophical Transactions* (beginning vol. XLV) contains "A Collection of Electrical Experiments communicated to the Royal Society by Wm. Watson, F. R. S., and read at several meetings between October 29, 1747, and Jan. 21, following." These comprise all the papers brought together in Watson's third pamphlet,[11] and they include Watson's long quotation from Franklin and his statement of his own theory, which he claimed had been formulated (but not published) prior to the receipt of Franklin's paper.[*]

The contributions by Ellicott were not published in the same issue of the *Transactions* as Watson's, but in the following one (No. 486), "for the months of February and March 1748," actually printed under the date 1749. They were referred to by Franklin in a note to his "Opinions and Conjectures concerning the properties and effects of the electrical matter . . . 1749," which was sent to Collinson from Philadelphia, 29 July 1750. Franklin said: "See the ingenious essays on Electricity in the *Transactions* by Mr. Ellicot." The occasion was Franklin's statement of the basic principles of his theory in this fifth communication on the subject. Franklin's first four propositions are:

§ 1. The electrical matter consists of particles extremely subtile, since it can permeate common matter, even the densest metals, with such ease and freedom as not to receive any perceptible resistance.

§ 2. If any one should doubt whether the electrical matter passes through the substance of bodies, or only over and along their surfaces, a shock from an electrified large glass jar, taken through his own body, will probably convince him.

§ 3. Electrical matter differs from common matter in this, that the parts of the latter mutually attract, those of the former mutually repel each other. Hence the appearing divergency in a stream of electrified effluvia.

§ 4. But though the particles of electrical matter do repel each other, they are strongly attracted by all other matter.[12]

In Ellicott's publication, to which Franklin drew the reader's atten-

[*] See page 442 above.

tion, there are three fundamental propositions and a variety of experiments to illustrate them:

First, that the several electrical phænomena are produced by means of effluvia.

Secondly, that the particles composing these effluvia strongly repel each other.

Thirdly, that the said particles are strongly attracted by most if not all other bodies whatsoever.[13]

Ellicott had also observed the difference in effect when a pointed and a blunt conductor were brought near a charged body, a phenomenon which he attributed to " the different density of the effluvia at the extremities of the two bodies; for I have already shewn the effluvia will be much denser at the extremity of a pointed body than at an obtuse one." [14]

The similarity between the conclusions of Ellicott and of Franklin are noteworthy. Unfortunately, when Ellicott's papers were read at the Royal Society on 25 February 1747/8, 24 March 1747/8, and 19 May 1748, the basic principles of the Franklinian theory had already been made known in the portions of Franklin's letter of 1 June 1747 read by Watson at the Royal Society on 21 January 1747/8. Franklin was pleased to refer to Ellicott's paper in support of his views, but plainly those views had been formulated and made public before Ellicott's papers were read.

The partial similarity between the views of Ellicott and those of Watson and Franklin is not surprising, since we have already seen that in Franklin's day men were beginning to see that electrical phenomena might be explained by use of the concept of a kind of electric matter. Franklin's originality did not consist in inventing out of whole cloth the idea of an electric matter so much as to give that idea the needed precision, to see the implication of a conservation principle, and to apply this concept in strikingly new ways. And this is precisely the point made by Wilcke. After saying that many elements of the Franklinian theories and concepts were scattered through the literature, Wilcke said:

Still, great credit must be given to Mr. Franklin for these theories. For not only did he clarify them, but he also applied them with ingenuity to the charging—or shock experiments which are generally associated with the names of Leyden and of Muschenbroek. These hitherto had no natural explanation which could be put to proof. If he advanced thereto by means a trifle too artificial, still his explanations are less artificial than others still more incredible. Notwithstanding, Mr. Franklin did not elaborate his experiments to the extent of denying any natural scientist a wide field for further useful efforts, which he might initiate more successfully by following those tracks which Mr. Franklin had already traced. This theory is based generally on the following:

> The entire physical world is permeated throughout by a subtile matter which contains the cause and origin of all physical phenomena.

> The particles of this fine matter which one may call ether, fire, or light etc. mutually repel one other.

> However, these particles will be strongly attracted by particles of the common matter of which bodies consist.

> If one piece of physical matter contains so much of that electric fluid as it can hold without this being accumulated on the surface, then that piece of physical matter is in a natural state in respect to electricity.

> Should it contain more, it will be electrified positively or plus, or should it contain less, it will be electrified negatively, or minus.

> All electrical phenomena are caused by the passage of this matter from one body to another, and by the relative distribution or efflux of it.

These are briefly the main principles of this theory. As simple as these appear to us, just so extended is their application to experience. We can hardly call it a theory or hypothesis: since it contains in truth nothing but the empirical principles which one finally accepts. The repulsion of particles of electric matter in particular is just such an empirical principle. In truth, however, in this way one does not explain anything, but merely indicates a law which nature follows in such phenomena. Experiments and phenomena can thus be explained in a very simple and natural manner and may furthermore be expressed by a few laws in spite of their number and variety. Nay, the theory of electricity is thus reduced to principles just as simple and as general as the theory of the universe and the movement of celestial bodies. One cannot deny that this still remains subject to many and long standing metaphysical objections: however, if we consider further that all other explanations which may derive from pressure, mere attraction, or elasticity, might also be subject to as many objections, and that we still finally must leave off at some general principles derived from experience which do not allow further explanation, we shall become milder in our judgment. Basically it is the same whether we stop at the repelling force, or whether we assume the equally incomprehensible infinite set of small springs, forcibly bent, by which we hope to explain elasticity. For our knowledge will never penetrate deeper than nature's first motives. Explanation will not become more comprehensible, profound or natural, by assuming a learned aspect.

> The natural explanation and further elaboration of the doctrine of the two contrary electric states is a particular merit of this theory, and

of the present treatise. This was already known during Du Fay's time and has always been a matter of entirely differing opinions. The general laws on which these experiments are based are the following: that two electric bodies repel one another; that they will not draw fire from one another and will not deprive one another of their electric state. Experiments easily proved the inadequacy of these laws. Du Fay discovered that electric bodies attract one another. Thus he differentiated between the electricity of glass and the electricity of resin. Messrs. Richmann and Gralath demonstrated that bodies electric *per se* draw more intense sparks from each other than from non-electric bodies. Messrs. Klingenstierna and Strömer, two Swedish natural scientists and professors from Upsala, made public similar experiments with shock-glasses. There is no lack of papers in which mention is made of these exceptions to the general laws. However, we may rightly affirm that no one else gave so much attention to these remarkable phenomena as Mr. Franklin. Also no one else gave an explanation so natural as his. Even today some persons are satisfied by explaining these phenomena through mere differences in the degrees and strength of electricity. However, such a theory does not explain these phenomena and is true only in limited cases. Electricity had always been explained by the mere redundance or deficiency of electric matter; still, no one had ever combined the two phenomena, and it was Mr. Franklin who first demonstrated clearly that both the redundance or deficiency of electric matter in a body may produce electric phenomena. This is a consequence which might have been understood a long while ago, because no redundance can take place in one body, unless another body suffers a deficiency at the same time. This brings forth a difference of the state of the body in respect to electric matter. The explanation is as natural as it is adequate for all and every phenomenon. This subject is too complex to be dealt with here in more detail. I have done this in a separate treatise entitled: *Dissertatio Physica Experimentalis, de Electricitatibus Contrariis.* This treatise covers everything that belongs to the essence and history of this important subject. In this treatise I also advanced my arguments, which I believe convincingly prove that the two contrary electric states are not caused by the variance of electric force. This distinction is the most important discovery in the entire science of electricity. Furthermore, it seems to be the only way by which we may expect to obtain a thorough knowledge of the phenomena which play such an important role in all of nature. Mr. Franklin discovered the diversity of electric states on bodies, making use only of electricity created through rubbing glass. In the beginning he did not know that bodies electric *per se* can produce exactly this different effect, if brought near to one another. Mr. Kinnersley too, discovered this distinction and informed Mr. Franklin about it, a thing which we in our country have known for a long time. Indeed, we do not owe Mr. Franklin this distinction at all; yet, we do owe him the discovery that these two electric states may be brought forth in one and the same body electric *per se,* and beyond that his simple and natural explanation of this distinction.

Another topic discussed by Wilcke in his introduction was Franklin's part in discovering that lightning is an electric discharge:

It is a well known fact that we are indebted to Mr. Franklin for *our knowledge of electricity in thunderstorms*. Although, before Franklin all kinds of ideas were advanced on the similarity of lightning and electricity, hitherto these have remained merely conjectures. Although Mr. Franklin was not the first person who attempted these experiments, he contrived and presented them so clearly that his claim to having invented them cannot be contested. He composed a comprehensive treatise on the creation of electricity in clouds from the sea. He believes that electricity can be created in the sea through friction between salt particles, an electric *per se*, and water, a non-electric body, in conjunction with the assistance of the common and electric fluids rising in vapors. However, subsequently he changed his opinion and ascribes this effect in part to the friction of the air, and in part to the great rarification and expansion of the bodies rising in vapors. This enables them to absorb a larger quantity of matter and act as negative bodies as long as they are empty. Or if they have absorbed their natural quantity, then compressed by winds they will throw off their surplus, as if it were a sponge which is squeezed out. Yet, the most important statements Mr. Franklin makes on this subject are his *thoughts and proposals for drawing off thunderstorms and lightning*. Although these thoughts were generally acclaimed, they are as a rule not correctly understood.

REFERENCES

1. Rey, 1951: intro., p. xl.
2. Galvani, 1953: 31n.
3. Benjamin, 1898: 395-403.
4. See Benjamin, 1898: 403; Heathcote, 1950; Cohen, 1951.
5. See Benjamin, 1898: 541.
6. See Roller and Roller, 1954: 48.
7. Franklin, 1941: Letter II; 1769: Letter II.
8. E. g., Haüy, 1807: 1: 386, art. 416.
9. See Crombie, 1953a: concluding chapter.
10. Franklin, 1758: translator's preface.
11. Watson, 1746b.
12. Franklin, 1941: 213; 1769: 54.
13. Ellicott, 1748: 196; see also p. 207.
14. *Ibid.*, 220.

Bibliography

BIBLIOGRAPHY

The following Bibliography contains the names of books and articles which I have studied in the preparation of this book. Wherever possible, I have referred to collected works of authors rather than listing all of the separate publications and in many instances I have cited a widely used translation as well as, or in place of, the original. The Bibliography contains the major primary scientific writings (books and articles) relative to the main subject of the book, from the seventeenth and eighteenth centuries, and some scientific writings of the last hundred and fifty years that bear on topics discussed. There are also included bibliographical and biographical studies of the major figures, relevant philosophical and methodological writings and some secondary works that have been particularly helpful. But I have not included all of the articles dealing with the main subjects of the book, to be found in the scientific and learned journals of the eighteenth century, notably the *Philosophical Transactions* of the Royal Society of London, the annual volumes of *Histoire* and *Mémoires* of the Académie Royale des Sciences (Paris), etc., although I have made a systematic examination of them.

All of the entries in this Bibliography are arranged alphabetically under the name of the author, bibliographer, or editor, but not translator; collected works are listed under the name of the author, not the editor. The form of citation is that recommended by Dr. John F. Fulton in Fulton (1934).

ABRAHAM, JAMES JOHNSTON. 1933. Lettsom. His life, times, friends and descendants. London, William Heinemann, Medical Books.

ABRO, A. D'. 1950. The evolution of scientific thought. From Newton to Einstein. Second edition, revised and enlarged. New York, Dover Publications.

——. 1951. The rise of the new physics. Its mathematical and physical theories. (Formerly titled "Decline of mechanism.") Second edition. 2 v. New York, Dover Publications.

[Académie des Sciences de l'Institut de France]. 1931. Les membres et les correspondants de l'Académie Royale des Sciences, 1666-1793. Paris, au Palais de l'Institut.

ADAMS, C. RAYMOND. 1950. Benjamin Thompson, Count Rumford. *Scientific Monthly* 71: 380-386.

ADAMS, C. W. 1946. The age at which scientists do their best work. *Isis* 36: 166-169.

ADAMS, GEORGE. 1784. An essay on electricity; in which the theory and practice of that useful science, are illustrated by a variety of experiments, arranged in a methodical manner. To which is added, an essay on magnetism. London, printed for and sold by the author.

——. 1794. Lectures on natural and experimental philosophy. . . . 5 v. London, printed by R. Hindmarsh; sold by the author.

——. 1799. An essay on electricity, explaining the principles of that useful science; and describing the instruments, contrived either to illustrate the theory, or render the practice entertaining. Fifth edition, with corrections and additions, by William Jones. London, J. Dillon and Co., for, and sold by, W. and S. Jones.

ÆPINUS, FRANZ ULRICH THEODOR. 1756. Mémoire concernant quelques nouvelles expériences électriques remarquables. *Histoire de l'Académie Royale des Sciences et Belles Lettres*, Berlin, 105-121.

——. 1759? Tentamen theoriæ electricitatis et magnetismi: Accedunt dissertationes duæ, quarum prior, phænomenon quoddam eletricum, altera, magneticum, explicat. St. Petersburg, Typis Academiae Scientiarum.

ALBRECHT, GUSTAV. 1885. Geschichte der Elektricität mit Berücksichtigung ihrer Anwendungen. Wien, Pest, Leipzig, A. Hartleben's Verlag.

ALDRIDGE, ALFRED OWEN. 1950. Benjamin Franklin and Jonathan Edwards on lightning and earthquakes. *Isis* **41**: 162-164.

[American Philosophical Society.] 1884. Early proceedings of the American Philosophical Society for the Promotion of Useful Knowledge, compiled . . . from the manuscript minutes of its meetings from 1744 to 1838. Philadelphia, Press of McCalla & Stavely. *Proc. Amer. Philos. Soc.* **22** (3).

——. 1906. The record of the celebration of the two hundredth anniversary of the birth of Benjamin Franklin, under the auspices of the American Philosophical Society. Philadelphia, printed for the American Philosophical Society.

——. 1908. Calendar of the papers of Benjamin Franklin in the Library of the American Philosophical Society. Edited by I. Minis Hays. 5 v. Philadelphia, printed for the American Philosophical Society.

AMPÈRE, ANDRÉ-MARIE. 1826. Théorie des phénomènes électro-dynamiques, uniquement déduite de l'expérience. Paris, chez Méquignon-Marvis.

——. 1883. Théorie mathématique des phénomènes électro-dynamiques, uniquement déduite de l'expérience. Deuxième édition, conforme à la première publié en 1826. Paris, A. Hermann.

ANDRADE, E. N. DA C. 1935. Newton's early notebook. *Nature* **135**: 360.

——. 1943. Newton and the science of his age. *Proc. Royal Soc. A*, **181**: 227-243.

——. 1947. Newton. Pages 3-23 of: The Royal Society: Newton Tercentenary Celebrations, 15-19 July 1946. Cambridge, Univ. Press.

——. 1950a. Robert Hooke. *Proc. Royal Soc. A*, **201**: 439-473. (Wilkins Lecture.)

——. 1950b. Isaac Newton. New York, Chanticleer Press.

——. 1953. A Newton collection. *Endeavour* **12**: 68-75.

——. 1954. Sir Isaac Newton. London, Collins. (Brief Lives, No. 11.)

[Anon.] 1773. Extrait de la doctrine de M. Franklin, sur l'electricité. *Observations sur la physique, sur l'histoire naturelle et sur les arts* [Paris, Au Bureau du Journal de Physique], septembre 1773: 204-209.

ARCY, PATRICK D'. 1749. Mémoire sur l'électricité, contenant la description d'un électromètre, ou d'un instrument servant à mesurer la force électrique. *Histoire de l'Académie Royale des Sciences*, Mémoires, 63-74.

ARNOLD, HOWARD PAYSON. 1899. Historic side-lights. New York and London, Harper & Brothers.

ARTHUS, MAURICE. 1943. Philosophy of scientific investigation. Preface to *De l'anaphylaxie à l'immunité*, Paris, 1921. Translated from the French, with an introduction by Henry E. Sigerist. Foreword by Warfield T. Longcope, Baltimore, The Johns Hopkins Press. (Reprinted from *Bull. Hist. Medicine.* **14**: 366-390, 1943.)

AUERBACH, FELIX. 1923. Entwicklungsgeschichte der modernen Physik. Zugleich eine Übersicht ihrer tatsachen Gesetze und Theorien. Berlin, Verlag von Julius Springer.

AYKROYD, W. R. 1935. Three philosophers (Lavoisier, Priestley and Cavendish). London, William Heinemann (Medical Books).

[Babson Collection.] 1950. A descriptive catalogue of the Grace K. Babson Collection of the works of Sir Isaac Newton, and the material relating to him, in the Babson Institute Library, Babson Park, Mass. With an introduction by Roger Babson Webber. New York, Herbert Reichner.

BACHELARD, GASTON. 1927. Étude sur l'évolution d'un problème de physique: la propagation thermique dans des solides. Paris, Librairie Philosophique J. Vrin.

[BACON, FRANCIS.] 1861. The works of Francis Bacon, Baron of Verulam, Viscount St. Albans, and Lord High Chancellor of England. Collected and edited by James Spedding, Robert Leslie Ellis, and Douglas Denon Heath. 15 v. Boston, Brown and Taggard.

——. 1878. Novum organum. Edited with introduction, notes, etc. by Thomas Fowler. Oxford, Clarendon Press.

[——]. 1905. The philosophical works of Francis Bacon. Reprinted from the texts and translations, with the notes and prefaces, of Ellis and Spedding. Edited with an introduction by John M. Robertson. London, George Routledge and Sons; New York, E. P. Dutton.

BAINTON, ROLAND H. 1953. Hunted heretic. The life and death of Michael Servetus, 1511-1553. Boston, Beacon Press.

BAKER, HENRY. 1748. A letter . . . concerning several medical experiments of electricity. *Phil. Trans.* **45**: 270-275.

BALL, W. W. ROUSE. 1889. A history of the study of mathematics at Cambridge. Cambridge, Univ. Press.

——. 1893. An essay on Newton's " Principia." London, New York, Macmillan.

——. 1915. A short account of the history of mathematics. Sixth edition. London, Macmillan.

BARLES, JEAN. 1937. Le schisme maçonnique anglais de 1717. (Création de la Grande Loge de Londres). Vingt-septième partie. Autres notes sur Desaguliers. *Les Archives de Trans en Provence.* **61**: 281-288.

BARROW, ISAAC. 1669. Lectiones XVIII, Cantabrigiæ in scholis publicis habitæ; in quibus opticorum phænomeῶn genuinæ rationes investigantur, ac exponuntur. London, Typis Gulielmi Godbid, & prostant venales apud Johannem Dunmore & Octavianum Pulleyn juniorem.

——. 1714. Euclide's elements: the whole fifteen books compendiously demonstrated. With Archimedes' theorems of the sphere and cylinder, investigated by the method of indivisibles. To which is added in this edition, Euclide's data with Marinus's preface. And a brief treatise of regular solids. London, printed and sold by W. Redmayne, R. Mount, and J. and B. Sprint.

——. 1734. The usefulness of mathematical learning explained and demonstrated: being mathematical lectures read in the publick schools at the University of Cambridge. Translated by John Kirby. London, printed for Stephen Austen.

——. 1735. Geometrical lectures: explaining the generation, nature and properties of curve lines. Read in the University of Cambridge. Translated from the Latin edition, revised corrected and amended by the late Sir Isaac Newton, by Edmund Stone. London, printed for Stephen Austen.

[——]. 1860. The mathematical works of Isaac Barrow. Edited for Trinity College by William Whewell. Cambridge, printed at the Univ. Press.

[——]. 1916. The geometrical lectures of Isaac Newton. Translated, with notes and proofs, and a discussion on the advance made therein on the work of his predecessors in the infinitesimal calculus, by J. M. Child. Chicago and London, Open Court. (The Open Court Series of Classics of Science and Philosophy, No. 3.)

[BARTRAM, JOHN]. 1849. Memorials of John Bartram and Humphrey Marshall, with notices of their botanical contemporaries, by William Darlington. Philadelphia, Lindsay & Blakiston.

BASTHOLM, E. 1950. The history of muscle physiology. From the natural philosophers to Albrecht von Haller. A study of the history of medicine. Copenhagen, Ejnar Munksgaard. (Acta Historica Scientiarum Naturalium et Medicinalium, 7.)

BATES, RALPH S. 1945. Scientific societies in the United States. New York, John Wiley & Sons. (A publication of the Technology Press, Massachusetts Institute of Technology.)

BAUER, EDMOND. 1949. L'électromagnétisme hier et aujourd'hui. Paris, Albin Michel.

BAUMGARTEN, EDUARD. 1936. Benjamin Franklin, der Lehrmeister der Amerikanischen Revolution. Frankfurt am Main, Vittorio Klostermann.

BAXTER, ANDREW. 1745. An enquiry into the nature of the human soul, wherein the immateriality of the soul is evinced from the principles of reason and philosophy. Third edition. 2 v. London, printed for A. Millar.

BECCARIA, GIAMBATTISTA. 1754. Lettre sur l'électricité, adressée a M. l'Abbé Nollet. Traduite de l'Italien par M. de Lor. Paris, chez Ganeau.

——. 1772. Elettricismo artificiale di Giambattista Beccaria delle scuole pie all'altezza reale del signor Duca di Chablais. Colophon, in Torino.

——. 1776. A treatise upon artificial electricity, in which are given solutions of a number of interesting electric phœnomena, hitherto unexplained. To which is added an essay on the mild and slow electricity which prevails in the atmosphere during serene weather. Translated from the Italian. London, printed for J. Nourse.

——. 1793. Dell' elettricismo opere del P. Giambattista Beccaria delle scuole pie con molte note nuovamente illustrate. . . . 2 v. Macerata.

BECKER, CARL L. 1946. Benjamin Franklin: a biographical sketch. Ithaca, New York, Cornell Univ. Press. (Reprinted from Dictionary of American Biography 6: 585-598.)

BECKET, J. B. 1773. An essay on electricity, containing a series of experiments introductory to the study of that science; in which are included some of the latest discoveries; intended chiefly with a view of facilitating its application, and extending its utility in medical purposes. Bristol, printed for J. B. Becket.

BECQUEREL, ANTOINE CÉSAR. 1834. Traité expérimental de l'électricité et du magnétisme, et de leurs rapports avec les phénomènes naturels. 2 v. Paris, Firmin Didot Frères.

BECQUEREL, ANTOINE CÉSAR, and ALEXANDRE EDMOND BECQUEREL. 1858. Résumé de l'histoire de l'électricité et du magnétisme, et des applications de ces sciences à la chimie, aux sciences naturelles et aux arts. Paris, Librairie de Firmin Didot Frères.

BEER, G. R. DE. 1951. Voltaire, F.R.S. Notes and Records Royal Society of London 8: 247-252.

——. 1953. Sir Hans Sloane and the British Museum. Published for the trustees of the British Museum. London, New York, Toronto, Geoffrey Cumberlege, Oxford Univ. Press.

BELL, A. E. 1947. Christian Huygens and the development of science in the seventeenth century. New York, Longmans Green; London, Edward Arnold.

BELL, WHITFIELD J., JR., 1955a. Franklin's papers and The papers of Benjamin Franklin. Penna. Hist. 22: 3-19.

——. 1955b. Early American science, needs and opportunities for study. Williamsburg, Va., Institute of Early American History and Culture.

BENJAMIN, PARK. 1898. A history of electricity (The intellectual rise in electricity) from antiquity to the days of Benjamin Franklin. New York, John Wiley & Sons. [A previous version was published in 1895 by D. Appleton & Co., New York, under a similar title.]

BENTHAM, MURIEL A. 1937. Some seventeenth century views concerning the nature of heat and cold. Annals of Science 2: 431-450.

BENTLEY, RICHARD. 1838. Sermons preached at Boyle's lecture; remarks upon a discourse of free-thinking; proposals for an edition of the Greek testament; etc. etc. Edited, with notes, by the Rev. Alexander Dyce. London, Francis Macpherson. (The works of Richard Bentley, D. D., collected and edited by the Rev. Alexander Dyce, 3, Theological writings.)

[BERKELEY, GEORGE]. 1951. The works of George Berkeley, Bishop of Cloyne. Edited by A. A. Luce and T. E. Jessop. Vol. 4, edited by A. A. Luce. De Motu with an English translation. The analyst. A defence of free-thinking in mathematics. Reasons for not replying to Mr. Walton's Full Answer. Arithmetica and miscellanea mathematica. Of infinities. [Etc.] London, Edinburgh, Thomas Nelson and Sons.

BERNARD, CLAUDE. 1927. An introduction to the study of experimental medicine. Translated by Henry Copley Greene. With an introduction by Lawrence J. Henderson. New York, Macmillan.

[——]. 1939. Claude Bernard, extraits de

son œuvre, par E. Dhurout. Avec un exposé de sa philosophie emprunté à l'œuvre de Henri Bergson. Paris, Librairie Félix Alcan.

BERZELIUS, JÖNS JACOB. 1811. Essai sur la nomenclature chimique. *Journal de Physique, de Chimie et d'Histoire Naturelle* **73**: 253-286.

BEVERIDGE, W. I. B. 1950. The art of scientific investigation. New York, W. W. Norton.

BILLY, ANDRÉ. 1932. Diderot. Paris, Les Éditions de France.

BIRCH, THOMAS. 1756-1757. The history of the Royal Society of London, for Improving of Natural Knowledge, from its first rise. A supplement to the *Philosophical Transactions*. 4 v. London, printed for A. Millar.

BIRKHOFF, GEORGE DAVID. 1938. Electricity as a fluid. *Jour. Franklin Inst.* **226**: 315-325.

BLACK, JOSEPH. 1803. Lectures on the elements of chemistry. Published by John Robison. 2 v. Edinburgh, Mundell and Son, for Longman and Rees, London, and William Creech, Edinburgh.

BLOCH, ERNST. 1914. Die chemischen Theorien bei Descartes und den Cartesianern. *Isis* **1**: 590-636.

——. 1926. Das chemische Affinitätsproblem, geschichtlich betrachtet. *Isis* **8**: 119-156.

BLOCH, LÉON. 1908. La philosophie de Newton. Paris, Félix Alcan.

BOAS, MARIE. 1950. Boyle as a theoretical scientist. *Isis* **41**: 261-268.

——. 1952. The establishment of the mechanical philosophy. *Osiris* **10**: 412-541.

BOERHAAVE, HERMAN. 1727. A new method of chemistry; including the theory and practice of that art. Translated by P. Shaw and E. Chambers. With notes. 2 v. London, J. Osborn and T. Longman.

——. 1732. Elementa chemiæ, quæ anniversario labore docuit, in publicis, privatisque, scholis. 2 v. Lugduni Batavorum, apud Isaacum Severinum.

——. 1735. Elements of chemistry: being the annual lectures of Herman Boerhaave. Translated from the Latin by Timothy Dallowe. 2 v. London, printed for J. and J. Pemberton, J. Clarke, A. Millar, and J. Gray.

——. 1741. A new method of chemistry; including the history theory, and practice of the art. Translated, from the original Latin of Dr. Boerhaave's *Elementa chemiæ* as published by himself, by Peter Shaw. Second edition. 2 v. London, printed for T. Longman. [A "third edition" appeared in 1753.]

——. 1748. Elemens de chymie. Traduits du Latin par J. N. S. Allamand. 2 v. La Haye, chez J. Néaulme.

[——]. 1939. Memorialia Herman Boerhaave, optimi medici. Haarlem, De Erven F. Bohn. N. V. [A collection of commemorative essays, upon the occasion of the 200th anniversary of Boerhaave's death.]

BOFFITO, G. 1929. Gli strumenti della scienza e la scienza degli strumenti, con l'illustrazione della Tribuna di Galileo. Firenze, Libreria Internazionale Seeber.

BORDEAUX, ALBERT. 1920. Histoire des sciences physiques, chimiques, et géologiques au XIXe siècle. Paris, Liége, Librairie Polytechnique Ch. Béranger.

BORN, MAX. 1943. Experiment and theory in physics. Cambridge, Univ. Press.

——. 1949. Natural philosophy of cause and chance. Being the Waynflete Lectures . . . , Oxford, 1948. Oxford, Clarendon Press.

BOSE, GEORG MATTHIAS. 1745. Abstract of a letter from Monsieur De Bozes, professor of experimental philosophy, at the Academy of Wirtemberg, to Monsieur De Maizau. Communicated by Mr. Baker from Mr. Ellis, and translated out of the Latin by Mr. Baker. *Phil. Trans.* **43**: 419-421. [Abstract of a letter read 23 May.]

BOSSCHA, J., ed. 1905. La correspondance de A. Volta et M. van Marum. Leiden, A. W. Sijthoff.

BOSSUT, CHARLES. 1803. A general history of mathematics, from the earliest times to the middle of the eighteenth century. Translated from the French. London, printed for J. Johnson.

BOULLANGER, ——. 1750. Traité de la cause et des phenomenes de l'électricité. 2 v.

Paris, de l'Imprimerie de la Veuve David et se vend chez Pecquet, Libraire.

BOUTROUX, PIERRE. 1921. L'enseignement de la mécanique en France au XVIIᵉ siècle. *Isis* 4: 276-294.

BOWDOIN, JAMES. 1783. Observations on light, and the waste of matter in the sun and fixt stars, occasioned by the constant efflux of light from them: with a conjecture, proposed by way of query, and suggesting a mean, by which their several systems might be preserved from the disorder and final ruin, to which they seem liable by that waste of matter, and by the law of gravitation. *Memoirs Amer. Acad. Arts and Sciences* 1: 195-207.

BOYER, CARL B. 1939. The concepts of the calculus. A critical and historical discussion of the derivative and the integral. New York, Columbia Univ. Press.

BOYLE, ROBERT. n. d. The sceptical chymist. Introduction by M. M. Pattison Muir. London, J. M. Dent & Sons; New York, E. P. Dutton. (Everyman's Library.)

——. 1675. Experiments and notes about the mechanical origine or production of electricity. London, printed by E. Flesher for R. Davis, Bookseller in Oxford. [Facsimile edition, printed by the Burndy Library, 1945.]

[——]. 1744. The works of the Honourable Robert Boyle. 5 v. To which is prefixed the life of the author. Edited by Thomas Birch. London, printed for A. Millar.

[——]. 1772. The works of the Honourable Robert Boyle. 6 v. To which is prefixed the life of the author. A new edition. Edited by Thos. Birch. London, printed for J. and F. Rivington, L. Davis, W. Johnston, S. Crowder, T. Payne, G. Kearsley, J. Robson, B. White, T. Becket, and P. A. DeHondt, T. Davies, T. Cadell, Robinson and Roberts, Richardson & Richardson, J. Knox, W. Woodfall, J. Johnson, and T. Evans.

——. 1927. Electricity & magnetism, 1675-6. Oxford, Old Ashmolean. (Old Ashmolean Reprints, 7). [A reprint, " prepared for members of the British Asso-

ciation meeting in 1926 in Oxford " by R. T. Gunther, of Boyle: Experiments and notes about . . . electricity, 1675; Experiments and notes about . . . magnetism, 1676.]

BRASCH, FREDERICK E., ed. 1928. Sir Isaac Newton, 1727-1927, a bicentenary evaluation of his work. A series of papers prepared under the auspices of the History of Science Society, . . . Baltimore, Williams & Wilkins.

——. 1942. James Logan, a colonial mathematical scholar, and the first copy of Newton's *Principia* to arrive in the colony. *Proc. Amer. Philos. Soc.* **86**: 3-12.

——. 1952. A survey of the number of copies of Newton's *Principia* in the United States, Canada, and Mexico. *Scripta Mathematica* 18: 53-67.

BRETT-JAMES, NORMAN G. 1926. The life of Peter Collinson. London, published for the author by Edgar G. Dunstan & Co., and sold at the Friends' Bookshop.

BREWSTER, SIR DAVID. 1831. The life of Sir Isaac Newton. London, John Murray. (Reprinted, 1839, New York, Harper & Brothers.)

——. 1855. Memoirs of the life, writings, and discoveries of Sir Isaac Newton. 2 v. Edinburgh, Thomas Constable and Co.; London, Hamilton, Adams, and Co. (Also, Edinburgh, Thomas Constable and Co.; Boston, Little, Brown, and Co.)

BRIDENBAUGH, CARL. 1938. Cities in the wilderness. The first century of urban life in America, 1625-1742. New York, Ronald Press.

BRIDENBAUGH, CARL, and JESSICA BRIDENBAUGH. 1942. Rebels and gentlemen: Philadelphia in the age of Franklin. New York, Reynal & Hitchcock.

BRIDGMAN, P. W. 1927. The logic of modern physics. New York, Macmillan.

——. 1936. The nature of physical theory. Princeton, Princeton Univ. Press. (Published on the Louis Clark Vanuxem Foundation.) [Facsimile reprint: New York, Dover Publications.]

——. 1941. The nature of thermodynamics. Cambridge, Harvard Univ. Press.

——. 1950. Reflections of a physicist. New York, Philosophical Library.

——. 1952. The nature of some of our physical concepts. New York, Philosophical Library. (Reprinted from *British Jour. for the Philos. of Science* 1: 257-272, 1951; 2: 25-44, 142-160, 1951.)

BRINTON, CRANE. 1950. Ideas and men. The story of western thought. New York, Prentice-Hall.

BROAD, C. D. 1926. Francis Bacon and scientific method. *Nature* 118: 487-488, 523-524.

——. 1927. Sir Isaac Newton. Annual lecture on a master mind. Henriette Hertz Trust of the British Academy. London, for the British Academy; Oxford Univ. Press, Humphrey Milford.

BRODETSKY, S. 1929. Sir Isaac Newton: a brief account of his life and work. Second edition. London, Methuen.

BROUGHAM, HENRY LORD, and E. J. ROUTH. 1855. Analytical view of Sir Isaac Newton's Principia. London, Longman, Brown, Green, and Longmans.

BROWN, G. BURNISTON. 1950. Science: its method and its philosophy. New York, W. W. Norton.

BROWN, HARCOURT. 1934. Scientific organizations in seventeenth century France (1620-1680). Baltimore, Williams & Wilkins. (History of Science Society Publications, new series V.)

BROWN, SANBORN C. 1947. The discovery of convection currents by Benjamin Thompson, Count of Rumford. *Amer. Jour. Physics* 15: 273-274.

——. 1949. Count Rumford and the caloric theory of heat. *Proc. Amer. Philos. Soc.* 93: 316-325.

BRUCE, WILLIAM CABELL. 1942. Benjamin Franklin self-revealed. A biographical and critical study based mainly on his own writings. Third ed. revised. 2 v. in one. New York, G. P. Putnam's Sons.

BRUNET, PIERRE. 1926. Les physiciens Hollandais et la méthode expérimentale en France au XVIIIᵉ siècle. Paris, Librairie Scientifique Albert Blanchard.

——. 1929. Maupertuis. 2 v. 1: Etude biographique; 2: L'œuvre et sa place dans la pensée scientifique et philosophique du XVIIIᵉ siècle. Paris, Librairie Scientifique Albert Blanchard.

——. 1931. L'introduction des théories de Newton en France au XVIIIᵉ siècle. I: Avant 1738. Paris, Librairie Scientifique Albert Blanchard.

——. 1940. L'œuvre scientifique de Charles François du Fay (1698-1739). *Petrus Nonius* 3: 77-95.

——. 1947. Les premières recherches expérimentales sur la foudre et l'électricité atmosphérique. *Lychnos*, 1946-1947: 117-148 .

——. 1948. Les origines du paratonnerre (discussions et réalisations). *Revue d'Histoire des Sciences et de leurs Applications* 1: 213-253.

BRUNSCHVICG, LÉON. 1929. Les étapes de la philosophie mathématique. Troisième édition. Paris, Librairie Félix Alcan.

——. 1949. L'expérience humaine et la causalité physique. 3ᵉ édition. Paris, Presses Universitaires de France. (Bibliothèque de Philosophie Contemporaine.)

BUFFON, GEORGES-LOUIS LECLERC. 1860. Correspondance inédite de Buffon, à laquelle ont été réunies les lettres publiées jusqu'à ce jour, recueillie et annotée par Henri Nadault de Buffon. 2 v. Paris, Librairie de L. Hachette et Cie.

BURR, ALEX. C. 1933. Notes on the history of the concept of thermal conductivity. *Isis* 20: 246-259.

——. 1934. Notes on the history of the experimental determination of the thermal conductivity of gases. *Isis* 21: 169-186.

BURTT, EDWIN ARTHUR. 1932. The metaphysical foundations of modern physical science. A historical and critical essay. Revised edition. London, Routledge & Kegan Paul. (International Library of Psychology, Philosophy and Scientific Method.)

BUSH, VANNEVAR. 1945. Science, the endless frontier: a report to the President. Washington, U. S. Govt. Print. Office.

BUTTERFIELD, H. 1949. The origins of modern science, 1300-1800. London, G. Bell and Sons. (An American reprint by Macmillan.)

CABANÈS, A. n. d. Marat inconnu: l'homme privé, le médecin, le savant. Deuzième édition, refondue et augmentée. Paris, Albin Michel.

CAJORI, FLORIAN. 1919. A history of the conceptions of limits and fluxions in Great Britain from Newton to Woodhouse. Chicago, London, Open Court. (The Open Court Series of Classics of Science and Philosophy, No. 5.)

——. 1921. Note on the Fahrenheit scale. *Isis* 4: 17-22.

——. 1922a. On the history of caloric. *Isis* 4: 483-492.

——. 1922b. Newton's discovery of gravitation. *Univ. of Calif. Chronicle* 24: 232-238.

——. 1922c. Newton and the law of gravitation. *Archivio di Storia della Scienza* 3: 201-204.

——. 1924. The growth of legend about Sir Isaac Newton. *Science* 59: 390-392.

——. 1925. The Baconian method of scientific research. *Scientific Monthly* 20: 85-91.

——. 1926a. Sir Isaac Newton's early study of the Apocalypse. *Popular Astronomy* 34: 75-78.

——. 1926b. Ce que Newton doit à Descartes. *L'Enseignement Mathématique* 25: 7-11.

——. 1928a. Newton's twenty years' delay in announcing the law of gravitation. Pages 127-188 of: Sir Isaac Newton, 1727-1927. A bicentenary evaluation of his work: a series of papers prepared under the auspices of the History of Science Society, . . . Baltimore, William & Wilkins.

——. 1928b. Sir Isaac Newton on gravitation. *Scientific Monthly* 27: 47-53.

——. 1938. A history of physics in its elementary branches, including the evolution of physical laboratories. Revised and enlarged edition. New York, Macmillan.

CAMERON, HECTOR CHARLES. 1952. Sir Joseph Banks, K. B., P. R. S., the autocrat of the philosophers. London, Batchworth Press.

CAMPBELL, LEWIS, and WILLIAM GARNETT. 1882. The life of James Clerk Maxwell. With a selection from his correspondence and occasional writings, and a sketch of his contributions to science. London, Macmillan.

CAMPBELL, WILLIAM J. 1918. The collection of Franklin imprints in the museum of the Curtis Publishing Company. With a short-title check list of all the books, pamphlets, broadsides, &c., known to have been printed by Benjamin Franklin. Philadelphia, Curtis Publishing Company.

CANDOLLE, ALPHONSE DE. 1885. Histoire des sciences et des savants, depuis deux siècles, précédée et suivie d'autres études sur des sujets scientifiques, en particulier sur l'hérédité et la sélection dans l'espèce humaine. Deuxième édition, augmenté. Genève-Bâle, Lyon, H. Georg.

CANTON, JOHN. 1754. A letter to the Right Honourable the Earl of Macclesfield, President of the Royal Society, concerning some new electrical experiments. *Phil. Trans.* 48: 780-785.

CASSIRER, ERNST. 1902. Leibniz' System in seinen wissenschaftlichen Grundlagen. Marburg, N. G. Elwert'sche Verlagsbuchhandlung.

——. 1911. Das Erkenntnisproblem in der Philosophie und Wissenschaft der neueren Zeit. Zweiter Band. Zweite durchgesehene Auflage. Berlin, Verlag Bruno Cassirer.

——. 1943. Newton and Leibniz. Galileo and the scientific revolution. *Philos. Rev.* 52: 366-391.

——. 1946. Galileo's Platonism. Pages 277-297 of: Studies and essays in the history of science and learning, offered in homage to George Sarton, on the occasion of his sixtieth birthday, 31 August 1944, edited by M. F. Ashley Montagu. New York, Henry Schuman.

——. 1950. The problem of knowledge. Philosophy, science, and history since Hegel. Translated by William H. Woglom and Charles W. Hendel. New Haven, Yale Univ. Press.

——. 1953. The philosophy of symbolic forms. Vol. 1: Language. Translated by Ralph Manheim. Preface and introduction by Charles W. Hendel. New Haven, Yale Univ. Press.

CAVALLO, TIBERIUS. 1803. The elements

of natural or experimental philosophy. 4 v. London, printed by Luke Hansard, for T. Cadell and W. Davies.

CAVENDISH, HENRY. 1879. The electrical researches of the Honourable Henry Cavendish, F. R. S., written between 1771 and 1781, edited from the original manuscripts in the possession of the Duke of Devonshire, K. G., by J. Clerk Maxwell. Cambridge, Univ. Press.

——. 1921. The scientific papers of the Honourable Henry Cavendish, F. R. S. Vol. 1, the electrical researches. Edited from the published papers, and the Cavendish manuscripts in the possession of His Grace the Duke of Devonshire, by James Clerk Maxwell. Revised by Sir Joseph Larmor. Cambridge, Univ. Press.

CHALMERS, GORDON KEITH. 1936. Three terms of the corpuscularian philosophy. Modern Philology 33: 243-260.

CHALMERS, T. W. 1949. Historic researches. Chapters in the history of physical and chemical discovery. London, Morgan Brothers.

CHAUVEAU, B. 1922. Électricité atmosphérique. Premier fascicule. Introduction historique. Paris, Librairie Octave Doin, Gaston Doin, Éditeur.

CHEVREUL, EUGÈNE. 1866. Introduction à l'histoire des connaissances chimiques. Connexions des sciences du domaine de la philosophie naturelle, exposées conformément à la méthode a posteriori expérimentale sous le double rapport de l'analyse et de la synthèse. Paris, L. Guerin.

CHILD, J. M. 1927. Newton and the art of discovery. Pages 117-129 of: Isaac Newton, 1642-1727: a memorial volume edited for the Mathematical Association by W. J. Greenstreet. London, G. Bell and Sons.

CHINARD, GILBERT. 1943. The American Philosophical Society and the world of science (1768-1800). Proc. Amer. Philos. Soc. 87: 1-11.

CHIPMAN, R. A. 1954. An unpublished letter of Stephen Gray on electrical experiments, 1707-1708. Isis 45: 33-40.

CHURCH, A. H. (Compiler). 1908. The Royal Society—Some account of the " Letters and Papers " of the period

1741-1806 in the archives. With an index of authors. Oxford, printed for the author.

CHWOLSON, O. D. 1925. Die Evolution des Geistes der Physik, 1873-1923. Braunschweig, Verlag von Friedr. Vieweg & Sohn Akt.-Ges.

CLAIRAUT, ALEXIS CLAUDE. 1739. Sur les explications cartésienne et newtonienne de la réfraction de la lumière. Histoire de l'Académie Royale des Sciences, Mémoires, 259-275.

CLARE, MARTIN. 1735. The motion of fluids, natural and artificial; in particular that of the air and water, in a familiar manner, proposed and proved, by evident and conclusive experiments with many useful remarks. Done with such plainness and perspicuity, as that they may be understood by the unlearned. For whose sake there is added a short explanation of such uncommon terms, which in treating on this subject could not, without affectation, be avoided. With plain draughts of such experiments and machines, which, by description only, might not readily be comprehended. London, printed for Edward Symon. [A third edition was printed in London in 1747.]

——. 1737. The motion of fluids, natural and artificial; in particular that of the air and water: in a familiar manner proposed and proved by evident and conclusive experiments, to which are added many useful remarks. Done with such plainness and perspicuity, as that they may be understood by the unlearned. For whose sake is annexed, a short explanation of such uncommon terms, which in treating on this subject could not, without affectation, be avoided. With plain draughts of such experiments and machines, which, by description only, might not readily be comprehended. The second edition, corrected and improved. London, printed for Edward Symon. [A third edition appeared in 1747.]

CLARK, G. N. 1937. Science and social welfare in the age of Newton. Oxford, Clarendon Press.

——. 1947. The seventeenth century. Second ed. Oxford, Clarendon Press.

CLARK-KENNEDY, A. E. 1929. Stephen

Hales, D. D., F. R. S.: An eighteenth century biography. Cambridge, Univ. Press.

CLARKE, SAMUEL. 1717. A collection of papers, which passed between the late learned Mr. Leibnitz, and Dr. Clarke, in the years 1715 and 1716. Relating to the principles of natural philosophy and religion. With an appendix. To which are added, letters to Dr. Clarke concerning liberty and necessity; from a gentleman of the University of Cambridge: with the doctor's answers to them. Also remarks upon a book, entituled, *A philosophical enquiry concerning human liberty*. London, printed for James Knapton.

——. 1732. A discourse concerning the being and attributes of God, the obligations of natural religion, and the truth and certainty of the Christian revelation. The eighth edition. London, printed by W. Botham for James and John Knapton.

CLIFFORD, WILLIAM KINGDON. 1879. Seeing and thinking. London, Macmillan. (Nature Series.)

——. 1886. Lectures and essays. Edited by Leslie Stephen and Frederick Pollock. With an introduction by F. Pollock. Second edition. London, New York, Macmillan.

COHEN, ERNST, and W. A. T. COHEN-DE MEESTER. 1941. Katalog der wiedergefundenen Manuskripte und Briefwechsel von Herman Boerhaave. *Nederlandsche Akademie van Wetenschappen* (Tweedie Sectie) 40: 1-45.

COHEN, I. BERNARD. 1940. The first explanation of interference. *Amer. Jour. Physics* 8: 99-106.

——. 1943a. Franklin's experiments on heat absorption as a function of color. *Isis* 34: 404-407.

——. 1943b. Benjamin Franklin and the mysterious " Dr. Spence ": the date and source of Franklin's interest in electricity. *Jour. Franklin Inst.* 235: 1-26.

——. 1945a. American physicists at war: [1] from the Revolution to the World Wars, [2] from the First World War to 1942. *Amer. Jour. Physics* 13: 223-235, 333-346.

——. 1945b. How practical was Benjamin Franklin's science? *Penna. Mag. Hist. and Biog.* 69: 284-293.

——. 1950a. Some early tools of American science. An account of the early scientific instruments and mineralogical and biological collections in Harvard University. With a foreword by Samuel Eliot Morison. Cambridge, Harvard Univ. Press.

——. 1950b. A sense of history in science. *Amer. Jour. Physics* 18: 343-359.

——. 1951. Guericke and Dufay. *Annals of Science* 7: 207-209.

——. 1952a. Prejudice against the introduction of lightning rods. *Jour. Franklin Inst.* 253: 393-440.

——. 1952b. The two hundredth anniversary of Benjamin Franklin's two lightning experiments and the introduction of the lightning rod. *Proc. Amer. Philos. Soc.* 96: 331-366.

——. 1953. Benjamin Franklin: His contribution to the American tradition. New York, Bobbs-Merrill. (Makers of the American Tradition Series.)

——. 1954a. Review-discussion: Some recent books on the history of science. *Jour. Hist. Ideas* 15: 163-192.

——. 1954b. Neglected sources for the life of Stephen Gray. *Isis* 45: 41-50.

——. 1955a. Franklin, Boerhaave, Newton, Boyle & the absorption of heat in relation to color. *Isis* 46: 99-104.

——. 1955b. Present status and needs of the history of science. *Proc. Amer. Philos. Soc.* 99: 343-347.

——. 1955c. An interview with Einstein. *Scientific American* 193 (1) : 68-73.

COHEN, I. BERNARD, and ROBERT SCHOFIELD. 1952. Did Diviš erect the first European protective lightning rod, and was his invention independent? *Isis* 43: 358-364.

[COLDEN, CADWALLADER.] 1919, 1920. The letters and papers of Cadwallader Colden: vol. 3, 1743-1747; vol. 4, 1748-1754. New York, printed for the Society (Coll. of the New-York Hist. Soc.).

COLE, F. J. 1930. Early theories of sexual generation. Oxford, Clarendon Press.

COLEBY, L. J. M. 1952. John Francis Vigani, first professor of chemistry in the University of Cambridge. *Annals of Science* 8: 46-60.

COLLIER, KATHARINE BROWNELL. 1934. Cosmogonies of our fathers. Some theories of the seventeenth and the eighteenth centuries. New York, Columbia Univ. Press.

CONANT, JAMES B. 1947. On understanding science. An historical approach. New Haven, Yale Univ. Press. (The Terry Lectures.)

—— (ed.) . 1950. Robert Boyle's experiments in pneumatics. Cambridge, Harvard Univ. Press. (Harvard Case Histories in Experimental Science: Case 1.)

——. 1951. Science and common sense. New Haven, Yale Univ. Press.

[CONDUITT, JOHN.] 1806. Memoirs of Sir Isaac Newton sent by Mr. Conduitt to Monsieur Fontenelle in 1727. Pages 158-167 of Edmond Turnor: Collections for the history of the town and soke of Grantham. Containing authentic memoirs of Sir Isaac Newton. . . . London, printed for William Miller by W. Bulmer and Co. [On pp. 172-173: A remarkable and curious conversation between Sir Isaac Newton and Mr. Conduitt.]

[Conservatoire National des Arts et Métiers.] 1905. Ministère du Commerce, des Postes et des Télégraphes. Catalogue officiel des collections du Conservatoire National des Arts et Métiers. Deuxième fascicule. Physique. Paris, E. Bernard.

CORNELL, E. S. 1936. Early studies in radiant heat. *Annals of Science* 1: 217-225.

——. 1938. The radiant heat spectrum from Herschel to Melloni—I. The work of Herschel and his contemporaries; II. The work of Melloni and his contemporaries. *Annals of Science* 3: 119-137, 402-416.

CORRIGAN, J. FREDERICK. 1924. Stephen Gray (1696-1736), an early electrical experimenter. *Science Progress* 19: 102-114.

COTES, ROGER. 1738. Hydrostatical and pneumatical lectures. Published with notes by his successor Robert Smith. London, printed for the editor.

[COULOMB, CHARLES AUGUSTIN DE.] 1884. Collection de mémoires relatifs a la physique, publiés par la Société Française de Physique. Tome 1. Mémoires de Charles Augustin de Coulomb. Paris, Gauthier-Villars.

——. 1890. Vier Abhandlungen über die Elektricität und den Magnetismus. Uebersetzt und herausgegeben von Walter König. Leipzig, Verlag von Wilhelm Engelmann. (Ostwald's Klassiker d. exacten Wiss., Nr. 13.)

COULSON, THOMAS. 1950. Joseph Henry, his life and work. Princeton, Princeton Univ. Press.

COWPER, WILLIAM. 1724. Myotomia reformata, or an anatomical treatise on the muscles of the human body. Illustrated with figures after the life. To which is prefix'd an introduction concerning muscular motion. London, printed for Robert Knaplock, and William and John Innys; and Jacob Tonson.

CRAIG, JOHN. 1946. Newton at the mint. Cambridge, Univ. Press.

CRANE, VERNER WINSLOW. 1936. Benjamin Franklin, Englishman and American. The Colver Lectures, 1935. Baltimore, Williams & Wilkins (published for Brown Univ.) .

CREW, HENRY. 1935. The rise of modern physics. Second ed. Baltimore, Williams & Wilkins.

CROMBIE, A. C. 1948. Some reflections on the history of science and its conception of nature. *Annals of Science* 6: 54-75.

——. 1953*a*. Augustine to Galileo: the history of science A. D. 400-1650. Cambridge, Harvard Univ. Press.

——. 1953*b*. Robert Grosseteste and the origins of experimental science, 1100-1700. Oxford, Clarendon Press.

CRU, R. LOYALTY. 1913. Diderot as a disciple of English thought. New York, Columbia Univ. Press.

CURTI, MERLE. 1943. The growth of American thought. New York, London, Harper & Brothers.

CURTI, MERLE, RICHARD H. SHRYOCK, THOMAS C. COCHRAN, and FRED HARVEY HARRINGTON. 1950. An American history. 2 v. New York, Harper & Brothers.

DALTON, JOHN. 1808, 1810, 1827. A new system of chemical philosophy. Part 1, Manchester: printed by S. Russell for R. Bickerstaff, London. Part 2, Manchester: printed by Russell & Allen for R. Bickerstaff, London. Part first of vol. 2, Manchester, printed by the Executors of S. Russell for George Wilson. (Facsimile reprint by William Dawson, London.)

DANNEMANN, FRIEDRICH. 1914? Die Entdeckung der Elektrizität. Leipzig, R. Voigtländers Verlag. (Voigtländers Quellenbücher, Band 75.)

DARLINGTON, WILLIAM. 1849. Memorials of John Bartram and Humphry Marshall, with notices of their botanical contemporaries. Philadelphia, Lindsay & Blakiston.

DARMSTAEDTER, ERNST. 1927. Hermann Boerhaaves Briefe an Johann Bapt. Bassand in Wien. München, Verlag der Münchner Drucke.

DARMSTAEDTER, LUDWIG. 1908. Handbuch zur Geschichte der Naturwissenschaften und der Technik. In chronologischer Darstellung. Zweite, umgearbeitete und vermehrte Auflage. Unter Mitwirkung von R. du Bois-Reymond und D. C. Schaefer, herausgegeben von L. Darmstaedter. Berlin, Verlag von Julius Springer.

DARROW, KARL K. 1926. Introduction to contemporary physics. New York, D. Van Nostrand.

DARWIN, ROBERT WARING. 1786. New experiments on the ocular spectra of light and colours; communicated by Erasmus Darwin, M. D., F. R. S. *Phil. Trans.* 76: 313-348. [Reprinted, pp. 534-566, Darwin, Erasmus: Zoonomia; or, the laws of organic life, 1. London, printed for J. Johnson, 1794.]

DAUJAT, JEAN. 1945. Origines et formation de la théorie des phénomènes électriques et magnétiques. 3 v. 1: Antiquité et moyen age; 2: XVIIᵉ siècle; 3: XVIIIᵉ siècle. Paris, Hermann. (Actualités Scientifiques et Industrielles, 989, 990, 991.)

DAUMAS, MAURICE. 1953. Les instruments scientifiques aux XVIIᵉ et XVIIIᵉ siècles. Paris, Presses Universitaires de France.

DAVIS, TENNEY L. 1926. The first edition of the *Sceptical Chymist. Isis* 8: 71-76.

——. 1928. The vicissitudes of Boerhaave's textbook of chemistry. *Isis* 10: 33-46.

——. 1931. Boyle's conception of element compared with that of Lavoisier. *Isis* 16: 82-91.

DAVY, SIR HUMPHRY. 1840. Historical sketch of electrical discovery. The collected works of Sir Humphry Davy, Bart. Edited by his brother John Davy. 8: Agricultural lectures, part 2, and other lectures, 256-273. London, Smith, Elder.

DE LAUNAY, LOUIS. 1925. Le grand Ampère, d'après des documents inédits. Paris, Librairie Académique Perrin.

DE MORGAN, AUGUSTUS. 1862. Contents of the *Correspondence of scientific men of the seventeenth century*, printed at the University Press, Oxford, in two volumes octavo, 1841, under the superintendence of the late Professor Rigaud, from the originals in the collection of the right honourable The Earl of Macclesfield. Oxford, Univ. Press.

——. 1885. Newton: his friend: and his niece. Edited by his [De Morgan's] wife, and by his pupil, Arthur Cowper Ranyard. London, Elliot Stock.

——. 1914. Essays on the life and work of Newton. Edited, with notes and appendices, by Philip E. B. Jourdain. Chicago, London, Open Court.

DE MORGAN, SOPHIA E. 1882. Memoir of Augustus De Morgan, by his wife Sophia Elizabeth De Morgan. With selections from his letters. London, Longmans, Green.

DESAGULIERS, J. T. 1734. The constitutions of the Free-Masons. Containing the history, charges, regulations, &c. of that most ancient and right worshipful fraternity. For the use of the Lodges. London, printed Anno 5723, re-printed in Philadelphia by special order, for the use of the Brethren in North-America. (Facsimile edition by the R. W. Grand Lodge of Pennsylvania. In the year of Masonry 5906, A. D. 1906.)

——. 1734-1744. A course of experimental philosophy. 2 v. London, printed for

J. Senex; W. Innys and R. Manby; and John Osborn and Thomas Longman.

———. 1739-1740a. Some thoughts and conjectures concerning the cause of elasticity. *Phil. Trans.* 41 (1) : 175-185.

———. 1739-1740b. [I] Some thoughts and experiments concerning electricity. [II] Experiments made before the Royal Society, Feb. 2, 1737-8. [III] An account of some electrical experiments made before the Royal Society on Thursday the 16th of February 1737-8. [IV] An account of some electrical experiments made at his Royal Highness the Prince of Wale's house at Cliesden, on Tuesday the 15th of April 1738, when the electricity was conveyed 420 feet in a direct line. *Phil. Trans.* 41 (1) : 186-193, 193-200, 200-208, 209-210.

———. 1740-1741a. [I] Some things concerning electricity. [II] An account of some electrical experiments made before the Royal Society, on Thursday the 22d of January 1740-1. [III] Electrical experiments made before the Royal Society, on Thursday, March 15th 1740-1. *Phil. Trans.* 41 (2) : 634-637, 637-639, 639-640.

———. 1740-1741b. Several electrical experiments, made at various times, before the Royal Society. *Phil. Trans.* 41 (2) : 661-667.

———. 1742. A dissertation concerning electricity. London, W. Innys & T. Longman.

———. 1742-1743a. Some further observations concerning electricity. *Phil. Trans.* 42: 14-18.

———. 1742-1743b. Some conjectures concerning electricity, and the rise of vapours. *Phil. Trans.* 42: 140-143.

DESCARTES, RENÉ. 1903. Discourse on the method of rightly conducting the reason, and seeking truth in the sciences. Translated from the French, and collated with the Latin, by John Veitch. Chicago, Open Court. (Religion of Science Library, No. 38.)

[DIDEROT, DENIS.] 1871. Encyclopédie, ou Dictionnaire raisonné des sciences, des arts et des metiers, par une société de gens de lettres. Mis en ordre & publié par M. Diderot; & quant à la partie mathématique, par M. d'Alembert. 36 v.

Lausanne et Berne, chez les Sociétes Typographiques.

———. 1875a. De l'interprétation de la nature. Pages 1-62 of vol. 2 of: Œuvres complètes de Diderot, ed. by J. Assézat. Paris, Garnier Frères.

———. 1875b. Plan d'une université pour le gouvernement de Russie. Pages 409-534 of vol 3 of: Œuvres complètes de Diderot, ed. by J. Assézat. Paris, Garnier Frères.

[———]. 1916. Diderot's early philosophical works. Translated and edited by Margaret Jourdain. Chicago, London, Open Court. (The Open Court Series of Classics of Science and Philosophy, No. 4.)

[———.] 1951. Diderot et l'encyclopédie. Exposition commémorative du deuxième centenaire de l'Encyclopédie. Paris, Bibliothèque Nationale.

DIECKMANN, HERBERT. 1943. The influence of Francis Bacon on Diderot's *Interprétation de la nature. Romanic Review* 34: 303-330.

———. 1948. " Le philosophe ": texts and interpretations. Genève, E. Droz. (Washington University Studies, N. S., Language and Literature, No. 18.)

DIECKMANN, HERBERT, and I. BERNARD COHEN. 1955. The first edition of Diderot's *Pensées sur l'interprétation de la nature*, A note concerning Diderot and Franklin. *Isis* 46: 251-272.

DONOVAN, M. 1815. Second reply to Mr. De Luc's observations on a paper entitled " Reflections on the inadequacy of the principal hypotheses to explain the phaenomena of electricity." *Phil. Mag.* 46: 13-14.

DREYER, J. L. E. 1924. An address delivered by the President, Dr. J. L. E. Dreyer, on the desirability of publishing a new edition of Isaac Newton's collected works. *Monthly Notices of the Royal Astronomical Society* 84: 298-304.

DRUDE, PAUL. 1902. The theory of optics. Translated from the German by C. Riborg Mann and Robert A. Millikan. New York, London, Longmans, Green.

DUANE, WILLIAM. 1859. Letters to Benjamin Franklin from his family and friends, 1751-1790. New York, C. Benjamin Richardson.

DU BOIS-REYMOND, EMIL. 1852. On animal electricity: being an abstract of the discoveries of Emil Du Bois-Reymond. Edited by H. Bence Jones. London, John Churchill.

DUBOS, RENÉ. 1950. Louis Pasteur, free lance of science. Boston, Little, Brown.

DUCARLA, M. 1784. Du feu complet. Paris, chez Moutard. (Mémoires du musée de Paris: sciences, No. 1, première livraison.)

DU FAY, CHARLES-FRANÇOIS DU CISTERNAY. 1733-1734. A letter . . . concerning electricity. *Phil. Trans.* 38: 258-266.

——. 1733a. Premier mémoire sur l'électricite: Histoire de l'électricité. *Histoire de l'Academie Royale des Sciences*, Mémoires, 23-35.

——. 1733b. Second mémoire sur l'électricité: Quels sont les corps qui sont susceptibles d'électricité. *Histoire de l'Académie Royale des Sciences*, Mémoires, 73-84.

——. 1733c. Troisième mémoire sur l'électricité: Des corps qui sont le plus vivement attirés par les matières electriques, & de ceux qui sont les plus propres à transmettre l'électricité. *Histoire de l'Académie Royale des Sciences*, Mémoires, 233-254.

——. 1733d. Quatrième mémoire sur l'électricité: De l'attraction & répulsion des corps électriques. *Histoire de l'Académie Royale des Sciences*, Mémoires, 457-476.

——. 1734a. Cinquième mémoire sur l'électricité: Où l'on rend compte des nouvelles découvertes sur cette matière, faites depuis peu par M. Gray; et où l'on examine quelles sont les circonstances qui peuvent apporter quelque changement à l'électricité pour l'augmentation ou la diminution de sa force, comme la température de l'air, le vuide, l'air comprimé, &c. *Histoire de l'Académie Royale des Sciences*, Mémoires, 341-361.

——. 1734b. Sixième mémoire sur l'électricité: Où l'on examine quel rapport il y a entre l'électricité, & la faculté de rendre de la lumière, qui est commune à la plûpart des corps électriques, &

ce qu'on peut inférer de ce rapport. *Histoire de l'Académie Royale des Sciences*, Mémoires, 503-526.

——. 1737a. Septième mémoire sur l'électricité: contenant quelques additions aux Mémoires précédents. *Histoire de l'Académie Royale des Sciences*, Mémoires, 86-100.

——. 1737b. Huitiéme mémoire sur l'électricité. *Histoire de l'Académie Royale des Sciences*, Mémoires, 307-325.

DUGAS, RENÉ. 1950. Histoire de la mécanique. Préface de Louis de Broglie. Neuchâtel, Éditions du Griffon. (Bibliothèque Scientifique, 16: Philosophie et Histoire.)

DUHEM, PIERRE. 1902. Le mixte et la combinaison chimique. Essai sur l'évolution d'une idée. Paris, Gauthier-Villars.

——. 1908. ΣΩΖΕΙΝ ΤΑ ΦΑΙΝΟΜΕΝΑ. Essai sur la notion de théorie physique de Platon a Galilée. Paris, Librairie Scientifique A. Hermann.

——. 1954. The aim and structure of physical theory. Foreword by Prince Louis de Broglie. Translated from the French by Philip P. Wiener. Princeton, Princeton Univ. Press.

DUNSHEATH, P. 1951. The electric current. Based on the Christmas Lectures delivered at the Royal Institution. London, G. Bell and Sons.

[DUVEEN, DENIS I.] 1952. Catalogue of printed works by, and memorabilia of, Antoine Laurent Lavoisier, 1743-1794. New York, Grolier Club.

DVOICHENKO-MARKOFF (MARKOV), EUFROSINA. 1947. Benjamin Franklin, the American Philosophical Society, and the Russian Academy of Science. *Proc. Amer. Philos. Soc.* 91: 250-257.

——. 1950. The American Philosophical Society and early Russian-American relations. *Proc. Amer. Philos. Soc.* 94: 549-610.

EARNEST, ERNEST. 1940. John and William Bartram, botanists and explorers: 1699-1777, 1739-1823. Philadelphia, Univ. of Penna. Press. (Pennsylvania Lives.)

EDDY, GEORGE SIMPSON. 1924. Dr. Benjamin Franklin's library. *Proc. Amer. Antiquarian Soc.* 34 (2) : 206-226.

EDLESTON, J. 1850. Correspondence of Sir Isaac Newton and Professor Cotes, including letters of other eminent men . . . ; together with an appendix containing other unpublished letters and papers by Newton. . . . London, John W. Parker; Cambridge, John Deighton.

EINSTEIN, ALBERT. 1905. Ueber einen die Erzeugung und Verwandlung des Lichtes betreffenden heuristischen Gesichtspunkt. *Annalen der Physik* 17: 132-148.

——. 1949. Autobiographical notes. Pages 1-96 of: Albert Einstein: philosopher-scientist. Edited by Paul Arthur Schilpp. Evanston, Ill., Library of Living Philosophers.

——. 1950. Out of my later years. New York, Philosophical Library.

ELLICOTT, JOHN. 1748. Several essays towards discovering the laws of electricity . . . read on the 25th of Feb. 1747, and at two meetings soon after. *Phil. Trans.* 45: 195-224.

ELLIS, GEORGE E. 1871. Memoir of Sir Benjamin Thompson, Count Rumford, with notices of his daughter. Published in connection with an edition of Rumford's complete works by the American Academy of Arts and Sciences. Boston, Amer. Acad. Arts and Sciences.

EMERY, CLARK. 1942. " Sir " John Hill versus the Royal Society. *Isis* 34: 16-20.

ENESTRÖM, GUSTAF. 1910-1913. Verzeichnis der Schriften Leonhard Eulers. 2 v. Leipzig, Druck und Verlag von B. G. Teubner. (Jahresbericht der deutschen Mathematiker-Vereinigung: der Ergänzungsbände, 4. Band, Lieferung 1 u. Lieferung 2.)

ESPENSCHIED, LLOYD. 1955. The electrical flare of the 1740's. *Electrical Engineering* 74: 392-397.

EULER, M., LE FILS. 1759. Recherches sur la cause physique de l'électricité. *Histoire de l'Académie royale des sciences et belles lettres.* Année MDCCLVII, Berlin, Chez Haude et Spener.

EULER, LEONHARD. 1802. Letters of Euler on different subjects in physics and philosophy, addressed to a German princess. Translated from the French by Henry Hunter, with original notes, and a glossary of foreign and scientific terms. Second ed. 2 v. London, printed for Murray and Highley, etc. [One of many editions; see the bibliography by ERNESTRÖM (1910-1913) .]

EVE, A. S. 1939. Rutherford. Being the life and letters of the Rt. Hon. Lord Rutherford, O. M. With a foreword by Earl Baldwin. New York, Macmillan; Cambridge, Univ. Press.

FARADAY, MICHAEL. 1838, 1844, 1855. Experimental researches in electricity. 3 v. London, [1 & 2] Richard and John Edward Taylor; [3] Richard Taylor and William Francis.

[——]. 1899. The letters of Faraday and Schœnbein, 1836-1862. With notes, comments, and references to contemporary letters. Ed. by Georg W. A. Kahlbaum and Francis V. Darbishire. London, Williams & Norgate; Bâle: Benno Schwabe.

[——]. 1932-1936. Faraday's diary: being the various philosophical notes of experimental investigation made by Michael Faraday, . . . during the years 1820-1862, . . . and published for the first time under the editorial supervision of Thomas Martin, with a foreword by Sir William H. Bragg. 7 v. and index. London, G. Bell and Sons.

FARBER, EDUARD. 1952. The evolution of chemistry. A history of its ideas, methods, and materials. New York, Ronald Press.

FARRINGTON, BENJAMIN. 1949. Francis Bacon: philosopher of industrial science. New York, Henry Schuman. (The Life of Science Library.)

FAUCHET, ABBÉ. 1790. Éloge civique de Benjamin Franklin, prononcé le 21 juillet 1790, dans la Rotonde, au nom de la Commune de Paris. Paris, chez J.-R. Lottin, [&] G. L. Bailly, et au Palais-Royal, [chez] Vict. Desenne, [&] J. Cussac.

FAŸ, BERNARD. 1929. Franklin, the apostle of modern times. Boston, Little, Brown.

FISCH, HAROLD. 1953. The scientist as priest: A note on Robert Boyle's natural theology. *Isis* 44: 252-265.

FLEMING, DONALD. 1952. Latent heat and the invention of the Watt engine. *Isis* 43: 3-5.

FONTENELLE, BERNARD LeBOVIER DE. 1766. Éloge de M.'Du Fay. Pages 560-578 of vol. 2 of: Éloges des académiciens de l'Académie Royale des Sciences, morts depuis l'an 1699. Nouvelle édition. Paris, chez les Libraires Associés.

FORD, EDWARD. 1946. David Rittenhouse, astronomer-patriot, 1732-1796. Philadelphia, Univ. of Penna. Press (Pennsylvania Lives.)

FORD, PAUL LEICESTER. 1889. Franklin bibliography: a list of books written by, or relating to Benjamin Franklin. Brooklyn, N.Y., [privately printed].

——. 1899. The many-sided Franklin. New York, Century.

FORD, WORTHINGTON CHAUNCEY (ed.). 1905. List of the Benjamin Franklin papers in the Library of Congress. Washington, Govt. Print. Office.

FOURIER, JOSEPH. n.d. The analytical theory of heat. Translated, with notes, by Alexander Freeman. New York, G. E. Stechert. (A facsimile reprint.)

FOVEAU DE COURMELLES [Dr.]. 1907. Le bilan scientifique du XIXᵉ siècle. Paris, A. Maloine.

FOWLER, THOMAS. 1881. Bacon. London, Sampson Low, Marston, Searle, & Rivington.

FOX, R. HINGSTON. 1919. Dr. John Fothergill and his friends. Chapters in eighteenth century life. London, Macmillan.

FRANK, PHILIPP. 1949. Modern science and its philosophy. Cambridge, Harvard Univ. Press.

[FRANKLIN, BENJAMIN.] 1744. A catalogue of choice and valuable books, consisting of near 600 volumes, in most faculties and sciences, viz. divinity, history, law, mathematics, philosophy, physic, poetry, &c., which will begin to be sold for ready money only, by Benj. Franklin, at the Post-Office in Philadelphia, on Wednesday, the 11th of April 1744, at nine a clock in the morning; and for dispatch, the lowest price is mark'd in each book. [Philadelphia], [printed by Benjamin Franklin]. (I have used: "A facsimile of the unique copy in the Curtis Collection of Franklin Imprints, in the University of Pennsylvania Library, with a note by Carl Van Doren. Printed in an edition of 250 copies on

the occasion of the meeting of the Bibliographical Society of America in Philadelphia, June 5th, 1948.")

——. 1752. Expériences et observations sur l'électricité. Traduites de l'anglois. Paris, chez Durand.

——. 1756. Expériences et observations sur l'électricité. Traduites de l'anglois. Seconde edition. Par M. d'Alibard. Paris, chez Durand.

——. 1758. Des Herrn Benjamin Franklins, Esq. Briefe von der Elektricität. Aus dem Engländischen übersetzt, nebst Anmerkungen von J. C. Wilcke. Leipzig, Verlegts Gottfried Kiesewetter, Buchh. in Stockholm.

——. 1769. Experiments and observations on electricity, made at Philadelphia in America. To which are added letters and papers on philosophical subjects. London, printed for David Henry; and sold by Francis Newbery.

——. 1773. Œuvres de M. Franklin, docteur ès loix. Traduites de l'anglois sur la quatrième édition, par M. Barbeu Dubourg. Avec des additions nouvelles. 2 v. Paris, chez Quillau l'aîné, Esprit, et l'auteur.

——. 1774. Experiments and observations on electricity, made at Philadelphia in America. To which are added letters and papers on philosophical subjects. Fifth ed. London, printed for F. Newbery.

——. 1779. Political, miscellaneous, and philosophical pieces, . . . now first collected, with explanatory plates, notes, and an index to the whole, by Benjamin Vaughan. London, printed for J. Johnson.

[——]. 1806. The complete works in philosophy, politics, and morals, of the late Dr. Benjamin Franklin, now first collected and arranged with memoirs of his early life, written by himself. Second edition. 3 v. London, printed for J. Johnson, and Longman, Hurst, Rees, Orme, and Brown.

[——]. 1840. The works of Benjamin Franklin: containing several political and historical tracts not included in any former edition, and many letters official and private, not hitherto published; with notes and a life of the author by Jared Sparks. 10 v. Revised edition. Philadelphia, Childs & Peterson.

[———]. 1905-1907. The writings of Benjamin Franklin. Collected and edited with a life and introduction by Albert Henry Smyth. 10 v. New York, Macmillan.

[———]. 1926. Poor Richard's almanack. Selections from the prefaces, apothegms, and rimes, with a facsimile in reduction of the almanac for 1773. Edited by Benjamin E. Smith. New York, Century.

[———]. 1941. Benjamin Franklin's experiments. A new edition of Franklin's *Experiments and observations on electricity*. Edited, with a critical and historial introduction, by I. Bernard Cohen. Cambridge, Harvard Univ. Press.

[———]. 1945. A Benjamin Franklin reader. Edited by Nathan G. Goodman. New York, Thomas Y. Crowell.

[———]. 1949a. The will of Benjamin Franklin, 1757. Now reproduced in facsimile together with an introduction by Carl Van Doren. Philadelphia, Franklin Institute.

[———]. 1949b. Memoirs. Parallel text edition, comprising the texts of Franklin's original manuscript, the French translation by Louis Guillaume le Veillard, the French translation published by Buisson, and the version edited by William Temple Franklin, his grandson. Edited, with an introduction and explanatory notes, by Max Farrand. Berkeley, Los Angeles, Univ. of Calif. Press (in cooperation with the Huntington Library).

[———]. 1950a. The letters of Benjamin Franklin & Jane Mecom. Edited with an introduction by Carl Van Doren. Princeton, Princeton Univ. Press, published for the American Philosophical Society. (Memoirs of the Amer. Philos. Soc. 27.)

[———]. 1950b. Benjamin Franklin's letters to the press, 1758-1775. Collected and edited by Verner W. Crane. [Published for the Institute of Early American History and Culture at Williamsburg, Virginia.] Chapel Hill, Univ. of North Carolina Press.

[———]. 1954. Some account of the Pennsylvania Hospital. Printed in facsimile, with an introduction by I. Bernard Cohen. Baltimore, Johns Hopkins Press.

[FRANKLIN, BENJAMIN, and WINSTON CHURCHILL]. 1951. An exhibition celebrating the bicentennial of the University of Pennsylvania Library. At the University Museum, Philadelphia. Foreword by Harold E. Stassen. Philadelphia, [Univ. of Pennsylvania].

[Franklin Institute.] 1943. Meet Dr. Franklin. Philadelphia, Franklin Institute. (A series of papers on various aspects of Franklin's career by Carl Van Doren, Robert A. Millikan, Max Farrand, Conyers Read, Verner W. Crane, Robert E. Spiller, George Wharton Pepper, Gilbert Chinard, Lawrence C. Wroth, Bernhard Knollenberg, Carl R. Woodward, Julian P. Boyd.)

FREUD, SIGMUND. 1932. Leonardo da Vinci. A psychosexual study of an infantile reminiscence. Translated by A. A. Brill. New York, Dodd, Mead.

———. 1934. Gesammelte Schriften. Zwölfter Band: Schriften aus den Jahren 1928 bis 1933, Vermischte Schriften. Wien, Internationaler Psychoanalytischer Verlag.

FREUND, IDA. 1904. The study of chemical composition. An account of its method and historical development, with illustrative quotations. Cambridge, Univ. Press. (Cambridge Physical Series.)

FROBENIUS, SIGISMUND AUGUST. 1729-1730. An account of a spiritus vini æthereus, together with several experiments tried therewith. *Phil. Trans.* 36: 283-289.

———. 1740-1741. Abstracts of the original papers communicated to the Royal Society by Sigismond Augustus Frobenius, M. D. concerning his spiritus vini æthereus. *Phil. Trans.* 41: 864-870.

FROST, PERCIVAL. 1880. Newton's *Principia*, first book, sections I., II., III., with notes and illustrations, and a collection of problems, principally intended as examples of Newton's methods. London, Macmillan.

FROST, WALTER. 1927. Bacon und die Naturphilosophie. München, Verlag Ernst Reinhardt. (Geschichte der Philosophie in Einzeldarstellungen, Abt. V,

Die Philosophie der neueren Zeit II, Band 20.)

FUETER, EDUARD. 1941. Geschichte der exakten Wissenschaften in der schweizerischen Aufklärung (1680-1780). Aarau, Leipzig, H. R. Sauerländer. (Veröffentlichungen d. Schweiz. Gesellsch. f. Gesch. d. Med. u. d. Naturwiss., 12.)

FULTON, JOHN F. 1931. The rise of the experimental method: Bacon and the Royal Society of London. *Yale Jour. Biol. and Med.* 3: 299-320.

——. 1932a. Robert Boyle and his influence on thought in the seventeenth century. *Isis* 18: 77-102.

——. 1932b. A bibliography of the Honourable Robert Boyle, Fellow of the Royal Society. *Oxford Bibliog. Soc. Proc. and Papers* 3: 1-172, 339-365.

——. 1934. The principles of bibliographical citation. *Bull. Med. Libr. Assoc.* 22: 183-197.

——. 1935. A bibliography of two Oxford physiologists: Richard Lower, 1631-1691; John Mayow, 1643-1679. *Oxford Bibliog. Soc. Proc. and Papers* 4: 1-62.

——. 1950. Humanism in an age of science, being a Ludwig Mond Lecture delivered at the Manchester School of Medicine on 6 October 1949. New York, Henry Schuman.

——. 1951. The impact of science on American history. *Isis* 42: 176-191.

——. 1953a. Michael Servetus and the lesser circulation of the blood through the lungs. Pages 62-71 of: Autour de Michel Servet et de Sebastien Castellion, recueil publié sous la direction de B. Becker. Haarlem, H. D. Tjeenk Willink & Zoon.

——. 1953b. Michael Servetus, humanist and martyr. With a bibliography of his works and census of known copies by Madeline E. Stanton. New York, Herbert Reichner.

FULTON, JOHN F., and CHARLOTTE H. PETERS. 1937. Works of Joseph Priestley, 1733-1804. Preliminary short title list. New Haven, Laboratory of physiology, Yale Univ. School of Medicine.

GALDSTON, IAGO. 1944. Descartes and modern psychiatric thought. *Isis* 35: 118-128.

GALILEI, GALILEO. 1914. Dialogues concerning two new sciences. Translated from the Italian and Latin into English by Henry Crew and Alfonso de Salvio. With an introduction by Antonio Favaro. New York, Macmillan. [Reissued by the Macmillan Company, 1933. Facsimile reprint by Editorial Board of Northwestern University Studies, Evanston, Illinois, 1946; reissued by Dover Publications, New York, n. d.]

——. 1953a. Dialogue on the two world systems. In the Salusbury translation. Revised and annotated, and with an introduction, by Giorgio de Santillana. Chicago, Univ. of Chicago Press.

——. 1953b. Dialogue concerning the two chief world systems—Ptolemaic and Copernican. Translated by Stillman Drake. Foreword by Albert Einstein. Berkeley, Los Angeles, Univ. of California Press.

GALVANI, LUIGI. 1953. Commentary on the effects of electricity on muscular motion. Translated into English by Margaret Glover Foley. With notes and a critical introduction by I. Bernard Cohen. Together with a facsimile of Galvani's *De viribus electricitatis in motu musculari commentarius* (1791), and a bibliography of the editions and translations of Galvani's book prepared by John Farquhar Fulton and Madeline E. Stanton. Norwalk, Burndy Library.

GARNETT, WILLIAM. 1886. Heroes of science. Physicists. London, Society for Promoting Christian Knowledge. New York, E. & J. B. Young and Co. [Contains chapters on Boyle, Franklin, Cavendish, Rumford, Young, Faraday, and Clerk Maxwell.]

[GAUGER, NICOLAS.] 1713. La mécanique du feu, ou l'art d'en augmenter les effets, & d'en diminuer la dépense . . . par Mr. G * * *. Paris, chez Jacques Estienne.

——. 1715. Fires improv'd: being a new method of building chimneys, so as to prevent their smoaking: in which a small fire shall warm a room much better than a much larger made the common way. With tne manner of altering such chimneys as are already built, so that they shall perform the same effects. Made English and improved by J. T. Desaguliers. London, J. Sennex & E. Curll.

——. 1736. Fires improved: or, a new method of building chimnies so as to prevent their smoking. In which a small fire shall warm a room much better than a large one made the common way. And the method of altering such chimnies as are already built, so that they shall perform the same effects. Made English from the French original by J. T. Desaguliers. The second edition, with an appendix, containing several farther improvements made by the translator and others. London, J. Sennex & E. Curll.

GEIKIE, SIR ARCHIBALD. 1917. Annals of the Royal Society Club. The record of a London dining-club in the eighteenth & nineteenth centuries. London, Macmillan.

GERLAND, E. 1892. Geschichte der Physik. Leipzig, Verlagsbuchhandlung von J. J. Weber.

GERLAND, E., and F. TRAUMÜLLER. 1899. Geschichte der physikalischen Experimentierkunst. Leipzig, Verlag von Wilhelm Engelmann.

GIBBS, F. W. 1951. Peter Shaw and the revival of chemistry. *Annals of Science,* 7: 211-237.

GIBSON, R. W. 1950. Francis Bacon: a bibliography of his works and of Baconiana to the year 1750. Oxford, at the Scrivener Press.

GIRVIN, HARVEY F. 1948. A historical appraisal of mechanics. Scranton, Pa., International Textbook.

GLADSTONE, J. H. 1872. Michael Faraday. London, Macmillan.

GLANSDORFF, MAXIME. 1947. La philosophie de Newton. *Synthèses,* 2e année, 25-39.

GLAZEBROOK, R. T. 1900. James Clerk Maxwell and modern physics. New York, Macmillan. (The Century Science Series.)

GLIOZZI, MARIO. 1937. L'elettrologia fino al Volta. 2 v. Napoli, Luigi Loffredo.

GOODMAN, NATHAN G. 1938. Life of Benjamin Franklin year by year. 1706-1790. Philadelphia, Franklin Institute. (Poor Richard Pamphlet, 1.)

GORDON, MARGARET MARIA (BREWSTER). 1870. The home life of Sir David Brewster. By his daughter. Second edition. Edinburgh, Edmonston and Douglas.

'sGRAVESANDE, WILLEM JACOBA. 1726. Mathematical elements of natural philosophy, confirm'd by experiments; or, an introduction to Sir Isaac Newton's philosophy. Written in Latin. Translated into English by J. T. Desaguliers. 2d edition, corrected. 2 v. London, printed for J. Senex, W. and J. Innys; and J. Osborn and T. Longman.

——. 1737. Mathematical elements of natural philosophy, confirm'd by experiments: or, an introduction to Sir Isaac Newton's philosophy. Written in Latin. Translated into English by J. T. Desaguliers. 5th ed. 2 v. London, printed for J. Senex, W. Innys, R. Manby, and T. Longman.

——. 1747 Mathematical elements of natural philosophy, confirm'd by experiments: or, an introduction to Sir Isaac Newton's philosophy. Written in Latin. Translated into English by J. T. Desaguliers. 6th edition. 2 v. London, printed for W. Innys, T. Longman and T. Shewell, C. Hitch, and M. Senex.

GRAY, GEORGE J. 1907. A bibliography of the works of Sir Isaac Newton. Together with a list of books illustrating his works. With notes. Second edition, revised and enlarged. Cambridge, Bowes and Bowes.

GRAY, STEPHEN. 1731-1732a. A letter . . . containing several experiments concerning electricity. *Phil. Trans.* 37: 18-44.

——. 1731-1732b. A letter concerning the electricity of water. *Phil. Trans.* 37: 227-230.

——. 1731-1732c. A letter . . . containing a farther account of his experiments concerning electricity. *Phil. Trans.* 37: 285-290.

——. 1731-1732d. Two letters . . . containing farther accounts of his experiments concerning electricity. *Phil. Trans.* 37: 397-407.

[GREEN, GEORGE.] 1903. Mathematical papers of the late George Green. Edited by N. M. Ferrers. Paris, Librairie Scientifique A. Hermann. (Facsimile reprint of original edition.)

GREEN, H. GWYNEDD. 1946. A biography of George Green, mathematical physicist of Nottingham and Cambridge, 1793-1841. Pages 545-594 of: Studies and essays in the history of science and learning, offered in homage to George Sarton, on the occasion of his sixtieth birthday, 31 August 1944, edited by M. F. Ashley Montagu. New York, Henry Schuman.

GREENE, EVARTS BOUTELL. 1943. The revolutionary generation, 1763-1790. New York, Macmillan. (A history of American life, 4.)

GREENHILL, GEORGE. 1923. Definitions and laws of motion in the " Principia." Nature 111: 224-226, 395-396.

GREENSTREET, W. J. 1927. Isaac Newton, 1642-1727. A memorial volume, edited for the Mathematical Association. London, G. Bell and Sons.

[GREGORY, DAVID.] 1937. David Gregory, Isaac Newton and their circle. Extracts from David Gregory's memoranda, 1677-1708. Edited by W. G. Hiscock. Oxford, printed for the editor.

GRIMAUX, ÉDOUARD. 1896. Lavoisier 1743-1794, d'après sa correspondance, ses manuscrits, ses papiers de famille et d'autres documents inédits. Deuxième édition. Paris, Félix Alcan.

GROSS, B. 1944. On the experiment of the dissectible condenser. Amer. Jour. Physics 12: 324-329.

GUERLAC, HENRY. 1950. Temps moderne. Comité International des Sciences Historiques, Rapports, 182-211. [Paris, published by UNESCO.]

——. 1951. The continental reputation of Stephen Hales. Archives Internationales d'Histoire des Sciences, 4 (vol. 30 d'Archeion) : 393-404.

——. 1952. Science in western civilization. A syllabus. New York, Ronald Press.

——. 1954a. John Mayow and the aerial nitre. Actes du VIIe Congres International d'Histoire des Sciences, Jérusalem (4-12 Août 1953) . [Paris, Hermann & Cie., Académie Internationale d'Histoire des Sciences], 332-349.

——. 1954b. The poet's nitre. Isis 45: 243-255.

——. 1954c. Lavoisier and his biographers. Isis 45: 51-62.

GUICHARD, M. 1937. Essai historique sur les mesures en chimie. I: (a) Avant Lavoisier, (b) avec Lavoisier; II: (c) Après Lavoisier. Paris, Hermann. (Actualités Scientifiques et Industrielles, 567, 568.)

GUILLEMIN, ERNST ADOLPH. 1932. Early developments in electromagnetic theory. With two unpublished letters by André Marie Ampère. Isis 18: 118-126.

HAAS, ARTHUR ERICH. 1913. Die Elektronenhypothese in ihrem Verhältnis zu älteren physikalischen Theorien. Archiv für des Geschichte der Naturwissenschaften und der Technik 6: 144-149.

HADAMARD, JACQUES. 1945. An essay on the psychology of invention in the mathematical field. Princeton, Princeton Univ. Press.

HAGBERG, KNUT. 1952. Carl Linnæus. Translated from the Swedish by Alan Blair. London, Jonathan Cape.

HALBERTSMA, K. T. A. 1949. A history of the theory of colour. Amsterdam, Swets & Zeitlinger.

HALE, EDWARD E., EDWARD E. JR. 1888. Franklin in France. From original documents. 2 v. Boston, Roberts Brothers.

HALE, GEORGE ELLERY. 1913, 1914, 1915. National Academies and the progress of research. I: The work of European Academies. II: The first half century of the National Academy of Sciences. III: The future of the National Academy of Sciences. Science 38: 681-698; 39: 189-200; 40: 907-919; 41: 12-22.

HALES, STEPHEN. 1738. Statical essays: containing vegetable staticks; or, an account of some statical experiments on the sap in vegetables. 1. The third edition, with amendments. London, printed for W. Innys, R. Manby, T. Woodward, and J. Peele.

——. 1740. Statical essays: containing haemastatics; or, an account of some hydraulic and hydrostatical experiments made on the blood and blood-vessels of animals. To which is added an appendix containing observations and experiments relating to several subjects in the first volume. With an index to both volumes. 2. The second edition, corrected. London, printed for W. Innys, R. Manby, and T. Woodward.

——. 1743. A description of ventilators: whereby great quantities of fresh air may with ease be conveyed into mines, gaols, hospitals, work-houses and ships, in exchange for their noxious air. . . . (read before the Royal Society in May 1741). London, W. Innys, M. Manby, & T. Woodward.

——. 1750. Some considerations on the causes of earthquakes. *Phil. Trans.* 46: 669-681.

——. 1779, 1780. La statique des végétaux, et celle des animaux; expériences lues a la Société Royale de Londres. Première partie: La statique des végétaux; seconde partie: La statique des animaux. Paris, L'Imprimerie de Monsieur. [" La statique des végétaux, et l'analyse de l'air; ouvrage traduit de l'anglois par M. le Comte de Buffon . . . , nouvelle édition revue par M. Sigaud de la Fond"; " Hæmastatique, ou la statique des animaux . . . , ouvrage traduit de l'anglois par M. de Sauvages."]

HALL, A. R. 1948. Sir Isaac Newton's note-book, 1661-1665. *Cambridge Hist. Jour.* 9: 239-250.

——. 1952. Ballistics in the seventeenth century. A study in the relations of science and war, with reference principally to England. Cambridge, Univ. Press.

——. 1954. The scientific revolution, 1500-1800. The formation of the modern scientific attitude. London, Longmans, Green.

[HALLEY, EDMOND.] 1932. Correspondence and papers of Edmond Halley, preceded by an unpublished memoir of his life by one of his contemporaries and the " eloge " by D'Ortous de Mairan. Arranged and edited by Eugene Fairfield MacPike. Oxford, Clarendon Press.

HAMILTON, ALEXANDER. 1948. Gentleman's progress. The itinerarium of Dr. Alexander Hamilton, 1744. Edited with an introduction by Carl Bridenbaugh. Chapel Hill, Univ. of North Carolina Press. [Published for the Institute of Early American History and Culture.]

HARASZTI, ZOLTÁN. 1950. Young John Adams on Franklin's iron points. *Isis* 41: 11-14.

HARRIS, JOHN. 1736. Lexicon technicum: or, an universal dictionary of arts and sciences: explaining not only the terms of art, but the arts themselves. 2 v. The fifth edition. Now digested into one alphabet, with very considerable additions and improvements from later discoveries in mathematicks and philosophy, &c. London, printed for J. Walthoe, Mess. Knapton, D. Midwinter, A. Bettesworth and C. Hitch, E. Symon, T. Ward and E. Wicksteed, B. Motte and C. Bathurst, A. Ward, J. Clark, D. Brown, T. Wotton, T. Hatchett and E. Comins. [The preface contain's Newton's De Natura acidorum (1692) in a Latin and an English version.]

HARRISON, CHARLES T. 1933. Bacon, Hobbes, Boyle, and the ancient atomists. *Harvard Studies and Notes in Philology and Literature* 15: 191-218.

HARTLEY, HAROLD. 1933. [The bicentenary of Joseph Priestley.] *Jour. Chem. Soc.* 915-920.

HARTOG, SIR PHILIP. 1931. Joseph Priestley and his place in the history of science. *Proc. Royal Inst. of Great Britain* 26: 395-430.

——. 1933. Joseph Priestley, 1733-1804. *Jour. Chem. Soc.*, 896-902.

——. 1941. The newer views of Priestley and Lavoisier. *Annals of Science* 5: 1-56.

HARVEY, WILLIAM. 1931. Exercitatio anatomica de motu cordis et sanguinis in animalibus. An English translation, with annotations, by Chauncey D. Leake. Springfield, Illinois, Charles C Thomas.

HAÜY, RENÉ JUST. 1787. Exposition raisonnée de la théorie de l'électricité et du magnétisme, d'après les principes de M. Æpinus. Paris, chez la Veuve Desaint.

——. 1803. Traité élémentaire de physique. 2 v. Paris, de l'imprimerie de Delance et Lesueur.

——. 1806. Traité élémentaire de physique. Seconde édition, revue et considérablement augmentée. 2 v. Paris, chez Courcier.

——. 1807. An elementary treatise on

natural philosophy. Translated from the French by Olinthus Gregory. 2 v. London, printed for George Kearsley.

HAWKINS, RICHMOND LAURIN, ed. 1933. Newly discovered French letters of the seventeenth, eighteenth, and nineteenth centuries. Cambridge, Harvard Univ. Press.

HAYES, I. MINIS, ed. 1908. Calendar of the papers of Benjamin Franklin in the library of the American Philosophical Society. 5 v. Philadelphia, printed for the Amer. Philos. Soc.

HAZARD, PAUL. 1946. La pensée européenne au XVIIIeme siècle de Montesquieu a Lessing. 3 v. 1: première partie: Le procès du Christianisme; deuxième partie: La cité des hommes. 2: Désagrégation. 3: Notes and références. Paris, Boivin.

——. 1953. The European mind. The critical years (1680-1715). Translated by J. Lewis May. New Haven, Yale Univ. Press. [The title of the original French volume was: La crise de la conscience européenne (1935).]

HEATHCOTE, N. H. DE V. 1950. Guericke's sulphur globe. Annals of Science 6: 293-305.

——. 1955. Franklin's introduction to electricity. Isis 46: 29-35.

HEAVISIDE, OLIVER. 1893, 1899, 1912. Electromagnetic theory. 3 v. London, " The Electrician " Printing & Publishing Co., Ltd. [A one-volume reprint has been made by Dover Publications, New York, 1950.]

HEISENBERG, WERNER. 1952. Philosophic problems of nuclear science. Translated by F. C. Hayes. New York, Pantheon Books.

HELLER, AUGUST. 1882. Geschichte der Physik von Aristoteles bis auf die neueste Zeit. Zwei Bände. I. Band: Von Aristoteles bis Galilei. Stuttgart, Verlag Von Ferdinand Enke.

HELLOT, JEAN. 1739. Sur la liqueur éthérée de M. Frobenius. Histoire de l'Académie Royale des Sciences, Mémoires, 62-83.

HELMHOLTZ, HERMANN VON. 1881. On the modern development of Faraday's conception of electricity. Jour. Chem. Soc. 39: 277-304.

HENNIG, RICHARD. 1910. Die angebliche Kenntnis des Blitzableiters vor Franklin. Archiv für die Geschichte der Naturwissenschaften und der Technik 2: 97-136.

HENRY, JOSEPH. 1874. Report of the Secretary, Joseph Henry, for the year 1874. Annual Report of the Board of Regents of the Smithsonian Institution . . . for the year 1874, [Washington, Govt. Print. Office, 1875], 7-48.

——. 1886-1887. Scientific writings of Joseph Henry. 2 v. Washington, published by the Smithsonian Institution (Smithsonian Miscellaneous Collections, 30).

HERTZ, HEINRICH. 1893. Electric waves: being researches on the propagation of electric action with finite velocity through space. Authorised English translation by D. E. Jones. With a preface by Lord Kelvin. London, New York, Macmillan.

——. 1899. The principles of mechanics, presented in a new form. With an introduction by H. von Helmholtz. Authorised English translation by D. E. Jones and J. T. Walley. London, Macmillan.

HERTZBERGER, MENNO. 1927. Short-title catalogue of books written and edited by Herman Boerhaave. Compiled with the assistance of E. J. Van Der Linden. Preface by J. G. De Lint. Amsterdam, Menno Hertzberger.

HESSEN, B. 1946. The social and economic roots of Newton's Principia. Sydney, Current Book Distributors. [Reprint of article appearing in: Science at the cross roads. Papers presented to the International Congress of the History of Science and Technology held in London from June 29th to July 3rd, 1931, by the delegates of the U. S. S. R. London, Kniga, Ltd.]

HEYL, PAUL R. 1925. Fundamental concepts in physics in the light of recent discoveries. The eighteenth century: the century of materialism. Science 61: 221-225.

HILL, JOHN. 1751. A review of the works of the Royal Society of London; containing animadversions on such of the papers as deserve particular observation. London, printed for R. Griffiths.

HISCOCK, W. G. 1936. The war of the scientists: New light on Newton and Gregory. *The Times Literary Supplement*, 11 Jan.

HOADLY, BENJAMIN, and BENJAMIN WILSON. 1756. Observations on a series of electrical experiments. London, printed for T. Payne. [A second edition, "with alternations and the addition of some experiments, letters, and explanatory notes," was published in 1759.]

HOBHOUSE, STEPHEN. 1948. Selected mystical writings of William Law. Edited, with notes and twenty-four studies in the mystical theology of William Law and Jacob Boehme, and an enquiry into the influence of Jacob Boehme on Isaac Newton. Foreword by Aldous Huxley. New York, London, Harper Brothers.

HOBSON, E. W. 1923. The domain of natural science. The Gifford Lectures delivered in the University of Aberdeen in 1921 and 1922. Cambridge, Univ. Press.

HOCKETT, HOMER CAREY. 1943. Political and social growth of the American people, 1492-1865. Third edition. New York, Macmillan.

HOFF, HEBBEL, E. 1936. Galvani and the pre-Galvanian electrophysiologists. *Annals of Science* 1: 157-172.

HOFMANN, JOS. E. 1949. Die Entwicklungsgeschichte der Leibnizschen Mathematik während des Aufenthaltes in Paris (1672-1676). München, Leibniz Verlag (Bischer R. Oldenbourg Verlag).

HOLMES, THOMAS J. 1940. Cotton Mather. A bibliography of his works. 3 v. Cambridge, Harvard Univ. Press.

HOOKE, ROBERT. 1665. Micrographia: or some physiological descriptions of minute bodies made by magnifying glasses. With observation and inquiries thereupon. London, printed by Jo. Martyn and Ja. Allestry. [Facsimile reprint in: Early Science in Oxford, ed. by R. T. Gunther, 13, Oxford, 1938.]

HOOYKAAS, R. 1948. The discrimination between "natural" and "artificial" substances and the development of corpuscular theory. *Archives Internationales d'Histoire des Sciences* 1: 640-651.

———. 1949. The experimental origin of chemical atomic and molecular theory before Boyle. *Chymia* 2: 65-80.

HOPPE, EDMUND. 1884. Geschichte der Elektrizität. Leipzig, Johann Ambrosius Barth.

———. 1926. Geschichte der Optik. Leipzig, Verlagsbuchhandlung J. J. Weber.

———. 1928. Histoire de la physique. Traduit de l'allemand par Henri Besson. Paris, Payot. (Bibliothèque scientifique.)

HORNBERGER, THEODORE. 1945. Scientific thought in the American colleges 1638-1800. Austin, Univ. of Texas Press.

HORSLEY, SAMUEL. 1770. Difficulties in the Newtonian theory of light, considered and removed. *Phil. Trans.* 60: 417-440. [A supplement to a former paper, concerning difficulties in the Newtonian theory of light. *Phil. Trans.* 61: 547-558.]

HOUSTON, EDWIN J. 1906. Franklin as man of science and an inventor. *Jour. Franklin Inst.* 161: 241-316, 321-383.

HOWLDY, THOMAS. 1815. On the Franklinian theory of the Leyden jar; with remarks on Mr. Donovan's experiments. *Philos. Mag.* 46: 401-408.

HUGHES, ARTHUR. 1951-1952. Science in English encyclopædias, 1704-1875. *Annals of Science* 7: 340-370; 8: 323-367.

HUJER, KAREL. 1952. Father Procopius Diviš—the European Franklin. *Isis* 43: 351-357.

HUME, DAVID. 1882. Essays: Moral, political, and literary. Edited, with preliminary dissertations and notes, by T. H. Green and T. H. Grose. 2 v. New edition. London, Longmans, Green. [Vol. 2 contains pp. 1-135, An enquiry concerning human understanding.]

HUMPHREYS, A. W. 1937. The development of the conception and measurement of electric current. *Annals of Science* 2: 164-178.

HUMPHREYS, WILLIAM J. 1942. A review of the papers on meteorology and climatology published by the American Philosophical Society prior to the twentieth century. *Proc. Amer. Philos. Soc.* 86: 29-33.

HUNTER, JOHN. 1773. Anatomical observations on the torpedo. *Phil. Trans.* **63**: 481-489.

HUSSAKOF, L. 1916. Benjamin Franklin and Erasmus Darwin: with some unpublished correspondence. *Science*, N. S., **43**: 773-775.

HUYGENS, CHRISTIAAN. 1912. Treatise on light. In which are explained the causes of that which occurs in reflexion, & in refraction, and particularly in the strange refraction of Iceland crystal. Translated by Silvanus P. Thompson. London, Macmillan. (Facsimile edition, Univ. of Chicago Press.)

——. 1937. Traité de la lumière. Où sont expliquées les causes de ce qui luy arrive dans la reflexion, & dans la refraction. Et particulièrement dans l'étrange refraction du cristal d'islande. Pages 451-537 of: Œuvres complètes de Christiaan Huygens, publiées par la Société Hollandaise des Sciences. Tome dix-neuvième. The Hague, Martinus Nijhoff. [The original edition, in French, was first published in Leyden, 1690.]

[——]. 1950. Œuvres complètes de Christiaan Huygens, publiées par la Société Hollandaise des Sciences, tome vingt-deuxième: Supplément à la correspondance, Varia, Biographie de Chr. Huygens, Catalogue de la vente des livres de Chr. Huygens. The Hague, Martinus Nijhoff.

[HUYGENS, CHRISTIAAN, and AUGUSTIN JEAN FRESNEL.] 1945. Huygens-Fresnel. La teoría ondulatoria de la luz. Introducción y notas de Cortés Pla. Buenos Aires, Editorial Losada.

INGEN-HOUSZ, JEAN. 1785. Nouvelles expériences et observations sur divers objets de physique. Paris, chez P. Théophile Barrois le jeune, Librairie.

——. 1789. Sur les métaux comme conducteurs de la chaleur. *Observations sur la physique, sur l'histoire naturelle et sur les arts* **24**: 68-380.

[Institut de France.] 1939. Index biographique des membres et correspondants de l'Académie des Sciences de 1666 à 1939. Paris, Gauthier-Villars.

JACQUOT, JEAN. 1952. Sir Charles Cavendish and his learned friends.—I. Before

the Civil War; II. The years of exile. *Annals of Science* **8**: 13-27, 175-191.

JALLABERT, LOUIS. 1749. Expériences sur l'électricité, avec quelques conjectures sur la cause de ses effets. Paris, chez Durand [&] chez Pissot.

JEANS, J. H. 1908. The mathematical theory of electricity and magnetism. Cambridge, Univ. Press.

JONES, BENCE. 1870. The life and letters of Faraday. 2 v. London, Longmans, Green.

JONES, HAROLD SPENCER. 1947. Sir Isaac Newton (1642-1727). *Ciel et Terre* **63**: 73-85.

[JONES, RICHARD FOSTER.] 1951. The seventeenth century. Studies in the history of English thought and literature from Bacon to Pope, by Richard Foster Jones, and other writings in his honor. Stanford, Stanford Univ. Press.

JORGENSON, CHESTER E. 1935. The new science in the almanacs of Ames and Franklin. *New England Quart.* **8**: 555-561.

JOURDAIN, LAURA, and GEORGE SARTON. 1923. Philip E. B. Jourdain (1879-1919). *Isis* **5**: 126-133.

JOURDAIN, PHILIP E. B. 1913. The principle of least action. Chicago, Open Court.

——. 1914a. The principles of mechanics with Newton, from 1666 to 1679. *The Monist* **24**: 187-224.

——. 1914b. The principles of mechanics with Newton from 1679 to 1687. *The Monist* **24**: 515-564.

——. 1915a. Newton's hypothesis of ether and of gravitation from 1672 to 1679. *The Monist* **25**: 79-106.

——. 1915b. Newton's hypothesis of ether and of gravitation from 1679 to 1693. *The Monist* **25**: 233-254.

——. 1915c. Newton's hypothesis of ether and of gravitation from 1693 to 1726. *The Monist* **25**: 418-440.

——. 1920a. Elliptic orbits and the growth of the third law with Newton. *The Monist* **30**: 183-198.

——. 1920b. Newton's theorems on the attraction of spheres. *The Monist* **30**: 199-202.

[KALM, PETER.] 1937. The America of 1750: Peter Kalm's travels in North America. The English version of 1770. Revised from the original Swedish and edited by Adolph B. Benson. With a translation of new material from Kalm's diary notes. 2 v. New York, Wilson-Erickson.

[KELVIN], WILLIAM THOMSON. 1872. Reprint of papers on electrostatics and magnetism. London, Macmillan. [A second edition appeared in 1884.]

KERKER, MILTON. 1955. Herman Boerhaave and the development of pneumatic chemistry. *Isis* 46: 36-49.

KEYNES, LORD. 1947. Newton the man. Pages 27-34 of: The Royal Society: Newton Tercentenary Celebrations, 15-19 July 1946. Cambridge, Univ. Press.

KEYS, ALICE MAPELSDEN. 1906. Cadwallader Colden: a representative eighteenth century official. New York, Columbia Univ. Press; Macmillan Company, agents.

KILGOUR, FREDERICK G. 1949. The rise of scientific activity in colonial New England. *Yale Jour. Biol. and Med.* 22: 123-138.

KING, LORD PETER. 1830. The life of John Locke, with extracts from his correspondence, journals, and commonplace books. New edition, with considerable additions. 2 v. London, Henry Colbourn and Richard Bentley.

KNIGHT, GOWAN. 1744. An account of some magnetical experiments, shewed before the Royal Society, by Mr. Gowan Knight, on Thursday the 15th of November, 1744. *Phil. Trans.* 43: 161-166.

KOYRÉ, ALEXANDRE. 1939. Etudes Galiléennes. I: A l'aube de la science classique; II: La loi de la chute des corps: Descartes et Galilée; III: Galilée et la loi d'inertie. Paris, Hermann. (Actualités Scientifiques et Industrielles, 852, 853, 854.)

——. 1943a. Galileo and the scientific revolution of the seventeenth cenutry. *Philos. Rev.* 52: 333-348.

——. 1943b. Galileo and Plato. *Jour. Hist. of Ideas* 4: 400-428.

——. 1944. Entretiens sur Descartes. New York, Paris, Brentano's.

——. 1945. Discovering Plato. Translated by Leonora Cohen Rosenfield. New York, Columbia Univ. Press.

——. 1950. The significance of the Newtonian synthesis. *Jour. of General Education* 4: 256-268. [Reprinted from *Archives Internationales d'Histoire des Sciences*, 1950, no. 11; 291-311.]

——. 1952. An unpublished letter of Robert Hooke to Isaac Newton. *Isis* 43: 312-337.

——. 1953. Experiment in measurement. Bibliography. *Proc. Amer. Philos. Soc.* 97: 222-237.

——. 1955. Pour une édition critique des œuvres de Newton. *Revue d'Histoire des sciences* 8: 19-37.

KRAUS, MICHAEL. 1949. The Atlantic civilization: eighteenth-century origins. Ithaca, Cornell Univ. Press, for the American Historical Association.

KUBIE, LAWRENCE S. 1953-1954. Some unsolved problems of the scientific career. *Amer. Scientist* 41: 596-613; 42: 104-112.

KUHN, THOMAS S. 1951. Newton's "31st query" and the degradation of gold. *Isis* 42: 296-298.

——. 1952. Robert Boyle and structural chemistry in the seventeenth century. *Isis* 43: 12-36.

LABAREE, LEONARD W. 1954. The papers of Benjamin Franklin. *Manuscripts* 7: 36-39.

LANGE, FREDERICK ALBERT. 1950. The history of materialism, and criticism of its present importance. Authorized translation by Ernest Chester Thomas. Third edition. 3 v. in one. Introduction by Bertrand Russell. New York, Humanities Press.

LAPLACE, PIERRE SIMON DE. 1821. Précis de l'histoire de l'astronomie. Paris: Mme Ve Courcier, Libraire pour les sciences. ["Le précis . . . forme le livre V de la cinquième edition de mon Exposition du Système du Monde, actuellement sous presse."]

LARMOR, JOSEPH. 1924. On editing Newton. *Nature* 113: 744.

——. 1937. Origins of Clerk Maxwell's electric ideas: as described in familiar letters to William Thomson. Cambridge, Univ. Press.

LAUE, MAX VON. 1950. History of physics. Translated by Ralph Oesper. New York, Academic Press.

LAVOISIER, ANTOINE. 1862. Œuvres de Lavoisier. Publiées par les soins de son excellence le ministre de l'instruction publique et des cultes. Tome 2, Mémoires de chimie et de physique. Paris, Imprimerie Impériale.

LE CAT, CLAUDE-NICOLAS. 1752. Remarques sur les principales expériences, & sur la doctrine du livre de M. Benjamin Franklin de Philadelphie en Amérique, concernant l'électricité. Lettres à M. Phineas Bond. *Jour. Œconomique* [Paris, chez Antoine Boudet], novembre, 1752: 89-112.

[LEIBNIZ.] 1920. The early mathematical manuscripts of Leibniz. Translated from the Latin texts published by Carl Immanuel Gerhardt, with critical and historical notes by J. M. Child. Chicago, London, Open Court.

LE MONNIER, LOUIS G. 1746. Recherches sur la communication de l'électricité. *Histoire de l'Académie Royale des Sciences*, Mémoires 447-464.

LENOBLE, ROBERT. 1943. Mersenne, ou la naissance du mécanisme. Paris, Librairie Philosophique J. Vrin. (Bibliothèque d'Histoire de la Philosophie.)

LEROUX, LUCIEN. 1925. Nicolas Lémery. *Isis* 7: 430-432.

LE ROY, JEAN BAPTISTE. 1753. Mémoire sur l'électricité, où l'on montre par une suite d'expériences, qu'il y a deux espèces d'électricités, l'une produite par la condensation du fluide électrique, & l'autre par sa raréfaction; & qu'elles ont chacune des phénomènes particuliers qui les caractérisent parfaitement. *Histoire de l'Academie Royale des Sciences*, Mémoires, 447-474.

LESLIE, JOHN. 1804. An experimental inquiry into the nature and propagation of heat. London, printed for J. Mawman.

——. 1835. Dissertation fourth: exhibiting a general view of the progress of mathematical and physical science, chiefly during the eighteenth century. Pages 573-677 of: Dissertations on the history of metaphysical and ethical, and mathematical and physical science, by Dugald Stuart, the Right Hon. Sir James Mackintosh, John Playfair and Sir John Leslie. Edinburgh, Adam and Charles Black. [Written for the seventh edition of the *Encyclopædia Britannica*.]

LETTSOM, JOHN COAKLEY. 1786. Memoirs of John Fothergill, M. D., &c. The fourth edition. London, printed for C. Dilly.

LIEBEN, FRITZ. 1953. Vorstellungen vom Aufbau der Materie im Wandel der Zeiten. Eine historische Übersicht. Wien, Franz Deuticke.

LIEBIG, JUSTUS VON. 1863. Rede in der öffentlichen Sitzung der k. Akademie der Wissenschaften am 28. März 1863 . . . : Francis Bacon von Verulam und die Geschichte der Naturwissenschaften. München, Auf Rosten der k. Akademie.

LILLEY, S. 1948. Attitudes to the nature of heat about the beginning of the nineteenth century. *Archives Internationales d'Histoire des Sciences* 1: 630-639.

LIN, CHI-KAI. 1931. L'origine et le développement de la méthode expérimentale. Paris, Les éditions Domat-Montchrestien, F. Loviton.

LINDSAY, ROBERT BRUCE, and HENRY MARGENAU. 1936. Foundations of physics. New York, John Wiley & Sons; London, Chapman & Hall.

LINGELBACH, WILLIAM E. 1955. Benjamin Franklin's papers and the American Philosophical Society. *Proc. Amer. Philos. Soc.* 99: 349-380.

[LINNAEUS.] 1821. A selection of the correspondence of Linnaeus, and other naturalists, from the original manuscripts. Edited by Sir James Edward Smith. 2 v. London, printed for Longman, Hurst, Rees, Orme, and Brown.

LLOYD, HUMPHREY. 1834. Report on the progress and present state of physical optics. *Report of the Fourth Meeting of the British Association for the Advancement of Science* (London, 1835), 295-413.

LOCKE, JOHN. 1823. Some thoughts concerning education. The works of John Locke. A new edition, corrected. 10 v. 9: 1-205. London, printed for T. Tegg, W. Sharpe and Son, etc.

LODGE, OLIVER J. 1889. Modern views on electricity. London, New York, Macmillan. (Nature Series.)

——. 1892. Lightning conductors and lightning guards. A treatise on the protection of buildings, of telegraph instruments and submarine cables, and of electric installations generally, from damage by atmospheric discharges. London, Whittaker; New York, Macmillan.

LORIA, GINO. 1920. Per la storia del Newtonianismo in Italia. *Atti della Società Italiana per il Progresso delle Scienze*, X Riunione, Pisa, Aprile 1919: 471-475.

McEACHRON, K. B. 1952. Lightning protection since Franklin's day. *Jour. Franklin Inst.* 253: 441-470.

MACH, ERNST. 1911. History and root of the principle of the conservation of energy. Translated from the German and annotated by Philip E. B. Jourdain. Chicago, London, Open Court.

——. 1919. The science of mechanics. A critical and historical account of its development. Translated from the German by Thomas J. McCormack. Fourth edition. Chicago, London. Open Court.

——. 1923. Die Principien der Wärmelehre. Historisch-Kritisch Entwickelt. 4. Auflage. Leipzig, Verlag von Johann Ambrosius Barth.

——. 1926. The principles of physical optics. An historical and philosophical treatment. Translated by John S. Anderson and A. F. A. Young. London, Methuen.

MACKENZIE, A. STANLEY (ed.). 1900. The laws of gravitation. Memoirs by Newton, Bouguer and Cavendish, together with abstracts of other important memoirs. Translated and edited by A. Stanley Mackenzie. New York, American Book Company.

McKIE, DOUGLAS. 1936. Antoine Lavoisier: the father of modern chemistry. Philadelphia, J. B. Lippincott.

——. 1942a. Newton and chemistry. *Endeavour* 1: 141-144.

——. 1942b. Some notes on Newton's chemical philosophy, written upon the occasion of the tercentenary of his birth.

Philos. Mag. and Jour. of Science 33: 847-870.

——. 1949. Antoine Laurent Lavoisier, F. R. S.—1743-1794. *Notes and Records Royal Soc. of London* 7: 1-41.

——. 1952. Antoine Lavoisier: scientist, economist, social reformer. New York, Henry Schuman. (The Life of Science Library.)

McKIE, D., and G. R. DE BEER. 1951, 1952. Newton's apple. *Notes and Records Royal Soc. of London* 9: 46-54, 333-335.

McKIE, DOUGLAS, and NIELS H. DE V. HEATHCOTE. 1935. The discovery of specific and latent heats. With a foreword by E. N. da C. Andrade. London, Edward Arnold.

MacLAREN, MALCOLM. 1943. The rise of the electrical industry during the nineteenth century. Princeton, Princeton Univ. Press.

MACLAURIN, COLIN. 1748. An account of Sir Isaac Newton's philosophical discoveries. Published from the author's manuscript papers. London, printed for the author's children, and sold by A. Millar and J. Nourse, . . .

MacLAURIN, LOIS MARGARET. 1928. Franklin's vocabulary. Garden City, N. Y., Doubleday, Doran. (Franklin Monographs.)

MACOMBER, HENRY P. 1951. A comparison of the variations and errors in copies of the first edition of Newton's *Principia*, 1687. *Isis* 42: 230-232.

——. 1953. A census of the owners of copies of the 1687 first edition (and the 1726 presentation issue) of Newton's *Principia. Papers Bibliog. Soc. of America* 47: 269-300.

MADDISON, R. E. W. 1951, 1952. Studies in the life of Robert Boyle. Part 1: Robert Boyle and some of his foreign visitors; part 2: Salt water freshened. *Notes and Records Royal Soc. of London* 9: 1-35, 196-216.

MAGIE, WILLIAM FRANCIS. 1935. A source book in physics. New York and London, McGraw-Hill. (Source Books in the History of the Sciences.)

MAHON, CHARLES. 1779. Principles of electricity, containing divers new theorems and experiments, together with an analysis of the superior advantages of high and pointed conductors. This treatise comprehends an explanation of an electrical returning stroke, by which fatal effects may be produced even at a vast distance from the place where the lightning falls. London, printed for P. Elmsly.

MAINDRON, ERNEST. 1888. L'Académie des Sciences: histoire de l'Académie—fondation de l'Institut National: Bonaparte membre de l'Institut National. Paris, Ancienne Librairie Germer Baillière, Félix Alcan, Éditeur.

MALEBRANCHE, NICOLAS. 1945. De la recherche de la vérité, où l'on traite de la nature de l'esprit de l'homme, et de l'usage qu'il en doit faire pour éviter l'erreur des sciences. Introduction et texte établi par Geneviève Lewis. 2 v. Paris, Librairie Philosophique J. Vrin. (Bibliothèque des textes philosophiques.)

MALLIK, D. N. 1921. Optical theories. Based on lectures delivered before the Calcutta University. Second edition, revised. Cambridge, Univ. Press.

MANGIN, ARTHUR. 1866. Le feu du ciel: histoire de l'électricité et de ses principales applications. Troisième édition. Tours, Alfred Mame et fils, éditeurs.

MARAT, JEAN PAUL. 1782. Recherches physiques sur l'électricité. Paris, de l'imprimerie de Clousier. . . .

MARTIN, BENJAMIN. 1738. The philosophical grammar; being a view of the present state of experimented physiology, or natural philosophy. Second edition. London, printed for John Noon.

——. 1746. An essay on electricity: being an enquiry into the nature, cause and properties thereof, on the principles of Sir Isaac Newton's theory of vibrating motion, light and fire; and the various phænomena of forty-two capital experiments; with some observations relative to the uses that may be made of this wonderful power of nature. Bath, printed for the author, and Mr. Leake, and Mr. Frederick, . . . [The bound copy I have used contains *A supplement: containing remarks on a rhapsody of adventures of a modern knight-errant in philosophy.*]

——. 1747. Philosophia Britannica: or a new and comprehensive system of the Newtonian philosophy, astronomy and geography. 2 v. Reading, printed by C. Micklewright and Co. for the author, and for M. Cooper, R. Raikes, B. Collins, J. Leake, and W. Frederick.

——. 1759. A supplement to the Philosophia Britannica. Appendix I, containing new experiments in electricity, and the method of making artificial magnets, 3-32. London, [no publisher].

MARTIN, EDWIN T. 1952. Thomas Jefferson: scientist. New York, Henry Schuman. (The Life of Science Library.)

MARTIN, THOMAS. 1949. Faraday's discovery of electro-magnetic induction. London, Edward Arnold.

MARTINEAU, HARRIET. 1855. The positive philosophy of Auguste Comte. Freely translated and condensed. New York, Calvin Blanchard.

MARX, ROSE S. 1934. A 13th century theory of heat as a form of motion. *Isis* 22: 19-20.

MASSON, FLORA. 1914. Robert Boyle: a biography. London, Constable.

MATHER, COTTON. 1721. The Christian philosopher: a collection of the best discoveries in nature, with religious improvements. London, printed for Eman. Matthews.

——. 1938. Manuductio ad ministerium. Directions for a candidate of the ministry. Reproduced from the original edition, Boston, 1726, with a bibliographical note by Thomas J. Holmes and Kenneth B. Murdock. New York, Columbia Univ. Press. (Facsimile Text Society, Pub. No. 42.)

MAXWELL, JAMES CLERK. n. d. Matter and motion. Reprinted: with notes and appendices by Sir Joseph Larmor. New York, Dover Publications.

——. 1873. A treatise on electricity and magnetism. 2 v. Oxford, Clarendon Press. (Third edition, revised by J. J. Thomson, issued by Oxford University Press, 1892; reprinted 1904; reprinted photographically, 1937, 1946.)

——. 1881. An elementary treatise on electricity. Edited by William Garnett. Oxford, Clarendon Press. (Clarendon Press Series.)

——. 1885. Theory of heat. Eighth edition. London, Longmans, Green.

——. 1888. An elementary treatise on electricity. Edited by William Garnett. Second edition. Oxford, Clarendon Press.

[——]. 1890. The scientific papers of James Clerk Maxwell. Edited by W. D. Niven. 2 v. Cambridge, Univ. Press. [A one-volume reprint has been made by Dover Publications, New York.]

[——]. 1931. James Clerk Maxwell: a commemoration volume, 1831-1931. Essays by Sir J. J. Thomson, Max Planck, Albert Einstein, *et al.* Cambridge, Univ. Press.

MAYO, LAWRENCE SHAW. 1948. The Winthrop family in America. Boston, Mass. Hist. Soc.

MAZEAS, GUILL. 1752. Letters of the Abbé Mazéas, F. R. S. to the Rev. Stephen Hales, D. D., F. R. S. concerning the success of the late experiments in France. Translated from the French by James Parsons, M. D., F. R. S. *Phil. Trans.* 47: 534-552.

MELDRUM, ANDREW NORMAN. 1910. The development of the atomic theory: (3) Newton's theory, and its influence in the eighteenth century. *Mem. and Proc. Manchester Lit. and Philos. Soc.* 55: 1-15.

——. 1919. The development of the atomic theory. London, Oxford Univ. Press.

——. 1930. The eighteenth century revolution in science—the first phase. Bombay, Longmans, Green.

——. 1933. Priestley's unique contribution to science; Priestley's work on nitrogen peroxide. *Jour. Chem. Soc.*, 902-915.

——. 1933-1934. Lavoisier's early work in science, 1763-1771. *Isis* 19: 330-363; 20: 396-425.

MENDENHALL, T. C. 1890. A century of electricity. Boston, New York, Houghton, Mifflin. (The Riverside Science Series, 1.)

MENTRÉ, M. F. 1905. La simultanéité des decouvertes scientifiques. Pages 916-924 of: Congrès International de Philosophie, 2me session, tenue à Genève du 4 au 8 septembre 1904: *Rapports et Comptes Rendus.* Genève, Henry Kündig.

MERTON, ROBERT K. 1937a. The sociology of knowledge. *Isis* 27: 493-503.

——. 1937b. Some economic factors in seventeenth-century English science. *Scientia* 62: 142-152.

——. 1938. Science, technology and society in seventeenth century England. *Osiris* 4: 360-632.

——. 1939. Science and the economy of seventeenth century England. *Science and Society* 3: 3-27.

MERZ, JOHN THEODORE. 1907-1912. A history of European thought in the nineteenth century. 2 v. Third unaltered edition. Edinburgh and London, William Blackwood and Sons.

MESMER, FRANZ. 1948. Mesmerism, by Dr. Mesmer, (1779). Being the first translation of Mesmer's historic *Mémoire sur la découverte du magnétisme animal* to appear in English. With an introductory monograph by Gilbert Frankau. London, Macdonald.

METCALF, SAMUEL L. 1843. Caloric: its mechanical chemical and vital agencies in the phenomena of nature. 2 v. London, William Pickering.

METZGER, HÉLÈNE. 1918. La genèse de la science des cristaux. Paris, Félix Alcan.

——. 1922. L'évolution du règne métallique d'après les Alchimistes du XVIIe siècle. *Isis* 4: 466-482.

——. 1923. Les doctrines chimiques en France du début du XVIIe à la fin du XVIIIe siècle. Tome I. Paris, Les Presses Universitaires de France.

——. 1926a. La philosophie de la matière chez Stahl et ses disciples. *Isis* 8: 427-464.

——. 1926b. Les concepts scientifiques. Paris, Librairie Félix Alcan. (Bibliothèque de Philosophie Contemporaine.)

——. 1927. La théorie de la composition des sels et la théorie de la combustion d'après Stahl et ses disciples. *Isis* 9: 294-325.

——. 1929a. Newton: la théorie de l'émission de la lumière et la doctrine chimique au XVIIIeme siècle. *Archeion* 11: 13-25.

——. 1929*b*. Newton et l'exposé de la doctrine chimique au XVIIIeme siècle. *Archeion* 11: 190-197.

——. 1930. Newton, Stahl, Boerhaave et la doctrine chimique. Paris, Librairie Félix Alcan. (Bibliothèque de Philosophie Contemporaine.)

——. 1935. La philosophie de la matière chez Lavoisier. Paris, Hermann. (Actualités Scientifiques et Industrielles, 218.)

——. 1938. Attraction universelle et religion naturelle chez quelques commentateurs anglais de Newton. Première partie: Introduction philosophique; deuxième partie: Newton-Bentley-Whiston-Tolland; troisième partie: Clarke – Cheyne – Baxter – Priestley. Paris, Hermann. (Actualités Scientifiques et Industrielles, 621, 622, 623.)

MEYER, ARTHUR WILLIAM. 1936. An analysis of the De generatione animalium of William Harvey. Stanford, Stanford Univ. Press; London, Oxford Univ. Press.

——. 1939. The rise of embryology. Stanford, Calif., Stanford Univ. Press.

MEYERHOF, MAX. 1935. Ibn An-Nafîs (XIIIth century) and his theory of the lesser circulation. *Isis* 23: 100-120.

MEYERSON, EMILE. 1930. Identity and reality. Authorized translation by Kate Loewenberg. London, George Allen & Unwin; New York, Macmillan. (Library of Philosophy.)

——. 1931. Du cheminement de la pensée. 3 v. 1: Le problème et la solution envisagée; 2: Le raisonnement mathématique; 3: Notes. Paris, Félix Alcan.

——. 1936. Essais. Préface de Louis de Broglie. Avertissement de Lucien Lévy-Bruhl. Paris, Librairie Philosophique J. Vrin.

MILES, HENRY. 1744-1745. A letter from the Reverend Henry Miles, D. D., F. R. S. to Mr. Henry Baker, F. R. S. of firing phosphorus by electricity. *Phil. Trans.* 43: 290-293.

——. 1745. A letter from the Reverend Henry Miles, D. D. and F. R. S. to the President; containing observations of luminous emanations from human bodies, and from brutes; with some remarks on electricity. *Phil. Trans.* 43: 441-446.

——. 1746. Part of a letter . . . concerning electrical fire. *Phil. Trans.* 44 (1) :78-81.

MILHAUD, GASTON. 1921. Descartes savant. Paris, Librairie Félix Alcan (Bibliothèque de Philosophie Contemporaine.)

MILLER, DAYTON CLARENCE. 1939. Sparks, lightning, cosmic rays. An anecdotal history of electricity. Christmas week lectures for young people, 1937, The Franklin Institute. New York, Macmillan.

MILLER, PERRY. 1949. Jonathan Edwards. New York, William Sloane Associates. (The American Men of Letters Series.)

——. 1953. The New England mind. From colony to province. Cambridge, Harvard Univ. Press.

——. 1954. The New England mind. The seventeenth century. Cambridge, Harvard Univ. Press.

MILLER, SAMUEL. 1803. A brief retrospect of the eighteenth century. Part first: Containing a sketch of the revolutions and improvements in science, arts, and literature, during that period. 2 v. New York, printed by T. and J. Swords.

MILLIKAN, ROBERT ANDREWS. 1917. The electron. Its isolation and measurement and the determination of some of its properties. Chicago, Univ. of Chicago Press.

——. 1943. Benjamin Franklin as a scientist. Pages 11-26 of: Meet Dr. Franklin. Philadelphia, Franklin Institute.

——. 1947. Electrons ($+$ and $-$), protons, photons, neutrons, mesotrons, and cosmic rays. Revised edition. Chicago, Univ. of Chicago Press. [The beginning of this book corresponds to Millikan (1917).]

——. 1948. Franklin's discovery of the electron. *Amer. Jour. Physics* 16: 319.

——. 1950. The autobiography of Robert A. Millikan. New York, Prentice-Hall.

MILLINGTON, E. C. 1945. Theories of cohesion in the seventeenth century. *Annals of Science* 5: 253-269.

——. 1947. Studies in capillarity and cohesion in the eighteenth century. *Annals of Science* 5: 352-369.

MISES, RICHARD VON. 1951. Positivism: a study in human understanding. Cambridge, Harvard Univ. Press.

MOLLOY, GERALD. 1888. Gleanings in science. A series of popular lectures on scientific subjects. London and New York, Macmillan.

MONTGOMERY, THOMAS HARRISON. 1900. A history of the University of Pennsylvania, from its foundation to A. D. 1770. Philadelphia, George W. Jacobs.

MORAND, SAUVEUR F., and JEAN A. NOLLET. 1749. Expériences de l'électricité appliquée a des paralytiques. *Histoire de l'Académie Royale des Sciences*, Mémoires, 28-39.

MORE, LOUIS TRENCHARD. 1914. The units of measure and the principle of relativity. *The Monist* 24: 225-258.

——. 1934. Isaac Newton: a biography, 1642-1727. New York, London, Charles Scribner's Sons.

——. 1944. The life and works of the Honourable Robert Boyle. New York, Oxford Univ. Press.

MORGAN, G. C. 1794. Lectures on electricity. 2 v. Norwich, J. March; sold by J. Johnson, London.

MORIN, P. E. 1819. Essai sur la nature et les propriétés d'un fluide impondérable, ou nouvelle théorie de l'univers matériel. Le Puy, chez J. G. Guilhaume; Paris, chez Delaunay, chez Gœury.

MORISON, SAMUEL ELIOT. 1936. Harvard College in the seventeenth century. 2 v. Cambridge, Harvard Univ. Press.

MORISON, SAMUEL ELIOT, and HENRY STEELE COMMAGER. 1942. The growth of the American republic. 1. Third edition. New York, London, Oxford Univ. Press.

MORLEY, JOHN. 1886. Diderot and the encyclopædists. 2 v. London, Macmillan.

MORNET, DANIEL. 1911. Les sciences de la nature en France, au XVIIIe siècle. Un chapitre de l'histoire des idées. Paris, Librairie Armand Colin.

——. 1929. French thought in the eighteenth century. Translated by Lawrence M. Levin. New York, Prentice-Hall.

MORTON, CHARLES. 1940. Compendium physicæ. Edited, with an introduction and notes, by Theodore Hornberger. With a biographical introduction by Samuel Eliot Morison. Boston, Colonial Soc. of Mass. (Publications of the Colonial Society of Massachusetts, **33**, Collections.)

MOSZKOWSKI, ALEXANDER. 1921. Einstein the searcher: His work explained from dialogues with Einstein. Translated by Henry L. Brose. London, Methuen & Co. Ltd.

MOTT, FRANK LUTHER, and CHESTER E. JORGENSON (eds.), 1936. Benjamin Franklin: representative selections, with introduction, bibliography, and notes. New York, American Book Company. (American Writers Series.)

MOTTELAY, PAUL FLEURY. 1922. Bibliographical history of electricity and magnetism, chronologically arranged. With an introduction by Silvanus P. Thompson and foreword by Sir R. T. Glazebrook. London, Charles Griffin; Philadelphia, J. B. Lippincott.

MOUY, PAUL. 1934. Le développement de la physique cartésienne, 1646-1712. Paris, Librairie Philosophique J. Vrin. (Bibliothèque d'Histoire de la Philosophie.)

MUNBY, A. N. L. 1952. The distribution of the first edition of Newton's *Principia*. The Keynes Collection of the works of Sir Isaac Newton at King's College, Cambridge. *Notes and Records Royal Soc. of London* 10: 28-39, 40-50.

MUSSCHENBROEK, PIETER VAN. 1744. The elements of natural philosophy. Translated from the Latin by John Colson. 2 v. London, printed for J. Nourse.

——. 1769. Cours de physique expérimentale et mathématique. Traduit par M. Sigaud de la Fond. 3 v. Paris, chez Ganeau.

NASH, LEONARD K. 1950. The atomic-molecular theory. Cambridge, Harvard Univ. Press. (Harvard Case Histories in Experimental Science: Case 4.)

——. 1952. Plants and the atmosphere. Cambridge, Harvard University Press. (Harvard Case Histories in Experimental Science: Case 5.)

[National Resources Committee.] 1938, 1940, 1941. Research—a national resource. 1: Relation of the federal government to research: report of the Science Committee to the National Resources Committee. 2: Industrial research: report of the National Research Council to the National Resources Planning Board. 3: Business research: report of an advisory committee to the National Resources Planning Board. Washington, U. S. Govt. Print. Office.

NEAVE, E. W. J. 1936. Joseph Black's lectures on the elements of chemistry. *Isis* 25: 372-390.

——. 1950-1951-1952. Chemistry in Rozier's journal.—I. The journal and its editors; II. The phlogiston theory; III. Pierre Bayen; IV. C. L. Berthollet, and V. Fixed air; VI. Hepatic air, and VII. The Dutch chemists; VIII. Chemical affinity, and IX. Nomenclature. *Annals of Science* 6: 416-421; 7: 101-106, 144-148, 284-299, 393-400; 8: 28-45.

NEEDHAM, JOSEPH. 1934. A history of embryology. Cambridge, Univ. Press.

NEEDHAM, TURBERVILL. 1746. Extract of a letter . . . concerning some new electrical experiments lately made at Paris. *Phil. Trans.* 44 (1) : 247-263.

NETTLES, CURTIS P. 1938. The roots of American civilization: a history of American colonial life. New York, F. S. Crofts.

NEUBURGER, MAX. 1926. Lord Bacon's relations to medicine: a memorial on the occasion of the three hundredth anniversary of his death (April 9, 1626). *Medical Life* 33 (April 1926) : 149-169.

NEUMANN, C. 1870. Ueber die Principien der Galilei-Newton'schen Theorie. Akademische Antrittsvorlesung gehalten in der Aula der Universität Leipzig am 3. November 1869. Leipzig, Druck und verlag von B. G. Teubner.

NEURATH, OTTO. 1915. Prinzipielles zur Geschichte der Optik. *Archiv für die geschichte der naturwissenschaften und der technik* 5: 371-389.

NEWELL, LYMAN C. 1928. Count Rumford—scientist and philanthropist. *Science* 68: 67-73.

NEWTON, ISAAC. 1671/2. A letter of Mr. Isaac Newton, professor of the mathematicks in the University of Cambridge; containing his new theory about light and colours: sent by the author to the publisher from Cambridge, Febr. 6. 1671/72; in order to be communicated to the R. Society. *Phil. Trans.*, numb. 80 (vol. 6) : 3075-3087. [This letter is reproduced in facsimile in Newton (1956a) , and Sarton (1930a) , and is reprinted in Roberts & Thomas (1934: 71-91) .]

——. 1687. Philosophiæ naturalis principia mathematica. London, Jussu Societatis Regis ac Typis Josephi Streater. Prostant venales apud Sam. Smith . . . ; nonnullos bibliopolas. (Reproduced in facsimile by William Dawson & Sons, London.)

——. 1723. Philosophiæ naturalis principia mathematica. Editio ultima, cui accedit analysis per quantitatum series, fluxiones ac differentias cum enumeratione linearum tertii ordinis. Amsterdam, Sumptibus Societatis. [A reprint of the second edition, edited by Cotes, and published in London in 1713.]

——. 1728a. Optical lectures read in the publick schools of the University of Cambridge, Anno Domini 1669. Never before printed. Translated into English out of the original Latin. London, printed for Francis Fayram.

——. 1728b. A treatise of the system of the world. Translated into English. London, printed for F. Fayram.

——. 1729a. Lectiones opticæ annis MDCLXIX, MDCLXX, & MDCLXXI in scholis publicis habitæ, et nunc primum ex Mss. in lucem editæ. London, apud Guil. Innys.

——. 1729b. The mathematical principles of natural philosophy. Translated into English by Andrew Motte. To which are added: The laws of the moon's motion, according to gravity, by John Machin. 2 v. London, printed for Benjamin Motte. [This translation is based on the second edition of the *Principia*, in Latin, edited by Cotes, and published in London in 1713.]

——. 1733. Observations upon the prophecies of Daniel, and the apocalypse of St. John. In two parts. London, printed by J. Darby and T. Browne, and sold by J. Roberts, J. Tonson, W. Innys and R. Manby, . . .

[——]. 1779-1785. Opera quæ exstant omnia. Commentariis illustrabat Samuel Horsley. 5 v. London, excudebat Joannes Nichols.

——. 1833. Philosophiæ naturalis principia mathematica. Perpetuis commentariis illustrata, communi studio PP. Thomæ Le Seur et Francisci Jacquier. Editio nova, summa cura recensita. 2 v. Glasguæ: Georgius Brookman; London, T. T. et J. Tegg.

[——]. 1850. Correspondence of Sir Isaac Newton and Professor Cotes, including letters of other eminent men, now first published from the originals in the Library of Trinity College, Cambridge; together with an appendix, containing other unpublished letters and papers by Newton; with notes, synoptical view of the philosopher's life, and a variety of details illustrative of his history, by J. Edleston. London, John W. Parker; Cambridge, John Deighton.

——. 1898. Optik, oder Abhandlung über Spiegelungen, Brechungen, Beugungen und Farben des Lichts. (1704). Uebersetzt und herausgegeben von William Abendroth. 2 v. Leipzig, Verlag von Wilhelm Engelmann. (Ostwald's Klassiker der Exacten Wissenschaften, 96-97.)

——. 1934. Sir Isaac Newton's mathematical principles of natural philosophy and his system of the world. Translated into English by Andrew Motte in 1729. The translations revised, and supplied with an historical and explanatory appendix, by Florian Cajori. Berkeley, Univ. of California Press.

[——]. 1950. Sir Isaac Newton: Theological manuscripts. Selected and edited, with an introduction, by H. McLachlan. Liverpool, Univ. Press.

——. 1952. Opticks, or a treatise of the reflections, refractions, inflections, & colours of light. Based on the fourth edition: London, 1730. With a foreword by Albert Einstein, an introduction by Sir Edmund Whittaker, a preface by I. Bernard Cohen, and an analytical table of contents, prepared by Duane H. D. Roller. New York, Dover Publications.

——. 1956a. [Sir Isaac Newton's papers and letters on physical subjects, and related documents. Edited by I. Bernard Cohen with the assistance of R. E. Schofield. Cambridge, Harvard Univ. Press. In press.

——. 1956b. [Correspondence of Isaac Newton. Edited by H. W. Turnbull. Cambridge, Univ. Press.] In press.

NICHOLS, EDWARD L. 1906. Franklin's researches in electricity. Pages 103-121 of: The record of the celebration of the birth of Benjamin Franklin. Philadelphia, printed for the Amer. Philos. Soc.

NICOLINI, FAUSTO. 1932. Lumières nouvelles sur quelques ouvrages de Diderot d'après la correspondance inédite de l'abbé Galiani. Études Italiennes, nouvelle série, 2: 87-103, 161-173, 209-219.

NICOLSON, MARJORIE HOPE. 1930. Conway Letters. The correspondence of Anne, Viscountess Conway, Henry More, and their friends, 1642-1684. Collected from manuscript sources & edited with a biographical account. New Haven, Yale Univ. Press.

——. 1946. Newton demands the muse. Newton's Opticks and the eighteenth century poets. Princeton, Princeton Univ. Press. (History of Ideas Series, No. 2.)

——. 1950. The breaking of the circle. Studies in the effect of the "new science" upon seventeenth century poetry. [The Norman Wait Harris lectures delivered at Northwestern University, July 1949.] Evanston, Northwestern Univ. Press.

NOAD, HENRY M. 1855. A manual of electricity. Part 1: Electricity and galvanism. Fourth edition, entirely re-written. London, George Knight.

NOLLET, JEAN A. 1745. Conjectures sur les causes de l'électricité des corps. Histoire de l'Académie Royale des Sciences, Mémoires, 107-151.

——. 1746a. Essai sur l'électricité des corps. Paris, chez les frères Guérin.

——. 1746b. Observations sur quelques nouveaux phénomènes d'électricité. Histoire de l'Académie Royale des Sciences, Mémoires. 1-23.

——. 1748. Éclaircissemens sur plusieurs faits concernant l'électricité. Histoire de *l'Académie Royale des Sciences*, Mémoires, 164-199.

——. 1749. Expériences et observations faites en différens endroits de l'Italie. *Histoire de l'Académie Royale des Sciences*, Mémoires, 444-488. [This article consists of five parts of which the first, pp. 445-460, deals with electricity.]

——. 1751-1752. Extracts of two letters to Mr. William Watson, F. R. S. relating to the extracting electricity from the clouds. Translated from the French. *Phil. Trans.* 47: 553-558.

——. 1752. Lectures in experimental philosophy. Translated from the French by John Colson. London, printed for J. Wren.

——. 1753a. Comparaison raisonnée des plus célebres phénomènes de l'électricité, tendant à faire voir que ceux qui nous sont connus jusqu'à présent, peuvent se rapporter à un petit nombre de faits qui sont comme les sources de tous les autres. *Histoire de l'Académie Royale des Sciences*, Mémoires, 429-446.

——. 1753b. Examen de deux questions concernant l'électricité, pour servir de suite au mémoire intitulé, Comparaison raisonnée des plus célèbres phénomènes de l'électricité, &c. *Histoire de l'Académie Royale des Sciences*, Mémoires, 475-514.

——. 1753c. Lettres sur l'électricité. Dans lesquelles on examine les dernieres découvertes qui ont été faites sur cette matiere, & les conséquences que l'on en peut tirer. A Paris, Chez Hippolyte-Louis Guérin & Louis-François Delatour.

——. 1754. Recherches sur les causes particulières des phénomènes électriques, et sur les effets nuisibles ou avantageux qu'on peut en attendre. Nouvelle édition. Paris, chez H. L. Guerin & L. F. Delatour.

——. 1762. Réflexions sur quelques phénomènes; cités en faveur des électricités en plus & en moins. *Histoire de l'Académie Royale des Sciences*, Mémoires, première partie, 137-160; seconde partie, 270-292.

——. 1764. Leçons de physique expérimentale. Tome sixième. Paris, Chez Hippolyte-Louis Guérin & Louis-François Delatour. [This sixth volume contains the portions devoted to magnetism and electricity.]

NORINDER, HAROLD. 1952. Experimental lightning research. *Jour. Franklin Inst.* 253: 471-504.

NUNN, T. PERCY. 1907. The aim and achievements of scientific method: an epistemological essay. London, Macmillan.

OLDFIELD, R. C., and KATHLEEN OLDFIELD. 1951. Hartley's 'Observations on man.' *Annals of Science* 7: 371-381.

OLMSTED, J. M. D. 1938. Claude Bernard, Physiologist. New York and London, Harper & Brothers Publishers.

OLSCHKI, LEONARDO. 1927. Galilei und seine Zeit. Geschichte der neusprachlichen wissenschaftlichen Literatur, Dritter Band. Halle (Saale), Max Niemeyer Verlag.

——. 1942. The scientific personality of Galileo. *Bull. Hist. of Medicine,* 12: 248-273.

——. 1943. Galileo's philosophy of science. *Philos. Rev.* 52: 349-365.

ORNSTEIN, MARTHA. 1938. The rôle of scientific societies in the seventeenth century. (History of medicine series, 6). Chicago, Univ. Press (1913, 1928).

OSEEN, C. W. 1939. Johan Carl Wilcke; experimental-fysiker. Uppsala, Almquist & Wiksells.

OSMOND, PERCY H. 1944. Isaac Barrow. His life and times. London, Society for Promoting Christian Knowledge.

OSTWALD, WILHELM. 1896. Elektrochemie: ihre Geschichte und Lehre. Leipzig, Verlag von Veit & Comp.

——. 1906. Individuality and immortality. The Ingersoll Lecture, 1906. Boston, New York, Houghton, Mifflin.

——. 1910. La science et l'histoire des sciences. *La Revue du Mois* 9: 513-525.

——. 1912. L'évolution de l'électrochimie. Traduit de l'allemand par E. Philippi. Paris, Librairie Félix Alcan.

PABST, ADOLF. 1932. Charles-François du Fay, a pioneer in crystal optics. *Amer. Mineralogist* 17 :569-572.

PAFFRATH-FELDKIRCH, J. 1915. Tiberius Cavallos Beiträge zur Lehre von der

Elektrizität. *Archiv für die geschichte der naturwissenschaften und der technik* 5: 86-92.

PAPANASTASSIOU, CH. E. 1935. Les théories sur la nature de la lumière de Descartes à nos jours et l'évolution de la théorie physique. Paris, Jouve.

PARKER, IRENE. 1914. Dissenting academies in England, their rise and progress and their place among the educational systems of the country. Cambridge, Univ. Press.

PARRINGTON, VERNON LOUIS. 1927. Main currents in American thought: an interpretation of American literature from the beginnings to 1920. 1. The colonial mind, 1620-1800. New York, Harcourt, Brace.

PARTINGTON, J. R. 1939. The origins of the atomic theory. *Annals of Science* 4: 245-282.

——. 1948. A short history of chemistry. Second edition. London, Macmillan.

——. 1949. An advanced treatise on physical chemistry. 4 v. London, New York, Longmans, Green.

——. 1954. Seventeenth-century chemistry, the phlogiston theory and Dalton's atomic theory. *Nature* 174: 291 ff.

PARTINGTON, J. R., and DOUGLAS MCKIE. 1937-1938-1939. Historical studies on the phlogiston theory. I: The levity of phlogiston; II: The negative weight of phlogiston; III: Light and heat in combustion; IV: Last phases of the theory. *Annals of Science* 2: 361-404; 3: 1-58, 337-371; 4: 113-149.

PARTON, JAMES. 1864. Life and times of Benjamin Franklin. 2 v. New York, Mason Brothers.

PASCAL, BLAISE. 1937. The physical treatises of Pascal. The equilibrium of liquids, and, The weight of the mass of the air. Translated by I. H. B. and A. G. H. Spiers, with introduction and notes by Frederick Barry. New York, Columbia Univ. Press. (Records of Civilization, No. 28.)

PASSMORE, J. A. 1952. Hume's intentions. Cambridge, Univ. Press.

PATTERSON, LOUISE DIEHL. 1948. Robert Hooke and the conservation of energy. *Isis* 38: 151-156.

——. 1949-1950. Hooke's gravitation theory and its influence on Newton. I: Hooke's gravitation theory; II: The insufficiency of the traditional estimate. *Isis* 40: 327-341; 41: 32-45.

——. 1952. Pendulums of Wren and Hooke. *Osiris* 10: 277-321.

PATTERSON, THOMAS S. 1931. John Mayow in contemporary setting. A contribution to the history of respiration and combustion. *Isis* 15: 47-96, 504-546.

PEACOCK, GEORGE. 1855. Life of Thomas Young, M. D., F. R. S., &c. London, John Murray.

PELSENEER, JEAN. n. d. L'évolution de la notion de phénomène physique des primitifs à Bohr et Louis de Broglie. Bruxelles, Office International de Librairie, Office des Cours du Cercle des Sciences.

——. 1929. Un lettre inédite de Newton. *Isis* 12: 237-254.

——. 1930. Une opinion inédite de Newton sur " L'Analyse des anciens " à propos de l'*Analysis geometrica* de Hugo de Omerique. *Isis* 14: 155-165.

——. 1932. Le dernier autographe de Newton. *Isis* 17: 331.

——. 1936. Une lettre inédite de Newton à Pepys (23 décembre 1693). *Osiris* 1: 497-499.

——. 1938. Newtons äpple. *Lychnos*, Annual of the Swedish History of Science Society, 366-371.

——. 1939. Lettres inédites de Newton. *Osiris* 7: 523-555.

——. 1947. L'origine Protestante de la science moderne. *Lychnos*, 1946-1947, 246-248.

PEMBERTON, HENRY. 1728. A view of Sir Isaac Newton's philosophy. London, printed by S. Palmer.

PERAZICH, GEORGE, and PHILIP M. FIELD. 1940. Industrial research and changing technology. Philadelphia, Work Projects Administration. (National Research Project: Report No. M-4.)

PETTINGILL, GEORGE E. 1951. Franklin's electrical machine. *Jour. Franklin Inst.* 251: 188.

PICARD, ÉMILE. 1927. Un double centenaire: Newton et Laplace, leur vie et leur œuvre. Paris, Palais de l'Institut

(Institut de France, Académie des Sciences).

——. 1930. Un coup d'œil sur l'histoire des sciences et des théories physiques. Paris, Gauthier-Villars.

PICKARD, MADGE E. 1946. Government and science in the United States: Historical backgrounds. *Jour. Hist. of Medicine and Allied Sciences* 1: 254-289, 446-481.

PIGGOTT, STUART. 1950. William Stukeley: an eighteenth-century antiquary. Oxford, Clarendon Press.

PLANCK, MAX. 1949. Scientific autobiography and other papers. With a memorial address by Max von Laue. Translated from the German by Frank Gaynor. New York, Philosophical Library.

PLAYFAIR, JOHN. 1835. Dissertation third: exhibiting a general view of the progress of mathematical and physical science since the revival of letters in Europe. Pages 433-572 of: Dissertations on the history of metaphysical and ethical, and mathematical and physical science, by Dugald Stuart, the Right Hon. Sir James Mackintosh, John Playfair, and Sir John Leslie. Edinburgh, Adam and Charles Black. (Available also as vol. 2 of *The Works of John Playfair*, 1822, Edinburgh, printed for Archibald Constable & Co.) [Written for, and prefixed to, the Supplement to the fourth, fifth, and sixth editions of the *Encyclopædia Britannica*.]

PLEDGE, H. T. 1939. Science since 1500. A short history of mathematics, physics, chemistry, biology. London, His Majesty's Stationery Office.

POGGENDORFF, J. C. 1883. Histoire de la physique. Cours fait a l'Université de Berlin. Traduction de MM. E. Bibart et G. de la Quesnerie. Paris, Dunod.

POINCARÉ, H. 1913. Dernières pensées. Paris, Ernest Flammarion. (Bibliothèque de Philosophie Scientifique.)

——. 1929. The foundations of science. Science and hypothesis; The value of science; Science and method. Translated by George Bruce Halsted. Lancaster, Pa., Science Press.

POINCARÉ, H., and FREDERICK K. VREELAND. 1904. Maxwell's theory and wireless telegraphy. Part 1: Maxwell's theory and Hertzian oscillations, by H. Poincaré, translated by Frederick K. Vreeland; part 2: The principles of wireless telegraphy, by Frederick K. Vreeland. New York, McGraw.

POINCARÉ, LUCIEN. 1907. The new physics and its evolution. Being the authorised translation of *La physique moderne, son évolution*. London, Kegan Paul, Trench, Trübner. (The International Scientific Series, 90.)

POISSON, SIMÉON DENIS. 1835. Théorie mathématique de la chaleur. Paris, Bachelier.

POLVANI, GIOVANNI. 1942. Alessandro Volta. Pisa, Domus Galilæana. (Studi di storia della scienze fisiche e mathematiche I.)

PONCELET, ABBÉ. 1766. La nature dans la formation du tonnerre, et la reproduction des êtres vivans, pour servir d'introduction aux vrais principes de l'agriculture. Paris, chez P. G. Le Mercier, & Ch. Saillant.

[Portsmouth Collection]. 1888. A catalogue of the books and papers written by or belonging to Sir Isaac Newton, the scientific portion of which has been presented by the Earl of Portsmouth to the University of Cambridge. Cambridge, Univ. Press.

POTAMIAN, BROTHER, and JAMES J. WALSH. 1909. Makers of electricity. New York, Fordham Univ. Press.

POWELL, BADEN. 1841. A general and elementary view of the undulatory theory, as applied to the dispersion of light, and some other subjects. Including the substance of several papers, printed in the *Philosophical Transactions*, and other journals. London, John W. Parker.

POWICKE, FREDERICK J. 1926. The Cambridge Platonists: a study. Cambridge, Harvard Univ. Press.

POYNTING, J. H., and SIR J. J. THOMSON. 1919. A text-book of physics. Heat. Fifth edition. London, Charles Griffin.

POYNTING, J. H., and SIR J. J. THOMSON. 1927. A text-book of physics. Properties of matter. Eleventh edition. London, Charles Griffin.

PRESTON, THOMAS. 1890. The theory of light. London, Macmillan. [Fifth edition, edited by Alfred W. Porter, was published by Macmillan, London, 1928.]

——. 1894. The theory of heat. London, Macmillan.

PRICE, DEREK J. 1952. The early observatory instruments of Trinity College, Cambridge. *Annals of Science* 8: 1-12.

[PRIESTLEY, JOSEPH.] 1771. Histoire de l'électricité, traduite de l'anglois de Joseph Priestley, avec des notes critiques. 3 v. Paris, chez Hérissant le fils. [Translated by a disciple of Nollet, who added many notes disparaging the work of Franklin.]

——. 1772. The history and present state of discoveries relating to vision, light, and colours. London, printed for J. Johnson.

——. 1775. The history and present state of electricity, with original experiments. The third edition, corrected and enlarged. 2 v. London, printed for C. Bathurst, and T. Lowndes; J. Rivington, and J. Johnson; S. Crowder, G. Robinson, and R. Baldwin; T. Becket, and T. Cadell.

——. 1781. Experiments and observations on different kinds of air. 1. The third edition, corrected. London, printed for J. Johnson.

[PRINGLE, SIR JOHN.] 1783. Six discourses delivered by Sir John Pringle, Bart. when President of the Royal Society; on occasion of six annual assignments of Sir Godfrey Copley's Medal. To which is prefixed the life of the author, by Andrew Kippis. London, printed for W. Strahan, and T. Cadell.

RAMSAUER, CARL. 1953. Grundversuche der Physik in historischer Darstellung. Erster Band: Von den Fallgesetzen bis zu den elecktrischen Wellen. Berlin, Göttingen, Heidelberg, Springer-Verlag.

RAMSAY, WILLIAM. 1918. The life and letters of Joseph Black, M. D. With an introduction dealing with the life and work of Sir William Ramsay, by F. G. Donnan, F. R. S. London, Constable.

RAMSEY, A. S. 1937. Electricity and magnetism. An introduction to the mathematical theory. Cambridge, Univ. Press.

——. 1940. An introduction to the theory of Newtonian attraction. Cambridge, Univ. Press.

RAYLEIGH, LORD. 1942. The life of Sir J. J. Thomson, O. M. Cambridge, Univ. Press.

——. 1943. The life of Sir J. J. Thomson, O. M., sometime Master of Trinity College, Cambridge. Cambridge, Univ. Press.

RÉAUMUR, RENÉ ANTOINE FERCHAULT DE. 1750. The art of hatching and bringing up domestick fowls of all kinds, at any time of the year: either by means of the heat of hot-beds, or that of common fire. London, printed for C. Davis, A. Millar, and J. Nourse.

REED, HOWARD S. 1949. Jan Ingenhousz, plant physiologist. With a history of the discovery of photosynthesis. *Chronica Botanica* 11: 286-391.

REY, JEAN. 1951. The essays of Jean Rey. A facsimile reprint of the original edition of 1630, with an introduction by Douglas McKie. London, Edward Arnold.

RICHARDS, HORACE C. 1942. Some early American physicists. *Proc. Amer. Philos. Soc.* 86: 22-28.

RIGAUD, STEPHEN PETER. 1838. Historical essay on the first publication of Sir Isaac Newton's *Principia*. Oxford, Univ. Press.

——. 1841. Correspondence of scientific men of the seventeenth century, including letters of Barrow, Flamsteed, Wallis, and Newton, printed from the originals in the collection of the Right Honourable the Earl of Macclesfield. 2 v. Oxford, Univ. Press. [For a table of contents and an index of these two volumes, see De Morgan (1862).]

ROBERTS, MICHAEL, and E. R. THOMAS. 1934. Newton and the origin of colours: a study of one of the earliest examples of scientific method. London, G. Bell & Sons. (Classics of Scientific Method.)

ROBINSON, BRYAN. 1743. A dissertation on the æther of Sir Isaac Newton. Dublin, printed by S. Powell, for Geo. Ewing and Wil. Smith.

——. 1745. Sir Isaac Newton's account of the æther, with some additions by way of appendix. Dublin, printed by S. Powell, for G. and A. Ewing, and W. Smith.

ROBISON, JOHN. 1822. System of mechanical philosophy. With notes by David Brewster. 4. Edinburgh, printed for John Murray, London.

ROE, ANNE. 1951. A psychological study of physical scientists. *Genetic Psychology Monographs* 43: 121-235.

ROHAULT, JACQUES. 1723. Rohault's system of natural philosophy, illustrated with Dr. Samuel Clarke's notes, taken mostly out of Sir Isaac Newton's philosophy. Done into English by John Clarke. 2 v. London, printed for James Knapton.

ROLLER, DUANE. 1950. The early development of the concepts of temperature and heat. The rise and decline of the caloric theory. Cambridge, Harvard Univ. Press. (Harvard case histories in experimental science, 3.)

ROLLER, DUANE, and DUANE H. D. ROLLER. 1953. Francis Hauksbee. *Scientific American* 189 (2) : 64-69.

ROLLER, DUANE, and DUANE H. D. ROLLER. 1954. The development of the concept of electric charge: electricity from the Greeks to Coulomb. Cambridge, Harvard Univ. Press. (Harvard case histories in experimental science, no. 8.)

ROLLER, DUANE, H. D. 1953. Did Bacon know Gilbert's *De Magnete*? *Isis* 44: 10-13.

ROMER, ALFRED. 1942a. The speculative history of atomic charges, 1873-1895. *Isis* 33: 671-683.

——. 1942b. The experimental history of atomic charges, 1895-1903. *Isis* 34: 150-161.

RONALDS, SIR FRANCIS. 1880. Catalogue of books and papers relating to electricity, magnetism, the electric telegraph, &c. Including the Ronalds Library. Compiled by Sir Francis Ronalds, with a biographical memoir. Edited by Alfred J. Frost. London, E. & F. N. Spon. Published by the [London, Eng.] Society of Telegraph Engineers.

RONCHI, VASCO. 1939. Storia della luce. Bologna, Nicolà Zanichelli editore.

ROSENBERGER, FERD. 1882, 1884, 1887-1890. Die Geschichte der Physik, in Grundzügen mit synchronistischen Tabellen. 3 v. Braunschweig, Druck und verlag von Friedrich Vieweg und Sohn.

——. 1895. Isaac Newton und seine physikalischen Principien. Ein Hauptstück aus der Entwickelungsgeschichte der modernen Physik. Leipzig, Johann Ambrosius Barth (Arthur Meiner).

——. 1898. Die moderne Entwicklung der elektrischen Principien. Fünf Vorträge. Leipzig, Verlag von Johann Ambrosius Barth.

ROSENFELD, L. 1927. La théorie des couleurs de Newton et ses adversaires. *Isis* 9: 44-65.

——. 1928. Le premier conflit entre la théorie ondulatoire et la théorie corpusculaire de la lumière. *Isis* 11: 111-122.

——. 1932. Marcus Marcis untersuchungen über das Prisma und ihr Verhältnis zu Newtons Farbentheorie. *Isis* 17: 325-330.

——. 1941. La genèse des principes de la thermodynamique. *Bulletin de la Société Royale des Sciences de Liége*, no. 3, 1941: 199-212.

ROUTH, E. J., and HENRY LORD BROUGHAM. 1855. Analytical view of Sir Isaac Newton's Principia. London, Longman, Brown, Green, and Longmans.

ROWLAND, HENRY A. 1899. The highest aim of the physicist. *Bull. Amer. Phys. Soc.* 1: 4-16.

Royal Society. 1947. The Royal Society: Newton Tercentenary Celebrations, 15-19 July 1946. Cambridge, Univ. Press.

ROZBROJ, HUGO. 1937. Jean-Paul Marat (1743-93) : ein Naturforscher und Revolutionär, sein Zusammentreffen in der Geisteswelt mit Goethe, Lamarck, Rousseau u. a. Berlin, Verlag Dr. Emil Ebering. (Historische Studien, Heft 315.)

RUFUS, W. CARL. 1948. David Rittenhouse as a Newtonian philosopher and defender. *Popular Astronomy* 56: 122-130.

RUMFORD, BENJAMIN THOMPSON, COUNT. 1798. An inquiry concerning the source of the heat which is excited by friction. *Phil. Trans.* 88 (1) : 80-102.

[RUSH, BENJAMIN]. 1948. The autobiography of Benjamin Rush. His "Travels through life," together with his Commonplace book for 1789-1813.

Now first printed in full from the original manuscripts in possession of the American Philosophical Society and The Library Company of Philadelphia. Edited, with an introduction and notes, by George W. Corner. Princeton, Princeton Univ. Press, published for the Amer. Philos. Soc. (Mem. Amer. Philos. Soc., **25**.)

[——]. 1951. Letters of Benjamin Rush. Edited by L. H. Butterfield. 2 v. **1**: 1761-1792; **2**: 1793-1813. Princeton, Princeton Univ. Press, published for the Amer. Philos. Soc. (Mem. Amer. Philos. Soc., **30**.)

RUSSELL, BERTRAND. 1937. A critical exposition of the philosophy of Leibniz, with an appendix of leading passages. New edition. London, George Allen & Unwin.

RUSSELL-WOOD, J. 1949. A biographical note on William Brownrigg, M. D., F. R. S. (1711-1800). *Annals of Science* **6**: 186-196.

——. 1950-1951. The scientific work of William Brownrigg, M. D., F. R. S. (1711-1800). *Annals of Science* **6**: 436-447; **7**: 77-94, 199-206.

RUSSO, FRANÇOIS. 1954. Histoire des sciences et des techniques. Bibliographie. Paris, Hermann. (Actualités scientifiques et industrielles, 1204.)

RUTENBERG, D. 1939. The early history of the potentiometer system of electrical measurement. *Annals of Science* **4**: 212-243.

RUTHERFORD, ERNEST, LORD. 1906. The modern theories of electricity and their relation to the Franklinian theory. Pages 123-157 of: The record of the celebration of the birth of Benjamin Franklin. Philadelphia, printed for the Amer. Philos. Soc.

——. 1913. Radioactive substances and their radiations. Cambridge, Univ. Press; New York, G. P. Putnam's Sons.

——. 1938. Forty years of physics. [Two lectures]: The history of radioactivity; The development of the theory of atomic structure. Pages 49-74 of: Background to modern science. New York, Macmillan; Cambridge, Univ. Press. (The Cambridge Library of Modern Science.)

SAINTE-BEUVE, C. A. 1905. Benjamin Franklin. Pages 311-373 of: Portraits of the eighteenth century, historic and literary. Part One. Translated by Katharine P. Wormeley. With a critical introduction by Edmond Scherer. New York, London. G. P. Putnam's Sons.

SANTILLANA, GEORGE DE. 1941. Aspects of scientific rationalism in the nineteenth century. *International Encyclopedia of Unified Science,* **2** (8) : 1-51.

SARTON, GEORGE. 1911. Les principes de la mécanique de Newton. Thèse présentée à la Faculté des Sciences de Gand pour l'obtention du grade scientifique de Docteur ès Sciences physiques et mathématiques, le 15 mai 1911. [Manuscript.]

——. 1930a. Discovery of the dispersion of light and of the nature of color (1672). With facsimile reproduction (no. X) of Newton's new theory about light and colors (*Phil. Trans.*, no. 80, Feb. 19, 1672: 3075-3078). *Isis* **14**: 326-341.

——. 1930b. Stephen Hales's library. *Isis* **14**: 422-423.

——. 1936. The study of the history of science. Cambridge, Harvard Univ. Press.

——. 1948a. The study of early scientific textbooks. *Isis* **38**: 137-148.

——. 1948b. The life of science: essays in the history of civilization. Foreword by Max H. Fisch. New York, Henry Schuman.

——. 1952. Horus: a guide to the history of science. A first guide for the study of the history of science, with introductory essays on science and tradition. Waltham, Chronica Botanica Company.

SAVÉRIEN, ALEXANDRE. 1775. Histoire des progrès de l'esprit humain dans les sciences naturelles et dans les arts qui en dépendent. Paris, chez Lacombe.

SAVIOZ, RAYMOND. 1948. Mémoires autobiographiques de Charles Bonnet de Genève. Paris, Librairie Philosophique J. Vrin.

SCHILPP, PAUL ARTHUR, ed. 1949. Albert Einstein: philosopher-scientist. Evanston, Ill., Library of Living Philosophers.

SCHLESINGER, ARTHUR M. 1946. An American historian looks at science and technology. *Isis* **36**: 162-166.

SCHONLAND, B. F. J. 1938. The lightning discharge, being the Halley Lecture delivered on 28 May 1937. Oxford, Clarendon Press.

——. 1950. The flight of thunderbolts. Oxford, Clarendon Press.

——. 1952. The work of Benjamin Franklin on thunderstorms and the development of the lightning rod. *Jour. Franklin Inst.* **253**: 375-392.

SCHRECKER, PAUL. 1946. Descartes and Leibniz in 1946. On their 350th and 300th birthdays. *Philosophy, Jour. British Inst. of Philosophy* **21**: 205-233.

——. 1948. Work and history. An essay on the structure of civilization. Princeton, Princeton Univ. Press.

SCHUHL, PIERRE MAXIME. 1949. Pour connaître la pensée de Lord Bacon. [Paris], Bordas.

SCHURMANN, PABLO F. 1938. Evolución de las teorías de la naturaleza de la luz. El nacimiento de la termodinámica. Montevideo, A. Monteverde.

SCHUSTER, ARTHUR. 1894-1895. On some remarkable passages in the writings of Benjamin Franklin. *Mem. and Proc. Manchester Lit. and Philos. Soc.* **9**: 152-164.

——. 1911. The progress of physics during 33 years (1875-1908). Four lectures delivered to the University of Calcutta during March 1908. Cambridge, Univ. Press.

[Science Museum, South Kensington.] 1905. Catalogue of the collections for teaching and research in the Science Museum, South Kensington. Part II, Physics. Second edition. London, printed for His Majesty's Stationery Office by Wyman and Sons.

SCOTT, J. F. 1938. The mathematical work of John Wallis, D.D., F.R.S. (1616-1703). With a foreword by E. N. da C. Andrade. London, Taylor and Francis.

——. 1952. The scientific work of René Descartes (1596-1650). With a foreword by H. W. Turnbull. London, Taylor & Francis.

SENEBIER, JEAN. An X [1802]. Essai sur l'art d'observer et de faire des expéri-

ences; seconde édition, considérablement changée et augmentée. 3 v. Genève, chez J. J. Paschoud, Libraire.

SHERRINGTON, SIR CHARLES. 1941. Man on his nature. The Gifford Lectures, Edinburgh, 1937-8. New York, Macmillan; Cambridge, Univ. Press.

SHRYOCK, RICHARD H. 1944. The need for studies in the history of American science. *Isis* **35**: 10-13.

——. 1947. American medical research, past and present. New York, Commonwealth Fund.

——. 1948. American indifference to basic science during the nineteenth century. *Archives Internationales d'Histoire des Sciences* **28**: 50-65.

——. 1951. Training historians of science in the United States. *Archives Internationales d'Histoire des Sciences* **30**: 595-599.

SIGAUD DE LA FOND, JEAN RENÉ. 1781. Précis historique et expérimental des phénomènes électriques, depuis l'origine de cette découverte jusqu'à ce jour. Paris, Rue et Hôtel Serpente.

SILBERSTEIN, LUDWIK. 1918. Elements of the electromagnetic theory of light. London, New York, Longmans, Green and Co.

SINGER, CHARLES. 1931. The story of living things. A short account of the evolution of the biological sciences. New York and London, Harper & Brothers Publishers.

SINGER, DOROTHEA WALEY. 1949-1950. Sir John Pringle and his circle.—I. Life; II. Public health; III. Copley discourses. *Annals of Science* **6**: 127-180, 229-247, 248-261.

SMITH, ADAM. 1869. Essays on I. Moral sentiments; II. Astronomical inquiries; III. Formation of languages; IV. History of ancient physics; V. Ancient logic and metaphysics; VI. The imitative arts; VII. Music, dancing, poetry; VIII. The external senses; IX. English and Italian verses. London, Alex. Murray & Son.

SMITH, HORACE WEMYSS. 1879-1880. Life and correspondence of the Rev. William Smith, D.D., . . . with copious extracts from his writings. 2 v. Philadelphia, S. A. George.

SMITH, PRESERVED. 1934. A history of modern culture. 2: The enlightenment, 1687-1776. New York, Henry Holt.

SMITH, WILLIAM. 1792. Eulogium on Benjamin Franklin. Philadelphia, Benjamin Franklin Bache.

SNELL, KARL. 1858. Newton und die mechanische Naturwissenschaft. Zu Newton's Gedächtniss im zweiten Säcularjahre seiner Geburt. Zweite Auflage. Leipzig, Arnoldische Buchhandlung.

SNOW, A. J. 1926. Matter and gravity in Newton's physical philosophy. A study in the natural philosophy of Newton's time. London, Oxford Univ. Press.

[SOTHEBY AND CO.] 1936. Catalogue of the Newton papers, sold by order of the Viscount Lymington to whom they have descended from Catherine Conduitt, Viscountess Lymington, greatniece of Sir Isaac Newton. Which will be sold by auction by Messrs. Sotheby and Co. . . . on Monday, July 13th, 1936, and following day, at one o'clock precisely. London, printed by H. Davy (for Sotheby and Co.) .

[SPINOZA, BARUCH.] 1928. The correspondence of Spinoza. Translated and edited, with introduction and annotations, by A. Wolf. London, George Allen & Unwin.

SPRAT, THOMAS. 1734. The history of the Royal Society of London, for the Improving of Natural Knowledge. Fourth edition. London, printed for J. Knapton, J. Walthoe, . . .

SPRIGGS, G. W. 1929. The Honourable Robert Boyle: a chapter in the philosophy of science. Archeion 11: 1-12.

STALLO, J. B. 1882. The concepts and theories of modern physics. New York, D. Appleton. (International Scientific Series, 38.)

STEARNS, RAYMOND PHINEAS. 1946. Colonial Fellows of the Royal Society of London, 1661-1788. Wm. and Mary Quart. 3: 208-268. [Originally written for Osiris (see entry immediately below) the publication of which was held up by the war, the article was first printed in 1946, and was later reprinted in 1951.]

——. 1948. Colonial Fellows of the Royal Society of London, 1661-1788. Osiris 8: 73-121.

——. 1951. Colonial Fellows of the Royal Society of London, 1661-1788. Notes and Records Royal Soc. of London 8: 178-246.

STEELMAN, JOHN R. 1947. Science and public policy. 1: A program for the nation; 2: The federal research program; 3: Administration for research; 4: Manpower for research; 5: The nation's medical research. Washington, D. C., U. S. Govt. Print. Office.

STEPHEN, LESLIE. 1881. History of English thought in the eighteenth century. 2 v. Second edition. London, Smith, Elder.

STEVENS, HENRY. 1881. Benjamin Franklin's life and writings. A bibliographical essay on the Stevens' collection of books and manuscripts relating to Dr. Franklin. London, printed by Messrs. Davy & Sons at the Dryden Press for the author.

STIMSON, DOROTHY. 1935. Puritanism and the new philosophy in 17th century England. Bull. Hist. of Medicine 3: 321-334.

——. 1948. Scientists and amateurs. A history of the Royal Society. New York, Henry Schuman. (The Life of Science Library.)

STONES, G. B. 1928. The atomic view of matter in the XVth, XVIth, and XVIIth centuries. Isis 10: 445-465.

STRONG, EDWARD W. 1936. Procedures and metaphysics: a study in the philosophy of mathematical-physical science in the sixteenth and seventeenth centuries. Berkeley, Univ. of California Press.

——. 1951. Newton's "Mathematical Way." Jour. Hist. of Ideas 12: 90-110.

——. 1952. Newton and God. Jour. Hist. of Ideas 13: 147-167.

STUART, ALEXANDER. 1731-1732. Experiments to prove the existence of a fluid in the nerves. Phil. Trans. 37: 327-331.

[STUKELEY, WILLIAM.] 1806. Letter from Dr. Stukeley to Dr. Mead, dated Grantham, 26th June 1727. Pages 174-181 of Edmond Turnor: Collections for the history of the town and soke of Grantham. Containing authentic memoirs of Sir Isaac Newton. . . . London, printed for William Miller by W. Bulmer.

[——.] 1882-1883-1887. The family memoirs of the Rev. William Stukeley, M. D. and the antiquarian and other correspondence of William Stukeley, Roger & Samuel Gale, etc. Published for the [Surtees] Society. Durham, Andrews & Co.; London, Whittaker, Bernard Quaritch; Edinburgh, William Blackwood & Sons. (Publications of the Surtees Society, **73**, 1880; **76**, 1883; **80**, 1885.)

Sullivan, J. W. N. 1938. Isaac Newton, 1642-1727. With a memoir of the author by Charles Singer. New York, Macmillan.

Susskind, Charles. 1950. Henry Cavendish, electrician. *Jour. Franklin Inst.* **249**: 181-188.

Sweet, Jessie M. 1952. Benjamin Franklin's purse. *Notes and Records Royal Soc. of London* **9**: 308-309.

Symmer, Robert. 1759. New experiments and observations concerning electricity. *Phil. Trans.* **51**: 340-389.

Thompson, Silvanus P. 1888. The influence machine, from 1788 to 1888. *Jour. Soc. Telegraph-Engineers and Electricians* **17**: 569-635.

——. 1898. Michael Faraday; his life and work. London, Cassell. (The Century Science Series.)

Thomson, G. P. 1930. The wave mechanics of free electrons. New York, McGraw-Hill.

Thomson, Sir J. J. 1888. Applications of dynamics to physics and chemistry. London, Macmillan.

——. 1893. Notes on recent researches in electricity and magnetism. Intended as a sequel to Professor Clerk-Maxwell's *Treatise on electricity and magnetism.* Oxford, Clarendon Press.

——. 1898. The discharge of electricity through gases. Lectures delivered on the occasion of the sesquicentennial celebration of Princeton University. New York, Charles Scribner's Sons.

——. 1904. Elements of the mathematical theory of electricity and magnetism. Third edition. Cambridge, Univ. Press.

——. 1906. Conduction of electricity through gases. Second edition. Cambridge, Univ. Press. (Cambridge Physical Series.)

——. 1907. The corpuscular theory of matter. London, Archibald Constable.

——. 1923. The electron in chemistry. Being five lectures delivered at the Franklin Institute, Philadelphia. Philadelphia, published by the Franklin Institute Press of J. B. Lippincott Company.

——. 1927. Newton's work in physics. Supplement to *Nature,* no. 2995: 36-40.

——. 1928. Beyond the electron. A lecture given at Girton College on 3 March 1928. Cambridge, Univ. Press.

——. 1936. Recollections and reflections. London, G. Bell and Sons.

Thomson, Thomas. 1812. History of the Royal Society from its institution to the end of the eighteenth century. London, printed for Robert Baldwin.

——. 1830. An outline of the sciences of heat and electricity. London, Baldwin & Cradock; Edinburgh, William Blackwood.

——. 1843. Sketch of the progress of physical science. Also, a course of lectures on astronomy, &c., by Dionysius Lardner. Third edition. New York, Greeley & McElrath. (New-York Tribune, [Extra], Useful Works for the People, No. 3.)

Thomson, Sir William (Baron Kelvin). 1889-1894-1891. Popular lectures and addresses. 3 v. **1**: Constitution of matter; **2**: Geology and general physics; **3**: Navigational affairs. London, New York, Macmillan. (Nature Series.)

——. 1902. Aepinus atomized. *Philos. Mag. and Jour. of Science* **3**, 6th ser., 257-283.

Thorndike, Lynn. 1924. *L'encyclopédie* and the history of science. *Isis* **6**: 361-386.

Thorpe, Francis Newton (ed.). 1893. Benjamin Franklin and the University of Pennsylvania. Washington, Govt. Print. Office. (Bureau of Education, Circular of Information No. 2, 1892, Whole number 188.)

Thorpe, Jocelyn. 1940. Stephen Hales, D. D., F. R. S.—1677-1761. *Notes and Records Royal Soc.* **3**: 53-63.

TODHUNTER, ISAAC. 1873. A history of the mathematical theories of attraction and the figure of the earth, from the time of Newton to that of Laplace. 2 v. London, Macmillan.

——. 1886. A history of the theory of elasticity and of the strength of materials, from Galilei to the present time. Edited and completed for the syndics of the University Press by Karl Pearson. 1: Galilei to Saint-Venant, 1639-1850. Cambridge, Univ. Press.

TOLLES, FREDERICK B. 1948. Meeting house and counting house: the Quaker merchants of colonial Philadelphia, 1682-1763. Chapel Hill, Univ. of North Carolina Press (published for the Institute of Early American History and Culture at Williamsburg, Virginia).

TORLAIS, JEAN. 1936. Un esprit encyclopédique en dehors de " L'encyclopédie." Réaumur, d'après des documents inédits. Paris, Desclée De Brouwer.

——. 1937. Un Rochelais grand-maître de la Franc-Maçonnerie et physicien au XVIIIᵉ siècle: Le Révérend J.-T. Désaguliers. La Rochelle, F. Pijollet, libraire-éditeur.

——. 1954. L'Abbé Nollet, 1700-1770: un physicien au siècle des lumières. Paris, Sipuco.

TOULMIN, STEPHEN. 1953. The philosophy of science. An introduction. London, Hutchinson's Univ. Library.

TOULOUSE, ÉDOUARD. 1910. Henri Poincaré. Paris, Ernest Flammarion.

TRESSAN, LOUIS ÉLISABETH DE LA VERGNE (COMTE DE). 1786. Essai sur le fluide électrique, considéré comme agent universel. 2 v. Paris, chez Buisson, Libraire.

TROWBRIDGE, JOHN. 1896. What is electricity? New York, D. Appleton. (The International Scientific Series, 75.)

——. 1917. Franklin as a scientist. Publ. Colonial Soc. of Mass. 18: 1-12.

——. 1922. The advance in electricity since the time of Franklin. Cambridge, Harvard Univ. Press.

[TRUE, FREDERICK W.] 1913. A history of the first half-century of the National Academy of Sciences, 1863-1913. Washington, [no publisher].

TRUESDELL, C. 1950. A new definition of a fluid. I. The Stokesian fluid. Journal de Mathématiques 29: 215-244.

——. 1951. A new definition of a fluid. II. The Maxwellian fluid. Journal de Mathématiques 30: 111-158.

——. 1952. The mechanical foundations of elasticity and fluid dynamics. Journal of Rational Mechanics & Analysis 1: 125-300.

——. 1954. Rational fluid mechanics, 1687-1765. Editor's introduction to vol. II 12 of Euler's works. Offprint from Leonhardi Euleri Commentationes Mechanicae ad Theoriam Corporum Fluidorum Pertinentes (Euleri Opera Omnia series II, 12). Zürich, Orell Füssli.

TURNBULL, HERBERT WESTREN (ed.). 1939. James Gregory. Tercentenary memorial volume. London, G. Bell & Sons.

——. 1945. The mathematical discoveries of Newton. London, Glasgow, Blackie & Son.

TURNER, DOROTHY M. 1927. Makers of science: electricity and magnetism. Introduction by Charles Singer. London, Oxford Univ. Press.

TURNOR, EDMOND. 1806. Collections for the history of the town and soke of Grantham. Containing authentic memoirs of Sir Isaac Newton, now first published from the original MSS. in the possession of the Earl of Portsmouth. London, printed for William Miller by W. Bulmer.

TYNDALL, JOHN. 1870. Faraday as a discoverer. New edition. London, Longmans, Green.

——. 1877. Lessons in electricity, at the royal institution, 1875-6. New York, D. Appleton.

VALLENTIN, ANTONINA. 1954. The drama of Albert Einstein. Translated by Moura Budberg. Garden City, N.Y., Doubleday.

VALLI, EUSEBIUS. 1793. Experiments on animal electricity, with their application to physiology. And some pathological and medical observations. London, printed for J. Johnson.

VAN DOREN, CARL (ed.). 1920. Benjamin Franklin and Jonathan Edwards: selections from their writings. Edited, with an introduction, by Carl Van Doren. New York, Chicago, Boston, Charles Scribner's Sons. (The Modern Student's Library.)

——. 1938. Benjamin Franklin. New York, Viking Press.

——. 1943. The beginnings of the American Philosophical Society. *Proc. Amer. Philos. Soc.* **87**: 277-289.

——. 1945. Benjamin Franklin's autobiographical writings. Selected and edited. New York, Viking Press.

——. 1950a. Jane Mecom: the favorite sister of Benjamin Franklin. Her life here first fully narrated from their entire surviving correspondence. New York, Viking Press.

—— (ed.). 1950b. The letters of Benjamin Franklin & Jane Mecom. Edited, with an introduction by Carl Van Doren. Princeton, Princeton Univ. Press, published for the Amer. Philos. Soc. (Mem. Amer. Philos. Soc. **27**.)

VAN MARUM, MARTIN. 1785. Description d'une très grande machine électrique, placée dans le Muséum de Teyler à Haarlem, et des expériments faits par le moyen de cette machine. Haarlem, chez Jean Enschedé et fils, et Jean Van Walré.

——. 1787. Première continuation des expériences, faites par le moyen de la machine électrique Teylerienne. Haarlem, chez Jean Enschedé et fils, et Jean Van Walré.

——. 1820. On the theory of Franklin, according to which electrical phenomena are explained by a single fluid. A memoir read at the Royal Institution of the Sciences at Amsterdam. Translated from the French. *Annals of Philosophy* **16**: 440-453.

VAVILOV, S. I. 1947. Newton and the atomic theory. Pages 43-61 of: The Royal Society: Newton Tercentenary Celebrations, 15-19 July 1946. Cambridge, Univ. Press.

——. 1948. Isaac Newton. Aus dem Russischen übersetzt von Josef Grün. Wien, "Neues Österreich" Zeitungs- und Verlagsgesellschaft m. b. H. (Wissenschaft für Jedermann.)

——. 1951. Isaac Newton. Berlin, Akademie-Verlag.

VENTURI, FRANCO. 1939. Jeunesse de Diderot (1713-1753). Traduit del'italien par Juliette Bertrand. Paris, Albert Skira.

VICTORY, BEATRICE MARGUERITE. 1915. Benjamin Franklin and Germany. [Philadelphia], Publications of the Univ. of Penna. (America Germanica, no. 21.)

VILLAMIL, R. DE. 1931. Newton: the man. Foreword by Albert Einstein. London, Gordon D. Knox.

[VOLTA, ALESSANDRO.] 1927. L'opera di Alessandro Volta. Scelta di scritti originali raccolti ed illustrati dal Prof. Francesco Massardi; pubblicati a cura della Associazione Elettrotecnica Italiana nel 1o centenario della morte. Milano, Presso la Sede Centrale dell'A.E.I. e presso l'Editore Ulrico Hoepli.

VOLTAIRE, FRANÇOIS. 1737. Elémens de la philosophie de Neuton. Nouvelle édition. "Londres," [no publisher].

——. 1909. Lettres philosophiques. Édition critique avec une introduction et un commentaire par Gustav Lanson. 2 v. Paris, Édouard Cornély.

——. 1926. Letters concerning the English nation. With an introduction by Charles Whibley. London, printed for Peter Davies.

WADE, IRA O. 1941. Voltaire and Madame du Châtelet. An essay on the intellectual activity at Cirey. Princeton, Princeton Univ. Press.

WALKER, EZ. 1813. On electricity. *Philos. Mag.* **42**: 161-163.

WALKER, W. CAMERON. 1934. The beginnings of the scientific career of Joseph Priestley. *Isis* **21**: 81-97.

——. 1936. The detection and estimation of electric charges in the eighteenth century. *Annals of Science* **1**: 66-100.

——. 1937. Animal electricity before Galvani. *Annals of Science* **2**: 84-113.

WALSH, JOHN. 1773. Of the electric property of the torpedo. In a letter from John Walsh to Benjamin Franklin. *Phil. Trans.* **63**: 461-480.

WATSON, E. C. 1954. Caricatures of Sir Isaac Newton by two famous artists. *Amer. Jour. Physics* **22**: 247-249.

WATSON, WILLIAM. 1745. Experiments and observations, tending to illustrate the nature and properties of electricity: by William Watson, Apothecary, F. R. S. *Phil. Trans.* **43**: 481-501. [Three letters read between 28 March and 24 October.]

——. 1746a. Experiments and observations tending to illustrate the nature and properties of electricity. In one letter to Martin Folkes, Esq; President, and two to the Royal Society. The third edition. London, printed for C. Davis. [The editions of this book have been discussed in a footnote on pages 391-392, above. The book consists of 3 letters, dated respectively 27 March 1746, 25 April 1745, and a third letter described as " Read before the Royal Society Oct. 24, 1745," and a " Continuation of the above, read Feb. 6, 1745." The first three letters were published in *Phil. Trans.* **43**: 481-501, 1745; the " Continuation " was published in the *Phil. Trans.* **44**: 41-50 (no. 478), 1746. It was reprinted in *Phil. Trans.* in an Appendix " Containing some papers which were not ready to be inserted in the order of their dates," but this reprint follows exactly the original printing.]

——. 1746b. A sequel to the experiments and observations tending to illustrate the nature and properties of electricity: wherein it is presumed, by a series of experiments expressly for that purpose, that the source of the electrical power, and its manner of acting are demonstrated. Addressed to the Royal Society. The second edition. London, printed for C. Davis.

——. 1748a. Experiences et observations, pour servir a l'explication de la nature et des proprieté's de l'électricité. Proposées en trois lettres à la Société Royale de Londres. Traduites de l'anglois d'après la seconde edition. Paris, chez Sebastien Jorry. (Recueil de traités sur l'électricité, traduits de l'allemand & de l'anglois. Seconde partie.)

——. 1748b. An account of the experiments made by some gentlemen of the Royal Society, in order to discover whether the electrical power would be sensible at great distances. With an experimental inquiry concerning the respective velocities of electricity and sound. To which are added, some further inquiries into the nature and properties of electricity. London, printed for C. Davis.

——. 1751-1752a. An account of Mr. Benjamin Franklin's treatise, lately published, intituled, " Experiments and observations on electricity, made at Philadelphia in America." *Phil. Trans.* **47**: 202-211.

——. 1751-1752b. An account of Professor Winkler's experiments relating to odours passing through electrised globes and tubes, being the extract and translation from the Latin of two letters sent by that gentleman to Cromwell Mortimer, M. D. Secretary of the Royal Society. With an account of the result of some experiments made here with globes and tubes, transmitted from Leipsic by Mr. Winkler to the Royal Society, in order to verify the facts beforementioned. *Phil. Trans.* **47**: 231-241.

——. 1751-1752c. An account of the phaenomena of electricity in vacuo, with some observations thereupon. *Phil. Trans.* **47**: 362-376.

——. 1751-1752d. A letter to the Royal Society, concerning the electrical experiments in England upon thunderclouds. *Phil. Trans.* **47**: 567-570.

——. 1753. An account of a treatise, presented to the Royal Society, intituled, " Letters concerning electricity; in which the latest discoveries upon this subject, and the consequences which may be deduced from them, are examined; by the Abbé Nollet, . . ." extracted and translated from the French. *Phil. Trans.* **48**: 201-216.

WECTER, DIXON. 1941. The hero in America, a chronicle of hero-worship. New York, Charles Scribner's Sons.

WEINSTEIN, ALEXANDER. 1943. Ode on Newton's theory of gravitation by Edmond Halley. *Science* **97**: 69-70.

WELD, CHARLES RICHARD. 1848. A history of the Royal Society, with memoirs of the presidents. Compiled from authentic documents. 2 v. London, John W. Parker.

WESTAWAY, F. W. 1919. Scientific method: its philosophy and its practice. New edition. London, Blackie and Son.

WEYL, HERMANN. 1949. Philosophy of mathematics and natural science. Revised and augmented English edition, based on a translation by Olaf Helmer. Princeton, Princeton Univ. Press.

WHEELER, LYNDE P. 1951. Josiah Willard Gibbs: the history of a great mind. New Haven, Yale Univ. Press.

[Wheeler Gift.] 1909. Catalogue of the Wheeler Gift of books, pamphlets and periodicals in the Library of the American Institute of Electrical Engineers. Edited by William D. Weaver, with introduction, descriptive and critical notes by Brother Potamian. 2 v. New York, Amer. Inst. Elec. Engineers.

WHELER, GRANVILLE. 1739-1740. Some electrical experiments, chiefly regarding the repulsive force of electrical bodies. *Phil. Trans.* 41 (1) : 98-111.

——. 1745. Two letters from the Rev. Mr. Granville Wheler, F. R. S. to the President, concerning a rotatory motion of glass tubes about their axes, when placed in a certain manner before the fire. *Phil. Trans.* 43: 341-348.

WHETHAM, WILLIAM CECIL DAMPIER. 1923. The theory of experimental electricity. Third edition. Cambridge, Univ. Press.

WHEWELL, WILLIAM. 1836. Report on the recent progress and present condition of the mathematical theories of electricity, magnetism, and heat. *Report of the fifth meeting of the British Association for the Advancement of Science*, Dublin, 1835, 1-34. London, John Murray.

——. 1858. Novum organon renovatum. Being the second part of the philosophy of the inductive sciences. The third edition, with large additions. London, John W. Parker and Son.

——. 1860. On the philosophy of discovery, chapters historical and critical; including the completion of the third edition of the philosophy of the induc-

tive sciences. London, John W. Parker and Son.

——. 1865. History of the inductive sciences: from the earliest to the present time. Third edition, with additions. 2 v. New York, D. Appleton.

WHITEHEAD, ALFRED NORTH. 1923. The first physical synthesis. Pages 161-178 of: Science and civilization: essays arranged and edited by F. S. Marvin. London, Oxford Univ. Press. (The Unity Series, 6.)

——. 1925. Science and the modern world. Lowell Lectures, 1925. New York, Macmillan

——. 1929. The aims of education and other essays. New York, Macmillan.

——. 1933. Adventures of ideas. New York, Macmillan.

WHITTAKER, SIR EDMUND. 1949. From Euclid to Eddington. A study of conceptions of the external world. [The Tarner Lectures, 1947.] Cambridge, Univ. Press.

——. 1951. A history of the theories of aether and electricity, 1: The Classical Theories. New York, Philosophical Library; Edinburgh & London, Thomas Nelson and Sons.

WIENER, PHILIP PAUL. 1932. The experimental philosophy of Robert Boyle (1626-91) . *Philos. Rev.* 41: 594-609.

WIGHTMAN, WILLIAM P. D. 1951. The growth of scientific ideas. New Haven, Yale Univ. Press.

WILDE, EMIL. 1843. Geschichte der Optik vom Ursprunge dieser Wissenschaft bis auf die gegenwärtige Zeit. Zweiter Theil. Von Newton bis Euler. Berlin, Rücker und Püchler.

WILLEY, BASIL. 1941. The eighteenth century background. Studies on the idea of nature in the thought of the period. New York, Columbia Univ. Press; London, Chatto and Windus.

——. 1950. The seventeenth century background. Studies in the thought of the age in relation to poetry and religion. New York, Columbia Univ. Press. (First published, 1934, London, Chatto and Windus.)

WILSON, BENJAMIN. 1746. An essay towards an explication of the phænomena of electricity, deduced from the æther of Sir Isaac Newton, contained in three papers which were read before The Royal Society. London, printed for C. Davis and M. Cooper.

——. 1752. A treatise on electricity. Second edition. London, printed and sold by C. Davis and R. Dodsley.

——. 1756. A retraction, by Mr. Benjamin Wilson, F. R. S. of his former opinion, concerning the explication of the Leyden experiment, *Phil. Trans.* 49 (2) : 682-683.

WILSON, BENJAMIN, and BENJAMIN HOADLY. 1756. Observations on a series of electrical experiments. London, printed for T. Payne.

WILSON, WILLIAM. 1950. A hundred years of physics. London, Gerald Duckworth. (100 Years Series.)

WINDRED, G. 1932. The relation between pure and applied electrical theory: with special reference to mathematical methods. *Isis* 18: 184-190.

——. 1933. The history of mathematical time. *Isis* 19: 121-153; 20: 192-219.

[WINKLER, JOHN HENRY.] 1744. Abstract of what is contained in a book concerning electricity, just published at Leipzic, 1744 by John Henry Wintler, Greek and Latin professor there; from Article 75 to Article 79. *Phil. Trans.* 43: 166-169.

[——]. 1744-1745. Regiæ Societati Anglicanæ Scientiarum quædam electricitatis recens observata exhibet J. Henricus Winkler, Gr. & Lat. Literarum Prof. Publ. Ordin. & Academiæ Lipsiensis h. t. Rector. *Phil. Trans.* 43: 307-315. Communication presented 21 March 1744-1745.

——. 1746. An extract of a letter . . . concerning the effects of electricity upon himself and his wife. *Phil. Trans.* 44 (1) : 211-212.

——. 1748. Essai sur la nature, les effets et les causes de l'électricité, avec une description de deux nouvelles machines a électricité. Traduit de l'allemand. (Recueil de traités sur l'électricité. Traduits de l'allemand & de l'anglois. Premiere partie.) Paris, chez Sebastien Jorry.

WINTHROP, JOHN. 1773. Remarks upon a passage in Castillione's *Life of Sir Isaac Newton*. *Phil. Trans.* 64: 153-157. (A communication dated 4 March 1773, and read 20 Jan. 1774.)

WINTHROP, ROBERT C. 1876. Washington, Bowdoin, and Franklin, as portrayed in occasional addresses. Boston, Little, Brown.

WINTNER, AUREL. 1941. The analytical foundations of celestial mechanics. Princeton, Princeton Univ. Press.

WITZ, A. 1921. L'Électricité, ses hypothèses et ses théories successives. Louvain, Fr. Ceuterick. (Extrait de la *Revue des Questions scientifiques*, 1920, 1921.)

WOLF, A. 1950. A history of science, technology, and philosophy in the 16th & 17th centuries. New edition, prepared by Douglas McKie. London, George Allen & Unwin; New York, Macmillan.

——. 1952. A history of science, technology, and philosophy in the eighteenth century. Second edition, revised by D. McKie. London, George Allen & Unwin.

WOLF, EDWIN, 2ND. 1954. The first books and printed catalogues of the Library Company of Philadelphia. *Penna. Mag. Hist. and Biog.* 78: 45-70.

WOLFSON, HARRY AUSTRYN. 1947. Philo. Foundations of religious philosophy in Judaism, Christianity, and Islam. 2 v. Cambridge, Harvard Univ. Press.

WOOD, ALEXANDER. 1954. Thomas Young, natural philosopher, 1773-1829. (Completed by Frank Oldham. With a memoir of Alexander Wood by Charles E. Raven.) Cambridge, Univ. Press.

WOODRUFF, LORANDE LOSS. 1917. Erasmus Darwin and Benjamin Franklin. *Science* 46: 291-292.

WRIGHT, JOHN K. 1944. Human nature in science. *Science* 100: 299-305.

WROTH, LAWRENCE C. 1943. Benjamin Franklin: the printer at work. Pp. 151-178 of: Meet Dr. Franklin. Philadelphia, Franklin Inst.

YOUNG, THOMAS. 1807. A course of lectures on natural philosophy and the mechanical arts. 2 v. London, printed for Joseph Johnson, by William Savage.

[——]. 1855. Miscellaneous works of the late Thomas Young. 3 v. Edited by George Peacock. London, John Murray.

ZELENY, JOHN. 1944. Observations and experiments on condensers with removable coats. *Amer. Jour. Physics* **12**: 329-339.

ZIRKLE, CONWAY. 1941. The jumar or cross between the horse and the cow. *Isis* **33**: 486-506.

Index

INDEX